MICHAEL POWER/ST. JOSEPH'S HIGH SCHOOL
300 Valermo Drive
Toronto, Ont.
M8W 2L1

PROPERTY OF
MICHAEL POWER/ST. JOSEPH'S HIGH SCHOOL

YEAR	NAME	GRADE	CONDITION RECEIVED	CONDITION RETURNED
86/87	Sandra	9		

THE McGRAW-HILL RYERSON MATHEMATICS PROGRAM CORE TEXTS

LIFE MATH 3

MATH 4
MATH 5
MATH 6

INTERMEDIATE MATHEMATICS 1
INTERMEDIATE MATHEMATICS 2

FOUNDATIONS OF MATHEMATICS FOR TODAY AND TOMORROW
FOUNDATIONS OF MATHEMATICS FOR TOMORROW: AN INTRODUCTION
FOUNDATIONS OF MATHEMATICS FOR TOMORROW: INTERMEDIATE
FOUNDATIONS OF MATHEMATICS FOR TOMORROW: SENIOR

APPLIED MATHEMATICS 9 (AMT^2)

APPLIED MATHEMATICS FOR TODAY: AN INTRODUCTION
APPLIED MATHEMATICS FOR TODAY: INTERMEDIATE
APPLIED MATHEMATICS FOR TODAY: SENIOR

TEACHER'S EDITIONS FOR:
MATH 4
MATH 5
MATH 6
INTERMEDIATE MATHEMATICS 1
INTERMEDIATE MATHEMATICS 2
APPLIED MATHEMATICS 9 (AMT^2)   I/P

TEACHER'S GUIDES FOR:
AMT: AN INTRODUCTION
AMT: INTERMEDIATE
FMT^2
FMT: INTERMEDIATE

APPLIED MATHEMATICS 9

Dino Dottori, B. Sc., M.S. Ed.
Head, Mathematics Department
Hill Park Secondary School
Hamilton, Ontario

George Knill, B. Sc., M.S. Ed.
Mathematics Consultant
Hamilton Board of Education
Hamilton, Ontario

John Seymour, B.A. M. Ed.
Principal
Stuart Scott Public School
Newmarket, Ontario

McGraw-Hill Ryerson Limited

Toronto, Montreal, New York, St. Louis, San Francisco, Auckland, Bogotá, Guatemala, Hamburg, Johannesburg, Lisbon, London, Madrid, Mexico, New Delhi, Panama, Paris, San Juan, São Paulo, Singapore, Sydney, Tokyo

Applied Mathematics 9   Revised

Copyright © McGraw-Hill Ryerson Limited, 1984
Copyright © McGraw-Hill Ryerson Limited, 1983

ISBN: 0-07-548825-6

2 3 4 5 6 7 8 9 0 JD 3 2 1 0 9 8 7 6 5

Illustrations by Frank Zsigo

A complete list of photo credits appears on page 535.

Printed and bound in Canada by John Deyell Company

Canadian Cataloguing in Publication Data

Dottori, Dino, date
  Applied mathematics 9:

(The McGraw-Hill Ryerson mathematics program)

For use in schools.
Includes index.
ISBN 0-07-548825-6

1. Mathematics - 1961-   I. Knill, George, date
II. Seymour, John, date   III. Title.
IV. Series

QA39.2.D68 1984   510   C84-098380-8

The metric usage in this text has been reviewed
by the Metric Screening Office of the Canadian Government
Specifications Board.
The Metric Commission has granted use of the
National Symbol for Metric conversion.

CONTENTS

WHOLE NUMBERS AND DECIMALS

1.1 WHOLE NUMBERS

Our solar system began to form more than 4 600 000 000 years ago. This number is read "four billion, six hundred million."

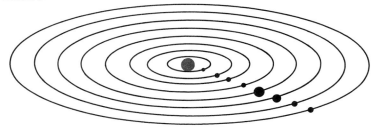

The following table gives the distance of the planets from the sun.

Planet	Distance
Earth	149 600 000 km
Jupiter	778 300 000 km
Mars	227 900 000 km
Mercury	57 900 000 km
Neptune	4 497 000 000 km
Pluto	5 900 000 000 km
Saturn	1 427 000 000 km
Uranus	2 870 000 000 km
Venus	108 200 000 km

In order to arrange the planets according to distance from the sun, we put the numbers on a place value chart.

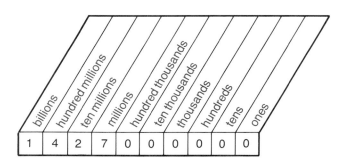

The number 1 427 000 000 is read "one billion, four hundred twenty-seven million."

The number 1 427 000 000 is larger than 1 426 000 000 because the 1 in the billions place means 1 000 000 000, one billion, while the 7 and 6 in the millions place mean 7 000 000 and 6 000 000 respectively.

7	000 000
1 427	000 000
1 426	000 000
6	000 000

Use the place value chart to list the planets in order from closest to the sun to farthest from the sun.

EXERCISE

A

1. Read the following numbers.
   (a) 620 000
   (b) 25 000
   (c) 8 432
   (d) 13 427 516
   (e) 3 516 000 000

2. State the place value of the indicated digit.
   (a) 32 427 000
   (b) 65 726 000
   (c) 32 518 000
   (d) 137 000 000
   (e) 26 350 000 000

3. What number does the 3 represent in these numbers?
   (a) 31 250 000
   (b) 52 135 000
   (c) 6 213 000
   (d) 13 251 000
   (e) 3 529 000 000

B

4. Write the following numbers.
   (a) twelve thousand
   (b) eight million
   (c) four thousand, eighteen
   (d) one hundred fifty thousand
   (e) seventy-five million
   (f) five billion, nine hundred million

APPLICATIONS

5. Arrange the planets according to diameter from smallest to largest.

Planet	Diameter
Earth	12 756 km
Jupiter	142 800 km
Mars	6 787 km
Mercury	4 878 km
Neptune	49 500 km
Pluto	3 000 km*
Saturn	120 600 km
Uranus	51 800 km
Venus	12 100 km

* Scientists provide an approximate diameter for Pluto.

CHALLENGE

Arrange these coins according to the following rules.
1. The quarter is just to the right of the half dollar.
2. Neither the penny nor the nickel is next to the dime.
3. Neither the nickel nor the penny is next to the quarter.
4. Neither the dime nor the nickel is next to the half dollar.

1.2 OPERATIONS WITH WHOLE NUMBERS

This exercise provides practice in addition, subtraction, multiplication, and division of whole numbers.

EXERCISE

A

1. Add.

   (a) $\begin{array}{r} 4712 \\ +2647 \\ \hline \end{array}$ (b) $\begin{array}{r} 65\,340 \\ +16\,435 \\ \hline \end{array}$

   (c) $\begin{array}{r} 6437 \\ 265 \\ 4218 \\ +8037 \\ \hline \end{array}$ (d) $\begin{array}{r} 75\,230 \\ 64\,395 \\ 5\,064 \\ +16\,321 \\ \hline \end{array}$

2. Subtract.

   (a) $\begin{array}{r} 7856 \\ -2143 \\ \hline \end{array}$ (b) $\begin{array}{r} 72\,586 \\ -31\,430 \\ \hline \end{array}$

   (c) $\begin{array}{r} 2150 \\ -1235 \\ \hline \end{array}$ (d) $\begin{array}{r} 67\,530 \\ -32\,430 \\ \hline \end{array}$

   (e) $\begin{array}{r} 2150 \\ -1945 \\ \hline \end{array}$ (f) $\begin{array}{r} 67\,530 \\ -27\,835 \\ \hline \end{array}$

3. Multiply.

   (a) $\begin{array}{r} 315 \\ \times 26 \\ \hline \end{array}$ (b) $\begin{array}{r} 637 \\ \times 53 \\ \hline \end{array}$

   (c) $\begin{array}{r} 534 \\ \times 82 \\ \hline \end{array}$ (d) $\begin{array}{r} 618 \\ \times 72 \\ \hline \end{array}$

4. Divide.

   (a) $36\overline{)4248}$ (b) $47\overline{)1269}$

   (c) $72\overline{)4752}$ (d) $124\overline{)30\,256}$

5. Perform the indicated operation.

   (a) $\begin{array}{r} 326 \\ \times 77 \\ \hline \end{array}$ (b) $\begin{array}{r} 2635 \\ -874 \\ \hline \end{array}$

   (c) $\dfrac{1768}{26}$ (d) $\begin{array}{r} 408 \\ \times 63 \\ \hline \end{array}$

   (e) $\begin{array}{r} 6024 \\ -5341 \\ \hline \end{array}$ (f) $\begin{array}{r} 7436 \\ \times 74 \\ \hline \end{array}$

   (g) $\begin{array}{r} 308 \\ \times 63 \\ \hline \end{array}$ (h) $\dfrac{18\,252}{78}$

6. Simplify.

   (a) $6324 + 2118 + 4752 + 3167$
   (b) $64\,236 - 35\,481$
   (c) 3634×27
   (d) $1488 \div 24$
   (e) $375\,128 + 637\,402$
   (f) 5724×613
   (g) $254\,683 - 215\,607$

7. Simplify.

   (a) $325 + 436 - 255$
   (b) $63 \times 24 \div 72$
   (c) $35 \times 47 + 63$
   (d) $12 \times 53 - 125$
   (e) $54 - 37 + 45$
   (f) $234 \times 527 + 1685$
   (g) $747 - 635 + 1245$
   (h) $18\,144 \div 12 \div 24$

8. The map shows the area of each of the Atlantic provinces.

Newfoundland
404 517 km²

Prince Edward Island
5 657 km²

New Brunswick
73 436 km²

Nova Scotia
55 491 km²

What is the total area of the Atlantic provinces?

9. A person uses about 87 360 L of water in one year.
   How much water would a person use in one week?

10. A space ship can travel 48 000 km each hour. Find the distances to the following bodies, given the time it takes to travel from Earth:
    (a) 8 h to the moon.
    (b) 2275 h to the planet Mercury.

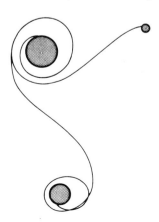

11. A cross-Canada jogging route is 5265 km long.

How many days would it take to jog across Canada averaging 65 km/d?

12. The land area of the earth is 149 000 000 km². The water area of the earth is 361 000 000 km².

What is the total area of the earth?

CHALLENGE

Place the numbers from 1 to 12 in the circles so that the numbers along each side add to 26.

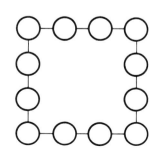

1.3 DECIMALS AND PLACE VALUE

The number 12 345.678 is read "twelve thousand, three hundred forty-five and six hundred seventy-eight thousandths." The position of each digit in the number determines the place value of the digit.

We can put the number on a place value chart.

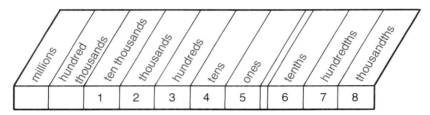

We can write numbers in expanded form as follows.

$$345 = 300 + 40 + 5$$
$$= 3 \times 100 + 4 \times 10 + 5 \times 1$$

$$45.6 = 40 + 5 + 0.6$$
$$= 4 \times 10 + 5 \times 1 + 6 \times 0.1$$

$$5.678 = 5 + 0.6 + 0.07 + 0.008$$
$$= 5 \times 1 + 6 \times 0.1 + 7 \times 0.01 + 8 \times 0.001$$

We can take numbers in expanded form and write them in standard form.

$$3 \times 1000 + 4 \times 100 + 2 \times 10 + 5 \times 1$$
$$= 3000 + 400 + 20 + 5$$
$$= 3425$$

$$4 \times 10 + 5 \times 1 + 7 \times 0.1 + 8 \times 0.01$$
$$= 40 + 5 + 0.7 + 0.08$$
$$= 45.78$$

In the number 6543 the 6 means 6000 because it has a face value of 6 and a place value of 1000.

$$\text{Total value} = \text{face value} \times \text{place value}$$
$$6000 = 6 \times 1000$$

In the number 543.21 the 2 has a place value of 0.1.

$$\text{Total value} = \text{face value} \times \text{place value}$$
$$0.2 = 2 \times 0.1$$

EXERCISE

A

1. Read the following numbers.
   (a) 4527
   (b) 6384
   (c) 5603
   (d) 7006
   (e) 175.61
   (f) 6462.7
   (g) 21.605
   (h) 0.5
   (i) 0.008

2. State the place value of the indicated digit.
   (a) 243.25
   (b) 125.6
   (c) 73.24
   (d) 12.012
   (e) 1.265
   (f) 3.007

3. State the total value of the indicated digit.
   (a) 243.75
   (b) 1527.6
   (c) 0.009
   (d) 6.763
   (e) 546 131.7
   (f) 124.8

B

4. Write the following numbers.
   (a) two thousand one hundred eleven
   (b) eleven thousand two hundred twenty
   (c) two hundred seven thousand
   (d) four and three tenths
   (e) ten and seven tenths
   (f) seven and twelve hundredths
   (g) one hundred twenty-five thousandths
   (h) four hundred fifty thousand

5. Write in expanded form.
   (a) 1247
   (b) 63 218
   (c) 12.37
   (d) 6.245
   (e) three thousand four
   (f) five and seven tenths
   (g) two hundred three thousandths
   (h) three and eight thousandths
   (i) twelve and five hundredths
   (j) eleven thousand two hundred

6. Write in standard form.
   (a) $300 + 20 + 5 + 0.6 + 0.08$
   (b) $2 \times 10 + 5 \times 1 + 3 \times 0.1 + 5 \times 0.01$
   (c) $7 \times 1 + 4 \times 0.1 + 5 \times 0.01 + 6 \times 0.001$
   (d) $5000 + 30 + 6$
   (e) $3 \times 10\ 000 + 2 \times 100 + 7 \times 1$
   (f) $4 + 0.06 + 0.008$
   (g) $5 \times 0.1 + 7 \times 0.001$
   (h) $3 \times 10 + 4 \times 0.1 + 6 \times 0.001$

APPLICATIONS

When you write a cheque, you must write the amount in words and also in numbers.

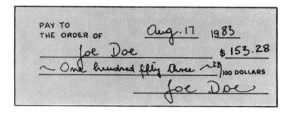

7. Write the words that correspond to these amounts.
   (a) $137.59
   (b) $2015.63
   (c) $67.09
   (d) $5005.05

8. Write these amounts in numbers.
   (a) one————————19/100 dollars
   (b) eleven————————50/100 dollars
   (c) forty-nine————————95/100 dollars
   (d) one hundred fifty————89/100 dollars

CHALLENGE

Place the numbers from 1 to 11 in the circles so that each row has the same sum.

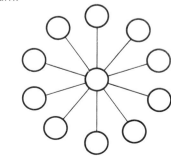

1.4 ADDITION AND SUBTRACTION WITH DECIMALS

In the Daytona 24 h endurance race, Derek Bell's lap times in minutes for five laps were:

2.034, 2.164, 1.966, 2.463, 2.111.

To find the total time for these five laps, we add:

```
  2.034
  2.164
  1.966
  2.463
+ 2.111
-------
 10.738
```

The time for the five laps was 10.738 min.

> To add decimals,
>   i) align the decimal points,
>   ii) add as with whole numbers.

REMEMBER:
ALWAYS ALIGN
THE DECIMAL
POINTS.

Example 1. Add. $65.35 + 746.8 + 0.375 + 74.03$

Solution:
```
    65.35
   746.8
     0.375
 + 74.03
 --------
  886.555
```

    Sometimes we add zeros as placeholders as in the following example.

Example 2. Calculate. $724.6 - 243.375$

Solution: (i) Rewrite the question, aligning the decimal points.
```
   724.6
 - 243.375
```

(ii) Insert zeros in the hundredths place and the thousandths place of 724.6.

(iii) Subtract as with whole numbers.
```
   724.600
 - 243.375
 ---------
   481.225
```

EXERCISE

B

1. Calculate.

   (a)
   ```
        3.65
       42.8
        5.375
    + 15.076
   ```

   (b)
   ```
      0.075
     25.0
      6.35
    + 4.06
   ```

   (c)
   ```
      4.3
    + 5.943
   ```

   (d)
   ```
     65.378
    - 21.65
   ```

   (e)
   ```
     41.26
    -  6.37
   ```

   (f)
   ```
     58.7
    + 4.635
   ```

   (g)
   ```
     75.0
    - 1.375
   ```

   (h)
   ```
        4.675
       28.03
        5.4
    + 368.27
   ```

2. Add.
   - (a) $4.65 + 0.375 + 56$
   - (b) $0.007 + 0.003 + 0.15$
   - (c) $56.3 + 7.25 + 58.3$
   - (d) $5.07 + 600.2 + 37.8$

3. Subtract.
   - (a) $43.475 - 21.633$
   - (b) $705.48 - 256.7$
   - (c) $5.38 - 2.375$
   - (d) $64.803 - 47.6$
   - (e) $285 - 49.6$
   - (f) $24 - 9.375$
   - (g) $6.047 - 3.248$

4. Simplify.
   - (a) $66.75 + 31.35 - 47.24$
   - (b) $5.675 + 8.43 - 2.718$
   - (c) $57.3 + 21.48 - 13.675$
   - (d) $24.67 - 18.35 + 4.36$
   - (e) $210.8 - 125.75 + 31.607$
   - (f) $7.5 - 3.008 + 4.63$

APPLICATIONS

5. In 1972, A. J. Foyt won the Daytona 500 in a Mercury with an average speed of 258.480 km/h. In 1979, Richard Petty won the race in an Oldsmobile with an average speed of 230.363 km/h.
   - (a) Which driver had the faster speed?
   - (b) How much faster was this speed?

6. Harriet sells real estate. In one month she made 5 sales and was paid these commissions:
$1265.00, $784.69, $565.80, $904.07, $671.75

What was Harriet's total commission for the month?

CHALLENGE

Place the numbers from 1 to 12 in the circles so that each side adds to 25.

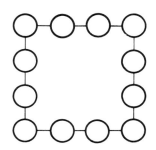

1.5 MULTIPLICATION AND DIVISION WITH DECIMALS

Gerry timed 1 lap at a go-cart track using a stop watch. The time for 1 lap was 1.268 min. How long would it take to complete 7 laps at that speed?

To find the answer, you multiply:
$1.268 \times 7 = 8.876$
It takes 8.876 min to complete the 7 laps.

To multiply decimals, we proceed as with whole numbers, then place the decimal point. To determine the number of decimal places in the answer, we count the number of decimal places in the factors.

Example 1. Multiply. 36.475×4.8

Solution:

```
   36.475          ←———— 3 decimal places
  ×  4.8           ←———— 1 decimal place
  291 800
 1459 00
 175.0800          ←———— 4 decimal places
```

$36.475 \times 4.8 = 175.08$

When dividing by decimal fractions, great care must be taken to place the decimal point correctly. Dividing by a decimal is like dividing by a whole number.

Example 2. Divide. $47.955 \div 5.75$

Solution I:

Multiply the divisor and dividend by 100 so that you divide by a whole number.

$$\frac{47.955 \times 100}{5.75 \times 100} = \frac{4795.5}{575}$$

```
            8.34
   575)4795.50
        4600
        1955
        1725
         2300
         2300
            0
```

Solution II:

Move the decimal point in the divisor two places to the right.
Move the decimal point in the dividend two places to the right and divide.

```
            8.34                8.34
  5.75)47.955        575)4795.50
       ^     ^                4600
                             1955
                             1725
                              2300
                              2300
                                 0
```

EXERCISE

B

1. Insert the decimal point in the answer. Add zeros if necessary.

   (a) $\begin{array}{r} 6.25 \\ \times\,3.8 \\ \hline 23750 \end{array}$

   (b) $\begin{array}{r} 98.1 \\ \times\,5.6 \\ \hline 54936 \end{array}$

   (c) $\begin{array}{r} 0.0025 \\ \times\,4.8 \\ \hline 12 \end{array}$

2. Multiply.

   (a) $\begin{array}{r} 43.5 \\ \times\,72 \end{array}$

   (b) $\begin{array}{r} 6.35 \\ \times\,63 \end{array}$

   (c) $\begin{array}{r} 0.349 \\ \times\,81 \end{array}$

   (d) $\begin{array}{r} 26.8 \\ \times\,4.7 \end{array}$

   (e) $\begin{array}{r} 3.75 \\ \times\,5.2 \end{array}$

   (f) $\begin{array}{r} 0.365 \\ \times\,0.54 \end{array}$

   (g) $\begin{array}{r} 66.8 \\ \times\,0.25 \end{array}$

   (h) $\begin{array}{r} 53.7 \\ \times\,0.48 \end{array}$

   (i) $\begin{array}{r} 725 \\ \times\,0.73 \end{array}$

3. Divide.

   (a) $42\overline{)71.4}$

   (b) $53\overline{)297.33}$

   (c) $6.5\overline{)37.7}$

   (d) $7.3\overline{)8.322}$

   (e) $0.375\overline{)17.55}$

   (f) $1.25\overline{)85.5}$

   (g) $87.5\overline{)222.25}$

   (h) $6.38\overline{)34.771}$

   (i) $0.05\overline{)3.19}$

   (j) $0.075\overline{)6.1425}$

4. Calculate.

   (a) 6.75×4.8

   (b) $12.88 \div 4.6$

   (c) $44.085 \div 5.35$

   (d) 32.6×0.425

   (e) $11.45 \div 0.25$

   (f) 0.575×1.24

   (g) 0.65×0.23

   (h) $0.5421 \div 0.078$

   (i) $\begin{array}{r} 675 \\ \times\,5.75 \end{array}$

   (j) $\begin{array}{r} 30\,305 \\ \times\,4.75 \end{array}$

   (k) $\begin{array}{r} 30\,527 \\ \times\,0.623 \end{array}$

   (l) $\begin{array}{r} 7346 \\ \times\,0.063 \end{array}$

APPLICATIONS

5. Badminton birds cost $0.67 each. What is the cost of 12 birds?

6. Go-cart fuel costs $0.528/L. What is the cost of 24.5 L of go-cart fuel?

7. A grade 9 class bought 32 tickets for a rock concert. The total cost was $280. What is the cost of one ticket?

8. Material for art class costs $1.25/m. One roll of material costs $22.50. How much material is in the roll?

CHALLENGE

Place the numbers from 1 to 9 in the circles so that each side adds to 17.

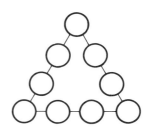

EXTRA EXTRA EXTRA EXTRA EXTRA

HIGHWAY INTERCHANGES

The interchanges on expressways are designed to make it easy for cars to change direction. There are many different designs for interchanges. The cloverleaf interchange (pictured above) is one of the most common. With this interchange, no left turns are necessary and it is not necessary to cross oncoming traffic.

EXERCISE

1. Sketch the diagram of the cloverleaf intersection shown at the right in your notebook. Trace the route you would take for each of the following.

   (a) You are driving east and you want to go south.
   (b) You are driving north and you want to go west.
   (c) You are driving west and you want to go east.

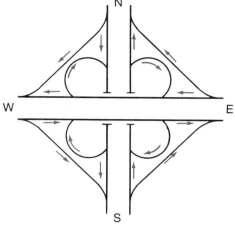

2. An all-directional interchange is shown at the right. The same exit is used for both left and right turns. It handles greater amounts of traffic at higher speeds.

   Sketch the diagram in your notebook. Trace the route you would take for each of the following.

   (a) You are driving west and you want to go south.
   (b) You are driving north and you want to go east.
   (c) You are driving south and you want to go east.

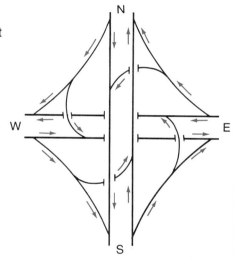

3. A partial diagram of a T-interchange is shown at the right. Complete the diagram so that cars travelling east can go north or south and cars travelling north or south can go west.

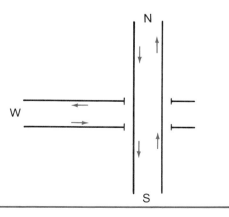

1.6 EXPONENTS AND POWERS

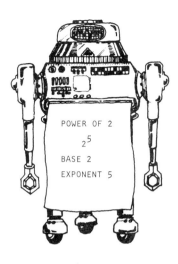

POWER OF 2

2^5

BASE 2

EXPONENT 5

2^5 means $2 \times 2 \times 2 \times 2 \times 2$

$2^5 = 32$

2^5 is read "two to the exponent five," or more simply "two to the fifth."

A number in exponential form can be written in standard form by first writing out the factors.

$$5^4 \quad = \quad 5 \times 5 \times 5 \times 5 \quad = \quad 625$$

exponential form ↗   expanded form   standard form ↗

Some numbers in standard form can be written in exponential form.

$125 = 5 \times 5 \times 5 = 5^3$

$49 = 7 \times 7 = 7^2$

EXERCISE

A

1. State the base and exponent.
   (a) 3^5 (b) 2^4 (c) 6^3
   (d) 7^5 (e) 11^6 (f) 8^7

2. State in exponential form.
   (a) $2 \times 2 \times 2 \times 2$ (b) $3 \times 3 \times 3$
   (c) $61 \times 61 \times 61$ (d) 475×475
   (e) $525 \times 525 \times 525 \times 525 \times 525$

B

3. Write in expanded form.
   (a) 5^3 (b) 3^5
   (c) 47^4 (d) 65^2
   (e) 375^3 (f) 425^3

4. Write as a power with base 2.
   (a) 8   (b) 16   (c) 32   (d) 64

5. Write in standard form.
   (a) 3^2 (b) 2^3 (c) 5^3
   (d) 6^2 (e) 6^3 (f) 7^3
   (g) 2^4 (h) 2^5 (i) 4^3

6. Which is larger?
   (a) 2^3 or 3^2
   (b) 3^5 or 5^3
   (c) 47^3 or 72^2

CHALLENGE

Find as many spelled-out numbers as you can.

Start in any square and move in any direction. Do not enter the same square twice while spelling a word.

S	X	T	Y
I	U	R	E
F	O	E	O
I	V	T	N

1.7 MULTIPLYING WITH POWERS

You can multiply $2^3 \times 2^5$ using exponents.

$2^3 = 2 \times 2 \times 2$

$2^5 = 2 \times 2 \times 2 \times 2 \times 2$

$2^3 \times 2^5 = \underbrace{(2 \times 2 \times 2)}_{\text{3 factors}} \times \underbrace{(2 \times 2 \times 2 \times 2 \times 2)}_{\text{5 factors}}$

$2^3 \times 2^5 = \underbrace{2 \times 2 \times 2 \times 2 \times 2 \times 2 \times 2 \times 2}_{\text{8 factors}}$

$= 2^8$

The 2 has been used as a factor 8 times.

TO MULTIPLY, ADD THE EXPONENTS IF THE BASES ARE THE SAME.

You can multiply numbers with the same base by adding the exponents.

$2^3 \times 2^5 = 2^{3+5} = 2^8$

$65^4 \times 65^7 = 65^{4+7} = 65^{11}$

You cannot multiply $3^5 \times 2^5$ using exponents because the bases are not the same.

EXERCISE

A

1. Find the missing exponent.
   (a) $3^2 \times 3^7 = 3^\blacksquare$
   (b) $7^2 \times 7^3 = 7^\blacksquare$
   (c) $23^3 \times 23^2 = 23^\blacksquare$
   (d) $41^3 \times 41^2 = 41^\blacksquare$
   (e) $25^2 \times 25^4 = 25^\blacksquare$
   (f) $4^8 \times 4^2 = 4^\blacksquare$

B

2. State the products in exponential form.
   (a) $3^2 \times 3^5$ (b) $2^4 \times 2^2$
   (c) $6^3 \times 6^2$ (d) $5^3 \times 5^2$
   (e) $4^3 \times 4^2$ (f) $7^3 \times 7^4$
   (g) $31^2 \times 31^3$ (h) $5^4 \times 5^3$
   (i) $35^3 \times 35^4$ (j) $25^2 \times 25^5$
   (k) $75^4 \times 75^7$ (l) $27^4 \times 27^5$
   (m) $395^3 \times 395^5$ (n) $5^3 \times 5^4$

3. State the products in exponential form.
   (a) 8×16 (b) 4×32
   (c) 9×27 (d) 25×125
   (e) 100×100 (f) 16×64
   (g) 125×125 (h) 100×1000

4. Which is larger?
   (a) $2^3 \times 2^2$ or 25
   (b) $6^2 \times 6^2$ or 200
   (c) $2^4 \times 2^2$ or 250
   (d) $2^3 \times 2^3$ or 3^4

CHALLENGE

The number $2^5 \times 9^2$ is an unusual one. Find its value. What is unusual about the value?

1.8 DIVIDING WITH POWERS

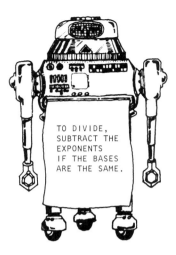

TO DIVIDE,
SUBTRACT THE
EXPONENTS
IF THE BASES
ARE THE SAME.

You can divide 3^6 by 3^2 by subtracting exponents because the bases are the same.

$$3^6 \div 3^2 = \frac{3^6}{3^2}$$
$$= \frac{3 \times 3 \times 3 \times 3 \times 3 \times 3}{3 \times 3}$$
$$= \frac{729}{9}$$
$$= 81$$
$$= 3^4$$
$$3^6 \div 3^2 = 3^{6-2} = 3^4$$
$$35^5 \div 35^3 = 35^{5-3} = 35^2$$

You cannot divide 5^6 by 3^6 using exponents because the bases are not the same.

EXERCISE

A

1. Find the missing exponent.
   (a) $3^7 \div 3^4 = 3^\blacksquare$
   (b) $6^7 \div 6^2 = 6^\blacksquare$
   (c) $4^8 \div 4^4 = 4^\blacksquare$
   (d) $5^{10} \div 5^5 = 5^\blacksquare$
   (e) $35^8 \div 35^6 = 35^\blacksquare$
   (f) $125^{11} \div 125^8 = 125^\blacksquare$

B

2. Write the quotients in exponential form.
   (a) $3^6 \div 3^4$ (b) $5^7 \div 5^4$
   (c) $5^7 \div 5^2$ (d) $6^8 \div 6^6$
   (e) $31^7 \div 31^5$ (f) $48^3 \div 48^2$
   (g) $15^7 \div 15^2$ (h) $75^9 \div 75^5$
   (i) $12^7 \div 12^5$ (j) $63^5 \div 63^3$

3. Write the quotients in exponential form.
   (a) $1246^7 \div 1246^5$
   (b) $6305^5 \div 6305^3$

4. Which is larger?
   (a) $3^7 \div 1^4$ or 5^2
   (b) $5^3 \div 5^2$ or $2^8 \div 2^4$
   (c) $65^4 \div 65^2$ or 4000
   (d) $39^6 \div 39^4$ or 15^2
   (e) $25^5 \div 25^3$ or $2^7 \div 2^4 \times 50$

CHALLENGE

Draw a clock face.
Draw a line across it so that the sum of the numbers on each side of the line is the same.

1.9 THE POWER LAW

In earlier chapters we saw that

2^5 means $2 \times 2 \times 2 \times 2 \times 2$ and $2^5 = 32$.

In this section we evaluate more complicated powers. We can evaluate $(5^2)^3$ in two ways:

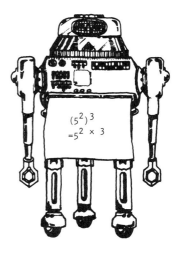

(i)   evaluating 5^2 first.
$$(5^2)^3 = (25)^3$$
$$= 25 \times 25 \times 25$$
$$= 15\,625$$

(ii) applying the multiplication rule first.
$$(5^2)^3 = 5^2 \times 5^2 \times 5^2$$
$$= 5^{2+2+2}$$
$$= 5^6$$
$$= 15\,625$$

$(5^2)^3 = 5^6$ suggests $(5^2)^3 = 5^{2 \times 3} = 5^6$

We find the power of a power by multiplying the exponents.
$$(3^4)^2 = 3^{4 \times 2} = 3^8$$

EXERCISE

B

1. Evaluate.
   (a) $(3^2)^3$ (b) $(3^3)^2$
   (c) $(5^3)^2$ (d) $(5^4)^1$
   (e) $(2^5)^2$ (f) $(2^2)^4$
   (g) $(2^4)^2$ (h) $(4^2)^2$
   (i) $(6^3)^2$ (j) $(5^0)^4$

2. Evaluate.
   (a) $(2^2)^2$ (b) $(3^3)^3$
   (c) $(1^2)^3$ (d) $(2^1)^3$
   (e) $(10^2)^3$ (f) $(10^3)^3$

C

3. Evaluate.
   (a) $(0.3^2)^2$ (b) $(0.2^2)^3$
   (c) $(1.1^1)^2$ (d) $(1.2^2)^0$
   (e) $(3.5^2)^3$ (f) $(0.7^3)^2$

CHALLENGE

Copy and complete the following.

$1^3 = 1$
$1^3 + 2^3 = 9$
$1^3 + 2^3 + 3^3 = $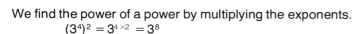
$1^3 + 2^3 + 3^3 + 4^3 = $ ▨
$1^3 + 2^3 + 3^3 + 4^3 + 5^3 = $ ▨

What pattern can you find here?

1.10 ORDER OF OPERATIONS

The following instructions are provided with some combination locks.

DEPRESS SHACKLE BEFORE DIALING A COMBINATION

Turn right two whole turns and stop at . . . . No 25

Turn left one whole turn past above number . . . . No 16
and stop at . . . .

Turn right, stop at . . . . No 32

PULL SHACKLE OPEN   TO CLOSE SNAP SHACKLE IN LOCK

If you do not follow these steps the lock will not open. You must perform these steps in the order given.

There is a definite order of operations when simplifying numerical expressions. The following chart helps us to remember the order of operations.

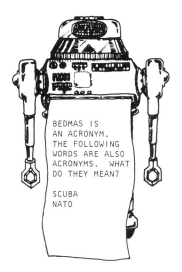

BEDMAS IS AN ACRONYM. THE FOLLOWING WORDS ARE ALSO ACRONYMS. WHAT DO THEY MEAN?

SCUBA
NATO

B	E	D M	A S
Do the computations in brackets first.	Simplify numbers with exponents and "of."	Divide or multiply in the order in which ÷ and × appear from left to right.	Add or subtract in the order in which + and − appear from left to right.

The word BEDMAS helps to remember the order.

When we write $5(12 - 4)$, we mean that 5 multiplies the quantity in the brackets.

$$5(12 - 4) = 5(8)$$
$$= 40$$

The following examples indicate the order in which the operations are performed.

Example 1. Simplify. $7 \times (8 - 3) + 7$

Solution: $7 \times (8 - 3) + 7$ ◀━━ Bracket
$= 7 \times 5 + 7$ ◀━━ Multiply
$= 35 + 7$ ◀━━ Add
$= 42$

Example 2. Simplify. $5 + 7 \times 2^3 - 9$

Solution: $5 + 7 \times 2^3 - 9$ ◀━━ Exponent
$= 5 + 7 \times 8 - 9$ ◀━━ Multiply
$= 5 + 56 - 9$ ◀━━ Add
$= 61 - 9$ ◀━━ Subtract
$= 52$

EXERCISE

A

1. Calculate.

   (a) $\frac{1}{2}$ of 10

   (b) $\frac{1}{3}$ of 30

   (c) $\frac{1}{2}$ of 14

   (d) $\frac{1}{4}$ of 20

   (e) $\frac{1}{2}$ of 24

   (f) $\frac{1}{4}$ of 24

   (g) $\frac{1}{4}$ of 44

   (h) $\frac{1}{5}$ of 30

B

2. Simplify.

   (a) $5 + 3 \times 7$

   (b) $25 - 3 \times 5$

   (c) $16 - 5 + 3$

   (d) $12 - 6 \times 0$

   (e) $0 \div 5 + 7$

   (f) $28 \div 4 \times 5$

   (g) $8 \times 4 \div 16$

   (h) $8 \times 2 - 2$

3. Simplify.

   (a) $3^2 - 1$

   (b) $2^2 + 3^2$

   (c) $3^2 - 2^3$

   (d) $(8 - 5)^2$

   (e) $8^2 - 4^3$

   (f) $24 - 3^2$

   (g) $(5 - 3)^3$

   (h) $1^2 + 2^2$

4. Calculate.

   (a) $3(2 + 4)$

   (b) $6(4 + 1)$

   (c) $(3 + 2)4$

   (d) $3 + (2 + 5)$

   (e) $(7 - 1) \div 2$

   (f) $12 \div (6 - 2)$

   (g) $4(6 + 1)$

   (h) $(10 - 8)^3$

   (i) $(5 - 2)^2$

5. Simplify.

   (a) $6 \times (5 + 2) - 7$

   (b) $7 \times 0 + 4 \times 6$

   (c) $(7 - 5) \times (4 + 8)$

   (d) $(6 - 2)^2 \div (2 \times 4)$

   (e) $2 \times 6 \div 3 \times 6$

   (f) $5 \times (3 + 8) - 8$

   (g) $(3^2 - 1) + 5 \times 12$

   (h) $(4 + 1)^2 \div (7 - 2)$

C

6. Calculate.

   (a) $5 \times 3^2 + 6(11 + 9)$

   (b) $12 \times 6 \div 3 \times 2 \div 12$

   (c) $(7^2 - 4) \div (4^2 - 7)$

   (d) $3(4 \times 9 - 24) + 7$

   (e) $5 \times 9 + (8 - 3) + 2^3$

   (f) $(1^3 + 2^2 + 3) \div 2^2$

   (g) $3^2 \times 2^3 \div 6^2$

   (h) $(5^2 + 5) \div (3 \times 5)$

   (i) $5(5 + 12 - 3)$

   (j) $4(3 + 5) - 3(2 + 7)$

7. Which is larger,
   $1^2 + 2^2 + 3^2$ or
   $(1 + 2 + 3)^2$?

CHALLENGE

Remove two toothpicks so that exactly two squares remain.

1.11 ROUNDING OFF NUMBERS

Statements such as
"There are 4 sharks" or
"There are 24 dolphins"
are considered exact because we can actually count the fish.

Sometimes exact numbers are not required and we use rounded numbers.

A statement such as

"The earth is 150 000 000 km from the sun" is an example of the use of a rounded number.

> To round off a number to a desired place value, we look at the face value of the digit to the right of the desired place value.
> (i) If the digit is less than 5, we round down.
> (ii) If the digit is 5 or greater, we round up.

This rule is applied to round off the numbers in the chart.

Number	Required place	Key digit	Rounded number
44 652	nearest hundred	44 6 52	44 700
725.327	nearest tenth	725.3 27	725.3
35 485	nearest thousand	35 4 85	35 000
3.275 84	nearest thousandth	3.2758 4	3.276

EXERCISE

A

1. Round to the nearest ten.
   (a) 375   (b) 283
   (c) 64 309   (d) 25 615

2. Round to the nearest thousand.
   (a) 26 623   (b) 34 438
   (c) 7385   (d) 64 805

3. Round to the nearest hundred.
   (a) 64 307   (b) 5718
   (c) 7216   (d) 8015

4. Round to the nearest ten thousand.
   (a) 65 772   (b) 435 207
   (c) 6 357 204   (d) 253 832

5. Round to the nearest tenth.
   (a) 75.25   (b) 6.375
   (c) 6.215   (d) 35.85

6. Round to the nearest hundredth.
   (a) 3.275   (b) 56.803
   (c) 0.488   (d) 0.0575

7. Round to the nearest thousandth.
   (a) 3.123 45   (b) 6.076 543
   (c) 0.03575   (d) 0.215 836

1.12 ESTIMATING

We find estimates using rounded numbers. For example, if cassettes cost $6.85 each, then an estimate for 8 cassettes is
$$8 \times \$7 = \$56.$$

To find an estimate, first round the numbers, then calculate using the rounded numbers.

IN ESTIMATING, CALCULATIONS MUST BE SIMPLE ENOUGH TO BE DONE MENTALLY.

Example. Estimate the answer.

(a) 21.6×47.2　　(b) $\dfrac{8.3 \times 61.7}{77}$

Solution: (a) $21.6 \times 47.2 \doteq 20 \times 50$
$$\doteq 1000$$

(b) $\dfrac{8.3 \times 61.7}{77} \doteq \dfrac{8 \times 60}{80}$
$$\doteq 6$$

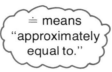

$\doteq$ means "approximately equal to."

EXERCISE

A

1. Estimate to insert the decimal.
   (a) $53.6 \div 28.7 = 186759$
   (b) $7485 \div 21.8 = 343348$
   (c) $3752 \div 846 = 443498$
   (d) $0.057 \div 8.65 = 658959$
   (e) $0.897 \div 0.513 = 174854$
   (f) $\dfrac{67.5 \times 81.3}{38.6} = 1421697$
   (g) $\dfrac{22\,400}{63.5 \times 88.6} = 3981444$

B

2. Estimate the answer.
   (a) 385×223
   (b) $5375 \div 21.6$
   (c) $0.065 \div 0.57$
   (d) $86.7 \div 8.75$
   (e) $\dfrac{7.75 \times 56.8}{3.75}$
   (f) $\dfrac{27.85}{2.95 \times 9.75}$

APPLICATIONS

3. Estimate the price of the following.
   (a) 6 pencils at $0.59 each
   (b) 8 pocket books at $1.95 each
   (c) 4 shovels at $19.95 each
   (d) 3 record albums at $11.95 each

4. Estimate these sums.
   (a) $8 + 13 + 21 + 32$
   (b) $3.7 + 8.2 + 9.7$
   (c) $\$1.95 + \$0.95 + \$7.95$
   (d) $\$2.25 + \$5.75 + \$9.20$

CHALLENGE

Move 4 toothpicks to make 3 squares.

1.13 VARIABLES IN ALGEBRAIC EXPRESSIONS

We use symbols to give us certain forms of information. What information is given to us by these road symbols?

In mathematical expressions, we use symbols.
Expressions such as
$$5a, n + 5, 2(\ell + w)$$
are called algebraic expressions. The letter symbols a, n, ℓ, and w are called variables.

A variable is a symbol used to represent one or more numbers.

When we write an expression such as 5a, the multiplication symbol is understood, so that 5a means $5 \times a$.

The value of an algebraic expression depends on the number used to replace the variable.
When a = 3, the value of 5a is $5 \times 3 = 15$.
When n = 8, the value of n + 5 is $8 + 5 = 13$.

Example 1. Evaluate $2x + 5$ when $x \in \{3, 4, 6.3\}$.

Solution:

When x = 3,
$$2x + 5 = 2(3) + 5$$
$$= 6 + 5$$
$$= 11$$

When x = 4
$$2x + 5 = 2(4) + 5$$
$$= 8 + 5$$
$$= 13$$

When x = 6.3
$$2x + 5 = 2(6.3) + 5$$
$$= 12.6 + 5$$
$$= 17.6$$

-y MEANS -1 x y

Algebraic expressions can contain more than one variable. For example $3x - 2y + 7z$ is an algebraic expression with three variables.

Example 2. Evaluate $3x - y + 7z$ for x = 5, y = 3, z = 4

Solution: $3x - y + 7z = 3(5) - (3) + 7(4)$
$$= 15 - 3 + 28$$
$$= 40$$

When we evaluate algebraic expressions we substitute first, then simplify using BEDMAS.

EXERCISE

A

1. Evaluate 5x when x equals
   (a) 3   (b) 5   (c) 7
   (d) 4   (e) 1   (f) 8

2. Evaluate 2x + 1 when x equals
   (a) 3   (b) 5   (c) 0
   (d) 6   (e) 2   (f) 9

3. Evaluate 3x − 2 when x equals
   (a) 1   (b) 3   (c) 10
   (d) 6   (e) 5   (f) 9

B

4. If x = 2 and y = 3, evaluate.
   (a) $x + y$ (b) $2x + y$
   (c) $x + 2y$ (d) $(x + y)^2$
   (e) $x^2 + y^2$ (f) $x^2 + 2xy + y^2$
   (g) $5x - 3y$ (h) xy
   (i) $4xy$ (j) $xy + 7$

5. Evaluate the following.
   (a) $3x + 7$ when $x = 5$
   (b) $2x - 6$ when $x = 3$
   (c) $x^2 + 1$ when $x = 4$
   (d) $x^2 + x$ when $x = 2$
   (e) $(x - 3)^2$ when $x = 5$
   (f) $x^2 - 3x + 2$ when $x = 4$
   (g) $7x - 4$ when $x = 1.5$
   (h) $17 - 3x$ when $x = 2.1$

C

6. If x = 5, which is larger?
   (a) $x + 3$ or $11 - x$
   (b) $x^2 + 5$ or $(x + 5)^2$
   (c) $x - 5$ or $x^2 - 20$
   (d) $3x + 7$ or $3(x + 2)$

7. What do these road symbols mean?
   (a)
   (b)

   (c)
   (d)

   (e)
   (f)

CHALLENGE

How many different squares are in this picture?

1.14 FORMULAS FROM GEOMETRY

We have found the area of a rectangle using the formula
$$\text{Area} = \text{length} \times \text{width}.$$

We can write this formula using variables:
$$A = \ell w \qquad \text{or} \qquad A = \ell \times w$$

Many formulas contain variables. In this section we shall work with formulas that deal with perimeter, area, and volume.

The perimeter, P, of a geometric figure is the distance around it. In this figure, the perimeter is 10 cm.

The area, A, of a geometric figure is the amount of surface it covers. In this figure the area is 6 cm².

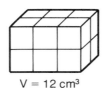

$V = 12 \text{ cm}^3$

The volume, V, of a geometric figure is the amount of space it occupies. In this figure, the volume is 12 cm³.

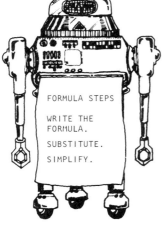

FORMULA STEPS

WRITE THE
FORMULA.
SUBSTITUTE.
SIMPLIFY.

Example. The formula for the area of a triangle is
$$A = \frac{1}{2}bh \qquad \text{or} \qquad A = \frac{1}{2} \times b \times h$$
where b is the length of the base and h is the height. Find the area of the triangle with base b = 12 cm and height h = 8 cm.

Solution: $A = \frac{1}{2}bh$

$A = \frac{1}{2}(12)(8)$

$\quad = 48$

The area is 48 cm².

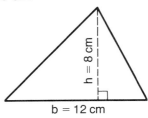

EXERCISE

B

1. The formula for perimeter of a rectangle is
   $P = 2 (\ell + w)$.

   Find the perimeter of each of these rectangles.

   (a)
   5 cm

   (b)
   3 cm
   8 cm

   12 cm

   (c) $\ell = 18$ cm and $w = 12$ cm
   (d) $\ell = 7$ cm and $w = 2$ cm

2. The perimeter of a square is
   $P = 4s$.

   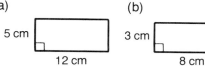

   Find the perimeter of these squares.

   (a)
   6 cm

   (b)
   7.5 cm

   (c) $s = 24$ cm
   (d) $s = 5.8$ cm

3. To find the perimeter of a triangle, add the lengths of the three sides.
   $P = a + b + c$

   Find the perimeter.

   (a)
   18 cm 9 cm
   16 cm

   (b) 3.5 cm
   6 cm 7.5 cm

   (c) $a = 8$ cm, $b = 7$ cm, $c = 7$ cm
   (d) $a = 5$ cm, $b = 8$ cm, $c = 9$ cm

4. The opposite sides of a parallelogram are equal. The formula for the perimeter is
   $P = 2 (a + b)$.

   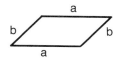

   Find the perimeter.

   (a)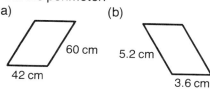
   60 cm
   42 cm

   (b)
   5.2 cm
   3.6 cm

   (c) $a = 25$ cm and $b = 16$ cm
   (d) $a = 7$ m and $b = 9$ m

5. The perimeter of a circle is called the circumference. The formulas for circumference are
   $C = \pi d$ or $C = 2\pi r$.

   d: diameter
   r: radius
   $\pi \doteq 3.14$

   Find the circumference.

   (a)
   65 cm

   (b)
   14 cm

   (c)
   30 cm

   (d)
   22 cm

   (e)
   26.5 cm

   (f)
   35 cm

6. To find the area of a rectangle, we use the formula
A = ℓw.

Find the area.

(a)

7.6 cm

(b)

4.3 cm

2.7 cm

8.5 cm

(c) ℓ = 38 cm, w = 23 cm
(d) ℓ = 6.5 cm, w = 6.2 cm

7. The formula for the area of a square is
A = s².

Find the area of each square.

(a)

75 cm

(b)

6.3 m

(c) s = 45 cm   (d) s = 3.2 cm

8. The formula for the area of a triangle is

$A = \frac{1}{2}bh.$

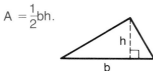

h

b

Find the area of each triangle.

(a)

4 cm

7 cm

(b)

3.4 cm

3.4 cm

(c) b = 35 cm, h = 24 cm
(d) b = 6.4 cm, h = 3.5 cm

9. The area of a parallelogram is found using the formula
A = bh.

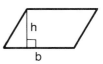

h

b

Find the area.

(a)

7 cm

6 cm

(b)

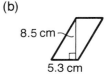

8.5 cm

5.3 cm

(c) b = 65 cm, h = 43 cm
(d) b = 8.3 cm, h = 5.7 cm

10. The formula for area of a circle is
A = πr².

π ≐ 3.14

Find the area.

(a)

15 cm

(b)

6.5 cm

(c) r = 75 cm   (d) r = 5.5 cm

11. A trapezoid has 2 of its four sides parallel. The formula for area of a trapezoid is

$A = \frac{1}{2} \times h (a + b).$

b

h

a

Find the area.

(a)

24 cm

35 cm

28 cm

(b)

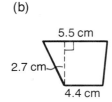

5.5 cm

2.7 cm

4.4 cm

(c) a = 44 cm, b = 56 cm, h = 36 cm
(d) a = 4.8 cm, b = 6.2 cm, h = 9 cm

12. The formula for the volume of a rectangular solid is
V = ℓwh.

Find the volume.

(a)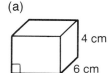

4 cm
6 cm
5 cm

(b)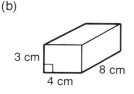

3 cm
8 cm
4 cm

(c) ℓ = 12 cm, w = 8 cm, h = 7 cm
(d) ℓ = 3.5 cm, w = 4.2 cm, h = 2.6 cm

13. The formula for volume of a cube is
V = s³.

s
s
s

Find the volume.

(a)

6 cm
6 cm
6 cm

(b)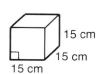

15 cm
15 cm
15 cm

(c) s = 12 cm
(d) s = 50 cm

14. The volume of a cylinder is found using the formula
V = πr²h.
π ≐ 3.14

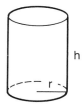

h
r

Find the volume.

(a)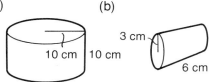

10 cm
10 cm

(b)
3 cm
6 cm

(c) r = 30 cm, h = 10 cm
(d) r = 50 cm, h = 12 cm

APPLICATIONS

A rectangular swimming pool is 4.8 m wide, 9.6 m long, and 1.5 m deep.

15. What is the distance around the edge of the pool?
16. What is the area of a solar blanket to just cover the pool?
17. Find the amount of water in the pool.

A large cylindrical storage tank is 7.5 m high and has a radius of 20 m.

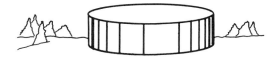

18. Find the diameter of the tank.
19. What is the area of the top of the tank?
20. What is the volume of the tank?

CHALLENGE

Copy this figure.
Place the numbers
5,6,7,8,9,10,11,12,13,14,15
in the circles so that the sum along any line is 30.

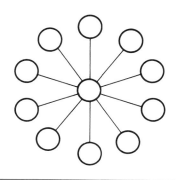

THE BINARY NUMBER SYSTEM

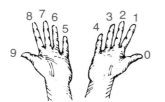

The human hands are the basis for the decimal number system which uses ten digits.

$$0, 1, 2, 3, 4, 5, 6, 7, 8, 9$$

Computers are electronic devices. Since electricity has only two states—"on" or "off"—computers have only two "fingers": 0 and 1.

0	1
no current flowing	current flowing
switch is off	switch is on
light is off	light is on
low voltage	high voltage
hole is not punched	hole is punched

The Binary Number System uses the digits 0 or 1 to represent numbers. The table at the left lists the numbers from 0 to 24 in Decimal and Binary.

Decimal	Binary
0	0
1	1
2	10
3	11
4	100
5	101
6	110
7	111
8	1000
9	1001
10	1010
11	1011
12	1100
13	1101
14	1110
15	1111
16	10000
17	10001
18	10010
19	10011
20	10100
21	10101
22	10110
23	10111
24	11000

The computer uses these four simple rules to add:

$$0 + 0 = 0$$
$$0 + 1 = 1$$
$$1 + 0 = 1$$
$$1 + 1 = 10 \text{ (or 0 and carry 1)}$$

The following are some examples of binary addition.

(a)
```
  101
+  10
─────
  111
```

(b)
```
  101
+ 110
─────
 1011
```

(c)
```
  111
+ 111
─────
 1110
```

EXERCISE

1. Complete the binary additions.

(a)
```
 1000
+ 101
```

(b)
```
 1010
+1101
```

(c)
```
 1101
+1011
```

2. Change each decimal number to a binary number and then add.

(a)
```
  13
+  9
```

(b)
```
  11
+ 12
```

(c)
```
  15
+  5
```

(d)
```
  14
+ 10
```

1.15 CHAPTER 1 REVIEW EXERCISE

B

1. Perform the indicated operation.
   (a) $\begin{array}{r} 3724 \\ +8168 \\ \hline \end{array}$
   (b) $\begin{array}{r} 3940 \\ -2652 \\ \hline \end{array}$
   (c) $56\overline{)1288}$
   (d) $\begin{array}{r} 6536 \\ \times 209 \\ \hline \end{array}$
   (e) $36 + 47 - 52 + 16$
   (f) $27 \times 15 - 306$
   (g) $36\,530 - 21\,607$
   (h) $32\,420 + 64\,585$
   (i) $5590 \div 86$

2. Simplify.
   (a) $\begin{array}{r} 431 \\ 2165 \\ 408 \\ +635 \\ \hline \end{array}$
   (b) $\begin{array}{r} 2\,526 \\ 75\,811 \\ 5\,218 \\ +21\,306 \\ \hline \end{array}$
   (c) $\begin{array}{r} 8107 \\ \times 513 \\ \hline \end{array}$
   (d) $\begin{array}{r} 375\,216 \\ -216\,375 \\ \hline \end{array}$
   (e) $\dfrac{21\,620}{92}$
   (f) $\begin{array}{r} 3645 \\ \times 808 \\ \hline \end{array}$
   (g) $256 + 725 - 538$
   (h) $1431 \div 27 \times 63$
   (i) $75 \times 81 + 17$
   (j) $623 \div 7 + 2512$
   (k) $(725)^2$

3. Simplify.
   (a) $\begin{array}{r} 32.675 \\ -18.426 \\ \hline \end{array}$
   (b) $\begin{array}{r} 3.25 \\ \times 6.4 \\ \hline \end{array}$
   (c) $\begin{array}{r} 5.755 \\ 36.85 \\ 432.6 \\ +40.24 \\ \hline \end{array}$
   (d) $36\overline{)172.8}$
   (e) $7.6\overline{)196.08}$
   (f) $3.65 + 24.72 + 657.4 + 13.307$
   (g) $37.65 + 21.83 - 42.64$
   (h) $604.8 - 425.6 + 140.7$

4. Round off as indicated.
   (a) 371 to the nearest ten
   (b) 0.371 to the nearest tenth
   (c) 76 134 218 to the nearest million
   (d) 54.925 to the nearest one

5. Estimate the answer.
   (a) 38.75×21.46
   (b) $320\,000 \div 18\,500$
   (c) $(407)^2$
   (d) $0.875 \div 0.45$
   (e) 72.375×2.85
   (f) 678.5×21.6

6. State the place value of the red digit.
   (a) 36 1⒉5   (b) 41.3⒍7   (c) 2⒍53
   (d) 5⒉5 702   (e) 0.1⒉4   (f) 83.7⒉

7. State the number represented by the red digit.
   (a) 12.⒍   (b) 43.3⒉1   (c) 53.6⒎5
   (d) 2954.⒊7   (e) 5.⒍07   (f) 2.4⒏8

8. Evaluate the following for $x = 8$.
   (a) $3x$ (b) $x + 3$ (c) x^3
   (d) $2x - 5$ (e) $25 - x$ (f) $16 - 2x$

9. Evaluate the following for $x = 2$ and $y = 5$.
   (a) $x + y$ (b) $2x + y$
   (c) $x + 2y$ (d) $2x + 2y$
   (e) $2(x + y)$ (f) $x^2 + y^2$

10. The formula for the distance, d metres, that an object falls in t seconds is $d = 4.9\,t^2$.
    Find the distance an object falls in
    (a) 3 s   (b) 7 s
    (c) 2.5 s   (d) 5.2 s

11. The following formula relates height (in centimetres) and mass (in kilograms) for young adults.
    $$m = \frac{6(h - 90)}{7}$$
    (a) Frank is 150 cm tall. What should his mass be?
    (b) Prepare a height chart.

Height	Mass
100 cm	
110 cm	
180 cm	

CHAPTER 1 TEST

1. Write these numbers using numerals.
   (a) four hundred sixty thousand
   (b) thirty thousand twelve
   (c) six and thirty-one thousandths
   (d) one hundred twenty-five thousandths

2. State the place value of the indicated digit.
   (a) 32 1**2**5   (b) 5.0**7**4   (c) 63.2**0**5   (d) 3 4**0**7.25

3. Round these numbers to the nearest hundred.
   (a) 35 647   (b) 2546   (c) 2546.7   (d) 345 638

4. Round these numbers to the nearest tenth.
   (a) 5.634   (b) 15.275   (c) 0.647   (d) 1.345

5. Perform the operation indicated.
   (a) $\begin{array}{r} 65\,208 \\ +\,17\,516 \\ \hline \end{array}$ 　　　　(b) $\begin{array}{r} 7.65 \\ -\,3.208 \\ \hline \end{array}$

   (c) $\begin{array}{r} 5.12 \\ \times\,3.07 \\ \hline \end{array}$ 　　(d) $\dfrac{17.86}{4.7}$

6. (a) Write 32 as a power with base 2.
   (b) Write 64 as a power with base 4.

7. Evaluate.
   (a) 3^2 (b) 2^3 (c) 5^3 (d) 4^1

8. Write the answer in exponential form.
   (a) $2^3 \times 2^5$ (b) $7^6 \div 7^3$ (c) $4^2 \div 4^2$ (d) $5^3 \times 5^2$

9. Simplify.
   (a) $16 - 4 \times 3$ 　　　　(b) $\dfrac{1}{3}$ of 36
   (c) $3^2 + 2^2$ 　　　　(d) $3(4 + 7)$
   (e) $4(5 + 3) - 7$ 　　　　(f) $4(3 + 7) - 2(8 - 5)$

10. Evaluate for $x = 2$ and $y = 3$.
    (a) $3x$ 　　　　(b) x^3 　　　　(c) $x + 3$
    (d) $x + y$ 　　　　(e) xy 　　　　(f) $2x + 3y$

PROBLEM SOLVING

REVIEW AND PREVIEW TO CHAPTER 2

USING YOUR CALCULATOR

The hand-held calculator makes quick and accurate computation possible for all of us. In order to get correct answers when using calculators, we must know basic arithmetic operations. The following sequence of operations can be used on most calculators.

Problem: 276 + 547 − 468

Display

| 0.00 |
| 276. |
| 547. |
| 823. |
| 468. |
| 355. |

Buttons Pressed

C
2 7 6
+
5 4 7
−
4 6 8
=

Problem: 7368 ÷ 307

Display

| 0.00 |
| 7368. |
| 307. |
| 24. |

Buttons Pressed

C
7 3 6 8
÷
3 0 7
=

Problem: 315 × 37

Display

| 0.00 |
| 315. |
| 37. |
| 11655 |

Buttons Pressed

C
3 1 5
×
3 7
=

The exercise on the opposite page can be worked with or without a calculator. These interesting questions will help you to recall some basic arithmetic facts.

EXERCISE

The following figure is called a magic square. All columns, rows, and diagonals add to the magic number 15.

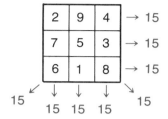

1. Copy and complete these magic squares.

   (a)

		8
	10	
12		16

   (b)

		7
8	3	10

   (c)

		15
		8
9		13

   (d)

7	17	15
		5

2. Determine which of these are magic squares.

   (a)

1	12	7	14
8	13	2	11
10	3	16	5
15	6	9	4

   (b)

0	14	18	28
22	24	4	10
12	2	30	16
26	20	8	6

   (c)

15	2	19	6	23
22	14	1	18	10
9	21	13	5	17
16	8	25	12	4
3	20	7	24	11

3. The large square is a magic square. Each small square is also magic.
   (a) Find the magic numbers.
   (b) Complete the magic squares.

71			8			53	46	51
66				5				
67		65	4		2	49		
26		24	44			42	62		60
	23			41				61
		20	40					56
35		33	80					
30				77		12		
31			76		74	13	18	11

4. Here are three magic squares, one inside another.
   (a) Find the magic numbers.
   (b) Complete the magic squares.

12				10		2
	20		35		14	
8		24		22		
9			25		33	
44				26	32	
47		13			30	
	1	4	5			38

USING YOUR CALCULATOR: ⊟

In this section we shall look at some features that are found on many calculators. For special features found on more advanced calculators, you should check the user's manual.

We can divide the calculator keys into 3 groups.

number keys	operation keys	special function keys
7 8 9	× ÷	M+ M− MR MC
4 5 6	+ −	% c/ce
1 2 3		+ − ·
0		

It is important to know how these keys work.

EXERCISE

1. Does your calculator have a constant for addition?
   Press.
   C 2 + 3 = = = =
   If your display reads:
   5—you do not have the repeating function.
   1.4—you have the repeating function.
   What will your calculator display after you press the following?
   (a) C 4 + 3 = = = =
   (b) C 1 + 5 = = =
   (c) C 3 + 2 = = = =
   (d) C 2 + = = = =
   (e) C 6 + 3 = = 6 = =
   (f) Start with 2 and make your calculator count by 3.
   (g) Start with 5 and make your calculator count by 5.

2. Does your calculator have a constant function for subtraction?
   Press.
   C 3 0 − 5 = = = =
   If your display reads:
   10—you have the repeating function
   25—you do not have the repeating function.
   What will your calculator display after you press the following?
   (a) C 2 3 − 2 = = = =
   (b) C 4 5 − 5 = = =
   (c) C 7 7 − 1 1 = = =
   (d) C 1 2 5 − 2 0 = =
   (e) C 3 5 − 5 = = 1 8 =
   (f) Start with 81 and make your calculator count backwards by 10.
   (g) Start with 120 and make your calculator count backwards by 15.

3. Does your calculator have a constant function for multiplication?
   Press.

   `C` `2` `×` `3` `=` `=` `=` `=`

   If your display reads:
   ЧВ—the 2 is the constant multiplier.
   ٦Ь２—the 3 is the constant multiplier.
   What will your calculator display after you press the following?

   (a) `C` `5` `×` `3` `=` `=`

   (b) `C` `3` `×` `2` `=` `=` `=`

   (c) `C` `4` `×` `1` `=` `=` `=`

   (d) `C` `1` `×` `4` `=` `=` `=`

   (e) `C` `2` `×` `3` `=` `5` `=`

   (f) Multiply 3 by 2 four times.
   (g) Start with 5 and multiply by 3 four times.

4. Does your calculator have a constant function for division?
   Press.

   `C` `8` `1` `÷` `3` `=` `=` `=` `=`

   If your display reads:
   ٦—you have the repeating function, ÷ 3.
   ２٦—you do not have the repeating function.
   What will your calculator display after your press the following?

   (a) `C` `1` `2` `5` `÷` `5` `=` `=`

   (b) `C` `1` `0` `2` `4` `÷` `2` `=` `=` `=`

   (c) `C` `4` `0` `9` `6` `÷` `4` `=` `=` `=`

   (d) `C` `7` `2` `9` `÷` `3` `=` `=` `=`

   (e) `C` `2` `1` `8` `7` `÷` `3` `=` `=` `9` `=`

   (f) Divide 16 384 by 2 five times.
   (g) Divide 59 049 by 3 four times.

Use the results of questions 1 to 4 to answer questions 5 to 15.
   i) Write what you think the answer is.
   ii) Check with a calculator.

5. `C` `+` `5` `=` `=` `=` `=`

6. `C` `÷` `5` `=` `=` `=`

7. `C` `−` `5` `=` `=` `=` `=`

8. `C` `÷` `5` `=` `=` `=` `=`

9. `C` `3` `+` `5` `=` `=` `=` `6` `=` `=`

10. `C` `3` `6` `−` `9` `=` `=` `=` `=`

11. `C` `3` `5` `−` `1` `2` `=` `=` `2` `=`

12. `C` `1` `×` `3` `=` `=` `=` `=`

13. `C` `2` `1` `8` `7` `÷` `3` `=` `=` `=` `=` `=`

14. `C` `1` `×` `4` `=` `=` `=` `=`

15. `C` `2` `×` `3` `=` `=` `4` `=` `=`

In these questions we look at +, −, ×, and ÷.

Press.

16. `C` `2` `+` `3` `=` `=` `+` `=` `=`

17. `C` `3` `+` `4` `=` `+` `=` `+` `=`

18. `C` `2` `×` `3` `=` `=` `×` `=` `=`

19. `C` `1` `×` `2` `=` `=` `×` `=` `×` `=`

20. `C` `6` `4` `÷` `2` `=` `=` `÷` `=`

21. `C` `7` `2` `9` `÷` `3` `=` `=` `=` `÷`

22. `C` `7` `8` `1` `2` `5` `÷` `5` `=` `=` `÷` `=`

23. `C` `1` `6` `3` `8` `4` `÷` `4` `=` `=` `÷` `=`

USING YOUR CALCULATOR: [M]

In this section we shall investigate the order in which your calculator performs calculations.

Not all calculators compute $2 + 3 \times 4$ in the same way.
$$2 + 3 \times 4 = 2 + 12$$
$$= 14$$

Using your calculator,

[C] [2] [+] [3] [×] [4] [=] $\begin{cases} 14 \\ 20 \end{cases}$

Some calculators are equipped with a priority level function. If your answer was 14, then your calculator performs $\times$ and $\div$ before $+$ and $-$.

If your answer was 20, then the priority level is determined by the person using the calculator.

To calculate $2 + 3 \times 4$, press:

[C] [3] [×] [4] [+] [2] [=] and the display is 14.

In order to perform more complicated computations using a calculator, we use the memory key M.

Example. Evaluate.
       (a) $3 \times 5 + 2 \times 8$
       (b) $(6 + 2) \times (12 - 8)$

Solution:
       (a) $3 \times 5 + 2 \times 8 = 15 + 16 = 31$

Press   [C] [3] [×] [5] [=] [M] [C] [2] [×] [8] [=] [+] [MR] [=]   The display is 31.
                        ↑   ↑

                      This key puts   This key recalls
                      the display   what is in the
                      into the   memory.
                      memory.

       (b) $(6 + 2) \times (12 - 8) = 8 \times 4 = 32$

Press   [C] [6] [+] [2] [=] [M] [C] [1] [2] [−] [8] [=] [×] [MR] [=]   The display is 32.

Check your user's manual for more information on memory keys.

EXERCISE

1. (a) Write what you think the display will read.
   (b) Check on your calculator.

   i) `C` `3` `+` `2` `=` `×` `5` `=`

   ii) `C` `3` `+` `2` `×` `5` `=`

   iii) `C` `2` `×` `5` `+` `3` `=`

2. (a) Write what you think the display will read.
   (b) Check on your calculator.

   i) `C` `2` `×` `6` `=` `M` `+` `6` `×`
      `7` `=` `+` `MR` `=`

   ii) `C` `4` `×` `5` `=` `M` `+` `7` `×`
       `8` `=` `−` `MR` `=`

   iii) `C` `5` `−` `2` `=` `M` `1` `2` `+`
        `3` `=` `÷` `MR` `=`

3. (a) Work these questions without a calculator.

   i) $2 \times 7 - 5$
   ii) $6 + 3 \times 2 - 5$
   iii) $(15 + 3) \div 2$
   iv) $7 \times (6 - 4)$
   v) $(8 + 20) - (4 + 12)$

   (b) Check your answers using your calculator.

4. Simplify using your calculator.
   (a) $6.25 + 3.1 \times 2.6$
   (b) $37.5 - 5.6 \times 3.7$
   (c) $5.65 \times 8.4 - 35.75$
   (d) $(8.3 + 2.7) \times 5.8$
   (e) $6.7 \times (12.7 - 4.9)$
   (f) $(4.49 + 5.87) \div 3.7$
   (g) $19.98 \div (11.7 - 6.3)$
   (h) $25.6 + 23.45 \times 3.5$

5. Simplify using your calculator.
   (a) $(5.6 + 7.2) \times (12.6 - 5.8)$
   (b) $7.3 \times 6.5 + 8.2 \times 9.1$
   (c) $(13.2 + 6.35) \div (4.65 - 2.35)$
   (d) $(4.6 + 2.7) \times (8.3 + 7.3)$
   (e) $5.65 + 3.7 \times 8.2 - 12.83$
   (f) $18.75 - 2.38 + 5.6 \times 2.7$

6. Simplify using your calculator.
   (a) $3.5 (2.6 + 4.2) - 6.25$
   (b) $(8.7 + 2.9) - (5.6 + 1.7)$
   (c) $6.75 \div 0.25 + 5.6 - 3.7$
   (d) $128.65 - 5.6 \times (56.3 - 47.2)$
   (e) $(6.71 - 5.36) + 3.6 \times 5.8$
   (f) $15.12 \div 5.6 - 6.84 \div 3.8$

THE EXPONENTIAL KEY

Some calculators have this key.
To compute $2^3 = 8$, press

`C` `2` `Yˣ` `3` `=`

and the display is 8.

7. Evaluate using your calculator.
   (a) 5^2 (b) 2^5
   (c) 8^2 (d) 2^8
   (e) 1.05^2 (f) 1.07^6
   (g) 1.06^8 (h) 1.04^{12}

Remember, if you do not have a Y^x key you can still evaluate 2^5 if you press

`C` `2` `×` `=` `=` `=` `=`

2.1 CHOOSING THE OPERATION

There is no quick and easy way to solve problems. However, a lot of our work can be simplified if we use an organized plan. Many problems require that we choose the correct operation: $+$, $-$, $\times$, $\div$. The following steps are helpful in solving problems.

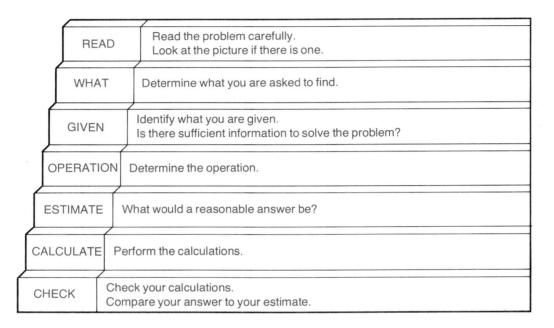

READ	Read the problem carefully. Look at the picture if there is one.
WHAT	Determine what you are asked to find.
GIVEN	Identify what you are given. Is there sufficient information to solve the problem?
OPERATION	Determine the operation.
ESTIMATE	What would a reasonable answer be?
CALCULATE	Perform the calculations.
CHECK	Check your calculations. Compare your answer to your estimate.

Example.

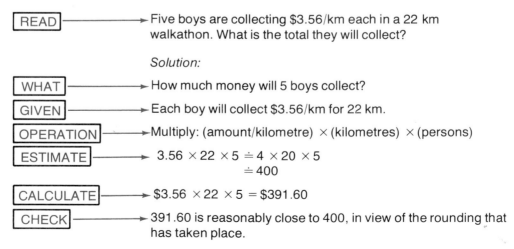

READ — Five boys are collecting $3.56/km each in a 22 km walkathon. What is the total they will collect?

Solution:

WHAT — How much money will 5 boys collect?

GIVEN — Each boy will collect $3.56/km for 22 km.

OPERATION — Multiply: (amount/kilometre) $\times$ (kilometres) $\times$ (persons)

ESTIMATE — $3.56 \times 22 \times 5 \doteq 4 \times 20 \times 5$
$\doteq 400$

CALCULATE — $3.56 \times 22 \times 5 = \$391.60$

CHECK — 391.60 is reasonably close to 400, in view of the rounding that has taken place.

$\therefore$ the boys will collect $391.60 in the walkathon.

EXERCISE

B

1. The approximate height to which a child will grow is found by doubling the height of the child on the second birthday.
   What will be the approximate full-grown height of a girl who is 78.4 cm tall on her second birthday?

2. Geraldine and her father drove east on the Trans Canada highway in separate cars. Geraldine drove at 80 km/h and her father drove at 90 km/h.

   They left from the same place at the same time.
   How far apart were they after 4 h?

3. When a spacecraft escapes the earth's gravitational pull, it must travel at least 11.8 km/s.
   How far would such a spacecraft travel in
   (a) 300 s?
   (b) 1 min?
   (c) 1 h?

4. In the election for mayor, the results are: Barkell 53 206 votes, Jones 9 561 votes, and Polaski 63 024 votes.
   (a) Who won the election?
   (b) What was the total number of votes cast in the election?

5. The Elmvale Corner Store had 65 loaves of bread to sell for $0.89 each. They sold 48 loaves.
   (a) How many loaves are left?
   (b) What is the value of the bread that is left?

6. John and Andy left Winnipeg at the same time, travelling in opposite directions. John drove at 75 km/h and Andy drove at 85 km/h.
   (a) How far did Andy drive in 3 h?
   (b) How far did John drive in 3 h?
   (c) How far apart were they after 3 h?

7. Mary and Gerrard like to solve puzzles.

   Mary can assemble the SUMA cube 13 times in the time it takes Gerrard to solve the RUBIK cube. It takes Mary 52 s to assemble a SUMA cube.
   How long does it take Gerrard to solve a RUBIK cube?

8.

   The moon completes a cycle around the earth every 28 d.
   How many cycles does the moon complete in 52 weeks?

10. A loaded truck has a mass of 5724 kg. The empty truck has a mass of 2653 kg. What is the mass of the load?

11. Lori's monthly salary is $1500. She pays $350 for rent, $265 for food and $154 for transportation.
How much money is left for other purposes?

12. Leap years are evenly divisible by 4. How many leap years are there between 1970 and 1999?

February				
	1	2	3	4	5
6	7	8	9	10	11	12
13	14	15	16	17	18	19
20	21	22	23	24	25	26
27	28	29				

13. It costs $25 to paint a white line down the centre of 1 km of highway. The line is 10 cm wide.

How much is saved on paint by painting a narrower line 8 cm wide?

14. A bicycle shop sold 65 bicycles during July for a total of $12 346.75.

What was the average price per bicycle?

15. The speed of light is 300 000 km/s.
(a) How far does light travel in 1 h?
(b) A light year is the distance light travels in one year.
How far does light travel in one year?

16. In 1963, Valentina Tereshkova, in the Russian Vostok, circled the earth 48 times in 70 h 50 min. In 1969, the Soyuz 5 spacecraft made 46 orbits in 68 h 57 min.
How much longer was the Soyuz flight than the Vostok flight?

17. NFL goalposts are 5.5 m apart. U.S. college football goalposts are 7.1 m apart.
How much wider are college goalposts than professional goalposts?

18. Radio waves travel at about 298 000 km/s.
How long will it take for a radio signal to go from the earth to the moon, a distance of 374 000 km?

19. From sea level to the top of the stratosphere, the temperature drops about 3°C/km.
(a) If this distance is 27 km, what is the total temperature change?
(b) What is the temperature at the top of the stratosphere when the temperature at sea level is 30°C?

20. A football stadium holds 52 000 people. Tickets cost $8.00 each and there are 4723 tickets left over.
    (a) How many tickets were sold?
    (b) What was the value of the tickets sold?

21. The average mass of an adult is approximately 68 kg. A commuter train carries about 45 000 persons per day. What mass is carried by the train in 5 d?

C

22. The Niagara Falls are located between Lake Ontario and Lake Erie. The falls are eating their way up the Niagara River at about 0.001 12 km/a.
    At this rate, how many years will it take to reach Lake Erie, a distance of 31.3 km?

23. Each North American clerk produces an average of 1.8 kg of waste paper each day. How much waste paper is produced by 15 clerks in 204 d?

24. Here are the diameters and the masses of the Canadian coins.

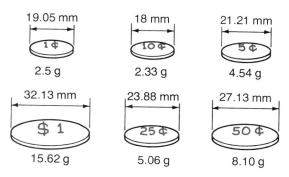

19.05 mm 1¢ 2.5 g
18 mm 10¢ 2.33 g
21.21 mm 5¢ 4.54 g
32.13 mm $1 15.62 g
23.88 mm 25¢ 5.06 g
27.13 mm 50¢ 8.10 g

    (a) How many half dollars placed end to end will form a strip 1 m long?
    (b) A roll of quarters contains 40 coins. What is the mass of a roll of quarters?
    (c) A mint set contains one of each coin. What is the mass of 5 mint sets?
    (d) A roll of dimes has a value of $5.00. How long a strip will a roll of dimes make if the coins are placed end to end?
    (e) Find the value of a strip of quarters placed end to end, 2.5 m long.
    (f) What is the mass of $20.00 in dollar coins?
    (g) Jim has 32 pennies, 46 dimes, 36 nickels, 24 quarters, and 16 half dollars in his collection.
        What is the mass of the coins?

CHALLENGE

A train is 1 km long. It is travelling at 1 km/h. How long will it take the train to completely pass through a tunnel 1 km long?

2.2 SOLVING PROBLEMS WITH AREA CODES

Canada, a vast country, stretches across the North American continent from the Atlantic to the Pacific Ocean. The size of the country makes it necessary to divide it into regions identified by codes.

The map shows how the country has been divided into area codes for dialing on the telephone.

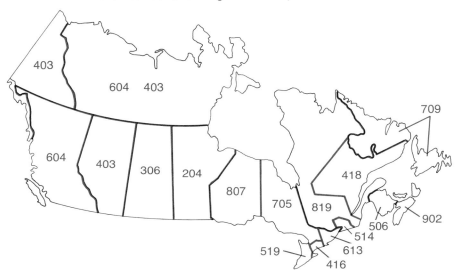

EXERCISE

A

1. State the telephone area code for these cities.
   (a) Regina   (b) Vancouver
   (c) Edmonton   (d) Winnipeg
   (e) Halifax   (f) Fredericton
   (g) St. John's   (h) Toronto

2. Name a city or town with the following area code.
   (a) 403   (b) 514   (c) 902
   (d) 416   (e) 819   (f) 506

3. What are the only two numbers used for the second digit of the telephone area code?

B

4. If you add the digits in the area code for Alberta, you get $4 + 10 + 3 = 17$, the number of clicks. Find the number of clicks in the area code for these places.
   (a) Victoria   (b) Ottawa
   (c) Quebec City   (d) Sydney
   (e) Saskatoon   (f) Hamilton

Dial phone   Touch phone

2.3 SOLVING PROBLEMS WITH TIME ZONES

The world has been divided into 24 time zones. We take the time at Greenwich, England, as our standard and then subtract or add to that time, depending on whether we are travelling west or east.

The following map shows the time zones across Canada.

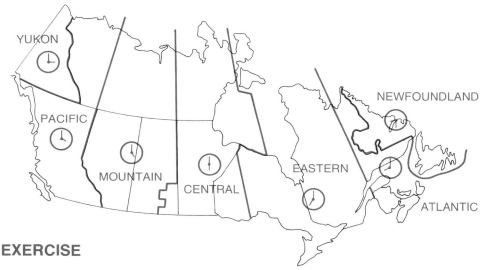

EXERCISE

A

1. Find the names of the 7 time zones.

B

2. If the Grey Cup parade was being held in Montreal at 10:00, at what time would people be viewing the parade on television in:
   (a) Halifax?   (b) Toronto?
   (c) Calgary?   (d) Regina?
   (e) Victoria?   (f) Whitehorse?

3. Name the time zone in which each of these communities is located.
   (a) Goose Bay   (b) Winnipeg
   (c) Moncton   (d) Edmonton
   (e) Vancouver   (f) your community

4. Why do the boundaries between the time zones seem to start as straight lines and then take a different path?

B.C.   ALTA.

2.4 SOLVING PROBLEMS WITH POSTAL CODES

The amount of mail being moved, and the desire to move the mail quickly have made it necessary to develop a postal code. The postal code enables a lot of the mail to be sorted by machine. Some countries have a numerical postal code. In Canada, the postal code consists of 3 numbers and 3 letters.

The following map indicates the postal zones for Canada.

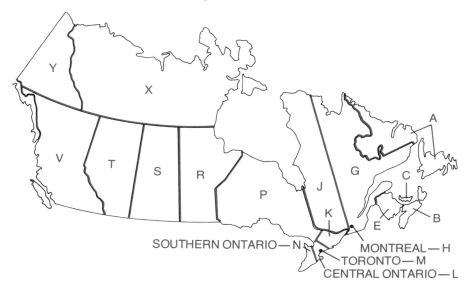

SOUTHERN ONTARIO — N
MONTREAL — H
TORONTO — M
CENTRAL ONTARIO — L

EXERCISE

A

1. How many postal zones are there in Canada?

B

2. (a) List the provinces alphabetically.
   (b) Beside each province, print the first letter of the postal code.
   (c) What are the first letters of the postal codes for the territories?

3. The postal code has 6 characters, such as V2B 3A5. What is the postal code for your home?

4. What is the first letter of the postal code for these places?
   (a) Kamloops   (b) Toronto
   (c) St. John's   (d) Calgary

EXTRAEXTRAEXTRAEXTRAEXTRA

THE AVERAGE PERSON

1. The average person blinks about 25 times each minute. About how many times will you blink in one hour?

2. The average person speaks about 125 words each minute. About how many words do you speak in one hour?

3. On the average, each of your feet will hit the ground or floor about 7000 times each day. How many times will your feet hit the ground or floor in one week?

4. From age 10 to age 14, people get, on the average, 2.7 colds each year. How many colds is that for the five years?

5. From age 15 to age 19 you can expect to get, on the average, 2.4 colds each year. About how many colds is that for the five years?

6. The average person thinks about 500 words each minute. About how many words can you think in one hour?

7. The average person laughs about 15 times each day. About how many times will you laugh in a year?

2.5 SOLVING PROBLEMS USING FORMULAS

Many problems can be solved using a formula. We have already used formulas from geometry in the previous chapter. In this section, we shall use some formulas in a general way to solve problems.

Example. In planning the school band banquet, the executive had to choose between two plans using these formulas.

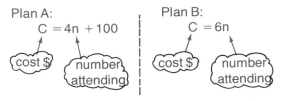

Plan A:
$$C = 4n + 100$$
cost $ number attending

Plan B:
$$C = 6n$$
cost $ number attending

Which plan gives the lower cost if 65 band members attend?

Solution: Plan A:
$$C = 4n + 100$$
$$= 4(65) + 100$$
$$= 260 + 100$$
$$= 360$$
∴ the cost for Plan A is $360.

Plan B:
$$C = 6n$$
$$= 6(65)$$
$$= 390$$
∴ the cost for Plan B is $390.
Plan A gives the lower cost.

EXERCISE

B

1. Suppose you want to add the natural numbers from 1 to 1000:

$$1 + 2 + 3 + \ldots + 999 + 1000$$

You can add the numbers directly or you can use the formula

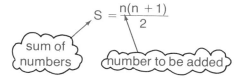

$$S = \frac{n(n+1)}{2}$$

sum of numbers

number to be added

Find the sum of the numbers from 1 to 1000.

2. The SONAR equipment on a ship measures the time it takes sound waves to reach an object and return.

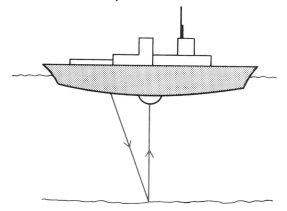

To find the distance from the ship to the object we use this formula.

$$d = 800\,t$$

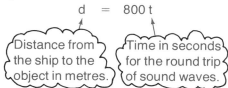

Distance from the ship to the object in metres.

Time in seconds for the round trip of sound waves.

(a) It took 4 s for the sound waves to reach the ocean floor and return. How deep was the ocean at that point?

(b) A submarine is 2250 m from a ship. How long will it take sound waves to reach the submarine and return?

3. The average mass for a young adult can be found using the formula:

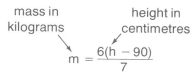

mass in kilograms

height in centimetres

$$m = \frac{6(h - 90)}{7}$$

Terry is 176 cm tall and has a mass of 74 kg. Use the formula to determine if Terry's mass is close to the average.

4. Gallileo dropped a cannonball from the top of the Leaning Tower of Pisa. It took 3.36 s for the cannonball to reach the ground.

Use the formula:

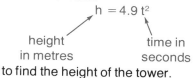

$$h = 4.9\,t^2$$

height in metres

time in seconds

to find the height of the tower.

5. School crests can be ordered according to two plans.

Plan 1:

$$C = 25 + 3n$$

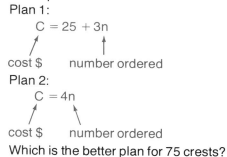

cost $

number ordered

Plan 2:

$$C = 4n$$

cost $

number ordered

Which is the better plan for 75 crests?

2.6 SOLVING PROBLEMS FROM PICTURES

In many problems, information is given in pictures. When we see information in pictures, we are doing the READ step.

Example.

READ ──────→ Find the length of material required to frame this picture.

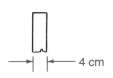

The frame material is 4 cm wide.

Solution:

WHAT ──────→ What is the total length of material?

GIVEN ──────→ The dimensions of the picture and the width of the frame.

OPERATION ──────→ Add the width of the frame to the dimensions of the picture, then add the lengths of the four pieces.

ESTIMATE ──────→ $28 + 33 + 28 + 33 \doteq 30 + 30 + 30 + 30$
$$\doteq 120$$

CALCULATE ──────→ $28 + 33 + 28 + 33 = 122$

CHECK ──────→ 122 is reasonably close to 120 in view of the rounding that has taken place.

122 cm of material are required.

You can also perform the calculations using the perimeter formula.

$$P = 2(\ell + w)$$
$$= 2(33 + 28)$$
$$= 2 \times 61$$
$$= 122$$

EXERCISE

B

1.

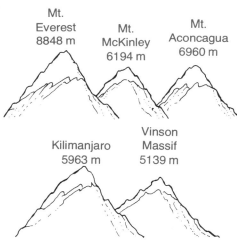

Vancouver 683 km   Winnipeg 1185 km

Montreal 3356 km

Find the distance from Winnipeg to
(a) Vancouver.   (b) Montreal.

2. Design a signpost to be placed at
Winnipeg given the following information.

Vancouver to Winnipeg	1868 km
Vancouver to Toronto	3983 km
Vancouver to Montreal	4222 km

3.

Mt.
Everest
8848 m

Mt.
McKinley
6194 m

Mt.
Aconcagua
6960 m

Vinson
Massif
5139 m

Kilimanjaro
5963 m

(a) List these mountain peaks giving the
tallest first.
(b) How much taller than Kilimanjaro is
Everest?
(c) How much taller than Kilimanjaro is
Mt. McKinley?

4. Here is a picture of the odometer on Bert
Hamston's car when he left Halifax and
when he arrived in Montreal.

Halifax	99085.3
Montreal	00356.7

How far is it from Halifax to Montreal?

C

5. The following map gives average driving
times in hours between certain Canadian
cities.

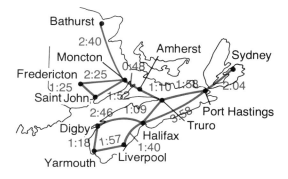

(a) What is the driving time from
    i) Bathurst to Halifax?
    ii) Sydney to Liverpool?
    iii) Fredericton to Amherst by way of
    Saint John?
    iv) Sydney to Halifax by way of
    Truro?
    v) Saint John to Halifax?

(b) How much longer is it to drive from
Fredericton to Moncton if you pass
through Saint John?

(c) How much shorter is it from Sydney
to Halifax if you through Truro?

(d)  A car rally starts at
Sydney on Saturday
morning at 08:00.
The route passes
through Halifax,
Yarmouth, Digby, Truro, Amherst,
Saint John and ends at Fredericton.
There is a 13 h stop in Digby.
At what time should the winning car
arrive in Fredericton?

2.7 WRITING PROBLEMS FROM PICTURES

Pictures often suggest problems. In this section we shall write our own problems from the information we see in pictures.

READ

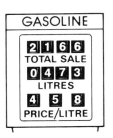

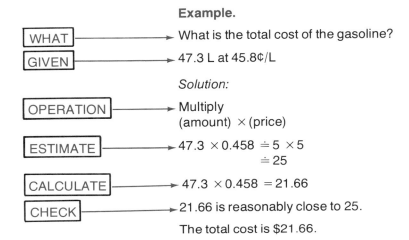

Example.

| WHAT | ──────→ What is the total cost of the gasoline? |
| GIVEN | ──────→ 47.3 L at 45.8¢/L |

Solution:

OPERATION ──────→ Multiply
(amount) × (price)

ESTIMATE ──────→ $47.3 \times 0.458 \doteq 5 \times 5$
$\doteq 25$

CALCULATE ──────→ $47.3 \times 0.458 = 21.66$

CHECK ──────→ 21.66 is reasonably close to 25.

The total cost is $21.66.

EXERCISE

Make up a problem from information in the pictures. Solve each problem.

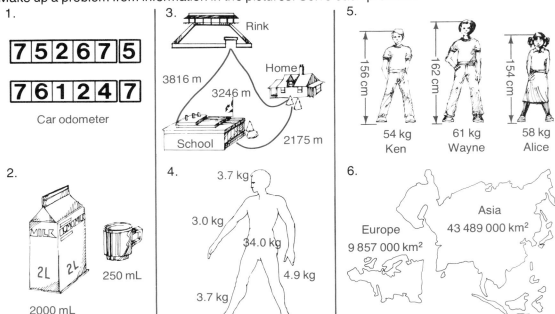

1.

7 5 2 6 7 5

7 6 1 2 4 7

Car odometer

2.

MILK
2L   2L   250 mL

2000 mL

3.

Rink

Home

3816 m

3246 m

School   2175 m

4.

3.7 kg

3.0 kg

34.0 kg

4.9 kg

3.7 kg

5.

156 cm   162 cm   154 cm

54 kg   61 kg   58 kg
Ken   Wayne   Alice

6.

Asia
43 489 000 km²

Europe
9 857 000 km²

2.8 WRITING THE PUNCH LINE

In this section, we complete the problem by asking a question based on the data. Some questions can have different punch lines.

WHAT

Example. The area of North America is 24 038 000 km² and the area of South America is 17 395 000 km².

Solution: A possible punch line is
"What is the combined area of North and South America?"
Combined area is:

$$
\begin{array}{r}
24\ 038\ 000 \\
17\ 395\ 000 \\
\hline
41\ 433\ 000
\end{array}
$$

∴ the combined area is 41 433 000 km².

EXERCISE

Write punch lines. Solve the problems.

B

1. This table gives the areas of the maritime provinces in square kilometres.

Province	Area (km²)
Newfoundland	404 517
P.E.I.	5 657
Nova Scotia	55 491
New Brunswick	73 436

2. This table gives the areas of the prairie provinces in square kilometres.

Province	Area (km²)
Manitoba	650 087
Saskatchewan	651 900
Alberta	661 185

3. In 1901, Pittsburgh won the pennant with 90 wins and 49 losses. In 1979, Pittsburgh won the pennant with 98 wins and 64 losses.

4. In Canada, pollution control costs about $105.00 per year per person.

5. In Canada, we produce about 263 tin cans per year per person.

6. The average body contains about 5.4 L of blood. The heart pumps the blood through the body 1350 times each day.

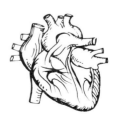

2.9 PROBLEMS WITH EXTRA INFORMATION

Sometimes we are presented with more information than is necessary to solve the problem. A good problem solver has to know what information to use and what to reject. In this set of problems, extra information that is not required is given. Identify the necessary information as part of your step GIVEN and solve the problem.

GIVEN

EXERCISE

B

1. Henry earns $4.75/h as a part-time gas station attendant. He is saving $195.00 to buy a portable tape deck.
   How much will he earn in 28 h?

2. How far will a car travel in 3.5 h at 85 km/h if it consumes gasoline at a rate of 18 L/100 km?

3. In 1968, Tom Cooke, an Englishman, planted six seed potatoes on 0.25 ha of land. He harvested about 745 kg of potatoes.
   How many kilograms of potatoes grew from each seed potato?

4. Each North American produces about 2.7 kg of trash per week. It costs $0.11 to dispose of 1 kg of trash.
   How much trash will a family of 5 produce in one year?

5. A houseboat travels 16 km/h in calm water. A speedboat goes 5 times faster. How long will it take the houseboat to travel 52 km?

6. A car salesman sold 24 cars and 7 vans. The commission on a car is $250 and the commission on a van is $300.
   What was the salesman's commission on the cars?

7. A riverfront lot is to be fenced on three sides, with the side along the river left open. The dimensions are 35 m, 83 m, 29 m, and 80 m along the river. The cost of fencing is $57/m.
   What is the cost of the fence?

CHALLENGE

Place the numbers from 0 to 8 in the circles so that the sum is 999.

$$
\begin{array}{cccc}
 & \bigcirc & \bigcirc & \bigcirc \\
 & \bigcirc & \bigcirc & \bigcirc \\
+ & \bigcirc & \bigcirc & \bigcirc \\
\hline
 & 9 & 9 & 9
\end{array}
$$

2.10 PROBLEMS WITH MISSING INFORMATION

In some problems, all the necessary information is not given. In these types of problems, you must determine what information is missing. For each problem in the exercise, supply the missing information and solve the problem.

EXERCISE

B

1. Four members of the student council are attending a conference in Ottawa. What is the cost of air fare?

2. Find the total cost of the following gasoline purchases.

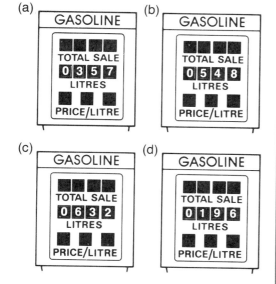

(a) GASOLINE — TOTAL SALE 0 3 5 7 LITRES — PRICE/LITRE

(b) GASOLINE — TOTAL SALE 0 5 4 8 LITRES — PRICE/LITRE

(c) GASOLINE — TOTAL SALE 0 6 3 2 LITRES — PRICE/LITRE

(d) GASOLINE — TOTAL SALE 0 1 9 6 LITRES — PRICE/LITRE

3. In hockey, a team gets 2 points for a win, and 1 point for a tie. How many points did the Edmonton Oilers have at the end of last season?

4. The school band washed 114 cars in a fund-raising car wash. How much did they earn?

5. How many buses holding 47 people each would be needed to transport the whole school on a field trip?

6. Samuel de Champlain carried out his explorations 111 a after Christopher Columbus discovered America. In what year did Champlain begin his explorations?

7. Two famous European volcanoes are Etna and Vesuvius. Mt. Etna is 2009 m higher than Mt. Vesuvius. How tall is Mt. Etna?

8. In 1977, the New York Yankees won the American League pennant by winning 100 games. How many games did they lose that year?

CHALLENGE

In each of the following words, four letters are missing. The first two letters of each word are the same as the last two letters, and in the same order. What are the words?

1. ▨ ▨ M A ▨ ▨
2. ▨ ▨ C I ▨ ▨
3. ▨ ▨ A S ▨ ▨

2.11 PROBLEMS WITHOUT NUMBERS

Some problems involve clear thinking and do not contain numbers, or require any computation. In the following exercise, you will solve problems using the given clues.

EXERCISE

A

1. Use the following clues to identify Jenny's present.
    i)   Jenny's present is in a small box.
    ii) The wrapping does not have striped paper.
    iii) The present has a ribbon.
    iv) The present has a bow.

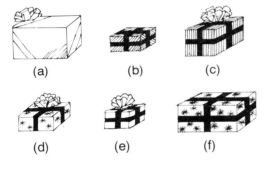

(a)   (b)   (c)

(d)   (e)   (f)

2. Six boys were in a race. Use the following clues to find the winner.
    i)   The winner has an even number.
    ii) The shortest boy lost.
    iii) The winner has white shorts.
    iv) The winner has a striped top.

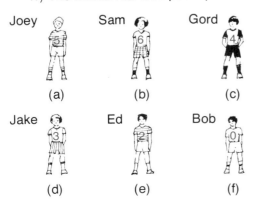

Joey   Sam   Gord

(a)   (b)   (c)

Jake   Ed   Bob

(d)   (e)   (f)

3. Use the following clues to find where Bill lives.
    i)   Bill lives in a big house.
    ii) Bill's house has a flat, black roof.
    iii) Bill's house is not a "split level."
    iv) Bill's house has a two-car garage.

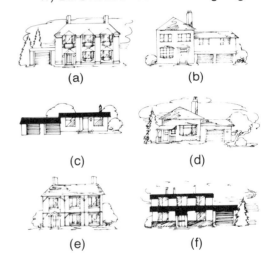

(a)   (b)

(c)   (d)

(e)   (f)

4. Some citizens gave the following description of a suspect:
    i)   short hair;   iii) glasses;
    ii) dark jacket;   iv) red hat.

(a)   (b)   (c)

(d)   (e)   (f)

Find the suspect.

B

5. Three sportscasters picked the following teams to win this week's football games.
Joe MacLean:
Vancouver, Calgary, Hamilton, Winnipeg
Ed Jones:
Calgary, Edmonton, Ottawa, Hamilton
Shirley Daw:
Winnipeg, Hamilton, Toronto, Ottawa
None of these sportscasters picked Montreal to win. Use this information to determine which teams played each other.

6. Gary's older brother is tall, fair, quite heavy, does not wear glasses, carries a briefcase, and was born in Regina.

Carl is tall, fair, from Regina, and does not wear glasses or carry a briefcase.

Murray is not short, does not wear glasses, carries a briefcase, is not dark, and comes from Regina.

Frank carries a briefcase, is not fair or too heavy, is not short, and wears glasses.

Is one of these three men Gary's older brother?

7. Ned, Tommy, and Anne rode their motorbikes to school. The other students wondered who owned which bike. Ned, Tommy, and Anne gave them these clues.

   i) Ned's bike is not the Yamaha.
   ii) The blue bike is a Honda.
   iii) Tommy's bike is not green.
   iv) The Harley Davidson is not black.
Who owns which bike?

CHALLENGE

Which of these points are inside the curve?

2.12 MAKING TABLES

Some problems are solved using tables. In this section we make tables using given information.

Example. Bert sells tickets for the school play. Tickets cost $4.25 each. Prepare a table for Bert so he can read the amount for up to 8 tickets.

Solution:

Number	1	2	3	4	5	6	7	8
Price	4.25	8.50	12.75	17.00	21.25	25.50	29.75	34.00

This is a horizontal table. We can also use vertical tables.
A table should have:

    1. lines drawn with a ruler;
    2. rows and columns labelled.

EXERCISE

B

1. Taxi fare is $1.25/km. Complete the table to show the cost of trips up to 10 km.

Distance (km)	Cost
1	
2	
3	
4	
5	
6	
7	
8	
9	
10	

2. The distance an object falls in metres can be found using the formula $d = 4.9 t^2$, where t is the length of time the object falls in seconds. Complete the table.

t(s)	d(m)
1	
2	
3	
4	
5	
6	

3. We can find the distance, in metres, that an alert driver is able to stop a car with good brakes on dry pavement by using this formula:
$d = 0.4 s + 0.02 s^2$
Complete the table.

s (km/h)	d (m)
20	
30	
40	
50	
60	
70	
80	
90	
100	

2.13 SOLVING PROBLEMS USING TABLES

We can solve problems using information in tables.

Boxes	Cost
1	1.89
2	3.78
3	5.67
4	7.56
5	9.45
6	11.34
7	13.23
8	15.12
9	17.01
10	18.90

Example. Terry sells homemade cookies at the farmer's market. The cookies cost $1.89 per box. Use the table at right to find the cost of 16 boxes.

Solution:

Cost of 10 boxes: $18.90
Cost of 6 boxes: $11.34

Add: $30.24

The cost of 16 boxes is $30.24

EXERCISE

A

1. The following table gives highway distances between some Canadian cities.

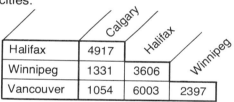

	Calgary	Halifax	Winnipeg
Halifax	4917		
Winnipeg	1331	3606	
Vancouver	1054	6003	2397

(a) How far is it from Calgary to Winnipeg?
(b) How far is it from Halifax to Vancouver?
(c) How much farther is it from Winnipeg to Halifax than from Winnipeg to Vancouver?
(d) It costs $3.75 to drive a large truck 1 km. What is the cost of driving this truck from Halifax to Vancouver?

2. The attendance at the swimming pool is shown in this table.

Admissions	Adult	Student
Thursday	147	42
Friday	178	53
Saturday	164	106

Find the total receipts if adults pay $1.25 and students pay $0.75.

3. This table shows the records of four teams in intramural sports.

Team	Won	Lost	Tied
Aces	5	5	0
Kings	7	2	1
Blues	3	6	1
Reds	4	6	0

Arrange the teams in order of standing based on 2 points for a win and 1 point for a tie.

4. The following table is used to determine the cost of concert tickets at $3.75 each.

Tickets	Cost	Tickets	Cost
1		6	
2		7	
3		8	
4		9	
5		10	

(a) Complete the table.

Use the table to find the cost of

(b) 14 tickets; (c) 20 tickets;
(d) 24 tickets; (e) 37 tickets.

2.14 A DECISION-MAKING MODEL

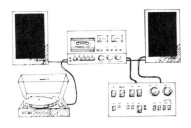

An important reason for studying mathematics is to develop the ability to make decisions when we solve problems. In some problems the solution is not immediately visible and there are alternatives — choices have to be made. In order to decide on the best choice, we need an organized plan. The following example illustrates the PACED plan for making decisions in problem solving.

PROBLEM
Identify the problem in a clear statement.

ALTERNATIVES
State the alternatives or options that are available.

Example. Chris won a $500.00 voucher in a contest and wants to buy a stereo. Find a system that comes closest to $500.00. His choices are:

Amplifier:	2-channel	$145.00
	4-channel	$179.50
Tape deck:	Playback	$ 85.00
	Play/record	$124.00
Turntable:	manual	$ 79.50
	automatic	$115.00
Speakers:	each	$ 75.00

CRITERIA
List reasons and constraints to be used in evaluating the alternatives.

Solution: The cost cannot exceed $500.00.
A 4-channel amplifier requires 4 speakers.
A 2-channel amplifier requires 2 speakers.

EVALUATE
Evaluate the alternatives based on the given criteria.

The total cost of a 4-channel amplifier and the 4 speakers that are needed is $479.50. Any tape deck and turntable will put this system over $500.00 so we can eliminate the system with the 4-channel amplifier. The other possible systems are listed below.

	System 1		System 2	
Amplifier	2-channel	145.00	2-channel	145.00
Tape deck	playback	85.00	play/record	124.00
Turntable	automatic	115.00	automatic	115.00
Speakers	(2)	150.00	(2)	150.00
Total		$495.00		$534.00

	System 3		System 4	
Amplifier	2-channel	145.00	2-channel	145.00
Tape deck	playback	85.00	play/record	124.00
Turntable	manual	79.50	manual	79.50
Speakers	(2)	150.00	(2)	150.00
Total		$459.50		$498.50

DECISION
Decide on the best alternative and solve the problem.

Using the tables, we see that System 4 best meets the requirements of the problem. Chris could buy a 2-channel amplifier, with play/record tape deck and manual turntable. A 2-channel amplifier requires 2 speakers.

EXERCISE

B

1. The following chart shows the number of cases of fruit delivered to four grocery stores.

Fruit	Store			
	Ideal	Foodland	Peter's	ABC
apples	24	37	32	28
peaches	12	20	17	22
pears	15	24	20	10
cherries	18	26	15	8

(a) What is the total value of the apples at $24/case?

(b) What is the total value of the peaches at $30/case?

(c) How many cases of fruit were delivered to Peter's?

(d) How many cases of fruit were delivered to Foodland?

(e) How many cases of fruit were delivered to the four stores?

(f) What is the cost to the ABC store if the fruit costs as follows:

apples $24   peaches $30
pears $28   cherries $32

2. Freddie operates a 10-bay garage. If he charges $20 for his service special, he will get 1200 jobs each week. For every $1 drop in price, he will get an extra 100 jobs per week. Complete the following table to find the amount Freddie should charge for the greatest receipts.

Charge	Number	Receipts
$20	1200	$24 000
$19		
$18		
$17		
$16		
$15		
$14		
$13		

3. Jim has $6 to spend on rides at the fall fair. Ride coupons are priced at 3/$1. Here is a list of rides and the number of coupons required. The better rides cost more coupons.

2 coupons
{ Ferris Wheel
  Carousel
  Moon Walk

3 coupons
{ Bumper cars
  Loop the Loop
  Rattler

4 coupons
{ Hi-Flyer
  Python
  Centrifuge

Jim will only go on a ride once.

(a) What are Jim's choices if he wants the best rides for his money?

(b) What are Jim's choices if he won't go on the Hi-Flyer and still wants the best rides?

4. The athletic council is planning an awards night. They want to charge $6.00 a student for food. Plan a menu based on the following prices per person.

Pizza $4.00
Fried chicken $4.50
Submarine $3.50
Milk $0.70
Pop $0.80
Milkshake $1.20
Ice cream $1.00

5. Janet and her mother have $50.00 for the purchase of new clothes. The choices are:

blouse $12.00   or   shirt $10.25
skirt $20.00   or   slacks $16.00
sweater $21.00

One choice must be a sweater. What selection brings the total bill closest to $50.00?

6. The Canadian Legion hockey team, consisting of 16 players, 2 coaches, and 2 trainers, plan to stay overnight while at a tournament. The organizers of the tournament have sent the following information about the rates of the motor inns.

Motor Inn	Single	Double	Extra Person	Maximum in a Room
Ambassador	29	34	4	4
Queens	30	35	5	4
York	34	40	4	5
Lake	33	41	4	5

Assume that accommodations are about equal.
Assume that the maximum number stay in each room.
Which hotel is the least expensive for the team?

7. The following is a restaurant menu:

```
❖◆❖◆❖◆❖◆❖◆❖◆❖◆❖◆❖◆❖◆❖
                 MENU
Appetizer
      soup . . . . . . . . . . . . . . . . . . . . $1.25
      juice . . . . . . . . . . . . . . . . . . . $1.10
Entree
      fish . . . . . . . . . . . . . . . . . . . . $5.45
      chicken . . . . . . . . . . . . . . . $6.95
      steak . . . . . . . . . . . . . . . . . $8.95
Dessert
      cake . . . . . . . . . . . . . . . . . . . $1.20
      pie . . . . . . . . . . . . . . . . . . . . $1.50
      ice cream . . . . . . . . . . . . . . $1.25
Beverage
      milk . . . . . . . . . . . . . . . . . . . . $0.85
      shake . . . . . . . . . . . . . . . . . . $1.50
❖◆❖◆❖◆❖◆❖◆❖◆❖◆❖◆❖◆❖◆❖
```

Each of 4 people selects 1 item from each category.
(a) What is the least expensive meal for one person?
(b) What is the most expensive meal for one person?
(c) What is the least possible cost if each of the 4 people has a different meal?

8. The following map shows the distances and speed limits on three routes from Foxhead to Barryfield.

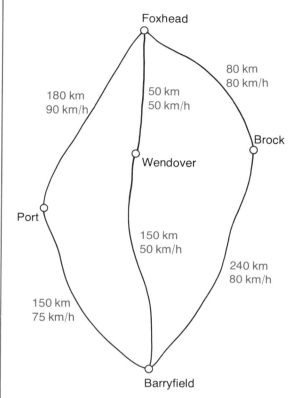

What route takes the shortest time if you drive at the speed limit?

CHALLENGE

How can you connect these links to make a 15-link chain by opening and closing just 3 links?

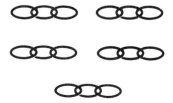

2.15 CHAPTER 2 REVIEW EXERCISE

1. The Dead Sea is 397 m below sea level. Death Valley is 86 m below sea level.
   (a) Which is lower?
   (b) By how much is it lower?

2. Find the cost of the following:

80¢   40¢

$1.20   50¢

   (a) a bowl of soup and a glass of milk;
   (b) a hamburger and a glass of milk;
   (c) a bowl of soup, two hamburgers, a glass of milk, and an ice cream bar.

3. A baseball stadium holds 53 285 people. There were 3750 empty seats during a game. How many people attended the game?

4. An auditorium holds 1250 people. Tickets for a play cost $6 each. There are 334 empty seats. What is the value of the tickets that have been sold?

5. Radio waves travel at 300 000 km/s.
   (a) How far does a radio wave travel in 1 min?
   (b) How long will it take a radio wave to reach the moon?

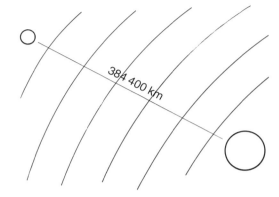

384 400 km

6. SONAR is used to detect objects under water. In order to locate an object, a sound wave is transmitted from the craft and reflected back. Sound waves travel 1600 m/s in sea water.
   (a) How far is the object if it takes 7 s for the sound waves to return to the source?
   (b) How far is an object if it takes 5.6 s for the sound waves to return to the source?

7. In 1961, Yuri Gagarin was the first man to orbit the earth in a Russian spacecraft. The flight lasted 1 h 48 min. In 1975, Vance Brand, Thomas Stafford, and Donald Slayton were in space for 217 h 30 min in a United States spacecraft.
   (a) How many years separated these events?
   (b) How much longer was the flight in 1975?

8. (a) Make up a problem from the information in this picture.
   (b) Solve the problem.

9. The following map shows the total area, in square kilometres, of the prairie provinces.

Alberta 661 185   Saskatchewan 651 900   Manitoba 650 087

   (a) Rank the provinces by total area from smallest to largest.
   (b) What is the total area of the prairie provinces?

10. The circumference of the earth is about 40 000 km, and the length of a standard paper clip is about 0.028 m.

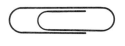

   (a) What is the circumference of the earth in metres?
   (b) How many paper clips are needed to make a chain around the earth?

11. One cubic centimetre (1 cm^3) of gold has a mass of 19.3 g.

BRICK 2453 cm^3

   (a) What is the mass of 25 cm^3 of gold?
   (b) What will be the volume of 4381.1 g of gold?
   (c) What is the mass of one of these gold bricks?

CHAPTER 2 TEST

1. A train with 563 people on board stopped at the commuter station. 112 people got off and 83 got on. How many people were on the train when it left the commuter station?

2. Light travels 300 000 km/s. How long does it take for light from the sun to reach the earth?

147 000 000 km

3. A formula for the amount of sleep you need is given by the formula

$$n = \frac{35 - a}{2} \qquad a < 20$$

where n is the hours of sleep, and a is your age. Use this formula to find the hours of sleep needed by a person 15 a old.

4. The frame on this window is 9 cm wide. How much material is needed to frame the window?

75

60

5. In an election, Smith received 14 107 votes, Jones received 9 467 votes, and Jacobs received 12 053 votes. By how many votes did Smith defeat Jones?

6. The attendance at a baseball park is shown in this table.

Day	Adults	Students
Tuesday	534	685
Thursday	628	890
Saturday	1115	1460

Find the total receipts for the three days if adults pay $2.25 each, and students pay $1.25.

7. The map at right shows three routes from Polaris to Moonglow. What is the shortest route between these two places?

Moonglow

112 km

73 km

63 km

Dipper

54 km

Saturn

Jupiter   68 km

Uranus

29 km

36 km

Polaris

FRACTIONS AND INTEGERS

REVIEW AND PREVIEW TO CHAPTER 3

EXERCISE 1   FACTORS

1. The factors of 18 are 1, 2, 3, 6, 9, and 18. Each of these factors divides 18 evenly. Find the factors of
   (a) 12   (b) 20   (c) 24
   (d) 30   (e) 36   (f) 42
   (g) 50   (h) 124   (i) 240

2. Find the missing factors.
   (a) $\square \times 5 = 150$
   (b) $11 \times \square = 550$
   (c) $27 \times \square = 135$
   (d) $\square \times 11 = 539$
   (e) $156 = \square \times 12$
   (f) $7 \times 8 \times \square = 504$

3. Complete these factor trees.
   (a)

   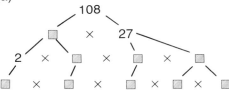

   (b)

   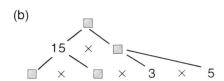

4. A prime number has only two different factors, itself and one. Write the number whose prime factors are:
   (a) 2, 3, 5   (b) 3, 3, 7
   (c) 2, 2, 2, 3, 5   (d) 3, 5, 5, 7
   (e) 2, 3, 3, 7   (f) 2, 3, 5, 7

5. Find the smallest number having the following factors.
   (a) 2, 3, 5   (b) 4, 5, 7
   (c) 15, 21, 35   (d) 3, 7, 12
   (e) 8, 9, 24   (f) 20, 24, 40
   (g) 20, 25, 30   (h) 49, 56, 63

6. As a product of its prime factors,
   $24 = 2 \times 2 \times 2 \times 3$
   $\quad = 2^3 \times 3$
   Write each of the following as a product of its prime factors.
   (a) 28   (b) 45   (c) 63
   (d) 72   (e) 64   (f) 48
   (g) 256   (h) 125   (i) 840

7. Write each of the following as a product of its prime factors.
   (a) 116   (b) 204   (c) 126
   (d) 336   (e) 112   (f) 196
   (g) 306   (h) 432   (i) 1008

8. Complete this double factor tree.

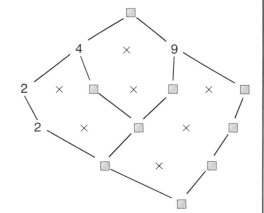

EXERCISE 2 GCF — GREATEST COMMON FACTOR

1. The common factors of 24 and 32 are 1, 2, 4, 8. Find the common factors of each pair of numbers.
   (a) 15, 20 (b) 12, 18 (c) 18, 27
   (d) 30, 35 (e) 16, 24 (f) 40, 50

2. The greatest common factor (GCF) of 24 and 32 is 8. Find the GCF of each of the following pairs of numbers.
   (a) 15, 20 (b) 16, 24 (c) 27, 36
   (d) 48, 72 (e) 64, 96 (f) 96, 168

3. Find the GCF of each group of numbers.
   (a) 33, 44, 55 (b) 18, 12, 15
   (c) 36, 48, 60 (d) 64, 80, 96
   (e) 24, 30, 36 (f) 30, 50, 45

4. Find the GCF of each group of numbers.
   (a) 40, 72, 108
   (b) 60, 75, 105
   (c) 54, 90, 126
   (d) 120, 168, 216
   (e) 72, 96, 120, 144
   (f) 162, 270, 324, 432

EXERCISE 3 LCM — LOWEST COMMON MULTIPLE

1. The lowest common multiple (LCM) of 4 and 6 is 12. Find the LCM of each pair of numbers.
   (a) 6, 12 (b) 16, 20 (c) 15, 25
   (d) 18, 24 (e) 18, 30 (f) 7, 6
   (g) 6, 5 (h) 12, 15 (i) 14, 21

2. Find the LCM of each group of numbers.
   (a) 9, 12, 15 (b) 15, 20, 25
   (c) 8, 12, 20 (d) 24, 30, 36
   (e) 10, 15, 20 (f) 35, 42, 105

3. Find the LCM of each group of numbers.
   (a) 5, 7, 15 (b) 8, 12, 15
   (c) 12, 32, 64 (d) 6, 16, 56
   (e) 10, 15, 25 (f) 14, 21, 28

4. Two gears should have 48 teeth and 20 teeth, respectively. Each gear has a broken tooth.

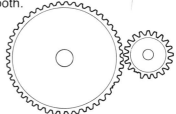

The broken teeth are matched now. After how many turns will they return to this position?

CHALLENGE

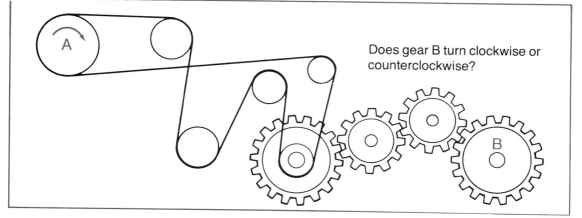

Does gear B turn clockwise or counterclockwise?

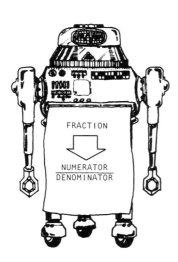

3.1 FRACTIONS

We use fractions to name part of a group. There are three boys and two girls in a group of five students.

A fraction will tell us what part of the group is boys, and what part of the group is girls.

We say three fifths of the students are boys, and we write $\frac{3}{5}$.

$\frac{2}{5}$ of the students are girls.

The numbers 2 and 5 are the terms of the fraction.

When we use a fraction to compare parts of a group, we are concerned only with the number of objects in the group, and not with their size. We can also use fractions to name part of a whole. When we consider a fraction of a square or rectangle, we are concerned with the size of each part as well as the number of parts.

Three of the eight squares that make up the rectangle at the left are shaded. Since all the squares are the same size, we can say that three eighths of the rectangle is shaded.

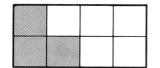

3 of the 8 parts are shaded.
$\frac{3}{8}$ of the rectangle is shaded.

Example . State fractions to describe the shaded parts.

(a)

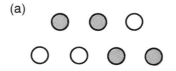

(b)

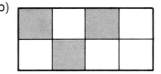

Solution:

(a) There are 7 objects in all.
4 objects are shaded.
$\frac{4}{7}$ of the group is shaded.

(b) There are 8 squares in all.
3 squares are shaded.
$\frac{3}{8}$ of the rectangle is shaded.

EXERCISE

A

1. State a fraction that indicates the part of the following that is shaded.

(a)

(b)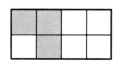

(c)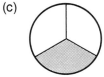

(d)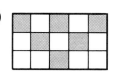

(e)

(f)

2. For each of the following, state a fraction that indicates the part that is not shaded.

(a)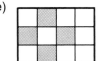

(b)

(c)

(d)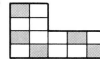

(e)

(f)

B

3. What part of the rectangle is labelled with the letter

(a) A?   (b) B?   (c) C?

A	A	A	A	B	B	B	B	B
B	C	B	C	A	A	A	A	A
B	C	B	C	A	A	A	A	A
B	C	B	C	A	A	A	A	A
B	C	B	C	A	A	A	A	A
B	C	B	C	A	A	A	A	A

4. In a survey of 25 students, 7 ate pizza, 12 ate hamburgers, and 6 ate hot dogs for lunch.
   What fraction of the students ate the following:
   (a) pizza?
   (b) hamburgers?
   (c) hot dogs?

5. What fraction of the dots lie inside each of these figures?

   (a) the triangle
   (b) the square
   (c) the circle
   (d) the circle, but not the square

6. Draw diagrams to show each of the following fractions.

   (a) $\frac{2}{3}$ (b) $\frac{3}{7}$ (c) $\frac{4}{5}$ (d) $\frac{5}{8}$

7. The bars below compare the top speeds of man on land, the dolphin in water, and the cheetah on land.

   Man

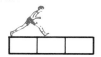

   Dolphin

   Cheetah

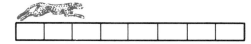

   Write fractions to compare these speeds.
   (a) man to dolphin
   (b) man to cheetah
   (c) dolphin to cheetah

3.2 EQUIVALENT FRACTIONS

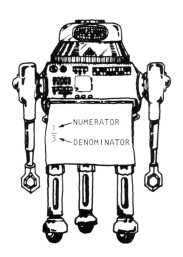

Consider the shaded area in these figures.

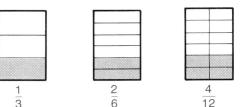

$$\frac{1}{3} \qquad \frac{2}{6} \qquad \frac{4}{12} \qquad \frac{8}{24}$$

Notice that the shaded area represents the same amount. Since each rectangle has been divided into a different number of parts, the fraction is expressed using different numerals.

$$\frac{1}{3} = \frac{2}{6} = \frac{4}{12} = \frac{8}{24}$$

because each fraction represents the same amount of the rectangle.

> To find an equivalent fraction, multiply or divide the numerator and the denominator by the same number.
>
> $$\frac{a}{b} = \frac{a \times c}{b \times c} \quad \text{and} \quad \frac{a}{b} = \frac{a \div c}{b \div c}$$

Example 1. Are $\frac{3}{4}$ and $\frac{15}{20}$ equivalent fractions?

Solution: $\frac{3}{4} = \frac{3 \times 5}{4 \times 5}$

$\quad\quad\quad = \frac{15}{20}$

$\quad \therefore \frac{3}{4}$ and $\frac{15}{20}$ are equivalent fractions.

Example 2. Express $\frac{6}{10}$ in lowest terms.

Solution: 2 is the largest whole number that divides both 6 and 10 evenly.

$$\frac{6}{10} = \frac{6 \div 2}{10 \div 2}$$

$$= \frac{3}{5}$$

$\frac{6}{10}$ expressed in lowest terms is $\frac{3}{5}$.

EXERCISE

A

1. State two equivalent fractions representing the shaded area for each of the following diagrams.

   (a)

   (b)

   (c)

   (d)

2. State two equivalent fractions for each of the following.

   (a) $\dfrac{1}{6}$ (b) $\dfrac{3}{5}$ (c) $\dfrac{4}{5}$

   (d) $\dfrac{3}{4}$ (e) $\dfrac{1}{2}$ (f) $\dfrac{1}{4}$

B

3. Find the value of ☐ that makes each statement true.

   (a) $\dfrac{5}{7} = \dfrac{☐}{42}$ (b) $\dfrac{7}{12} = \dfrac{☐}{48}$

   (c) $\dfrac{5}{6} = \dfrac{☐}{18}$ (d) $\dfrac{4}{6} = \dfrac{☐}{3}$

   (e) $\dfrac{12}{15} = \dfrac{48}{☐}$ (f) $4 = \dfrac{☐}{10}$

4. Which fractions are equivalent?

   (a) $\dfrac{1}{3}, \dfrac{3}{12}$ (b) $\dfrac{4}{9}, \dfrac{16}{27}$

   (c) $\dfrac{7}{8}, \dfrac{56}{24}$ (d) $\dfrac{1}{4}, \dfrac{2}{8}$

   (e) $\dfrac{4}{10}, \dfrac{2}{5}$ (f) $\dfrac{6}{7}, \dfrac{24}{27}$

5. Write each fraction in lowest terms.

   (a) $\dfrac{6}{8}$ (b) $\dfrac{10}{15}$ (c) $\dfrac{8}{10}$

   (d) $\dfrac{27}{30}$ (e) $\dfrac{12}{24}$ (f) $\dfrac{15}{18}$

   (g) $\dfrac{120}{140}$ (h) $\dfrac{65}{100}$ (i) $\dfrac{36}{144}$

6. Use equivalent fractions to order these fractions from smallest to largest.

   (a) $\dfrac{1}{2}, \dfrac{7}{8}, \dfrac{2}{3}, \dfrac{2}{5}, \dfrac{3}{4}$

   (b) $\dfrac{5}{3}, \dfrac{3}{2}, \dfrac{9}{8}, \dfrac{6}{5}, \dfrac{10}{3}$

   (c) $\dfrac{4}{5}, \dfrac{5}{4}, \dfrac{9}{2}, \dfrac{7}{8}, \dfrac{3}{1}$

APPLICATIONS

7. Sandra and Jennifer had a contest shooting free throws in basketball.

   Sandra made $\dfrac{6}{10}$ of her shots and

   Jennifer made $\dfrac{3}{5}$ of her shots.

   Who had the better shooting record for free throws?

8. Sandy earned 15 out of 20 on a test, and Terry got 18 out of 24 on a test.
   (a) Express these scores as fractions.
   (b) Who got the better mark?

CHALLENGE

Place the numbers from 1 to 8 in the boxes so that no two consecutive numbers are next to each other.

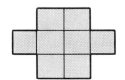

3.3 MULTIPLYING FRACTIONS

The rectangle at the left is divided into quarters. To find one-third of the quarters, we write:

$$\frac{1}{3} \text{ of } \frac{1}{4} = \frac{1}{3} \times \frac{1}{4}$$
$$= \frac{1 \times 1}{3 \times 4}$$
$$= \frac{1}{12}$$

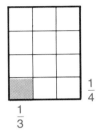

$\frac{1}{4}$

$\frac{1}{3}$

To multiply two fractions, we multiply the numerator by the numerator, and the denominator by the denominator.

$$\frac{a}{b} \times \frac{c}{d} = \frac{a \times c}{b \times d} = \frac{ac}{bd}$$

Example 1. Multiply. $\frac{2}{3} \times \frac{4}{5}$

Solution: $\frac{2}{3} \times \frac{4}{5} = \frac{2 \times 4}{3 \times 5}$
$$= \frac{8}{15}$$

Example 2. Multiply. $\frac{3}{5} \times 4$

Solution: $\frac{3}{5} \times 4 = \frac{3}{5} \times \frac{4}{1}$
$$= \frac{12}{5}$$
$$= 2\frac{2}{5}$$

To write 4 as a fraction, we write $\frac{4}{1}$

Example 3. Multiply. $1\frac{1}{2} \times 2\frac{3}{4}$

Solution: Change the mixed numbers to improper fractions.
$$1\frac{1}{2} \times 2\frac{3}{4} = \frac{3}{2} \times \frac{11}{4}$$
$$= \frac{33}{8}$$
$$= 4\frac{1}{8}$$

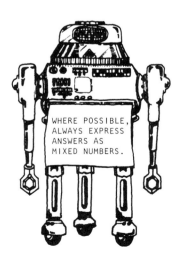

WHERE POSSIBLE, ALWAYS EXPRESS ANSWERS AS MIXED NUMBERS.

EXERCISE

A

1. Multiply these fractions. State your answers in lowest terms.

(a) $\dfrac{1}{2} \times \dfrac{1}{2}$ (b) $\dfrac{1}{3} \times \dfrac{1}{3}$

(c) $\dfrac{3}{4} \times \dfrac{1}{2}$ (d) $\dfrac{1}{4} \times \dfrac{3}{4}$

(e) $\dfrac{1}{2} \times \dfrac{2}{3}$ (f) $\dfrac{3}{4} \times \dfrac{1}{3}$

2. Evaluate.

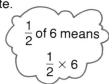

$\dfrac{1}{2}$ of 6 means

$\dfrac{1}{2} \times 6$

(a) $\dfrac{1}{2}$ of 8   (b) $\dfrac{1}{4}$ of 8

(c) $\dfrac{1}{5}$ of 20   (d) $\dfrac{3}{4}$ of 8

(e) $\dfrac{5}{8}$ of 8   (f) $\dfrac{1}{4}$ of 10

B

3. Multiply.
Express your answer in lowest terms.

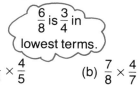

$\dfrac{6}{8}$ is $\dfrac{3}{4}$ in lowest terms.

(a) $\dfrac{1}{8} \times \dfrac{4}{5}$ (b) $\dfrac{7}{8} \times \dfrac{4}{7}$

(c) $\dfrac{1}{3} \times \dfrac{3}{8}$ (d) $\dfrac{2}{3} \times \dfrac{3}{4}$

(e) $\dfrac{5}{8} \times \dfrac{1}{5}$ (f) $\dfrac{4}{5} \times \dfrac{5}{8}$

4. Change to improper fractions.

(a) $2\dfrac{1}{3}$ (b) $2\dfrac{5}{8}$

(c) $1\dfrac{3}{4}$ (d) $4\dfrac{1}{3}$

5. Multiply.
Express your answers in lowest terms.

(a) $1\dfrac{1}{2} \times 4$ (b) $6\dfrac{1}{2} \times 8$

(c) $3 \times 2\dfrac{1}{2}$ (d) $1\dfrac{1}{2} \times 2\dfrac{1}{3}$

APPLICATIONS

6. The motor of a large truck takes 6 L of oil. The "low oil" light comes on when the oil is down by $\dfrac{1}{3}$.

(a) How much oil is left in the crankcase when the light comes on?

(b) How much oil should be added?

7. An airline company is having a seat sale. Calculate the sale price after these discounts.

(a) Fredericton to Toronto:

$126 with $\dfrac{1}{3}$ off

(b) Vancouver to Montreal:

$425 with $\dfrac{1}{5}$ off

(c) Winnipeg to Edmonton:

$248 with $\dfrac{1}{4}$ off

C

8. Evaluate xy if

(a) $x = \dfrac{1}{2}, y = \dfrac{3}{4}$

(b) $x = \dfrac{1}{3}, y = \dfrac{1}{2}$

(c) $x = 2\dfrac{1}{2}, y = 1\dfrac{2}{3}$

CHALLENGE

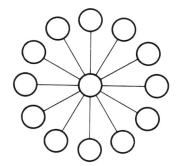

Write the numbers from 1 to 13 in the circles so that the sum along each line is 21.

3.4 DIVIDING FRACTIONS

Division is the inverse operation of multiplication.
Since $2 \times 5 = 10$,　then　$10 \div 5 = 2$
Similarly,

since $\frac{3}{4} \times \frac{1}{2} = \frac{3}{8}$,　then　$\frac{3}{8} \div \frac{1}{2} = \frac{3}{4}$

Also,　$\frac{3}{8} \times \frac{2}{1} = \frac{6}{8} = \frac{3}{4}$

Therefore,

$$\frac{3}{8} \div \frac{1}{2} = \frac{3}{8} \times \frac{2}{1}$$

We can divide by a fraction if we multiply by the reciprocal.

For example,

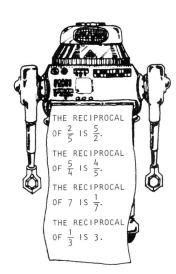

THE RECIPROCAL OF $\frac{2}{5}$ IS $\frac{5}{2}$.

THE RECIPROCAL OF $\frac{5}{4}$ IS $\frac{4}{5}$.

THE RECIPROCAL OF 7 IS $\frac{1}{7}$.

THE RECIPROCAL OF $\frac{1}{3}$ IS 3.

$1\frac{1}{3} \div \frac{2}{5} = \frac{4}{3} \div \frac{2}{5}$ ← Change the mixed number to an improper fraction.

$= \frac{4}{3} \times \frac{5}{2}$ ← Write the reciprocal of $\frac{2}{5}$.

$= \frac{20}{6}$

$= \frac{10}{3}$

To divide by a fraction, multiply by the reciprocal of the divisor.

$$\frac{a}{b} \div \frac{c}{d} = \frac{a}{b} \times \frac{d}{c} = \frac{ad}{bc}$$

Example 1. Divide.　$2\frac{2}{3} \div 1\frac{1}{4}$

Solution: $2\frac{2}{3} \div 1\frac{1}{4} = \frac{8}{3} \div \frac{5}{4}$ ← Write $2\frac{2}{3}$ as an improper fraction.

$= \frac{8}{3} \times \frac{4}{5}$ ← The reciprocal of $\frac{5}{4}$ is $\frac{4}{5}$.

$= \frac{32}{15}$

$= 2\frac{2}{15}$

Example 2. Divide.　$1\frac{1}{2} \div 3$

Solution: $1\frac{1}{2} \div 3 = \frac{3}{2} \div 3$ ← Write $1\frac{1}{2}$ as $\frac{3}{2}$.

$= \frac{3}{2} \times \frac{1}{3}$ ← The reciprocal of 3 is $\frac{1}{3}$.

$= \frac{1}{2}$

EXERCISE

A

1. State the reciprocal of each of the following.

   (a) $\frac{2}{3}$ (b) $\frac{4}{5}$ (c) $\frac{8}{7}$

   (d) $\frac{1}{2}$ (e) 8 (f) $1\frac{1}{3}$

   (g) $2\frac{1}{4}$ (h) 9 (i) 1

B

2. Write as improper fractions.

   (a) $1\frac{1}{2}$ (b) $2\frac{2}{3}$ (c) $3\frac{5}{8}$ (d) $4\frac{1}{4}$

   (e) $3\frac{2}{3}$ (f) $1\frac{3}{4}$ (g) $2\frac{3}{8}$ (h) $3\frac{1}{3}$

3. Write as mixed numbers.

   (a) $\frac{4}{3}$ (b) $\frac{5}{2}$ (c) $\frac{7}{3}$ (d) $\frac{7}{4}$

   (e) $\frac{13}{3}$ (f) $\frac{10}{3}$ (g) $\frac{8}{3}$ (h) $\frac{15}{2}$

4. Simplify and state your answer in lowest terms.

   (a) $\frac{1}{3} \div \frac{1}{2}$ (b) $\frac{3}{4} \div \frac{2}{3}$

   (c) $\frac{5}{8} \div \frac{2}{3}$ (d) $\frac{1}{6} \div \frac{1}{2}$

   (e) $\frac{1}{6} \div \frac{2}{3}$ (f) $4 \div \frac{1}{2}$

   (g) $\frac{1}{9} \div \frac{3}{4}$ (h) $\frac{5}{7} \div \frac{2}{7}$

   (i) $\frac{3}{4} \div 3$ (j) $\frac{5}{8} \div 5$

5. Simplify and state your answer in lowest terms.

   (a) $1\frac{1}{2} \div 1\frac{1}{3}$ (b) $6\frac{1}{4} \div 4\frac{1}{3}$

   (c) $1\frac{1}{3} \div 2\frac{1}{5}$ (d) $4\frac{1}{2} \div 6\frac{1}{3}$

   (e) $12\frac{1}{2} \div 4$ (f) $5 \div 1\frac{1}{2}$

   (g) $\frac{3}{5} \div \frac{6}{7}$ (h) $8\frac{1}{2} \div 1\frac{1}{3}$

   (i) $2\frac{1}{3} \div 2\frac{1}{3}$ (j) $5\frac{1}{2} \div 4$

APPLICATIONS

6. What is the average speed of a jet aircraft that travels 2800 km from Miami to Toronto in $2\frac{1}{2}$ h?

7. Strips of wallpaper are $\frac{6}{10}$ m wide. How many strips of wallpaper will it take to cover a bulletin board that is 8 m wide?

C

8. How many tables, each $2\frac{1}{2}$ m wide, can you put along the wall of the gym which is 21 m wide?

9. It takes $2\frac{1}{3}$ measures of flour to make a cake. How many cakes can you make from 14 measures of flour?

10. The electronics class is building a stereo. How many pieces of wire $1\frac{3}{10}$ m long can be cut from a spool with wire of length:

    (a) $344\frac{1}{2}$ m (b) 225 m

    (c) $125\frac{1}{2}$ m (d) $238\frac{1}{2}$ m

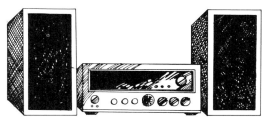

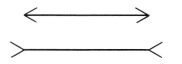

3.5 ADDING FRACTIONS

ALWAYS
WRITE ANSWERS
IN LOWEST
TERMS.

If fractions have the same denominator we can add the numerators.

Example 1. Evaluate. $\dfrac{1}{8} + \dfrac{3}{8}$

Solution: $\dfrac{1}{8} + \dfrac{3}{8} = \dfrac{1+3}{8}$

$= \dfrac{4}{8}$

$= \dfrac{1}{2}$

$$\dfrac{1}{8}$$
$$+\dfrac{3}{8}$$
$$\dfrac{4}{8}$$
$$\dfrac{1}{2}$$

To add fractions with the same denominator,

$$\frac{a}{b} + \frac{c}{b} = \frac{a+c}{b}$$

If fractions do not have the same denominator, we use equivalent fractions.

Example 2. Evaluate. $\dfrac{3}{4} + \dfrac{3}{8}$

Solution: $\dfrac{3}{4} + \dfrac{3}{8} = \dfrac{6}{8} + \dfrac{3}{8}$

$= \dfrac{9}{8}$

$= 1\dfrac{1}{8}$

$$\dfrac{3}{4}$$
$$\dfrac{3}{8}$$

$$1 \qquad + \qquad \dfrac{1}{8}$$

When adding mixed numbers like $1\dfrac{3}{5} + 4\dfrac{3}{4}$ we can use two methods.

METHOD I

$1\dfrac{3}{5} + 4\dfrac{3}{4} = \dfrac{8}{5} + \dfrac{19}{4}$

$\qquad = \dfrac{32}{20} + \dfrac{95}{20}$

$\qquad = \dfrac{127}{20}$

$\qquad = 6\dfrac{7}{20}$

METHOD II

$1\dfrac{3}{5} + 4\dfrac{3}{4} = 1\dfrac{12}{20} + 4\dfrac{15}{20}$

$\qquad = 5 + \dfrac{27}{20}$

$\qquad = 5 + 1\dfrac{7}{20}$

$\qquad = 6\dfrac{7}{20}$

To add fractions, we use equivalent fractions to get common denominators, and then add the numerators.

EXERCISE

A

1. Find the equivalent fraction.

   (a) $\dfrac{3}{4} = \dfrac{\square}{8}$ (b) $\dfrac{5}{10} = \dfrac{\square}{2}$

   (c) $4 = \dfrac{\square}{3}$ (d) $\dfrac{\square}{5} = \dfrac{4}{10}$

2. Find the lowest common denominator (L.C.D.).

   (a) $\dfrac{1}{2}, \dfrac{5}{8}$ (b) $\dfrac{2}{3}, \dfrac{3}{4}$

   (c) $3, \dfrac{2}{5}$ (d) $\dfrac{3}{4}, 2$

3. Add.

   (a) $\dfrac{1}{5} + \dfrac{2}{5}$ (b) $\dfrac{1}{3} + \dfrac{2}{3}$

   (c) $\dfrac{4}{5} + \dfrac{1}{5}$ (d) $\dfrac{5}{8} + \dfrac{3}{8}$

B

4. Add.

   (a) $\dfrac{2}{3} + \dfrac{3}{4}$ (b) $\dfrac{5}{8} + \dfrac{1}{4}$

   (c) $\dfrac{5}{8} + \dfrac{1}{2}$ (d) $\dfrac{2}{3} + \dfrac{5}{6}$

   (e) $2\dfrac{1}{3} + 1\dfrac{1}{2}$ (f) $5\dfrac{1}{4} + 2\dfrac{1}{2}$

5. Add.

   (a) $\dfrac{7}{8} + \dfrac{1}{4}$ (b) $\dfrac{2}{3} + \dfrac{1}{6}$

   (c) $\dfrac{2}{3} + \dfrac{1}{4}$ (d) $\dfrac{3}{4} + \dfrac{2}{3}$

   (e) $5\dfrac{1}{2} + 2\dfrac{1}{4}$ (f) $3\dfrac{1}{3} + 1\dfrac{3}{4}$

6. Evaluate.

   (a) $\dfrac{3}{4} + \dfrac{5}{8}$ (b) $\dfrac{5}{6} + \dfrac{1}{3}$

   (c) $\dfrac{3}{7} + \dfrac{1}{2}$ (d) $\dfrac{5}{8} + \dfrac{1}{2}$

   (e) $\dfrac{5}{8} + \dfrac{1}{6}$ (f) $\dfrac{3}{4} + \dfrac{1}{3}$

   (g) $\dfrac{2}{3} + \dfrac{5}{12}$ (h) $\dfrac{8}{9} + \dfrac{2}{3}$

7. Evaluate.

   (a) $9\dfrac{1}{3} + 4\dfrac{2}{3}$ (b) $6\dfrac{1}{2} + 4\dfrac{1}{4}$

   (c) $2\dfrac{1}{2} + 1\dfrac{2}{3}$ (d) $2\dfrac{2}{5} + 4\dfrac{1}{4}$

   (e) $1\dfrac{1}{5} + \dfrac{3}{4}$ (f) $7\dfrac{1}{2} + 8\dfrac{2}{3}$

8. Evaluate.

   (a) $\dfrac{1}{2} + \dfrac{2}{3} + \dfrac{1}{4}$ (b) $\dfrac{3}{4} + \dfrac{1}{2} + \dfrac{1}{3}$

   (c) $\dfrac{5}{8} + \dfrac{1}{4} + \dfrac{1}{2}$ (d) $\dfrac{1}{3} + \dfrac{1}{2} + \dfrac{1}{6}$

   (e) $2\dfrac{1}{2} + 3\dfrac{1}{4} + 1\dfrac{3}{4}$ (f) $6\dfrac{2}{3} + 2\dfrac{1}{3} + 2\dfrac{1}{2}$

9. A tank contains 123 L of milk. 165 L of milk are added to the tank. How much milk is now in the tank?

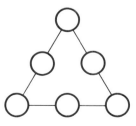

CHALLENGE

Put the numbers from 1 to 6 in the circles so that the sum along each side is 10.

3.6 SUBTRACTING FRACTIONS

If fractions have the same denominator we can subtract the numerators.

Example 1. Evaluate. $\dfrac{4}{5} - \dfrac{3}{5}$

$Solution:$ $\dfrac{4}{5} - \dfrac{3}{5} = \dfrac{4-3}{5}$

$$= \dfrac{1}{5}$$

$\dfrac{4}{5}$

$\dfrac{3}{5}$

$\dfrac{1}{5}$

> To subtract fractions with the same denominator,
> $$\dfrac{a}{b} - \dfrac{c}{b} = \dfrac{a-c}{b}$$

If fractions do not have the same denominator, we use equivalent fractions.

Example 2. Evaluate. $\dfrac{3}{4} - \dfrac{1}{2}$

$Solution:$ $\dfrac{3}{4} - \dfrac{1}{2} = \dfrac{3}{4} - \dfrac{2}{4}$

$$= \dfrac{1}{4}$$

When subtracting mixed numbers like $5\dfrac{1}{2} - 2\dfrac{2}{3}$

we sometimes have to regroup the numbers as follows.

WHY DOES
$5\dfrac{3}{6}$
$= 4\dfrac{9}{6}$?

METHOD I

$5\dfrac{1}{2} - 2\dfrac{2}{3} = 5\dfrac{3}{6} - 2\dfrac{4}{6}$

$= 4\dfrac{9}{6} - 2\dfrac{4}{6}$

$= 2\dfrac{5}{6}$

METHOD II

$5\dfrac{1}{2} - 2\dfrac{2}{3} = \dfrac{11}{2} - \dfrac{8}{3}$

$= \dfrac{33}{6} - \dfrac{16}{6}$

$= \dfrac{17}{6}$

$= 2\dfrac{5}{6}$

> To subtract fractions, we use equivalent fractions to get common denominators, and then subtract the numerators.

EXERCISE

B

1. Subtract.

(a) $\dfrac{5}{8} - \dfrac{1}{4}$

(b) $\dfrac{7}{10} - \dfrac{3}{10}$

(c) $\dfrac{5}{6} - \dfrac{2}{3}$

(d) $\dfrac{1}{2} - \dfrac{1}{3}$

2. Make a diagram to show each of the following subtractions.

(a) $\dfrac{2}{3} - \dfrac{1}{2}$

(b) $\dfrac{2}{3} - \dfrac{1}{6}$

(c) $\dfrac{3}{10} - \dfrac{1}{5}$

(d) $\dfrac{7}{8} - \dfrac{3}{4}$

3. Find the difference for each.

(a) $\dfrac{5}{8} - \dfrac{1}{8}$ (b) $\dfrac{3}{8} - \dfrac{1}{8}$

(c) $\dfrac{3}{4} - \dfrac{1}{4}$ (d) $\dfrac{7}{10} - \dfrac{3}{10}$

(e) $\dfrac{5}{6} - \dfrac{1}{6}$ (f) $\dfrac{2}{3} - \dfrac{1}{3}$

4. Subtract.

(a) $\dfrac{3}{4} - \dfrac{1}{2}$ (b) $\dfrac{5}{6} - \dfrac{1}{3}$

(c) $\dfrac{5}{8} - \dfrac{1}{4}$ (d) $\dfrac{7}{8} - \dfrac{3}{4}$

(e) $\dfrac{7}{10} - \dfrac{1}{5}$ (f) $\dfrac{4}{5} - \dfrac{3}{10}$

5. Find each difference.

(a) $5\dfrac{5}{8} - 2\dfrac{1}{4}$ (b) $4\dfrac{5}{6} - 1\dfrac{2}{3}$

(c) $7\dfrac{2}{3} - 3\dfrac{1}{3}$ (d) $5\dfrac{7}{10} - 1\dfrac{2}{5}$

(e) $3\dfrac{3}{4} - 1\dfrac{1}{2}$ (f) $10\dfrac{7}{8} - 5\dfrac{1}{2}$

6. Subtract.

(a) $\dfrac{4}{5} - \dfrac{3}{4}$ (b) $\dfrac{2}{3} - \dfrac{3}{8}$

(c) $\dfrac{1}{4} - \dfrac{1}{6}$ (d) $\dfrac{4}{5} - \dfrac{2}{3}$

7. Subtract.

(a) $4\dfrac{2}{3} - 1\dfrac{1}{2}$ (b) $7\dfrac{5}{6} - 2\dfrac{2}{3}$

(c) $6\dfrac{4}{10} - 2\dfrac{1}{3}$ (d) $3\dfrac{7}{8} - 1\dfrac{1}{2}$

8. Find the difference.

(a) $3\dfrac{1}{3} - 1\dfrac{2}{3}$ (b) $5\dfrac{1}{5} - 1\dfrac{1}{2}$

(c) $5\dfrac{1}{3} - 2\dfrac{3}{4}$ (d) $4\dfrac{3}{8} - 2\dfrac{3}{4}$

CHALLENGE

Start with the word "HAND" and change one letter at a time to form a new word until you reach "FOOT." The best solution has the fewest steps.

HAND

‾‾‾‾

‾‾‾‾

‾‾‾‾

‾‾‾‾

FOOT

3.7 SOLVING PROBLEMS WITH FRACTIONS

In this section we solve problems with fractions.

Example 1. Jim has $\frac{1}{2}$ of a pizza. He shares his half pizza by giving $\frac{1}{3}$ of his share to Chad. What fraction of the whole pizza does Chad receive?

Solution:

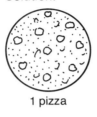 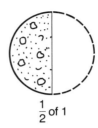 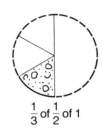

1 pizza $\frac{1}{2}$ of 1 $\frac{1}{3}$ of $\frac{1}{2}$ of 1

The fraction of the whole pizza is:

$$\frac{1}{3} \text{ of } \frac{1}{2} \text{ of } 1 = \frac{1}{3} \times \frac{1}{2} \times 1$$
$$= \frac{1}{6}$$

Chad receives $\frac{1}{6}$ of a pizza.

Example 2.

Hans takes $12\frac{3}{4}$ h to repair and paint the fender on a car. It takes $15\frac{1}{2}$ h for the paint to dry. How long does it take for the whole job to be completed?

Solution: The total time required is:

$$12\frac{3}{4} + 15\frac{1}{2} = 12\frac{3}{4} + 15\frac{2}{4}$$
$$= 12 + 15 + \frac{3}{4} + \frac{2}{4}$$
$$= 27 + \frac{5}{4}$$
$$= 27 + 1 + \frac{1}{4}$$
$$= 28\frac{1}{4}$$

$\therefore$ it takes $28\frac{1}{4}$ h for the whole job.

Do these steps mentally.

EXERCISE

B

1. Joan trained for a cross-country run. She ran $1\frac{1}{2}$ h on Monday, $2\frac{1}{4}$ h on Tuesday, and $2\frac{3}{4}$ h on Wednesday.

   What is the total number of hours she trained on Monday, Tuesday, and Wednesday?

2. Jacques tries to do weight training for 10 h each week. This week he has trained $1\frac{1}{4}$ h, $2\frac{1}{2}$ h, and $1\frac{1}{2}$ h.

   How many more hours must he train this week?

3. The price of a stock goes up and down in fractions of a dollar. A certain stock started at $\$7\frac{1}{4}$, then had an increase of $\$1\frac{1}{2}$, followed by a drop of $\$2\frac{1}{4}$.

   What is the new value of the stock?

4. An overseas telephone call was made during the $\frac{2}{3}$ off calling time. The regular rate for the call is $27.00.

   How much was actually paid for the call?

5. A portable stereo that normally sells for $459, is on sale at $\frac{1}{3}$ off.

   (a) What is the discount?
   (b) What is the sale price of the stereo?

6. There are 12 girls on the junior basketball team. After a game, they ordered pizza.

   Each player ate an average of $\frac{2}{3}$ of a pizza.

   How many pizzas did they eat?

7. 1 kg of roast beef will feed 3 people.
   (a) What fraction of a kilogram of beef is required for 1 person?
   (b) How many people can be fed with 15 kg of beef?

8. There are 1250 students in the school. Only 800 students can be seated in the gymnasium at one time.
   (a) What fraction of the student body can be seated in the gymnasium at one time?
   (b) What fraction of the student body cannot be seated in the gymnasium at one time?

3.8 CHANGING FRACTIONS TO DECIMALS

In archery class, Jennifer hit the target 14 times in 20 shots, while Gisele hit the target 18 times in 30 shots. Which girl has the better record?

Jennifer hit the target $\frac{14}{20}$ of the time.

Gisele hit the target $\frac{18}{30}$ of the time.

We compare these fractions by writing them as decimals.

$\frac{14}{20}$ means $14 \div 20$. $\frac{14}{20} = 0.7 \leftarrow$ $20\overline{)14.0}$ 0.7

$\frac{18}{30}$ means $18 \div 30$. $\frac{18}{30} = 0.6 \leftarrow$ $30\overline{)18.0}$ 0.6

Since $0.7 > 0.6$, Jennifer's record is better than Gisele's.

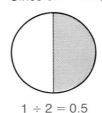

$1 \div 2 = 0.5$

To change a fraction to a decimal, divide the numerator by the denominator.

We can write a fraction as a decimal. The shaded portion of the circle represents 0.5 or $\frac{1}{2}$.

We change $\frac{1}{2}$ to 0.5 by dividing.

Example. Change to decimals.

(a) $\frac{3}{8}$ (b) $\frac{2}{3}$ (c) $\frac{7}{27}$

Solution: We divide the denominator into the numerator.

(a)
$$\begin{array}{r} 0.375 \\ 8\overline{)3.000} \\ 2\,4 \\ \hline 60 \\ 56 \\ \hline 40 \\ 40 \\ \hline 0 \end{array}$$

(b)
$$\begin{array}{r} 0.666 \\ 3\overline{)2.000} \\ 1\,8 \\ \hline 20 \\ 18 \\ \hline 20 \\ 18 \\ \hline 2 \end{array}$$

(c)
$$\begin{array}{r} 0.259259 \\ 27\overline{)7.000000} \\ 5\,4 \\ \hline 160 \\ 135 \\ \hline 250 \\ 243 \\ \hline 70 \\ 54 \\ \hline 160 \\ 135 \\ \hline 25 \end{array}$$

$\frac{3}{8} = 0.375$ $\frac{2}{3} = 0.\overline{6}$ $\frac{7}{27} = 0.\overline{259}$

When the division does not produce a remainder of 0, we have a repeating decimal. Decimals such as 0.375 are terminating decimals. Decimals such as 0.666... and 0.259259... are called periodic or non-terminating decimals. The period of a repeating decimal is the part of the decimal that repeats. The period of 0.259259... is 259 and we write $0.\overline{259}$.

EXERCISE

A

1. State the period of these decimals.
   (a) 0.333 3...   (b) 0.363 6...
   (c) 0.050 5...   (d) 2.425 425...
   (e) 72.777...   (f) 0.105 105...

B

2. State the decimal form of each fraction.
   (a) $\frac{1}{10}$ (b) $\frac{2}{10}$ (c) $\frac{3}{10}$
   (d) $\frac{7}{10}$ (e) $\frac{4}{10}$ (f) $\frac{8}{10}$
   (g) $\frac{25}{100}$ (h) $\frac{50}{100}$ (i) $\frac{75}{100}$
   (j) $\frac{5}{100}$ (k) $\frac{18}{100}$ (l) $\frac{65}{100}$

3. Write, using the bar above the period.
   (a) 3.222...   (b) 4.625 625...
   (c) 0.454 54...   (d) 0.035 353...
   (e) 5.212 12...   (f) 0.071 071...
   (g) 0.142 857 142 857 1...

4. Express as decimals.
   (a) $\frac{1}{4}$ (b) $\frac{3}{4}$ (c) $\frac{1}{8}$
   (d) $\frac{5}{8}$ (e) $\frac{3}{5}$ (f) $\frac{3}{2}$
   (g) $\frac{1}{9}$ (h) $\frac{1}{3}$ (i) $\frac{2}{11}$
   (j) $\frac{3}{11}$ (k) $\frac{2}{27}$ (l) $\frac{11}{15}$

5. Express as decimals.
   (a) $\frac{5}{12}$ (b) $\frac{7}{24}$ (c) $\frac{8}{15}$
   (d) $\frac{6}{18}$ (e) $\frac{9}{24}$ (f) $\frac{11}{21}$
   (g) $\frac{7}{66}$ (h) $\frac{8}{21}$ (i) $\frac{15}{31}$

6. In baseball, Henry hit 17 times during 24 at bats. Richard hit 21 times in 29 at bats. In order to find who is the better batter, we find the batting average:
$$average = \frac{number\ of\ hits}{number\ of\ at\ bats}$$
Find the averages to determine which player has the better record.

7. Edna hit the target 17 times in 24 throws of bean toss at the winter carnival. Jane hit the target 12 times in 18 throws. In order to find which girl had the better record at bean toss, we find the average:
$$average = \frac{number\ of\ hits}{number\ of\ tosses}$$
Find the averages to determine which girl has the better record.

CHALLENGE

Copy this figure in your notebook. Trace it without lifting your pencil or going over a line more than once.

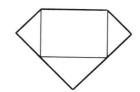

3.9 CHANGING DECIMALS TO FRACTIONS

We can change terminating decimals to fractions using place value.

Example 1. Change to fractions.
(a) 0.25   (b) 0.237   (c) 0.045

Solution:

(a) $0.25 = \dfrac{25}{100}$ (b) $0.237 = \dfrac{237}{1000}$ (c) $0.045 = \dfrac{45}{1000}$

$\quad\quad = \dfrac{1}{4}$ $\quad\quad\quad\quad\quad\quad = \dfrac{9}{200}$

To change repeating decimals to fractions, we eliminate the repeating portion of the decimal by subtraction.

Example 2. Change to fractions.
(a) 0.333...   (b) 0.454 545...   (c) $0.1\overline{35}$

Solution:

(a) $p = 0.333...$

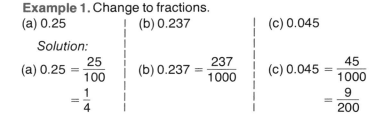

$\quad\quad 10p = 3.333...$
$\quad\quad\quad p = 0.333...$
$\quad\quad\quad 9p = 3$
$\quad\quad\quad\quad p = \dfrac{3}{9}$
$\quad\quad\quad\quad\quad = \dfrac{1}{3}$

(b) $p = 0.4545...$

$\quad\quad 100p = 45.4545...$
$\quad\quad\quad\, p = \,\,\,\,0.4545...$
$\quad\quad\, 99p = 45$
$\quad\quad\quad\, p = \dfrac{45}{99}$
$\quad\quad\quad\quad = \dfrac{5}{11}$

Locate the decimal after the first period.

(c) $p = 0.13535...$

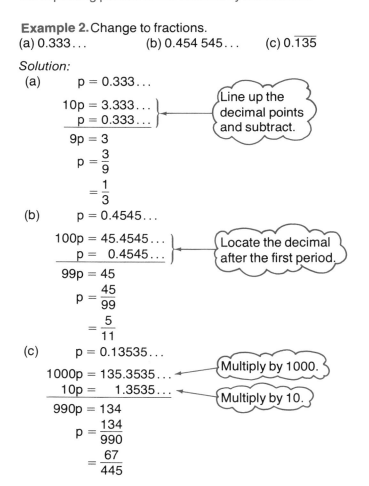

$\quad\, 1000p = 135.3535...$
$\quad\quad 10p = \,\,\,\,\,1.3535...$
$\quad\, 990p = 134$
$\quad\quad\quad p = \dfrac{134}{990}$
$\quad\quad\quad\quad = \dfrac{67}{445}$

Multiply by 1000.

Multiply by 10.

EXERCISE

A

1. State the period of each of these decimals.
   - (a) 0.252 525...
   - (b) 0.375 375...
   - (c) 0.322 222...
   - (d) 0.423 232...
   - (e) 0.305 305...
   - (f) 0.444 444...
   - (g) $0.\overline{235}$
   - (h) $0.6\overline{07}$
   - (i) $2.3\overline{253}$
   - (j) $4.6\overline{005}$

B

2. Change these decimals to fractions.
   - (a) 0.71
   - (b) 0.3
   - (c) 0.6
   - (d) 0.123
   - (e) 0.627
   - (f) 0.373
   - (g) 0.19
   - (h) 0.11
   - (i) 0.07
   - (j) 0.231

3. Change to fractions in lowest terms.
   - (a) 0.72
   - (b) 0.65
   - (c) 0.19
   - (d) 0.35
   - (e) 0.025
   - (f) 0.25
   - (g) 0.005
   - (h) 0.375
   - (i) 0.505
   - (j) 0.625

4. Change to fractions or mixed numbers in simplest form.
   - (a) 1.5
   - (b) 2.25
   - (c) 3.75
   - (d) 4.4
   - (e) 55.6
   - (f) 23.23
   - (g) 7.375
   - (h) 43.85
   - (i) 6.55
   - (j) 3.625

5. Change these repeating decimals to fractions.
   - (a) 0.666...
   - (b) $0.\overline{4}$
   - (c) 0.131 3...
   - (d) $0.\overline{54}$
   - (e) 0.555...
   - (f) 0.155 5...
   - (g) 2.272 7...
   - (h) 0.063 63...

6. Change these repeating decimals to fractions.
   - (a) $0.\overline{2}$
   - (b) $0.\overline{51}$
   - (c) $0.\overline{8}$
   - (d) $0.9\overline{2}$
   - (e) $0.\overline{23}$
   - (f) $0.5\overline{07}$

7. Change these repeating decimals to fractions. Explain your results.
   - (a) $0.\overline{5}$
   - (b) $0.\overline{9}$

CALCULATOR MATH

ROUNDING OFF

Some calculators round off, while others truncate, or "chop off" the extra digits without rounding. The following exercise demonstrates how your calculator handles the extra digits. The displays from two different kinds of calculators are shown.

Press	Calculator #1 Display	Calculator #2 Display
C	0	0.00
2	2.	2.
÷	2.	2.00
3	3.	3.
=	0.6666666	0.6666667
×	0.6666666	0.6666667
3	3.	3.
=	1.9999998	2

Notice that the two calculators give slightly different answers to the problem
$$2 \div 3 \times 3$$

The difference arises because calculator #1 truncates and drops the digits after dividing. Calculator #2 does two things: (i) only the display is rounded off; (ii) digits are saved in the memory and not dropped off.

The solution is
$$2 \div 3 \times 3 = 2$$
as we multiply and divide in order from left to right.

EXERCISE

Experiment with the following questions to determine whether the calculator you are using truncates, or rounds.
1. $5 \div 3 \times 3$
2. $6 \div 7 \times 7$
3. $1 \div 6 \times 6$
4. $2 \div 6 \times 6$
5. $8 \div 3 \times 3$

3.10 INTEGERS

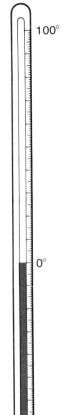

Numbers like +2, −5, −7, are called integers. These numbers are used to show direction above or below zero with temperature or sea level. Following are some examples of the use of integers.

1290 m above sea level	+1290
21°C below zero	−21
$125 profit	+125
$46 loss	−46
3 under par in golf	−3

The set of integers is:
$$I = \{\ldots, -3, -2, -1, 0, +1, +2, +3, \ldots\}$$

We can show the integers on a number line.

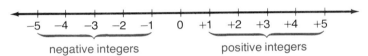

negative integers   positive integers

When we compare two integers on a number line, the number to the right is greater.

Since +2 is to the right of −3 on the number line, we say "+2 is greater than −3" and we write:
$$+2 > -3$$
We can also say "−3 is less than +2" and we write:
$$-3 < +2$$

Example. Draw graphs of the following on a number line.
    (a) integers less than +6
    (b) integers greater than −4

Solution: (a) $\{\ldots, -2, -1, 0, +1, +2, +3, +4, +5\}$

           (b) $\{-3, -2, -1, 0, +1, +2, +3, +4, \ldots\}$

The positive integers can be written without the + sign so that +2 and 2 are the same.

Now we have,
$$I = \{\ldots, -3, -2, -1, 0, 1, 2, 3, 4, \ldots\}$$

EXERCISE

A

1. Represent each phrase with an integer.
   - (a) 5°C below zero
   - (b) a loss of $7
   - (c) 12 m below sea level
   - (d) $64 profit
   - (e) 1542 m above sea level

2. State the next largest integer.
   - (a) −3
   - (b) 4
   - (c) 5
   - (d) −5
   - (e) 0
   - (f) 7

3. Which is the greater number?
   - (a) 6 or +3
   - (b) −5 or 2
   - (c) −3 or −5
   - (d) 2 or −2
   - (e) −5 or 5
   - (f) 7 or 0
   - (g) 0 or −2
   - (h) 3 or −2

4. Which is the smaller number?
   - (a) +6 or 8
   - (b) 6 or 9
   - (c) 3 or −2
   - (d) −3 or 5
   - (e) −4 or 1
   - (f) −9 or −11
   - (g) 0 or −3
   - (h) 3 or 0

B

5. List the following sets in brace brackets,
   { }.
   - (a) the even integers
   - (b) the odd integers
   - (c) the integers less than 3
   - (d) the integers less than −1
   - (e) the positive integers
   - (f) integers greater than −3
   - (g) integers between −4 and 3

6. State these sets.
   - (a)

   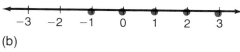

   - (b)

   - (c)

   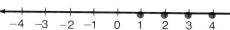

7. Draw number lines and graph these sets.
   - (a) {. . . 0, 2, 4, 6, 8}
   - (b) {−3, −2, −1, 0, 1, 2, 3}
   - (c) {−4, −2, 0, 2, 4}
   - (d) {. . . , −3, −2, −1, 1, 2, 3}
   - (e) {. . . , −10, −5, 0, 5, 10, . . . }
   - (f) {−2, 0, 2, 4,}
   - (g) {0, 3, 6, 9}

8. Replace ☐ with <, =, or > to make the
   following statements true.
   - (a) 5 ☐ 3
   - (b) −7 ☐ 0
   - (c) 1 ☐ −5
   - (d) +3 ☐ 3
   - (e) −1 ☐ −4
   - (f) 2 ☐ −9
   - (g) −7 ☐ −3
   - (h) −4 ☐ 4

9. Graph these sentences on an integer
   line.
   - (a) the negative integers
   - (b) integers that are multiples of 2
   - (c) the positive integers that are even
   - (d) the integers less than or equal to 5
   - (e) the integers greater than −5
   - (f) the integers less than 2
   - (g) the integers less than −2
   - (h) the integers less than 4 and greater
     than −5

CHALLENGE

Draw a clock face. Draw 2 lines to form
3 groups so that the sum of the
numbers in each group is the same.

3.11 ADDING INTEGERS

Consider a large vat with many ⊞ and ⊟ cubes in it. These ⊞ and ⊟ cubes control the temperature of the solution. We shall call this a biotemp solution.

The ⊞ cubes are like hot coals except that they never lose their heat. The ⊟ cubes are like ice cubes except that they never melt. If the same number of ⊞ cubes and ⊟ cubes are in the vat, the temperature of the solution is 0°. For each ⊞ cube added, the solution temperature goes up one degree. For each ⊟ cube added the temperature goes down one degree.

We can use our biotemp solution to explain how we add integers. The temperature of the solution changes when we add ⊞ or ⊟ cubes. Each ⊞ cube we add raises the temperature 1°. Each ⊟ cube we add lowers the temperature 1°. If three of these ⊟ cubes are added, the temperature goes down 3°. The following table shows how this works.

Solution Temperature	Cubes Added	New Temperature	Addition Statement
5°	3 ⊞	8°	$5 + 3 = 8$
3°	2 ⊟	1°	$3 + (-2) = 1$
0°	4 ⊟	-4°	$0 + (-4) = -4$
-2°	4 ⊞	2°	$-2 + 4 = 2$
-6°	3 ⊟	-9°	$-6 + (-3) = -9$
-4°	3 ⊞	-1°	$-4 + 3 = -1$

When we add a negative integer, we write the negative integer in brackets, for example, $2 + (-3)$.

Integer addition can also be related to a number line. To show $-3 + (-5)$ we start at 0, move 3 to the left for -3, then 5 more to the left for -5.

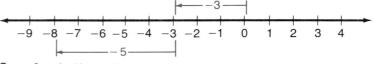

So, $-3 + (-5) = -8$.

To show $3 + (-5)$ we start at 0, move 3 to the right for 3, then 5 to the left for -5.

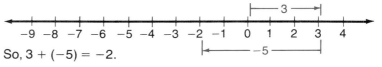

So, $3 + (-5) = -2$.

EXERCISE

A

1. Complete the following table.

Solution Temperature	Cubes Added	New Temperature	Addition Statement
5°	3 ⊟		
4°	4 ⊟		
−3°	5 ⊞		
−2°	2 ⊞		
3°	5 ⊟		
0°	3 ⊞		
−7°	2 ⊟		
2°	5 ⊞		

2. Add.
   (a) $3 + 5$
   (b) $3 + (-5)$
   (c) $-2 + 5$
   (d) $-2 + (-5)$
   (e) $-3 + 3$
   (f) $-3 + 5$
   (g) $2 + (-7)$
   (h) $-7 + 2$

3. Add.

   (a) $\begin{array}{r} 3 \\ +4 \\ \hline \end{array}$
   (b) $\begin{array}{r} 2 \\ 7 \\ \hline \end{array}$
   (c) $\begin{array}{r} -5 \\ -3 \\ \hline \end{array}$

   (d) $\begin{array}{r} -6 \\ 3 \\ \hline \end{array}$
   (e) $\begin{array}{r} -6 \\ 6 \\ \hline \end{array}$
   (f) $\begin{array}{r} 8 \\ -6 \\ \hline \end{array}$

   (g) $\begin{array}{r} -6 \\ -6 \\ \hline \end{array}$
   (h) $\begin{array}{r} 3 \\ 3 \\ \hline \end{array}$
   (i) $\begin{array}{r} -7 \\ -5 \\ \hline \end{array}$

B

4. Add.
   (a) $2 + (-3)$
   (b) $-5 + 7$
   (c) $-5 + (-7)$
   (d) $-7 + (-5)$
   (e) $-8 + 3$
   (f) $3 + (-8)$
   (g) $6 + (-5)$
   (h) $-5 + (-6)$

5. Add.
   (a) $2 + 7 + 5$
   (b) $2 + (-7) + 5$
   (c) $-3 + 6 + (-4)$
   (d) $-4 + 5 + (-3)$
   (e) $-3 + (-5) + 4$
   (f) $6 + (-4) + 5$
   (g) $-6 + (-6) + 12$
   (h) $-3 + (-2) + 1$

APPLICATIONS

6. The temperature in Kamloops is 3°C. What is the temperature after
   (a) a rise of 8°C?
   (b) a drop of 7°C?

7. The temperature in Dawson City is −4°C. What is the temperature after
   (a) a rise of 3°C?
   (b) a rise of 7°C?
   (c) a drop of 4°C?
   (d) a drop of 9°C?

8. The temperature in Edmonton at midnight was −1°C. The hourly temperature changes are shown below. Complete the table.

Time	Temperature Change	New Temperature
01:00	−2°C	
02:00	−3°C	
03:00	−2°C	
04:00	−1°C	
05:00	1°C	
06:00	2°C	

C

9. Add.
   (a) $236 + (-116)$
   (b) $358 + (-462)$
   (c) $-625 + 340$
   (d) $-417 + (-206)$

   (e) $\begin{array}{r} -315 \\ -206 \\ \hline \end{array}$
   (f) $\begin{array}{r} 307 \\ 512 \\ \hline \end{array}$

   (g) $\begin{array}{r} -718 \\ 216 \\ \hline \end{array}$
   (h) $\begin{array}{r} 503 \\ -704 \\ \hline \end{array}$

CHALLENGE

Arrange these numbers into pairs that add up to 26.
2, 4, 6, 8, 10, 12,
14, 16, 18, 20, 22, 24

3.12 SUBTRACTING INTEGERS

The biotemp solution also helps to explain the subtraction of integers. For each ⊞ cube removed from the solution, the temperature drops 1°C.

For each ⊟ cube removed from the solution, the temperature rises 1°C. Removing cubes is the same as subtracting or taking away.

The following table shows how this works.

Solution Temperature	Cubes Removed	Final Temperature	Subtraction Statement
5°C	3 ⊞	2°C	$5 - 3 = 2$
4°C	6 ⊞	−2°C	$4 - 6 = -2$
5°C	3 ⊟	8°C	$5 - (-3) = 8$
4°C	4 ⊞	0°C	$4 - 4 = 0$
−2°C	5 ⊟	3°C	$-2 - (-5) = 3$

Every integer has an opposite.

The opposite of 5 is −5.
The opposite of −12 is 12.

Subtraction is the inverse of addition.

Notice that $3 - (-4) = 7$ and $3 + (+4) = 7$.

Therefore, to subtract −4 we add the opposite integer, which is +4.

Subtraction Statement	Addition Statement
$5 - 3 = 2$	$5 + (-3) = 2$
$3 - 9 = -6$	$3 + (-9) = -6$
$5 - (-3) = 8$	$5 + 3 = 8$
$4 - 5 = -1$	$4 + (-5) = -1$
$-7 - (-3) = -4$	$-7 + 3 = -4$
$2 - (-6) = 8$	$2 + 6 = 8$
$-2 - (-6) = 4$	$-2 + 6 = 4$

EXERCISE

A

1. State the opposite of each of the following integers.

   (a) 3   (b) −25   (c) 17
   (d) 0   (e) −1   (f) −16
   (g) −(−5)   (h) −715   (i) 324

B

2. (a) Complete the table.

Solution Temperature	Cubes Removed	Final Temperature
5°	2⊞	
3°	2⊟	
−7°	2⊞	
−5°	3⊟	
1°	5⊞	
−3°	4⊟	
9°	6⊞	
9°	6⊟	
−1°	5⊟	

   (b) Write a subtraction statement and an addition statement for each question in part (a).
   Here are the first two.
   $5 − 2 = 5 + (−2) = 3$
   $3 − (−2) = 3 + 2 = 5$

3. Simplify.

   (a) $11 − 8$ (b) $6 − (−3)$
   (c) $5 − (−1)$ (d) $−5 − (−8)$
   (e) $−3 − 7$ (f) $7 − 12$
   (g) $0 − (−5)$ (h) $0 − 7$

4. Subtract.

   (a) 25   (b) 17   (c)   4
        18   17   9
        ——   ——   ——

   (d) −8   (e) 15   (f)   4
         3   −7   −8
        ——   ——   ——

   (g) −6   (h) 12   (i)   0
        −7   −5   −3
        ——   ——   ——

5. Simplify.

   (a) $−6 − 9$ (b) $−1 − 1$
   (c) $20 − (−7)$ (d) $2 − 49$
   (e) $−32 − (−3)$ (f) $−8 − 10$
   (g) $−10 − 15$ (h) $−51 − 9$

6. Simplify.

   (a) $17 + (−7) − 10$
   (b) $− 28 + 3 − 1$
   (c) $36 − (−4) + (−5)$
   (d) $− 10 − 5 + (−2)$
   (e) $−5 − 10 − 7$
   (f) $−3 + (5 − 3)$
   (g) $(4 − 2) + (2 − 4)$
   (h) $6 − (3 − 5) − (−2)$

APPLICATIONS

7. Subtract integers to find the answer.

   (a) What is the difference in temperature?
   Dawson City: −18°C
   Death Valley: 56°C

   (b) What is the difference in altitude?
   Mt. Everest: 8708 m above sea level
   Death Valley: 86 m below sea level

   (c) What is the difference in golf scores?
   Peter Gardner: 18 over par
   Joe Carole: 4 under par

   (d) What is the difference in depth?
   Atlantic Ocean: 3864 m
   Pacific Ocean: 4212 m

   (e) What is the difference in Winnipeg's temperatures?
   January: −18°C
   July: 19°C

CHALLENGE

If you are in a line-up for a movie and you are 15th from the front and 15th from the end, how many are in the line?

3.13 MULTIPLYING INTEGERS

Suppose we want to add ⊞ cubes to the biotemp solution in groups of three. If we add five groups of three ⊞ cubes, the temperature of the solution will rise 15°. $5 \times (+3) = +15$

If we add four groups of ⊟ cubes, the temperature of the solution will drop by 12°. $4 \times (-3) = -12$

What happens to the temperature of the solution if you remove five groups of three ⊞ cubes?

What happens to the temperature of the solution if you remove four groups of three ⊟ cubes?

Multiplication of integers, as with whole numbers, is based on repeated addition. $4 \times 5 = 5 + 5 + 5 + 5$
$$= 20$$

The product of two positive integers is positive.

$$4 \times (-5) = (-5) + (-5) + (-5) + (-5)$$
$$= -20$$

The product of a positive integer and a negative integer is negative.

Observe the patterns in these tables.

$3 \times 3 = 9$	$3 \times 3 = 9$
$3 \times 2 = 6$	$2 \times 3 = 6$
$3 \times 1 = 3$	$1 \times 3 = 3$
$3 \times 0 = 0$	$0 \times 3 = 0$
$3 \times (-1) = -3$	$(-1) \times 3 = -3$
$3 \times (-2) = -6$	$(-2) \times 3 = -6$
$3 \times (-3) = -9$	$(-3) \times 3 = -9$

The product of a negative integer and a positive integer is negative.

We can find the pattern for multiplying two negative integers in this table.

$(-4) \times 3 = -12$	$3 \times (-4) = -12$
$(-4) \times 2 = -8$	$2 \times (-4) = -8$
$(-4) \times 1 = -4$	$1 \times (-4) = -4$
$(-4) \times 0 = 0$	$0 \times (-4) = 0$
$(-4) \times (-1) = 4$	$-1 \times (-4) = 4$
$(-4) \times (-2) = 8$	$-2 \times (-4) = 8$
$(-4) \times (-3) = 12$	$-3 \times (-4) = 12$

The product of two negative integers is positive.

The pattern for multiplying integers is summarized in this table.

$$
\begin{array}{|c|}
\hline
\text{Rules of signs for integers} \\
a \times b = +ab \\
a \times (-b) = -ab \\
(-a) \times b = -ab \\
(-a) \times (-b) = +ab \\
\hline
\end{array}
$$

EXERCISE

A

1. Tell whether the answer is positive or negative.
   (a) $7 \times 4 = \blacksquare\ 28$
   (b) $5 \times (-3) = \blacksquare\ 15$
   (c) $(-7) \times (-2) = \blacksquare\ 14$
   (d) $(-6) \times 4 = \blacksquare\ 24$
   (e) $5 \times (-7) = \blacksquare\ 35$
   (f) $(-8) \times 0 = \blacksquare\ 0$

2. Multiply.
   (a) $(+2)(+3)$ (b) $(+3)(-5)$
   (c) $(-4)(6)$ (d) $0 \times (-3)$
   (e) -6×0 (f) $(-3) \times (-6)$
   (g) -5×7 (h) $8 \times (-2)$

3. Simplify.
   (a) -4×3 (b) $5 \times (-7)$
   (c) $5(-6)$ (d) -3×4
   (e) $-7(10)$ (f) $(-8)(-9)$
   (g) $-6 \times (-3)$ (h) -7×0

4. Simplify.
   (a) $6 \times (-5)$ (b) $(-1) \times 8$
   (c) $7 \times (-1)$ (d) -1×8
   (e) $-7 \times (-7)$ (f) $3 \times (-11)$
   (g) $(-12)(-4)$ (h) $-12 \times (-5)$

5. Simplify.
   (a) $(-3)^2$ (b) -3^2 (c) 5^2
   (d) $(-5)^2$ (e) $(-8)^2$ (f) 9^2
   (g) $(-11)^2$ (h) -7^2 (i) -11^2

B

6. Simplify.
   (a) 15×13 (b) -13×17
   (c) $25 \times (-22)$ (d) $(-41) \times (-7)$
   (e) $56 \times (-33)$ (f) -63×17
   (g) $25 \times (-3) \times 30$
   (h) $-24 \times 4 \times (-20)$
   (i) $-35 \times (-20) \times (-12)$
   (j) $63 \times (-5)^2 \times 5^2$

7. Which is greater?
   (a) $-6 \times (-4)$ or -5^2
   (b) -6^2 or $(-6)^2$
   (c) $23 \times (-1)$ or $(-4) \times (-5)$
   (d) -24×4 or $(-7)^2$
   (e) -12×4 or -7^2
   (f) $7 \times (-6)$ or $-6 \times (-7)$
   (g) $(-3^2) \times 5$ or $(-8)^2$

8. Simplify.

   $$-2(4-7) = (-2)(4) + (-2)(-7)$$

   (a) $3(2+5)$ (b) $4(5-8)$
   (c) $-4(2+7)$ (d) $3(6-9)$
   (e) $-5(8-3)$ (f) $-6(2-5)$
   (g) $-2(-4+4)$ (h) $-3(-7+2)$

C

9. Use the order of operations as stated in BEDMAS to simplify the following.
   (a) $2 \times 5 - 14$
   (b) $3 - 2 \times 5$
   (c) $-8(-2-7)$
   (d) $12 + (-6) \times 2$
   (e) $26 \times 0 + (-7)$
   (f) $5 - 3(-6)$
   (g) $5(-3)(-2) - (-5) \times 2$
   (h) $-2 \times (-5)^2 + 3 \times (-1)^2$
   (i) $(-3)^2 + (-4)^2 - (-2)^2$

APPLICATIONS

10. It is 27 km to the top of the stratosphere. As you go up, the temperature drops $3°C/km$.
    (a) What is the total temperature change?
    (b) What is the temperature at the top of the stratosphere if the temperature at sea level is $15°C$?

3.14 DIVIDING INTEGERS

Division is the inverse operation, or undoing, of multiplication.

If $(-10)(+2) = -20$,	then or	$(-20) \div (+2) = -10$ $(-20) \div (-10) = +2$
If $(+5)(+7) = +35$,	then or	$(+35) \div (+7) = +5$ $(+35) \div (+5) = +7$
If $(+4)(-8) = -32$,	then or	$(-32) \div (-8) = +4$ $(-32) \div (+4) = -8$
If $(-6)(-9) = +54$,	then or	$(+54) \div (-9) = -6$ $(+54) \div (-6) = -9$

The "sign" rules are summarized in the following table.

positive $\div$ positive = positive	$(+30) \div (+5) = +6$	$(+30) \div (+6) = +5$
positive $\div$ negative = negative	$(+30) \div (-5) = -6$	$(+30) \div (-6) = -5$
negative $\div$ positive = negative	$(-30) \div (+5) = -6$	$(-30) \div (+6) = -5$
negative $\div$ negative = positive	$(-30) \div (-5) = +6$	$(-30) \div (-6) = +5$

Example 1. Find the quotient.

(a) $\dfrac{-36}{+4}$ (b) $\dfrac{+18}{-6}$ (c) $\dfrac{-24}{-8}$

Solution:

(a) $\dfrac{-36}{+4} = -9$ (b) $\dfrac{+18}{-6} = -3$ (c) $\dfrac{-24}{-8} = +3$

Example 2. Find the value of ▨.

(a) $40 \div ▨ = -8$ (b) $-60 \div ▨ = -12$

Solution:

(a) Since $(-5) \times (-8) = 40$

$▨ = -5$

$40 \div (-5) = -8$

(b) Since $5 \times (-12) = -60$

$▨ = 5$

$-60 \div 5 = -12$

EXERCISE

A

1. Divide.

(a) $\dfrac{16}{-8}$ (b) $\dfrac{-12}{3}$ (c) $\dfrac{16}{4}$

(d) $\dfrac{-45}{-9}$ (e) $\dfrac{-36}{9}$ (f) $\dfrac{-56}{-7}$

(g) $\dfrac{0}{-2}$ (h) $\dfrac{-7}{7}$ (i) $\dfrac{5}{-5}$

B

2. Simplify.

(a) $20 \div (-5)$ (b) $-7 \div 7$
(c) $-63 \div (-7)$ (d) $(-35) \div (-7)$
(e) $9 \div (-9)$ (f) $0 \div (-5)$
(g) $-81 \div (-9)$ (h) $-72 \div 8$

3. Simplify.

(a) $12 \div (-6)$ (b) $-28 \div 4$
(c) $-30 \div (-6)$ (d) $-30 \div 5$
(e) $-44 \div (-4)$ (f) $45 \div 5$
(g) $-24 \div (-8)$ (h) $63 \div (-9)$

4. Simplify.

(a) $-45 \div 9$ (b) $-23 \div (-23)$
(c) $0 \div (-7)$ (d) $-21 \div (3)$
(e) $-48 \div 12$ (f) $-48 \div (-12)$
(g) $(-6)^2 \div 6$ (h) $(-5)^2 \div (-5)$

C

5. Simplify.

(a) $\dfrac{(-3) \times 8}{6}$ (b) $\dfrac{5 \times (-6)}{-10}$

(c) $2 \times \dfrac{(-12)}{-2}$ (d) $\dfrac{(-3)^2 \times 27}{3}$

(e) $\dfrac{27}{-3} \times \dfrac{5}{-1}$ (f) $-5 \times \dfrac{12}{-4}$

(g) $\dfrac{-8 \times 4}{-2 \times 8}$ (h) $\dfrac{27}{-3} \times \dfrac{7}{-1}$

6. Simplify.

(a) $80 \div (-10)$
(b) $(-60) \div 12$
(c) $(-168) \div 12$
(d) $(-138) \div (-23)$
(e) $(-406) \div (-29)$
(f) $(-243) \div (-9)$
(g) $184 \div (-23)$
(h) $169 \div 13$

7. Simplify.

(a) $(-255) \div 5 + 7$
(b) $5 + (-270) \div (-45)$
(c) $28 - 234 \div 26$
(d) $28 - 234 \div (-26)$
(e) $0 - 217 \div 31$
(f) $0 \times (-120) \div (-15)$

CHALLENGE

Arrange 14 chairs in a square room so there is the same number of chairs along each wall.

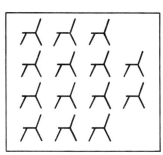

3.15 EXPRESSIONS WITH INTEGERS

In many expressions we replace the variables with integers. In these questions you substitute first, then evaluate.

Example 1. Evaluate these expressions for $x = -3$.

(a) $-5x$ (b) $4x + 3$ (c) $x^2 - 2x$

Solution: (a) $-5x = -5(-3)$
$$= 15$$

(b) $4x + 3 = 4(-3) + 3$
$$= -12 + 3$$
$$= -9$$

(c) $x^2 - 2x = (-3)^2 - 2(-3)$
$$= 9 + 6$$
$$= 15$$

Example 2. Evaluate the following expressions for
$x = 2$ and $y = -4$.

(a) $x + 2y$ (b) $x^2 + y^2$ (c) $x^2 - y$

Solution: (a) $x + 2y = (2) + 2(-4)$
$$= 2 - 8$$
$$= -6$$

(b) $x^2 + y^2 = (2)^2 + (-4)^2$
$$= 4 + 16$$
$$= 20$$

(c) $x^2 - y = (2)^2 - (-4)$
$$= 4 + 4$$
$$= 8$$

EXERCISE

A

1. If x = −2, evaluate.
   - (a) 2x
   - (b) 3x
   - (c) −4x
   - (d) −7x
   - (e) −x
   - (f) $x^2 + 3$
   - (g) 3x − 5
   - (h) 2x + 7

B

2. If x = 3, evaluate.
   - (a) $x^2 - 5$
   - (b) x − 5
   - (c) 2x − 7
   - (d) 3 − x
   - (e) x − 4
   - (f) x^3
   - (g) $5 - x^2$
   - (h) $x^2 - 5x$

3. If x = 3, y = −4, evaluate.
   - (a) x + y
   - (b) −x + y
   - (c) x − y
   - (d) −x − y
   - (e) $(x + y)^2$
   - (f) $x^2 + y^2$
   - (g) $x^2 + 3x + y^2 + 2y - 5$
   - (h) 2x − 3y + 7
   - (i) $5x - 2y + x^2 - 3$
   - (j) $7x - 2y + x^2 + y^2$

4. If x = −8 and y = 2, evaluate.
   - (a) −x
   - (b) −y
   - (c) −xy
   - (d) −(x + y)
   - (e) −(x − y)
   - (f) $x^2 + y^2$
   - (g) $x^2 - y^2$
   - (h) 2x − 3y

5. If x = −4, evaluate.
   - (a) $x^2 + 1$
   - (b) $x^2 - 12$
   - (c) 3x − 5
   - (d) $(2x)^2$
   - (e) $-2x^2$
   - (f) $-x^2 + 10$
   - (g) $(5 - x)^2$
   - (h) $(x + 1)^3$

CHALLENGE

CLOSED CURVE

Which points lie inside the closed curve?
Which points lie outside the closed curve?

CHALLENGE

Find the magic number and complete the magic square.

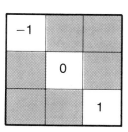

3.16 SCIENTIFIC NOTATION: LARGE NUMBERS

In science, we often have to use very large numbers. For example, the distance to the sun is approximately 147 000 000 km.

It may not be convenient to write all the zeros due to time and space. In order to simplify calculations with large numbers, scientists and technicians use "scientific notation" to write them.

To write 147 000 000 in scientific notation, we move the decimal point as shown.

$$1\ 47\ 000\ 000 = 1.47 \times 100\ 000\ 000$$
$$= 1.47 \times 10^8$$

Notice that the decimal point has been moved 8 places to the left, and the exponent of base 10 is 8.

Example 1. Express in scientific notation.

(a) 5300

(b) 625 000

Solution:

(a) $5300 = 5.300 \times 1000$
$$= 5.3 \times 10^3$$

(b) $625\ 000 = 6.25 \times 100\ 000$
$$= 6.25 \times 10^5$$

> You can find the exponent by counting the number of places the decimal point is moved.

Example 2. Express in standard notation.

(a) 3.5×10^4

(b) 6.3×10^7

Solution:

(a) $3.5 \times 10^4 = 3.5 \times 10\ 000$
$$= 35\ 000$$

(b) $6.3 \times 10^7 = 6.3 \times 10\ 000\ 000$
$$= 63\ 000\ 000$$

EXERCISE

A

1. Find the value of n in each statement.
   (a) $2500 = 2.5 \times 10^n$
   (b) $125 = 1.25 \times 10^n$
   (c) $21\,000 = 2.1 \times 10^n$
   (d) $275\,000 = 2.75 \times 10^n$
   (e) $26 = 2.6 \times 10^n$
   (f) $240 = 2.4 \times 10^n$
   (g) $6\,750\,000 = 6.75 \times 10^n$
   (h) $85\,600 = 8.56 \times 10^n$
   (i) $7\,400\,000 = 7.4 \times 10^n$

2. Find the value of n in each of the following.
   (a) $65\,200 = 6.52 \times 10^n$
   (b) $135\,000 = 1.35 \times 10^n$
   (c) $90\,000 = 9.0 \times 10^n$
   (d) $6\,120\,000 = 6.12 \times 10^n$
   (e) $5260 = 5.26 \times 10^n$
   (f) $820\,000 = 8.20 \times 10^n$
   (g) $15\,300\,000 = 1.53 \times 10^n$
   (h) $503\,000 = 5.03 \times 10^n$
   (i) $126 = 1.26 \times 10^n$

B

3. Write these numbers in scientific notation.
   (a) 5400
   (b) 520 000
   (c) 7 280 000
   (d) 6000
   (e) 3 020 000
   (f) 30 200 000

4. Write these numbers in scientific notation.
   (a) 93 000 000
   (b) 6 505 000 000 000
   (c) 2 353 000 000 000
   (d) 6 000 000 000 000
   (e) 2 570 000 000 000
   (f) 352 000 000 000 000

APPLICATIONS

5. Express the number in each statement using scientific notation.
   (a) The area of Canada is approximately $9\,970\,000 \text{ km}^2$.
   (b) There are about 96 000 km of railroad in Canada.
   (c) The moon is 356 000 km from the earth at its closest point.
   (d) The moon is 406 000 km from the earth at its farthest point.
   (e) One of Saturn's rings is 26 500 km wide.

C

6. The Andromeda Galaxy is the farthest object you can see with the unaided eye. The distance from the earth is about 22 000 000 000 000 000 km. Express this distance in scientific notation.

7. The radius of the universe is about 400 000 000 000 000 000 000 000 km. Express this distance in scientific notation.

8. Write these in standard notation.
   (a) 3.6×10^3 (b) 2.75×10^5
   (c) 6.35×10^2 (d) 5.0×10^5
   (e) 7.98×10^6 (f) 8.5×10^8

CALCULATOR MATH

Some calculators have scientific notation.

The display

$$2.50 \quad 07$$

is the product in scientific notation

$$2.50 \times 10^7$$

3.17 SCIENTIFIC NOTATION: SMALL NUMBERS

Scientists often use very small numbers. For example, the diameter of an atom is about

$$0.000\ 000\ 015\ \text{cm}$$

We can avoid writing all the zeros in very small numbers using scientific notation. To write 0.000 000 015 in scientific notation, we move the decimal point as shown.

from   to
here   here

$$0.000\ 000\ 015 = 1.5 \times 0.000\ 000\ 01$$
$$= 1.5 \times 10^{-8}$$

Notice that the decimal point has been moved 8 places to the right, and the exponent of 10 is -8.

Example 1. Express in scientific notation.

        (a) 0.035   (b) 0.000 062 5

Solution: (a) $0.035 = 3.5 \times 0.01$
$$= 3.5 \times 10^{-2}$$

        (b) $0.000\ 062\ 5 = 6.25 \times 0.000\ 01$
$$= 6.25 \times 10^{-5}$$

You can find the exponent by counting the number of places the decimal point is moved.

Example 2. Express in standard notation.

        (a) 1.6×10^{-5} (b) 5.08×10^{-2}

Solution: (a) $1.6 \times 10^{-5} = 1.6 \times 0.000\ 01$
$$= 0.000\ 016$$

        (b) $5.08 \times 10^{-2} = 5.08 \times 0.01$
$$= 0.050\ 8$$

EXERCISE

A

1. Find the value of n in each statement.
   - (a) $0.025 = 2.5 \times 10^n$
   - (b) $0.006\,5 = 6.5 \times 10^n$
   - (c) $0.37 = 3.7 \times 10^n$
   - (d) $0.000\,42 = 4.2 \times 10^n$
   - (e) $0.000\,003\,5 = 3.5 \times 10^n$
   - (f) $0.000\,065 = 6.5 \times 10^n$
   - (g) $0.000\,003\,75 = 3.75 \times 10^n$
   - (h) $0.004\,5 = 4.5 \times 10^n$
   - (i) $0.001\,03 = 1.03 \times 10^n$

2. Find the value of n in each of the following.
   - (a) $0.012\,5 = 1.25 \times 10^n$
   - (b) $0.000\,365 = 3.65 \times 10^n$
   - (c) $0.004\,26 = 4.26 \times 10^n$
   - (d) $0.000\,005 = 5.0 \times 10^n$
   - (e) $0.000\,053 = 5.3 \times 10^n$
   - (f) $0.75 = 7.5 \times 10^n$
   - (g) $0.060\,5 = 6.05 \times 10^n$
   - (h) $0.001\,28 = 1.28 \times 10^n$
   - (i) $0.000\,65 = 6.5 \times 10^n$

B

3. Write these numbers in scientific notation.
   - (a) 0.006 5
   - (b) 0.000 006 75
   - (c) 0.75
   - (d) 0.009 3
   - (e) 0.003 75
   - (f) 0.003 05

4. Write these numbers in scientific notation.
   - (a) 0.000 125
   - (b) 0.000 006 75
   - (c) 0.000 000 045
   - (d) 0.000 000 305
   - (e) 0.000 001 205
   - (f) 0.000 000 004 44

APPLICATIONS

5. Express the number in each statement using scientific notation.
   - (a) The hummingbird of Cuba has a mass of 0.001 98 kg.
   - (b) The world's smallest creature, the Rotifer, has a mass of 0.000 000 006 g.
   - (c) The mass of a proton is about: 0.000 000 000 000 000 000 001 67 g.
   - (d) The metric prefix "micro" means a multiplication factor of 0.000 001.
   - (e) The diameter of a molecule of water is 0.000 000 028 cm.
   - (f) Gold is a very maleable metal. One kilogram of gold can be stretched into a thread 0.000 5 cm in diameter, and 2400 km long.

6. Write each of the following numbers in standard notation.
   - (a) 2.5×10^{-3}
   - (b) 3.7×10^{-7}
   - (c) 1.25×10^{-6}
   - (d) 6.15×10^{-8}

CALCULATOR MATH

We use division to find a small number in scientific notation.

Press:

| 2 | . | 5 | ÷ | 1 | 0 | = |

| = | = | = | = | = | = |

The display

$$2.50 \quad -07$$

is the quotient in scientific notation 2.50×10^{-7}

THE WIND CHILL FACTOR

The wind chill factor is a number that tells us how cold we feel due to the temperature and wind speed. The faster your body loses heat, the colder you will feel. We can read the wind chill from the following chart.

WIND CHILL CHART

Wind Speed	Thermometer Reading (Degrees Celsius)														
	4	2	−1	−4	−7	−9	−12	−15	−18	−21	−23	−26	−29	−32	−34
Calm	4	2	−1	−4	−7	−9	−12	−15	−18	−21	−23	−26	−29	−32	−34
8 km/h	3	1	−3	−6	−9	−11	−14	−17	−21	−24	−26	−29	−32	−36	−37
16 km/h	−2	−6	−9	−13	−17	−19	−23	−26	−30	−33	−36	−39	−43	−47	−50
24 km/h	−6	−9	−12	−17	−21	−24	−28	−32	−36	−40	−43	−46	−51	−54	−57
32 km/h	−8	−11	−16	−20	−23	−27	−31	−36	−40	−43	−47	−51	−56	−60	−63
40 km/h	−9	−14	−18	−22	−26	−30	−34	−38	−43	−47	−50	−55	−59	−64	−67
48 km/h	−11	−15	−19	−24	−28	−32	−36	−41	−45	−49	−53	−57	−61	−66	−70
56 km/h	−12	−16	−20	−25	−29	−33	−37	−42	−47	−51	−55	−58	−64	−68	−72
64 km/h	−13	−17	−21	−26	−30	−34	−38	−43	−48	−52	−56	−60	−66	−70	−74

(Zones labelled on chart: Cold, Very Cold, Bitter Cold, Extremely Cold)

ESTIMATING THE WIND

Light wind under 20 km/h		Wind felt on face; extends a light flag; rustles and moves leaves
Moderate wind 21 to 40 km/h		Wind raises dust and loose paper; fine loose snow begins to drift; crested wavelets form on water.
Strong wind 41 to 60 km/h		Wind moves large branches; whistling is heard in telegraph wires; extensive drifting snow; difficulty walking against
Gale wind 61 to 90 km/h		Wind breaks off twigs; slight damage to structures, roof shingles, T.V. antennas; blowing snow reduces visibility.

EXERCISE

A

1. Find the wind chill temperature for the following combinations of wind speeds and thermometer readings.
   (a) 40 km/h and 4°C
   (b) 16 km/h and 4°C
   (c) 64 km/h and 2°C
   (d) 32 km/h and −4°C
   (e) 24 km/h and −23°C

B

2. Which of the following feels colder?
   (a) 16 km/h and −7°C, or 40 km/h and −1°C
   (b) 32 km/h and −15°C, or 48 km/h and −9°C
   (c) 40 km/h and −21°C, or 24 km/h and −26°C
   (d) 56 km/h and −12°C, or 32 km/h and −23°C
   (e) 48 km/h and 4°C, or 8 km/h and −9°C

3.18 CHAPTER 3 REVIEW EXERCISE

A

1. State these fractions in lowest terms.
   (a) $\dfrac{3}{12}$ (b) $\dfrac{5}{20}$
   (c) $\dfrac{12}{16}$ (d) $\dfrac{8}{12}$

B

2. Write these fractions in order from smallest to largest.
   $\dfrac{3}{4}, \dfrac{4}{5}, \dfrac{5}{9}, \dfrac{2}{3}, \dfrac{8}{11}, \dfrac{11}{15}$

3. Evaluate.
   (a) $\dfrac{1}{3}$ of 12   (b) $\dfrac{2}{5}$ of 15

4. Change to improper fractions.
   (a) $3\dfrac{1}{4}$ (b) $5\dfrac{2}{3}$

5. Multiply.
   (a) $\dfrac{3}{4} \times \dfrac{5}{6}$ (b) $\dfrac{4}{5} \times \dfrac{3}{5}$
   (c) $2\dfrac{1}{3} \times 3\dfrac{2}{3}$ (d) $4\dfrac{2}{5} \times 3\dfrac{1}{3}$

6. Divide.
   (a) $\dfrac{2}{3} \div \dfrac{3}{4}$ (b) $\dfrac{3}{5} \div \dfrac{4}{5}$
   (c) $3\dfrac{3}{4} \div 2\dfrac{3}{5}$ (d) $3\dfrac{1}{2} \div 1\dfrac{3}{4}$

7. Evaluate.
   (a) $\dfrac{3}{5} \times 4$ (b) $\dfrac{3}{5} \div 4$
   (c) $5 \times \dfrac{3}{4}$ (d) $4 \div \dfrac{2}{3}$

8. Evaluate.
   (a) $\dfrac{1}{2} + \dfrac{1}{3}$ (b) $\dfrac{3}{4} + \dfrac{4}{5}$
   (c) $\dfrac{3}{4} - \dfrac{1}{3}$ (d) $\dfrac{5}{6} - \dfrac{2}{3}$
   (e) $3\dfrac{2}{3} + 1\dfrac{1}{2}$ (f) $5\dfrac{1}{2} - 3\dfrac{2}{3}$
   (g) $5 - 2\dfrac{3}{4}$ (h) $3\dfrac{5}{8} + 2\dfrac{1}{4}$

9. Change these fractions to decimals.
   (a) $\dfrac{1}{4}$ (b) $\dfrac{3}{4}$ (c) $\dfrac{1}{5}$
   (d) $\dfrac{3}{8}$ (e) $\dfrac{5}{8}$ (f) $\dfrac{7}{8}$
   (g) $\dfrac{2}{5}$ (h) $\dfrac{3}{5}$ (i) $\dfrac{4}{5}$

10. Change these decimals to fractions.
    (a) 0.34   (b) 0.55   (c) 0.75
    (d) 0.57   (e) 0.25   (f) 0.36
    (g) 0.8   (h) 0.2   (i) 0.27
    (j) 0.125   (k) 0.875   (l) 0.625

11. Change these fractions to decimals.
    (a) $\dfrac{2}{3}$ (b) $\dfrac{3}{11}$ (c) $\dfrac{4}{9}$
    (d) $\dfrac{5}{9}$ (e) $\dfrac{7}{11}$ (f) $\dfrac{9}{11}$
    (g) $\dfrac{2}{7}$ (h) $\dfrac{4}{7}$ (i) $\dfrac{6}{7}$

12. Change these decimals to fractions.
    (a) 0.2222...   (b) 0.666...
    (c) 0.4444...   (d) 0.777...
    (e) 0.3535...   (f) 0.305 305...
    (g) $0.\overline{36}$ (h) $0.\overline{45}$
    (i) $0.\overline{325}$ (j) $0.\overline{25}$

13. Represent each phrase with an integer.
    (a) 3 m below sea level
    (b) a profit of $6
    (c) 1254 m above sea level
    (d) a profit of $0.25

14. Which is greater?
    (a) 5 or -5
    (b) -6 or -5
    (c) -3 or -4
    (d) -8 or -10

15. Write the opposite of each of these integers.
    (a) -4 (b) 6   (c) -11
    (d) 8   (e) -9 (f) $+6$

16. List the following sets.
    (a) the positive integers
    (b) the even integers
    (c) the negative integers
    (d) the integers greater than -3
    (e) the integers less than 7
    (f) the integers between -4 and 5
    (g) the integers less than or equal to 3
    (h) the integers greater than or equal to -4

17. Draw number lines and graph these sets.
    (a) $\{1, 2, 3, 4, \ldots\}$
    (b) $\{-2, -1, 0, 1, 2, 3\}$
    (c) $\{\ldots, -3, -2, -1\}$
    (d) $\{-4, -2, 0, 2, 4\}$
    (e) $\{\ldots, -7, -5, -3, -1, 1, 3, \ldots\}$

18. List these sets in brackets.

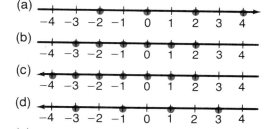

19. Simplify.
    (a) $-4 - 5$ (b) $5 - 9$
    (c) $7 + 4 - 3$ (d) $-2 + 5 - 7$
    (e) $-5 - 7 - 3$ (f) $5 - 6 + 7$

20. Simplify.
    (a) $3(5 - 9)$ (b) $-5(-3 + 7)$
    (c) $(5 - 8) - 3$ (d) $(5 - 8)(-3 - 4)$
    (e) $6(4 - 8) + 3(2 - 6)$
    (f) $-4(3 - 5) - 2(8 - 3)$
    (g) $3(5 - 2) - 6(0 - 3)$
    (h) $-5(4 - 9) + 3(-3 - 2)$

21. Write in scientific notation.
    (a) 25 000 000   (b) 360 000
    (c) 2 350 000   (d) 2350
    (e) 25   (f) 35 100
    (g) 1.25   (h) 0.25
    (i) 0.002 5   (j) 0.0375
    (k) 21.5   (l) 0.002 75

22. Write in standard notation.
    (a) 3.25×10^4
    (b) 5.45×10^5
    (c) 1.25×10^7
    (d) 2.05×10^{-3}
    (e) 1.55×10^{-5}
    (f) 6.25×10^3
    (g) 7.75×10^{-5}

23. If $x = -2$, evaluate.
    (a) $3x$ (b) $-4x$
    (c) $x + 5$ (d) $x - 7$
    (e) $-x$ (f) $-3x$
    (g) $5 - x$ (h) $2(x - 3)$

24. Evaluate for $x = 4$, and $y = -3$.
    (a) $x + y$ (b) $2x - y$
    (c) $2(x - y)$ (d) $-3x + 2y$
    (e) $5x + 2y$ (f) xy
    (g) $3xy$ (h) $xy - 4$
    (i) $(x + y + 2)^2$ (j) $(x - y)^2 + 3$

25. Harry takes 3 h to cut a lawn.
    How much of the lawn can Harry cut in 1 h?

26. John and Judy can pick a basket of blueberries in a half hour.
    How many baskets can they pick in an hour?

27. Sam crossed the lake in a power boat in $1\frac{1}{4}$ h. It took Mary $3\frac{2}{3}$ h to cross the same lake with a sailboat.
    What is the difference in time?

CHAPTER 3 TEST

1. Write each fraction in lowest terms.
   (a) $\dfrac{12}{16}$ (b) $\dfrac{5}{15}$ (c) $\dfrac{21}{35}$ (d) $\dfrac{63}{81}$

2. Order these fractions from smallest to largest.
   $\dfrac{3}{4}, \dfrac{5}{8}, \dfrac{7}{11}, \dfrac{35}{44}, \dfrac{15}{22}$

3. Simplify.
   (a) $\dfrac{2}{3} \times \dfrac{5}{8}$ (b) $\dfrac{2}{3}$ of 12   (c) $\dfrac{1}{8} \div \dfrac{1}{4}$
   (d) $\dfrac{3}{4} - \dfrac{2}{3}$ (e) $3\dfrac{1}{2} + 2\dfrac{3}{4}$ (f) $3\dfrac{1}{3} - 1\dfrac{5}{6}$

4. Change to decimals.
   (a) $\dfrac{5}{8}$ (b) $\dfrac{2}{3}$ (c) $\dfrac{5}{11}$ (d) $\dfrac{1}{9}$

5. Change to common fractions.
   (a) 0.53   (b) 0.007   (c) 0.777...   (d) 0.3535...

6. Graph on an integer line.
   (a) $\{1, 3, 5, 7, \dots\}$
   (b) $\{\dots, -3, 0, 3, 6, \dots\}$

7. List these sets.
   (a)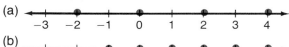
   (b)

8. Simplify.
   (a) $4 + (-7)$ (b) $-8 - 6$
   (c) $7 - 12$ (d) $-3 + (-8)$
   (e) $5 \times (-3)$ (f) $(-4)(-7)$
   (g) $-3(4 - 7)$ (h) $-28 \div (-7)$

9. Express in scientific notation.
   (a) 325 000   (b) 0.004 76

10. Express in standard notation.
    (a) 3.75×10^3 (b) 6.54×10^{-2}

11. It takes $4\dfrac{2}{3}$ h to clean the carpets in a house, and $5\dfrac{1}{2}$ h for the carpets to dry.
    How long does it take for the carpets to be cleaned and dried?

4

SQUARE ROOTS AND PYTHAGORAS

REVIEW AND PREVIEW TO CHAPTER 4

EXERCISE 1

1. Evaluate.

    (a) 3^2 (b) 2^3

    (c) 2^2 (d) 2^4

    (e) 2^5 (f) 2^6

    (g) 3^3 (h) 3^4

    (i) 5^2 (j) 4^3

2. Show that 2^6, 4^3, and 8^2 are the same number.

3. Which is greater?

    (a) 3^2 or 2^3?

    (b) 5^2 or 2^5?

    (c) $2^2 + 2^3$ or 2^5?

    (d) $4^3 - 4^1$ or 4^2?

    (e) $3^2 \times 3^2$ or 9^2?

4. Evaluate.

    (a) 125^2 (b) 420^2

    (c) 25^2 (d) 36^2

    (e) 100^2 (f) 1000^2

    (g) 64^2 (h) 50^2

    (i) 75^2 (j) 25^2

5. Determine whether these are equal.

    (a) 20^2 and 2×10^2

    (b) 25^2 and $(5^2)^2$

    (c) 30^2 and $60^2 \div 2$

    (d) 50^2 and $25^2 \div 4$

6. Simplify.

    (a) $3(4 - 7)$

    (b) $2(12 - 7) + 3(18 - 12)$

    (c) $(7 + 2)^2 - 1$

    (d) $(3 + 5)^2 - (9 - 7)^2$

    (e) $34 + 2(3 + 5) - 7$

    (f) $5(26 - 11) + 3(18 - 8)$

    (g) $(24 - 9)(14 - 9) \div (12 - 9)(11 - 6)$

7. Simplify.

    (a) $3(2.1 - 1.7)$

    (b) $2(5.8 - 2.6) + 3.7$

    (c) $3.2(4.5 - 2.7) + 1.25$

    (d) $4.4(2.5 + 1.6) - 1.75$

    (e) $34.75 - 2.4(1.6 + 3.5)$

    (f) $35.75 + 6.8 \times 4.9$

    (g) $82.25 - 5.6(3.8 + 3.5)$

8. Evaluate for $x = 3$.

    (a) x^2 (b) $2x$

    (c) $x + 2$ (d) $2x + 2$

    (e) $(x + 2)^2$ (f) $x^2 + 2$

    (g) $2x - 2$ (h) $10 - 3x$

9. Evaluate for $x = 3$, $y = 5$.

    (a) $x + y$ (b) $2x + 3y$

    (c) $x^2 + y^2$ (d) $(x + y)^2$

    (e) $3x - 2y$ (f) $2x - 3y$

    (g) $-x + y$ (h) $-x - y$

RIGHT ANGLES

These are examples of right angles.

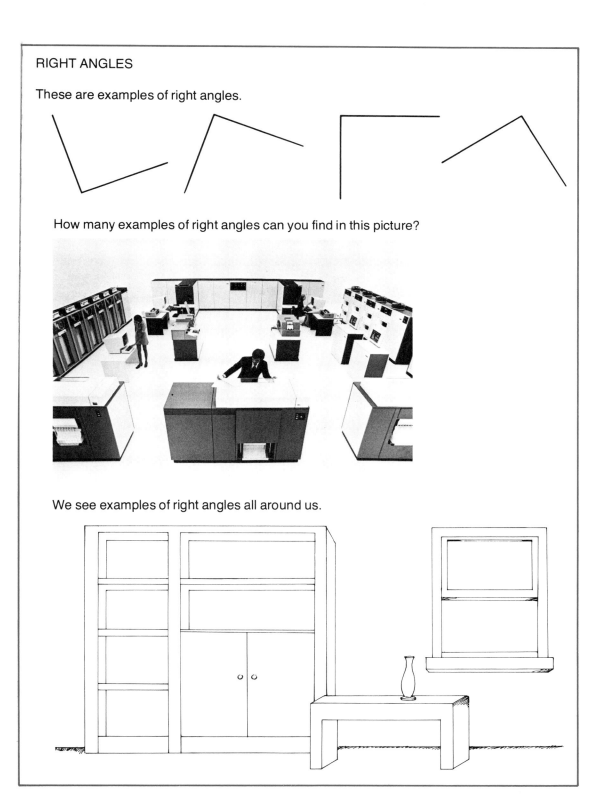

How many examples of right angles can you find in this picture?

We see examples of right angles all around us.

4.1 SQUARE ROOT

The idea of square root comes from numbers that can be shown as a square. The number 25 can be shown as a square.

$5 \times 5 = 25$ and   5 is the square root of 25.

We write: $\sqrt{25} = 5$

Every natural number has two square roots — one positive and one negative.

$$5 \times 5 = 25 \qquad \text{and} \qquad (-5) \times (-5) = 25$$

When we use the symbol $\sqrt{}$, we mean the positive square root.

> The square root of a number is a number which when multiplied by itself gives the first number.

The square root of a perfect square can be found by prime factoring.

To find $\sqrt{81}$, factor first.
$$81 = \underbrace{3 \times 3}_{9} \times \underbrace{3 \times 3}_{9}$$
$$= 9 \times 9$$
$$\sqrt{81} = 9$$

The square root is found by getting two identical factors.

Example. Find $\sqrt{324}$ using prime factoring.

Solution: $324 = 2 \times 2 \times 3 \times 3 \times 3 \times 3$
$$= 2 \times 3 \times 3 \times 2 \times 3 \times 3$$
$$= \underbrace{18}_{} \times \underbrace{18}_{}$$

Since $324 = 18 \times 18$
$$\sqrt{324} = 18$$

EXERCISE

A

1. Evaluate.

   (a) $\sqrt{36}$ (b) $\sqrt{9}$ (c) $\sqrt{49}$

   (d) $\sqrt{16}$ (e) $\sqrt{25}$ (f) $\sqrt{64}$

   (g) $\sqrt{81}$ (h) $\sqrt{4}$ (i) $\sqrt{1}$

B

2. Find the square roots by prime factoring.

   (a) $\sqrt{100}$ (b) $\sqrt{144}$ (c) $\sqrt{121}$

   (d) $\sqrt{169}$ (e) $\sqrt{256}$ (f) $\sqrt{225}$

3. Match each value in the left column with a value in the right column.

   (a) $\sqrt{9} + \sqrt{16}$ i) $\sqrt{25} + \sqrt{144}$

   (b) $\sqrt{36} + \sqrt{64}$ ii) $\sqrt{25}$

   (c) 17   iii) 7

   (d) 4 + 1   iv) 14

4. Evaluate.

   (a) $\sqrt{9} + \sqrt{25}$ (b) $\sqrt{36} - \sqrt{9}$

   (c) $5 \times \sqrt{25}$ (d) $20 \div \sqrt{16}$

4.2 ESTIMATING SQUARE ROOTS

In the previous section, we found square roots of perfect squares such as $\sqrt{25} = 5$ and $\sqrt{36} = 6$. In this section we shall find the approximate square roots of numbers by estimation.

Example. Find the square root of 71 to the nearest hundredth.

Solution: Since $\sqrt{64} = 8$ and $\sqrt{81} = 9$,

$\sqrt{71}$ lies between 8 and 9.

Estimate: $\sqrt{71} \doteq 8.5$
Test: $8.5^2 = 72.25$　　(too large)

Estimate: $\sqrt{71} \doteq 8.4$
Test: $8.4^2 = 70.56$　　(too small)
$\sqrt{71}$ lies between 8.4 and 8.5

Estimate: $\sqrt{71} \doteq 8.45$
Test: $8.45^2 = 71.402\ 5$　(too large)

Estimate: $\sqrt{71} \doteq 8.43$
Test: $8.43^2 = 71.064\ 9$　(too large)

Estimate: $\sqrt{71} \doteq 8.42$
Test: $8.42^2 = 70.896\ 4$　(too small)

71.064 9 is closer to 71 than 70.8964
$\therefore \sqrt{71} \doteq 8.43$ (to the nearest hundredth)

EXERCISE

B

1. Estimate to find the square root to the nearest tenth.

    (a) $\sqrt{29}$　　(b) $\sqrt{42}$　　(c) $\sqrt{50}$

    (d) $\sqrt{67}$　　(e) $\sqrt{88}$　　(f) $\sqrt{92}$

2. Estimate to find the square root to the nearest hundredth.

    (a) $\sqrt{56}$　　(b) $\sqrt{85}$　　(c) $\sqrt{19}$

    (d) $\sqrt{45}$　　(e) $\sqrt{72}$　　(f) $\sqrt{18}$

CALCULATOR MATH

If your calculator has a square root key, $\boxed{\sqrt{}}$, then to find $\sqrt{71}$, you press

and the display is: 8.4261497

Some calculators will round off and display: 8.43

EXTRA EXTRA EXTRA EXTRA EXTRA

KARL FRIEDRICH GAUSS (1777 – 1855)

Karl Gauss was a child prodigy. His astounding intelligence was recognized when he was two years old. At that age, he was able to perform lengthy additions. Although Gauss contributed to many branches of mathematics, his favourite branch was number theory. He is credited with devising a simple method of adding consecutive whole numbers. For example, to find the sum of the whole numbers from 1 to 12 we proceed as follows.

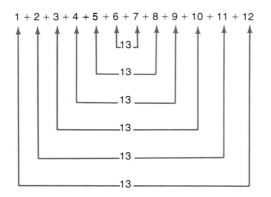

There are six pairs of numbers that total 13.

The sum of the numbers from 1 to 12 is 6×13 or 78.

To find the sum of the numbers from 23 to 31, we proceed as follows.

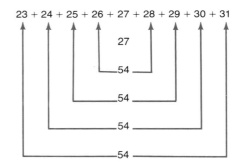

The sum of the numbers is

$$27 + 4 \times 54 = 27 + 216$$
$$= 243.$$

EXERCISE

1. Find the sum of the whole numbers from 1 to 20.

2. Find the sum of the whole numbers from 1 to 100.

3. Find the sum of the whole numbers from 1 to 500.

4. Find the sum of the whole numbers from 17 to 48.

5. Find the sum of the whole numbers from 8 to 68.

4.3 DETERMINING SQUARE ROOTS: NEWTON'S METHOD

Since $\sqrt{36} = 6$, then $\dfrac{36}{6} = 6$

To find $\sqrt{19}$, we can estimate $\sqrt{19} \doteq 4.5$

$\dfrac{19}{4.5} \doteq 4.2$ (4.2 is too small.)

(4.5 is too large.)

The average of 4.5 and 4.2 is a better estimate:

$\dfrac{4.5 + 4.2}{2} = 4.35$

$\sqrt{19} \doteq 4.35$ is better.

Repeating this process, estimate $\sqrt{19} \doteq 4.35$

$\dfrac{19}{4.35} \doteq 4.37$

The average is:
$\dfrac{4.35 + 4.37}{2} = 4.36$

Dividing again,

$\dfrac{19}{4.36} \doteq 4.36.$

$\therefore \sqrt{19} \doteq 4.4$ (to the nearest tenth)

This is called Newton's method, after Sir Isaac Newton. The flow chart at right helps to find square roots using Newton's method.

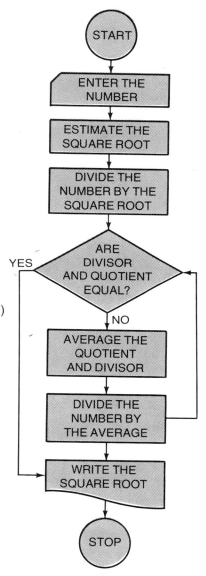

EXERCISE

B

1. Use Newton's method to evaluate to the nearest tenth.

   (a) $\sqrt{12}$ (b) $\sqrt{60}$

   (c) $\sqrt{45}$ (d) $\sqrt{17}$

   (e) $\sqrt{72}$ (f) $\sqrt{63}$

   (g) $\sqrt{85}$ (h) $\sqrt{92}$

2. Find the square root to the nearest tenth.

   (a) $\sqrt{84}$ (b) $\sqrt{59}$

   (c) $\sqrt{24}$ (d) $\sqrt{37}$

   (e) $\sqrt{41}$ (f) $\sqrt{30}$

3. $\neq$ means "is not equal to." Evaluate left side and right side separately to show the following.

   (a) $\sqrt{3} + \sqrt{7} \neq \sqrt{10}$

   (b) $\sqrt{12} + \sqrt{18} \neq \sqrt{30}$

   (c) $\sqrt{125} + \sqrt{250} \neq \sqrt{375}$

4.4 TABLE OF SQUARES AND SQUARE ROOTS

For convenience, the following table lists squares and square roots of whole numbers from 1 to 100.

n	$\sqrt{n}$	n^2	n	$\sqrt{n}$	n^2	n	$\sqrt{n}$	n^2	n	$\sqrt{n}$	n^2
1	1.000	1	26	5.099	676	51	7.141	2601	76	8.718	5776
2	1.414	4	27	5.196	729	52	7.211	2704	77	8.775	5929
3	1.732	9	28	5.292	784	53	7.280	2809	78	8.832	6084
4	2.000	16	29	5.385	841	54	7.349	2916	79	8.888	6241
5	2.236	25	30	5.477	900	55	7.416	3025	80	8.944	6400
6	2.450	36	31	5.568	961	56	7.483	3136	81	9.000	6561
7	2.646	49	32	5.657	1024	57	7.550	3249	82	9.055	6724
8	2.828	64	33	5.745	1089	58	7.616	3364	83	9.110	6889
9	3.000	81	34	5.831	1156	59	7.681	3481	84	9.165	7056
10	3.162	100	35	5.916	1225	60	7.746	3600	85	9.220	7225
11	3.317	121	36	6.000	1296	61	7.810	3721	86	9.274	7396
12	3.464	144	37	6.083	1369	62	7.874	3844	87	9.327	7569
13	3.606	169	38	6.164	1444	63	7.937	3969	88	9.381	7744
14	3.742	196	39	6.245	1521	64	8.000	4096	89	9.434	7921
15	3.873	225	40	6.325	1600	65	8.062	4225	90	9.487	8100
16	4.000	256	41	6.403	1681	66	8.124	4356	91	9.539	8281
17	4.123	289	42	6.481	1764	67	8.185	4489	92	9.592	8464
18	4.243	324	43	6.557	1849	68	8.246	4624	93	9.644	8649
19	4.359	361	44	6.633	1936	69	8.307	4761	94	9.695	8836
20	4.472	400	45	6.708	2025	70	8.367	4900	95	9.747	9025
21	4.583	441	46	6.782	2116	71	8.426	5041	96	9.798	9216
22	4.690	484	47	6.856	2209	72	8.485	5184	97	9.849	9409
23	4.796	529	48	6.928	2304	73	8.544	5329	98	9.900	9604
24	4.899	576	49	7.000	2401	74	8.602	5476	99	9.950	9801
25	5.000	625	50	7.071	2500	75	8.660	5625	100	10.000	10 000

To find $\sqrt{14}$, we look down the n column until we come to 14. Then we read:

$$\sqrt{14} \doteq 3.742$$

To find 14^2, we look down the n column until we come to 14. Then we read 14^2, across from 14 and under the n^2 column.

$$14^2 = 196$$

EXERCISE

A

1. Find the following square roots to the nearest tenth.

   (a) $\sqrt{29}$ (b) $\sqrt{33}$ (c) $\sqrt{42}$

   (d) $\sqrt{51}$ (e) $\sqrt{59}$ (f) $\sqrt{66}$

   (g) $\sqrt{75}$ (h) $\sqrt{89}$ (i) $\sqrt{91}$

2. Find the following square roots to the nearest hundredth.

   (a) $\sqrt{65}$ (b) $\sqrt{39}$ (c) $\sqrt{24}$

   (d) $\sqrt{67}$ (e) $\sqrt{83}$ (f) $\sqrt{55}$

3. Find the following squares.
   (a) 17^2 (b) 27^2 (c) 37^2
   (d) 42^2 (e) 53^2 (f) 68^2
   (g) 72^2 (h) 84^2 (i) 91^2

B

4. Evaluate to the nearest tenth.

   (a) $\sqrt{7} + \sqrt{12}$ (b) $\sqrt{20} + \sqrt{30}$

   (c) $\sqrt{27} + \sqrt{18}$ (d) $\sqrt{17} - \sqrt{12}$

   (e) $12^2 + 15^2$ (f) $\sqrt{95} + \sqrt{53}$

   (g) $\sqrt{77} + 8^2$ (h) $18^2 - 12^2$

APPLICATIONS

5. The speed of sound can be found using the formula:

$$V = 20 \times \sqrt{273 + t}$$

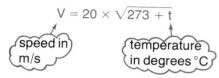
speed in m/s   temperature in degrees °C

Find the speed of sound at each of these temperatures.
(a) 10°C   (b) 13°C
(c) 28°C   (d) 21°C
(e) −10°C   (f) −23°C

CHALLENGE

SQUARE ROOTS BY SUBTRACTION?

There is an interesting way to find the square root of certain numbers by subtracting the odd numbers, 1, 3, 5, 7, 9, . . . in order. The following is an example.

To calculate $\sqrt{16}$ we proceed as follows.

Subtract the odd numbers from 16 in increasing value until the difference is 0.

$$\begin{array}{r} 16 \\ -\ 1 \\ \hline 15 \end{array} \qquad \begin{array}{r} 15 \\ -\ 3 \\ \hline 12 \end{array}$$

$$\begin{array}{r} 12 \\ -\ 5 \\ \hline 7 \end{array} \qquad \begin{array}{r} 7 \\ -\ 7 \\ \hline 0 \end{array}$$

Count the number of subtractions. The square root of 16 is the number of subtractions needed to reach zero.

$$\sqrt{16} = 4$$

Use this method to calculate the square root of the following numbers.

(a) 25   (b) 36   (c) 81   (d) 121

4.5 THE PYTHAGOREAN THEOREM

In ancient Egypt, the annual flood of the Nile River wiped out boundaries between farms. Surveyors called "rope stretchers" used ropes with knots to form right angles to renew boundaries. To form a right angle, they took a rope with 13 divisions formed by knots and stretched it between 3 stakes as shown. A triangle is formed with sides 3, 4, and 5 units long. The right angle is opposite the side which is 5 units long.

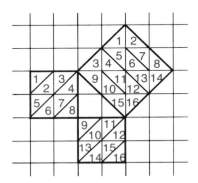

Notice the pattern in the floor tiles at left. This pattern suggests a relationship between the areas of the squares on the sides of a right triangle. The small triangles have been numbered to show the relationship. There are 16 triangles in the square on the hypotenuse (the longest side) and 8 triangles in each square on the other two sides. Although Pythagoras, a Greek mathematician who lived in 500 B.C., may not have discovered this relationship, he is credited with proving the theorem which bears his name.

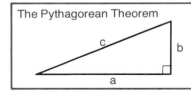

The Pythagorean Theorem

In any right triangle, the square on the hypotenuse is equal to the sum of the squares on the other two sides.
$$c^2 = a^2 + b^2$$

If we check the Egyptian rope stretchers' patterns using the theorem, we have:

$$5^2 = 3^2 + 4^2$$

25   9   16

25

Example 1. Calculate the length of the unknown side.

Solution: Using the theorem,
$$c^2 = 6^2 + 8^2$$
$$= 36 + 64$$
$$= 100$$
$$c = \sqrt{100}$$
$$c = 10$$

∴ the length of the side is 10 cm.

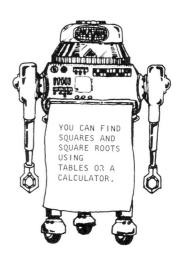

YOU CAN FIND
SQUARES AND
SQUARE ROOTS
USING
TABLES OR A
CALCULATOR.

Example 2. Calculate the length of the unknown side to the nearest hundredth.

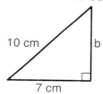

Solution: Using the thoerem,
$$10^2 = b^2 + 7^2$$
$$100 = b^2 + 49$$
$$51 = b^2$$
$$b = \sqrt{51}$$
$$b \doteq 7.141$$

What number added to 49 gives 100?

∴ the length of the side, rounded to the nearest hundredth, is 7.14 cm.

Example 3. Calculate the length of the unknown side.

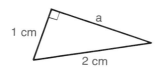

Solution: Using the theorem,
$$2^2 = 1^2 + a^2$$
$$4 = 1 + a^2$$
$$3 = a^2$$
$$a = \sqrt{3}$$
$$a \doteq 1.732$$

What number added to 1 gives 4?

∴ the length of the side, rounded to the nearest hundredth, is 1.73 cm.

EXERCISE

Round off answers to the nearest tenth.

B

1. Calculate the length of the unknown side.
   (a)   (b)

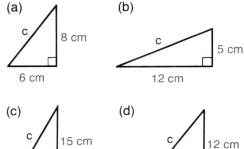

   (c)   (d)

2. Calculate the length of the hypotenuse.
   (a)   (b)

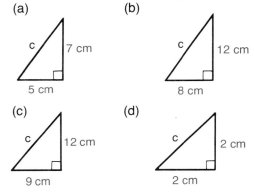

   (c)   (d)

3. Calculate the length of the hypotenuse.
   (a)   (b)

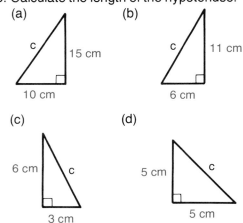

   (c)   (d)

4. Calculate the length of the unknown side.
   (a)   (b)

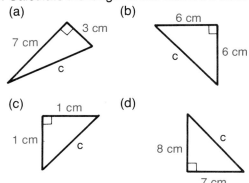

   (c)   (d)

5. Calculate the length of the unknown side.
   (a)   (b)

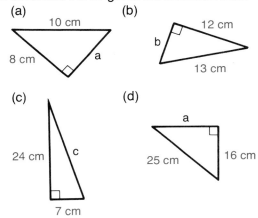

   (c)   (d)

6. Calculate the length of the unknown side.
   (a)   (b)

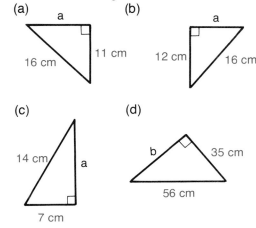

   (c)   (d)

APPLICATIONS

7. A ladder 6 m long leans against a wall. How high will the ladder reach up the wall?

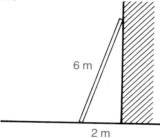

6 m

2 m

8. The foot of a ladder is 3.5 m from a wall. The ladder reaches 12 m up the wall. How long is the ladder?

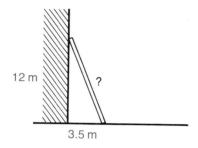

12 m

?

3.5 m

9. A vacant corner lot is 40 m by 60 m.

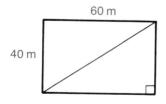

60 m

40 m

(a) What is the distance if you walk around the corner?
(b) What is the distance if you cut across the corner?
(c) How much shorter is it to cut across the corner?

10. Calculate the length of the wire, ℓ, that holds up the sign.

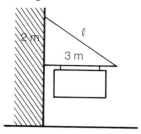

2 m

3 m

ℓ

11.

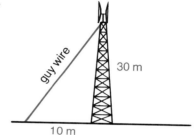

guy wire

30 m

10 m

(a) Find the length of the guy wire that fastens a radio tower as shown above.

(b)

It takes 5.3 m to fasten the guy line. How much cable is needed?

12.

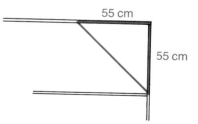

55 cm

55 cm

Find the length of the brace required to secure these shelves.

4.6 MORE APPLICATIONS OF SQUARE ROOT

Some problems are solved with formulas that have square roots. In these problems, you substitute for the variables and solve the problem.

Example 1. The time required for an object to fall a distance, h, is found using the formula
$$t = 0.45 \times \sqrt{h}$$
where h is the height in metres
t is the time in seconds.

How many seconds will it take for an object to fall from the top of the CN Tower which is 550 m high?

Solution: $t = 0.45 \times \sqrt{h}$

$t = 0.45 \times \sqrt{550}$

$\doteq 0.45 \times 23.452\,078$ (using a calculator)

$\doteq 10.553\,435$

∴ it takes an object 10.6 s to fall from the top of the CN Tower.

Example 2. The distance you can see to the horizon is given by the formula
$$d = 3.6 \times \sqrt{h}$$
where h is the height in metres
d is the distance in kilometres.

How far can you see from the top of the CN Tower which is 550 m high?

Solution: $d = 3.6 \times \sqrt{h}$

$d = 3.6 \times \sqrt{550}$

$\doteq 3.6 \times 23.452\,078$ (using a calculator)

$\doteq 84.427\,48$

∴ you can see 84.4 km from the top of the CN Tower.

EXERCISE

B

1. The formula for the length of the side of a square is
$$s = \sqrt{A}$$
where A is the area of the square
   s is the length of a side.
Find the lengths of the sides of these squares.

(a)

(b)

(c)

2. The formula
$$t = 0.45 \times \sqrt{h}$$

where t is the time in seconds
   h is the height in metres.

gives the time it takes an object to fall to the ground from a height h. How many seconds will it take for an object to fall from these heights?

(a) 10 m   (b) 30 m

(c) 50 m   (d) 125 m

(e) 150 m   (f) 200 m

3. The formula
$$d = 3.6 \times \sqrt{h}$$
where d is the distance in kilometres
   h is the height in metres
gives the distance you can see to the horizon.
How far can you see from these heights?

(a) 8 m   (b) 21 m
(c) 30 m   (d) 35 m
(e) 50 m   (f) 112 m
(g) from the top of Mount Kilimanjaro which is 5895 m high?

C

4. The formula
$$t = 2.01 \times \sqrt{L}$$

L = 1.44 m
where t is the time in seconds,
   L is the length in metres,
gives the time it takes for a pendulum to complete one swing. How long will it take for a pendulum 1.44 m long to make a complete swing?

CHALLENGE

Place the numbers from 1 to 9 in the circles so that each side of the triangle adds to 20.

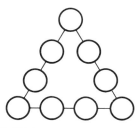

4.7 CHAPTER 4 REVIEW EXERCISE

1. Find the square root of each of the following numbers.
   (a) $\sqrt{16}$ (b) $\sqrt{36}$
   (c) $\sqrt{81}$ (d) $\sqrt{64}$
   (e) $\sqrt{25}$ (f) $\sqrt{49}$
   (g) $\sqrt{100}$ (h) $\sqrt{144}$

2. Find the square of each of the following numbers.
   (a) 15   (b) 17
   (c) 18   (d) 19
   (e) 22   (f) 25

3. Find the square roots by prime factoring.
   (a) $\sqrt{225}$ (b) $\sqrt{324}$
   (c) $\sqrt{256}$ (d) $\sqrt{400}$
   (e) $\sqrt{576}$ (f) $\sqrt{900}$
   (g) $\sqrt{729}$ (h) $\sqrt{441}$

4. Find the square root to the nearest tenth.
   (a) $\sqrt{27}$ (b) $\sqrt{35}$
   (c) $\sqrt{50}$ (d) $\sqrt{75}$
   (e) $\sqrt{110}$ (f) $\sqrt{125}$
   (g) $\sqrt{300}$ (h) $\sqrt{175}$

5. Find the square root to the nearest hundredth.
   (a) $\sqrt{7}$ (b) $\sqrt{18}$
   (c) $\sqrt{20}$ (d) $\sqrt{19}$

6. Replace ▨ with $<$, $>$, $=$, or $\neq$, to make true statements.
   (a) $\sqrt{9} + \sqrt{16}$ ▨ 5
   (b) $\sqrt{9 + 16}$ ▨ 5
   (c) $\sqrt{49} + \sqrt{25}$ ▨ 9
   (d) $\sqrt{49 + 25}$ ▨ 12
   (e) $\sqrt{25} + \sqrt{36}$ ▨ $\sqrt{25 + 36}$
   (f) $\sqrt{16} + \sqrt{49}$ ▨ $\sqrt{16 + 49}$

7. Replace ▨ with $<$, $>$, or $=$ to make true statements.
   (a) $\sqrt{15} + \sqrt{10}$ ▨ 5
   (b) $\sqrt{12} + \sqrt{13}$ ▨ 5
   (c) $\sqrt{25} - \sqrt{16}$ ▨ $\sqrt{9}$
   (d) $\sqrt{100} - \sqrt{36}$ ▨ $\sqrt{64}$
   (e) $\sqrt{25} + \sqrt{144}$ ▨ $\sqrt{169}$
   (f) $\sqrt{16} + \sqrt{30}$ ▨ 6

8. Use the Pythagorean Theorem to find the length of the unknown side.
   (a)
   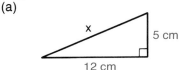
   (b)
   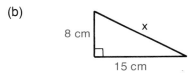
   (c)
   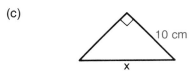
   (d)
   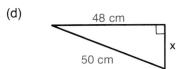
   (e)
   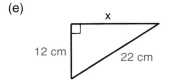
   (f)

9. A ladder 6 m long leans against a wall. The foot of the ladder is 1.5 m from the foot of the wall.
How high up the wall does the ladder reach?

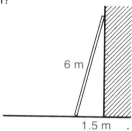

6 m

1.5 m

10. There is a short cut across a vacant corner lot as shown in the diagram. The dimensions of the lot are 24 m by 32 m. How much longer is it to walk around the corner than to take the short cut?

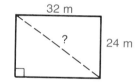

32 m

?

24 m

11. A store sign is supported by a guy wire connected 3 m above the sign and 6 m from the wall. It takes an extra 1.5 m of wire to fasten the ends.
How much wire is required to support the sign?

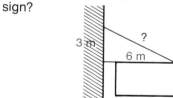

3 m

?

6 m

12. Find the length of material needed to build this bracket for a signpost.

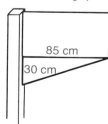

85 cm

30 cm

13. The formula
$$t = 0.45 \times \sqrt{h}$$
gives us the time, t, in seconds, for an object to fall from a height, h, in metres due to gravity. How long will it take for an object to reach the ground from the 300 m level of the Eiffel Tower in Paris?

14. The formula
$$d = 3.6 \times \sqrt{h}$$
gives us the distance, d, in kilometres, that you can see to the horizon from a height, h. How far can you see from the 300 m level of the Eiffel Tower?

15. The formula
$$s = \sqrt{A}$$
gives us the length of the side, s, of a square when we know the area, A. Find the lengths of the sides of these squares.

(a)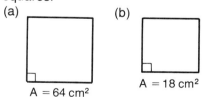

(b)

A = 64 cm²

A = 18 cm²

(c)

(d)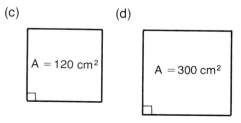

A = 120 cm²

A = 300 cm²

CHAPTER 4 TEST

1. Find the square root.

   (a) $\sqrt{81}$ (b) $\sqrt{225}$ (c) $\sqrt{1024}$ (d) $\sqrt{2401}$

2. Find the square root to the nearest tenth.

   (a) $\sqrt{75}$ (b) $\sqrt{83}$

3. Which is greater?

   (a) $\sqrt{3} + \sqrt{2}$ or $\sqrt{5}$

   (b) $\sqrt{16} + \sqrt{7}$ or   3

4. Calculate the length of the unknown side.

   (a) 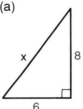   (b)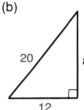

   (c) 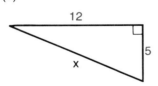   (d)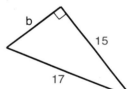

5. A ladder is 10.5 m long, and leans against a wall. The foot of the ladder is 3.5 m from the base of the wall.
   Find, to the nearest tenth of a metre, how high up the wall the ladder will reach.

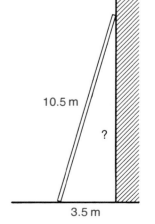

5

INTRODUCTION TO MICROCOMPUTERS

REVIEW AND PREVIEW TO CHAPTER 5

BITS AND BYTES

The smallest unit of information in a computer is called a bit. A bit is like a light switch. It can only be in one of two states— open or closed.

open bit

closed bit

1 bit gives 2^1 or 2 states.

When two bits are joined we can have 4 different states.

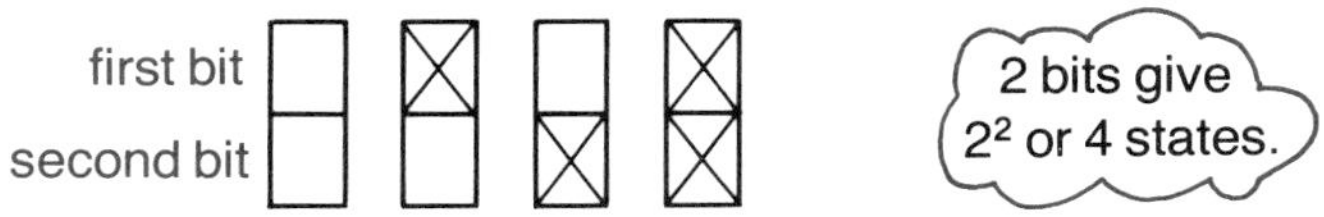

first bit

second bit

2 bits give 2^2 or 4 states.

When three bits are joined we can have 8 different states.

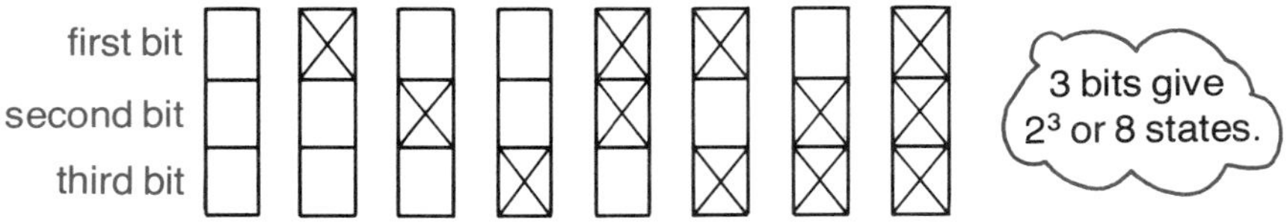

first bit

second bit

third bit

3 bits give 2^3 or 8 states.

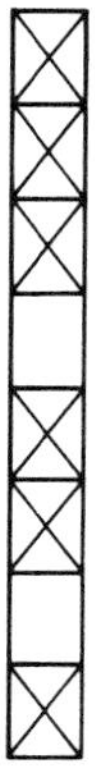

Present day computers use eight bits joined together. Each of these groups of eight bits is called a byte. Computers use bytes to store information. There are 2^8 or 256 possible different states in a byte. One of them is shown at the left.

Some more powerful computers use sixteen and thirty-two bits.

How many states are possible in a 16 bit computer?

EXERCISE

1. The sixteen possible states for 4 bits are shown below. Each state has been assigned a different character.

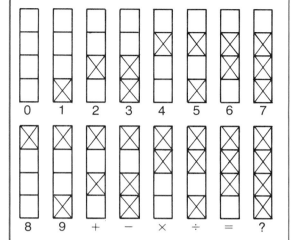

Complete each of the following. The first one is done for you.

(a)

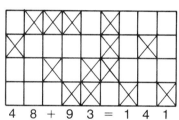

4 8 + 9 3 = 1 4 1

(b)

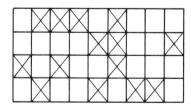

(c)

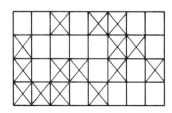

(d)

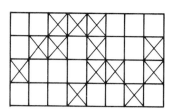

(e)

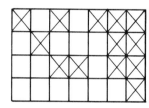

2. Solve.
(a)

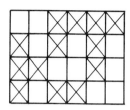

(b)

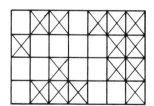

3. When five bits are joined, we can have 32 possible different states. Draw diagrams to show these states.

4. How many different states are possible when six bits are joined?

5. How many different states are possible when seven bits are joined?

5.1 USING FLOW CHARTS

Flow charts are used to show the order in which steps are performed in a problem. The following symbols are used in flow charting.

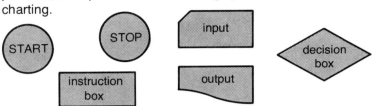

Example 1. Find the output of this flow chart.

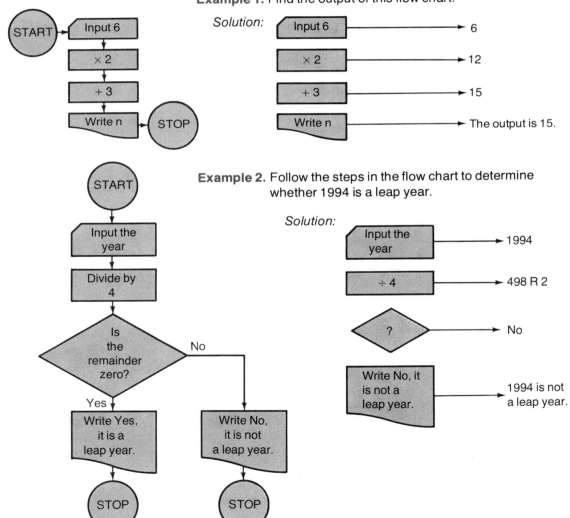

Solution:

Input 6	→ 6
× 2	→ 12
+ 3	→ 15
Write n	→ The output is 15.

Example 2. Follow the steps in the flow chart to determine whether 1994 is a leap year.

Solution:

Input the year	→ 1994
÷ 4	→ 498 R 2
?	→ No
Write No, it is not a leap year.	→ 1994 is not a leap year.

EXERCISE

B

1. Find the outputs.

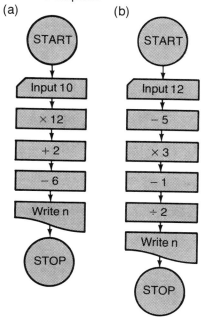

(a)

START
Input 10
× 12
+ 2
− 6
Write n
STOP

(b)

START
Input 12
− 5
× 3
− 1
÷ 2
Write n
STOP

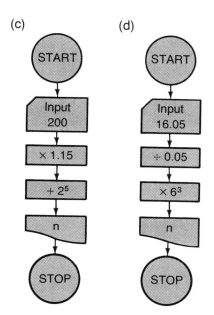

(c)

START
Input 200
× 1.15
+ 2⁵
n
STOP

(d)

START
Input 16.05
÷ 0.05
× 6³
n
STOP

2. (a) Find the output.
   (b) Can you explain the output?

START
Input any three digit number
Repeat the three digits.
Divide by 13
Divide by 11
Divide by 7
Write the answer
STOP

3. Find the output.

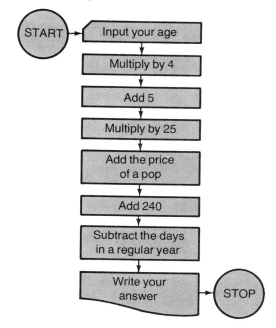

START
Input your age
Multiply by 4
Add 5
Multiply by 25
Add the price of a pop
Add 240
Subtract the days in a regular year
Write your answer
STOP

4. Find the output.

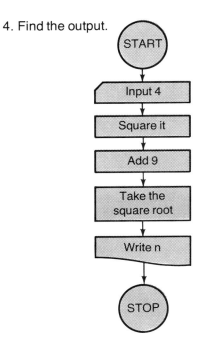

START

Input 4

Square it

Add 9

Take the
square root

Write n

STOP

5. Use the flow chart to determine which of the following numbers are divisible by 3.
   (a) 5124   (b) 914
   (c) 32 805   (d) 53 217

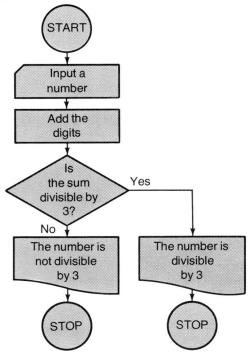

START

Input a
number

Add the
digits

Is
the sum
divisible by
3?

Yes

No

The number is
not divisible
by 3

The number is
divisible
by 3

STOP

STOP

6. We can find the height of the human body by measuring the length of the femur.

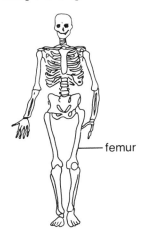

femur

Find the height of the human body if the length of the femur is
   (a) 42.55 cm (F)   (b) 41.92 cm (F)
   (c) 43.75 cm (F)   (d) 40.85 cm (M)
   (e) 44.50 cm (M)   (f) 43.15 cm (M)

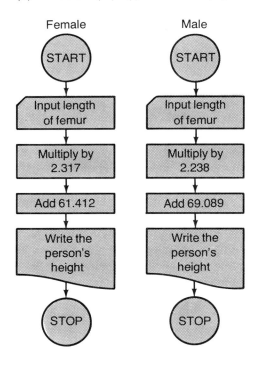

Female

START

Input length
of femur

Multiply by
2.317

Add 61.412

Write the
person's
height

STOP

Male

START

Input length
of femur

Multiply by
2.238

Add 69.089

Write the
person's
height

STOP

7. Use the output to flow chart (a) to find the outputs in (b) and (c).
   (a) How many days have you been alive?

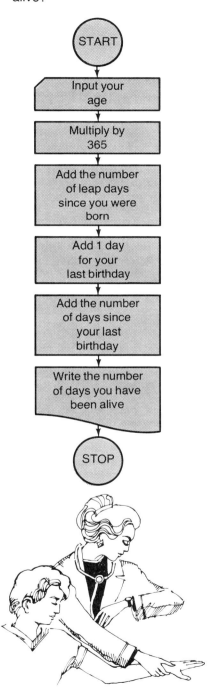

START

Input your age

Multiply by 365

Add the number of leap days since you were born

Add 1 day for your last birthday

Add the number of days since your last birthday

Write the number of days you have been alive

STOP

   (b) How many times has your heart beaten since you were born?

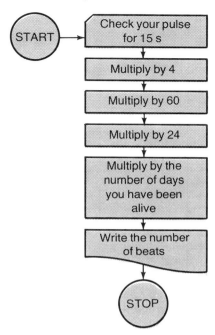

START → Check your pulse for 15 s

Multiply by 4

Multiply by 60

Multiply by 24

Multiply by the number of days you have been alive

Write the number of beats

STOP

   (c) How much air have you breathed since you were born?

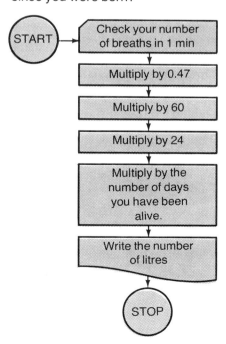

START → Check your number of breaths in 1 min

Multiply by 0.47

Multiply by 60

Multiply by 24

Multiply by the number of days you have been alive.

Write the number of litres

STOP

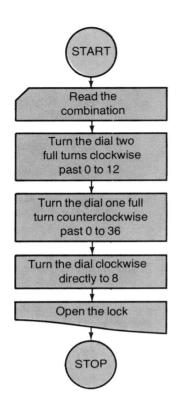

5.2 MAKING FLOW CHARTS

A list of instructions to be followed in a specific order can be placed in a flow chart.

We can make a flow chart to show how to open this combination lock.

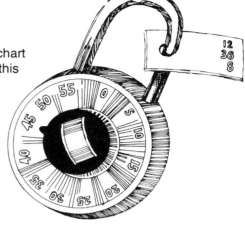

Example. Use these symbols to make a flow chart with an output of 3 when the input is 12.

| Input the number | − 15 | ÷ 7 | × 3 | Write the answer |

Solution: There are several flow charts that can be made using the symbols. Some of them are shown below. The flow chart that gives an output of 3 is shown in red

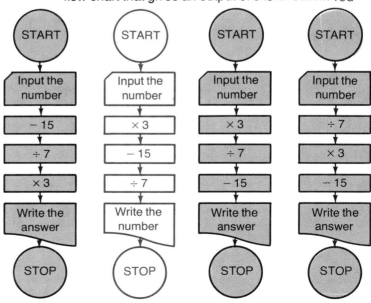

EXERCISE

A

1. Put the following instructions in the correct order.

    (a) Changing a light bulb
       Turn on the light switch.
       Put in the light bulb.
       Turn off the light switch.
       Take out the old light bulb.

    (b) Depositing money in your account
       Fill in the deposit slip.
       Receive a record slip of the transaction.
       Hand the slip and money to the teller.
       Decide the amount of your deposit.
       Teller counts your deposit money.
       Count your deposit money.

    (c) Getting a drink from a machine
       Walk away.
       Select the drink you want.
       Insert enough change.
       Lift cup from machine.
       Push selection button.
       Wait while cup is filled.
       Take your change.
       Drink your drink.

B

2. Draw flow charts for each of the following.
    (a) Write 16, add 4, divide by 10
    (b) Write 42, divide by 7, add 6, subtract 2
    (c) Write 0.5, multiply by 20, add 13
    (d) Write 2.5, add 0.25, multiply by 3.2

3. Mrs. Jack marks all of her tests out of 30, so she can use the same method for finding each student's percent. She uses m for the student mark.

$$\text{Students } \% = m \times 100 \div 30$$

   Use a flow chart to demonstrate this method for each of the following marks.

   Debbie 24   Lisa 18   Ruth 21
   John 12   Jeff 15   Alfie 27

4. Arrange these symbols into a flow chart so that an input of 24 gives an output of 15.

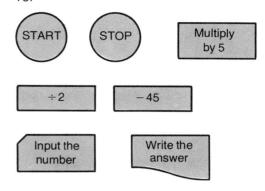

5. Arrange these symbols into a flow chart so that an input of 6 gives an output of 3.

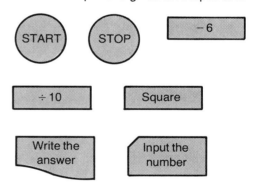

6. Arrange these symbols into a flow chart so that an input of 5 gives an output of 6.

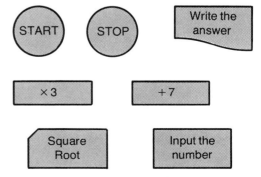

5.3 INTRODUCTION TO BASIC

To operate a computer, you must use a language that the computer understands. One of these languages is called BASIC. This is an acronym for Beginner's All-purpose Symbolic Instruction Code.

The following chart gives the BASIC notation for the operations we do in mathematics.

Operation	Mathematics	BASIC
addition	+	+
subtraction	−	−
multiplication	×	*
division	÷	/
raising to an exponent	exponent	↑

WHY DO YOU THINK THE COMPUTER USES * INSTEAD OF × FOR A MULTIPLICATION SIGN?

Example 1. Write these expressions in BASIC notation.
(a) $6 + 3$ (b) 6.5×4.3 (c) $12 \div 5$ (d) 5.7^3

Solution:

Expression	BASIC notation
(a) $6 + 3$	6+3
(b) 6.5×4.3	6.5*4.3
(c) $12 \div 5$	12/5
(d) 5.7^3	5.7↑3

When an expression contains more than one operation, the computer follows BEDMAS for the order of operations. The order of operations performed on the computer is the same as in mathematics.

Example 2. Write these expressions in BASIC notation.
(a) $5(6 + 4)$ (b) $3(-9)^2$ (c) $\dfrac{3 + 5}{2 \times 4}$

Solution:

Expression	BASIC notation
(a) $5(6 + 4)$	5*(6+4)
(b) $3(-9)^2$	3*(−9)↑2
(c) $\dfrac{3 + 5}{2 \times 4}$	(3+5)/(2*4)

Note in example 2(c), that expressions with fractions are written on one line.

Example 3. Evaluate each expression.

     (a) 5*6   (b) 3*(6+2)   (c) $(-3) \uparrow 2 / (3-1)$

Solution: (a) 5*6 means $5 \times 6 = 30$

        (b) 3*(6+2) means $3 \times (6 + 2) = 3 \times 8$

                                     $= 24$

        (c) $(-3) \uparrow 2 / (3-1)$ means $(-3)^2 \div (3 - 1) = 9 \div 2$

                                            $= 4.5$

EXERCISE

A

1. Evaluate these expressions.
   - (a) 8+12
   - (b) 3*7
   - (c) 6−10
   - (d) −12/3
   - (e) $5 \uparrow 3$
   - (f) $(-5) \uparrow 3$

B

2. Write these expressions in BASIC.
   - (a) 6×7
   - (b) $-6 \div 3$
   - (c) 5^3
   - (d) $3 + 9$
   - (e) $12 - 7$
   - (f) 3.5×2

3. Write these expressions in BASIC.
   - (a) $3(5 + 7)$
   - (b) $(6 + 4)(8 - 2)$
   - (c) $(5 - 3)^2$
   - (d) $(-3)^2 + 7$
   - (e) $\dfrac{(-4)^2}{2 \times 4}$
   - (f) $(3 \times 5)(-2)$

4. Evaluate these expressions.
   - (a) 5−3*2
   - (b) $3 \uparrow 2 - 5$
   - (c) $(8-9) \uparrow 2*5$
   - (d) $(3 \uparrow 2+6) / (1+2 \uparrow 2)$
   - (e) $(3+24)*(5 \uparrow 2-2*8)$
   - (f) $(5-3) \uparrow 3 / (-2)+5$

5. Which is greater?
   - (a) $5-3 \uparrow 2$ or $(5-3) \uparrow 2$
   - (b) $6 \uparrow 2 - 1$ or $6 \uparrow (2-1)$
   - (c) $12-2 \uparrow 2$ or $(12-2) \uparrow 2$
   - (d) $(2*3) \uparrow 2$ or $2*(3 \uparrow 2)$
   - (e) $3 \uparrow 2$ or $2 \uparrow 3$
   - (f) $2*3 \uparrow 2$ or $3*2 \uparrow 2$

6. Write these expressions in BASIC.
   - (a) $X + Y$
   - (b) $X \times Y$
   - (c) $3X$
   - (d) X^2
   - (e) $X^2 + Y^2$
   - (f) $(X + Y)^2$
   - (g) $2(L + W)$
   - (h) $2 \times 3.14 \times R$
   - (i) $3.14 \times R^2$
   - (j) $L \times W$
   - (k) $X \times Y \div Z$
   - (l) $X(Y - Z)$
   - (m) $(A + B) \times H \div 2$

This microcomputer system consists of a video display monitor, two disk drives, a printer, and a console.

5.4 "PRINT" AND "END" STATEMENTS

A set of instructions that tells a computer what to do is called a program. Each line of a program begins with a number. This number tells the computer the order in which the instructions are carried out. We usually number the statements 10,20,30,...

Following is an example of a simple program:

```
10 PRINT 12*16
20 END
```

Line 10 is a PRINT statement. This statement computes and prints the answer to 12 × 16.

Line 20 is an END statement. Every program should finish with an END statement. The END statement is the last statement in the program.

After typing in the program, we tell the computer to execute the program. To execute the program, you type RUN and press the RETURN key. Do not type a number in front of RUN.

Example 1. Write a program to compute:
$(13.5 - 2.7)^2$

Solution: First we write the expression in BASIC notation:
$(13.5-2.7) \uparrow 2$

The program is:
```
10 PRINT (13.5-2.7)↑2
20 END
```

Example 2. Write a program to compute:
3.14×7^2

Solution: First we write the expression in BASIC notation:
$3.14*7 \uparrow 2$

The program is:
```
10   PRINT   3.14*7↑2
20   END
```

Before typing in this program, we type NEW and press the return key to clear away any other programs that may be in the computer. In order to execute the program in Example 2, we type:

```
NEW
10 PRINT 3.14*7↑2
20 END
RUN
```

and the computer displays 153.86.

WE NUMBER
LINES
10,20,30...
SO THAT
WE CAN
INSERT OTHER
LINES LIKE
11,12,13,14,...
IF WE NEED TO.

EXERCISE

A

1. Explain what each of the following tells the computer to do.
   - (a) NEW
   - (b) PRINT
   - (c) END
   - (d) RUN

B

2. Calculate the output of the following programs.

   (a) `NEW`
   ```
   10 PRINT 5*6
   20 END
   RUN
   ```

   (b) `NEW`
   ```
   10 PRINT (-5)↑3
   20 END
   RUN
   ```

   (c) `NEW`
   ```
   10 PRINT (-3)↑2+4↑2
   20 END
   RUN
   ```

   (d) `NEW`
   ```
   10 PRINT (3+1)↑2/(6+2)
   20 END
   RUN
   ```

   (e) `NEW`
   ```
   10 PRINT (4+3)*(8-2)
   20 END
   RUN
   ```

   (f) `NEW`
   ```
   10 PRINT 25*5↑2
   20 END
   RUN
   ```

   (g) `NEW`
   ```
   10 PRINT 2*3.14*6
   20 END
   RUN
   ```

   (h) `NEW`
   ```
   10 PRINT 5*(3+7)
   20 END
   RUN
   ```

Write a program to compute each of the following.

3. 5.6×7.4

4. $12.8 - 5.9$

5. $856.2 + 753.4$

6. $14.31 \div 5.3$

7. 6.4^2

8. 1.02^5

9. 6.35^3

C

10. $\dfrac{5.7 + 2.8}{3.6^2}$

11. $\dfrac{8.5 \times 5.3}{2.8 \div 7}$

12. 3.14×5.6^2

13. $2(5.3 + 7.9)$

14. $\dfrac{1}{9}$ 15. $\dfrac{1}{7}$

16. $\dfrac{1}{11}$ 17. $\dfrac{7}{8}$

18. $\dfrac{36 - 25}{66}$

19. $25(19)^2$

20. $(3.2^2 + 4.8^2) - (3.2 + 4.8)^2$

21. $4 \times 3.14 \times 2.5^3 \div 3$

22. (a) Write computer programs to compute the following:
    - i) $(-6.5)^2 + (15.3)^2$
    - ii) $(-6.5 + 15.3)^2$
    - (b) Which is greater?

5.5 LET STATEMENTS

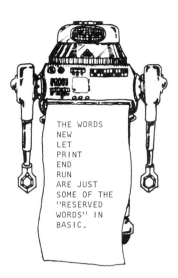

THE WORDS
NEW
LET
PRINT
END
RUN
ARE JUST
SOME OF THE
"RESERVED
WORDS" IN
BASIC.

A LET statement assigns a value to a variable. We can use any letter of the alphabet as a variable.

When we type

```
10 LET X = 5
```

the computer will replace X by 5 in the program.

Example 1. Write a program to compute:
X^2 when $X = -5$

Solution: First we write X^2 using BASIC notation:
$X \uparrow 2$

The program is:
```
NEW
10 LET X=-5
20 PRINT X↑2
30 END
RUN
```

We can have several variables in a program using LET statements.

Example 2. Write a program to compute:
$X^2 + Y^2$ when $X = 3.7$ and $Y = 4.5$

Solution: First we write $X^2 + Y^2$ using BASIC notation:
$X \uparrow 2 + Y \uparrow 2$

The program is:
```
NEW
10 LET X=3.7
20 LET Y=4.5
30 PRINT X↑2+Y↑2
40 END
RUN
```

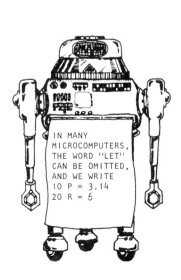

IN MANY
MICROCOMPUTERS,
THE WORD "LET"
CAN BE OMITTED,
AND WE WRITE
10 P = 3.14
20 R = 6

Example 3. Write a program to compute:
2PR when $P = 3.14$ and $R = 6$.

Solution: First we write 2PR in BASIC notation:
2PR means $2 \times P \times R$ which is $2*P*R$

The program is:
```
NEW
10 LET P=3.14
20 LET R=6
30 PRINT 2*P*R
40 END
RUN
```

EXERCISE

A

1. Explain what a LET statement tells the computer to do.

B

2. Calculate the output of the following programs.

(a)
```
NEW
10 LET X=5
20 PRINT X+5
30 END
RUN
```

(b)
```
NEW
10 LET X=-3
20 PRINT X+6
30 END
RUN
```

(c)
```
NEW
10 LET Y=7
20 PRINT Y↑3
30 END
RUN
```

(d)
```
NEW
10 LET X=5
20 LET Y=7
30 PRINT X+Y
40 END
RUN
```

(e)
```
NEW
10 LET X=7
20 LET Y=3
30 PRINT X-Y
40 END
RUN
```

(f)
```
NEW
10 LET P=3.14
20 LET R=10
30 PRINT P*R↑2
40 END
RUN
```

Write programs to compute the following.

3. $X + 4$ for $X = 5$

4. X^2 for $X = -2.5$

5. $Y + 3$ for $Y = 12$

6. Y^3 for $Y = -4$

7. $3X$ for $X = 7$

8. $2Y$ for $Y = -5$

C

9. X^5 for $X = -5$

10. Y^5 for $Y = 6$

11. $X + Y$ for $X = 3, Y = 2$

12. $(X + Y)^2$ for $X = 4, Y = 5$

13. $X^2 + Y^2$ for $X = 4, Y = 5$

14. $X^2 + Y^2$ for $X = 4, Y = -5$

15. $(X + Y)^2$ for $X = 4, Y = -5$

16. $X + Y + Z$ for $X = 1, Y = 2, Z = 3$

17. $X - Y + Z$ for $X = 7, Y = 9, Z = 5$

18. $(X + Y + Z)^2$ for $X = Y = Z = 3$

19. $5(X + Y)$ for $X = 3, Y = 6$

20. $2X + 3Y - 5$ for $X = 4, Y = 2$

A microcomputer chip

5.6 INPUT STATEMENTS

The computer is very useful when you want to do the same calculation over again with different numbers. We can do this using INPUT statements.

When we run a program with the statement

```
10 INPUT X
```

the computer will display a ? ▉ and wait for you to input a value for X. Once you input a value for X the computer will continue to the next instruction in the program.

The following program will add the two numbers that you INPUT.

```
NEW
10 INPUT X
20 INPUT Y
30 PRINT X+Y
40 END
RUN
```

The INPUT statements in lines 10 and 20 tell the computer that values will be inserted. When you RUN the program, the computer will ask for each value by displaying ? ▉ (or something similar). When all INPUT values have been entered, the computer continues to the end of the program.

Example. Find the output in this program:

```
NEW
10 INPUT X
20 INPUT Y
30 PRINT (X-Y)↑2
40 END
RUN
```

for (a) X = 12, Y = 7
(b) X = 3.8, Y = 1.8

Solution: First we change the BASIC notation to arithmetic:

$(X-Y) \uparrow 2$ means $(X - Y)^2$

(a) $(X - Y)^2 = (12 - 7)^2$
$= 5^2$
$= 25$

The output is 25.

(b) $(X - Y)^2 = (3.8 - 1.8)^2$
$= (2)^2$
$= 4$

The output is 4.

EXERCISE

A

1. Explain what an INPUT statement tells the computer to do.

B

Calculate the output of the following programs.

2. NEW
```
10 INPUT X
20 PRINT X+5
30 END
RUN
```
Use the following values.
(a) X = 10   (b) X = 4
(c) X = 15   (d) X = 18.6

3. NEW
```
10 INPUT S
20 PRINT S↑2
30 END
RUN
```
Use the following values.
(a) S = 3   (b) S = 6
(c) S = −4   (d) S = 5.8

4. NEW
```
10 INPUT R
20 PRINT 2*3.14*R
30 END
RUN
```
Use the following values.
(a) R = 10   (b) R = 15
(c) R = 20   (d) R = 4.5

5. NEW
```
10 INPUT X
20 INPUT Y
30 PRINT X−Y
40 END
RUN
```
Use the following values.
(a) X = 7, Y = 5
(b) X = 26.5, Y = 14

Write programs to compute the following.

6. X + 5 for the following values.
(a) X = 0   (b) X = 7
(c) X = −5   (d) X = 3.6

7. X^3 for the following values.
(a) X = 1   (b) X = 4
(c) X = 7   (d) X = −2

C

8. $(X + Y)^2$ for the following values.
(a) X = 4, Y = 3
(b) X = −3, Y = 3
(c) X = 6, Y = 0
(d) X = 3.5, Y = 1.5

9. $3.14R^2$ for the following values.
(a) R = 10
(b) R = 6.5
(c) R = 18.2

10. 2(L + W) for the following values.
(a) L = 7, W = 4
(b) L = 12, W = 5
(c) L = 6.3, W = 4.8

11. X + Y − Z for the following values.
(a) X = 5, Y = 7, Z = 6
(b) X = 3, Y = 2, Z = 5
(c) X = 24, Y = 16, Z = 8

UNIVERSAL PRODUCT CODE

To help speed customers through check-out counters, many supermarkets use Universal Product Codes which are printed on packages. An electronic reader scans the UPC and signals a computer to search its memory for the item. The name and the price of the item are then printed on the sales slip.

Each Universal Product Code encodes 12 digits. Six of them to the left of the "centre guard pattern" are each represented by a light space, a dark bar, a second light space and a second bar. The other six, to the right of the centre guard pattern, are each represented by a bar, a space, a bar and a space.

The digits are formed by patterns using 0 and 1, where a 0 is a blank and a 1 is a black line.

The following is an example of a Universal Product Code.

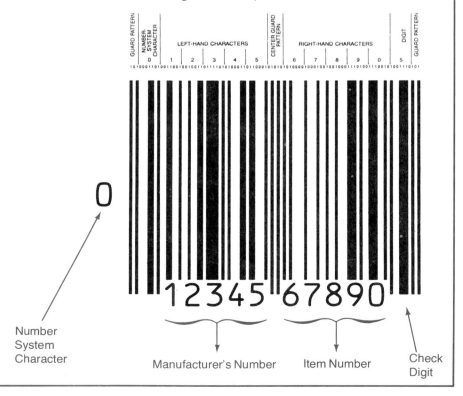

Number System Character

Manufacturer's Number

Item Number

Check Digit

The number system character is a 0 in this example. It indicates that the item is a standard supermarket item.

Notice that the 0 on the left has the pattern: 0001101
The 0 on the right has a pattern that is the reverse
of the 0 on the left.   1110010

This reversing is true for all the number patterns.

The only number not shown in "human-readable form" is the check digit. The check digit confirms that the other 11 digits have been scanned and decoded correctly. To find the value of the check digit for our example we proceed as follows.

1. Add the 2nd, 4th, 6th, 8th,
   and 10th digits. $1 + 3 + 5 + 7 + 9 = 25$

2. Multiply the sum of the
   1st, 3rd, 5th, 7th, 9th,
   and 11th digits by 3. $3 \times (0 + 2 + 4 + 6 + 8 + 0) = \underline{60}$

3. Add.   85

4. The check digit is the number that you add to 85 to give a multiple of 10. Since we add 5 to 85 to give 90, the check digit is 5.

EXERCISE

1. When it is on the left, a 0 has the pattern   0001101
   On the right, it has a pattern   1110010
   Determine the pattern for each of the other digits — on the left and on the right.

2. The check digit pattern has been cut off each of the following Universal Product Codes.
   Determine the check digit for each.

(a)

0   21120 05152

(b)

0   38000 41021

(c)

0   46000 09001

(d)

0   52600 11275

(e)

0   70290 01305

(f)

0   43800 00109

5.7 CHAPTER 5 REVIEW EXERCISE

A

1. Explain what these statements mean.
   (a) NEW   (b) PRINT
   (c) END   (d) RUN
   (e) LET   (f) INPUT

B

2. Arrange these symbols to make a flow chart so that the output is 4 when the input is 5.

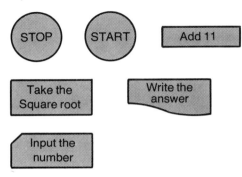

3. Work through the steps in each flow chart for the following numbers.
   (a) 7   (b) 12   (c) 25

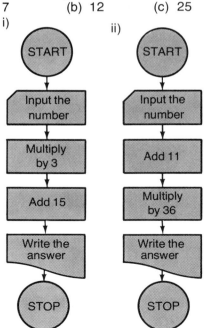

4. Follow the steps in the flow chart below for each set of digits.
   (a) 1,3,8,5   (b) 7,3,4,9
   (c) 8,3,6,4   (d) 2,8,1,5

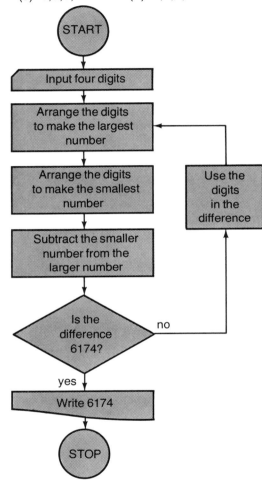

5. Evaluate these expressions.
   (a) $5*7$ (b) $4 \uparrow 3$
   (c) $28 / 7$ (d) $6+16$
   (e) $7-2 \uparrow 2$ (f) $(3*4) / (8 / 4)$
   (g) $(2+2 \uparrow 3)*(2 \uparrow 2+3)$
   (h) $(7-4) \uparrow 3+3$
   (i) $(2+3) \uparrow 2 / (20 / 4)$

6. Arrange these symbols to make a flow chart so that an input of 23 gives an output of 14.

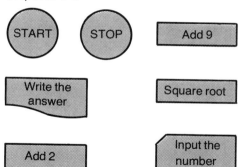

START   STOP   Add 9

Write the answer   Square root

Add 2   Input the number

7. Write these expressions in BASIC.
   (a) 5×12 (b) 7^2
   (c) $21 \div 3$ (d) $6^2 \div 4$

Calculate the outcomes of the following programs.

8. NEW
```
10 PRINT 3*12
20 END
RUN
```

9. NEW
```
10 PRINT 25↑2
20 END
RUN
```

10. NEW
```
10 PRINT 3.14*1000
20 END
RUN
```

11. NEW
```
10 LET X=7
20 PRINT X+12
30 END
RUN
```

12. NEW
```
10 LET N=12
20 PRINT N/3*2
30 END
RUN
```

13. NEW
```
10 LET P=3.14
20 LET R=6
30 LET H=10
40 PRINT P*R↑2*H
50 END
RUN
```

14. NEW
```
10 INPUT X
20 PRINT X+17
30 END
RUN
```
for the following INPUTS:
(a) $X = 3$ (b) $X = -12$
(c) $X = 13$ (d) $X = 17$

15. NEW
```
10 INPUT X
20 PRINT X↑2+3
30 END
RUN
```
for the following INPUTS:
(a) $X = 7$ (b) $X = 1.1$
(c) $X = 3$ (d) $X = 8$

16. NEW
```
10 INPUT X
20 INPUT Y
30 PRINT X+Y↑2
40 END
RUN
```
for the following INPUTS:
(a) $X = 12, Y = 2$
(b) $X = 7, Y = 11$
(c) $X = 3, Y = 8$

17. NEW
```
10 INPUT X
20 INPUT Y
30 PRINT X*Y+X/Y
40 END
RUN
```
for the following INPUTS:
(a) $X = 12, Y = 3$
(b) $X = 15, Y = 5$
(c) $X = 25, Y = 1$

18. Write a program to add $23.5 + 16.3$

CHAPTER 5 TEST

1. Find the output of each flow chart.

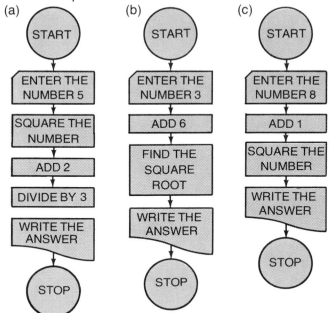

2. Arrange the following symbols into a flow chart so that an input of 6 gives an output of 5.

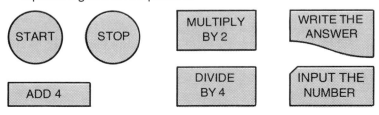

3. Write in BASIC computer language.
   (a) $3 \times 5(x + 2)$ (b) $5^2 - 12 \div 3$ (c) $3^2 + 4^2$

4. Evaluate.
   (a) $3 \uparrow 2 + 5$ (b) $(3 + 5) \uparrow 2$ (c) $4*6/3 - 7*2$

5. Calculate the output of these programs.

(a)
```
NEW
10 LET L=5
20 LET W=3
30 PRINT 2*(L+W)
40 END
RUN
```

(b) You input R = 5
```
NEW
10 INPUT R
20 PRINT 2*3.14*R
30 END
RUN
```

RATIO AND PROPORTION

REVIEW AND PREVIEW TO CHAPTER 6

THE RULE OF THREE

The problems in this section are solved using three steps. In the first step we state the given fact. In the second step, we reduce the fact to 1. In the third step, we multiply to get the desired result.

Example 1. In 10 a, the average North American consumes about 226 kg of fruit. How much fruit would an average North American consume in 25 a?

Solution:

Statement of fact: In 10 a, the consumption is 226 kg.

Reduce to 1: In 1 a, the consumption is $\dfrac{226}{10}$ kg.

Multiply: In 25 a, the consumption is

$$\frac{226}{10} \times 25 = 565$$

∴ the average North American consumes about 565 kg of fruit in 25 a.

Example 2. Find the cost of 8 golf balls, if the price is $27.00 for 12 golf balls.

Solution:

Statement of fact: 12 golf balls cost $27.00.

Reduce to 1: 1 golf ball costs $\dfrac{\$27.00}{12}$.

Multiply: 8 golf balls costs $\dfrac{\$27.00}{12} \times 8 = \$18.00$.

∴ 8 golf balls cost $18.00.

EXERCISE

1. If 10 stereo tapes cost $37.00, find the cost of 18 stereo tapes.

2. A Boeing 747 burns 6 t of fuel in 3 h. How much fuel is burned in 4.5 h?

3. There are 5 libraries for every 80 000 potential users.
   How many libraries are there for a city of 320 000 people?

4. If 5 m of chain cost $16.85, find the cost of 17 m of chain.

5.

The moon revolves about the earth 4 times in 118 days.
   (a) How long does it take the moon to revolve about the earth 15 times?
   (b) How many times does the moon revolve about the earth in 1416 days?

6. It takes 5.3 kJ of energy to melt 16 g of ice.
   (a) How much energy is required to melt 75 g of ice?
   (b) How many grams of ice can be melted by 50 kJ?

7. A car travels 315 km on 45 L of gasoline.
   (a) How far will this car travel on 37 L of gasoline?
   (b) How many litres will it take to travel 280 km?

8. If you climb a 3-storey building, you expend about 4.5 kJ of energy.
   How much energy is expended in climbing a 15-storey building?

9. It takes a radio signal about 1.3 s to travel from the earth to the moon, a distance of 374 000 km.

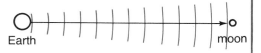

   (a) How far into space will a radio signal travel in 18 s?
   (b) How long will it take a radio signal to reach the sun, 150 000 000 km away?

10. Fred earns $42.75 for 9 h work as a playground supervisor.
    How much does Fred earn in 25 h?

CHALLENGE

Remove 4 toothpicks so that exactly 4 identical triangles remain.

6.1 RATIOS

A ratio is a comparison of two or more quantities. When we prepare orange juice from concentrate, we mix three cans of water with each can of concentrate.

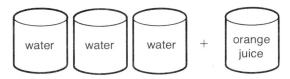

The ratio of water to concentrate is three to one and we write:

$$3:1 \quad \text{or} \quad \frac{3}{1}$$

The ratio of concentrate to water is one to three and we write:

$$1:3 \quad \text{or} \quad \frac{1}{3}$$

These are examples of two-term ratios.

Example 1.

Find these ratios:

(a) □ to ○   (b) △ to □   (c) ○ to △

Solution: △ △ △ △   □ □ □ □ □   ○ ○ ○
                 4   5   3

(a) □ to ○ is 5:3 or $\frac{5}{3}$ (b) △ to □ is 4:5 or $\frac{4}{5}$

(c) ○ to △ is 3:4 or $\frac{3}{4}$

Example 2. The number of tickets sold for a junior basketball game was 28 adults', 125 students', and 27 children's tickets.
Find the following ratios:
(a) students' to adults' tickets
(b) students' to children's tickets

Solution: (a) The ratio of students to adults is 125 to 28 and we write:

$$125:28 \quad \text{or} \quad \frac{125}{28}$$

(b) The ratio of students to children is 125 to 27 and we write:

$$125:27 \quad \text{or} \quad \frac{125}{27}$$

EXERCISE

A

1. Find the ratios.

(a) ☐ to ◯

(b) △ to ☐

(c) ◯ to △

2. Find these ratios in the following diagram.

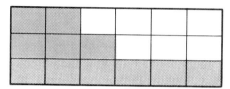

(a) red squares to black squares
(b) white squares to red squares
(c) white squares to black squares
(d) black squares to red squares
(e) white squares to all squares
(f) red squares to all squares

3. State these quantities as ratios.
(a) 15 boys to 11 girls
(b) 2 cats to 7 birds
(c) 35 hockey cards to 83 baseball cards
(d) 5 m to 9 m
(e) 12 kg to 1 kg

4. Ed is 12 a old, Margie is 11 a old, and Bonnie is 16 a old.
State the following ratios:
(a) Ed's age to Margie's age;
(b) Margie's age to Bonnie's age;
(c) Bonnie's age to Ed's age.

B

5. Find the following ratios:
(a)

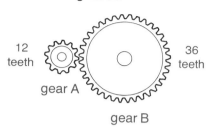

the number of teeth in gear A to gear B;

(b)

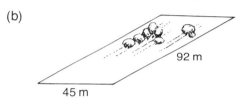

the ratio of length to width of the lot above;

(c)

the ratio of red circles to white circles.

6.

Find a ratio to compare the value of:
(a) a nickel to a dime;
(b) a penny to a nickel;
(c) a nickel to a quarter;
(d) a quarter to a dime.

7.

Find these ratios:
(a) length of AB to length of BD
(b) length of AC to length of CD
(c) length of AC to length of BD
(d) length of AD to length of BD
(e) length of BC to length of AD
(f) length of CD to length of BC

6.2 EQUIVALENT RATIOS

boys

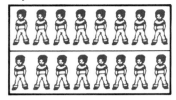

girls

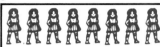

There are 16 boys and 8 girls in the class.

The ratio of boys to girls is 16 : 8.
This means that there are twice as many boys as girls. Another way to write the ratio of boys to girls is 2 : 1.
The ratios 16 : 8 and 2 : 1 are equivalent.

$$16 : 8 = 2 : 1 \qquad \text{or} \qquad \frac{16}{8} = \frac{2}{1}$$

The following ratios are equivalent:

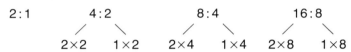

$$2 : 1 \qquad\qquad 4 : 2 \qquad\qquad\qquad 8 : 4 \qquad\qquad\qquad 16 : 8$$

$$2 \times 2 \quad 1 \times 2 \qquad 2 \times 4 \quad 1 \times 4 \qquad 2 \times 8 \quad 1 \times 8$$

The ratio 2 : 1 or $\frac{2}{1}$ is in lowest terms.

Example 1. Find the ratio of
$\bigcirc$ to $\triangle$ in
lowest terms.

$\bigcirc \triangle \triangle \triangle \triangle$
$\bigcirc \bigcirc \bigcirc \bigcirc \bigcirc$
$\bigcirc \triangle \bigcirc \triangle$

Solution: The ratio is: $\dfrac{9}{6} = \dfrac{9 \div 3}{6 \div 3}$

$$= \frac{3}{2}$$

Test for Equivalent Ratios

Are 5 : 8 and 15 : 24 equivalent ratios?

METHOD I
Express each ratio with the same denominator and compare numerators.

$5 : 8$

$$5 : 8 = \frac{5}{8}$$

$$= \frac{5 \times 3}{8 \times 3} = \frac{15}{24}$$

$15 : 24$

$$15 : 24 = \frac{15}{24}$$

METHOD II
Two ratios are equivalent if the cross products are equal.

$5 : 8 \qquad 15 : 24$

$$\frac{5}{8} \times \frac{15}{24}$$

$$5 \times 24 = 8 \times 15$$
$$120 = 120$$

$\therefore$ the ratios are equivalent.

EXERCISE

A

1. State each of the following ratios in lowest terms.

(a) $\dfrac{4}{16}$ (b) $\dfrac{8}{2}$ (c) $\dfrac{4}{10}$

(d) $5:10$ (e) $\dfrac{2}{4}$ (f) $21:3$

(g) $\dfrac{9}{15}$ (h) $\dfrac{18}{6}$ (i) $\dfrac{18}{9}$

(j) $7:21$ (k) $\dfrac{8}{12}$ (l) $8:20$

(m) $2:12$ (n) $\dfrac{14}{7}$ (o) $\dfrac{4}{18}$

2. State an equivalent ratio for each of the following.

(a) $\dfrac{3}{4}$ (b) $\dfrac{5}{8}$ (c) $3:2$

(d) $4:1$ (e) $5:6$ (f) $\dfrac{1}{3}$

B

3. Which of these pairs of ratios are equivalent ratios?
   (a) $10:4$ and $5:2$ (b) $6:3$ and $1:2$
   (c) $12:3$ and $5:1$ (d) $7:2$ and $21:6$
   (e) $5:3$ and $10:5$ (f) $1:6$ and $5:30$

4. Write the following ratios as fractions in lowest terms.
   (a) $12:4$ (b) $3:15$
   (c) $20:5$ (d) $20:4$
   (e) 40 kg to 20 kg   (f) 75 L to 25 L
   (g) 100 m to 5 m   (h) 225 kg to 9 kg

APPLICATIONS

5. Lou and Jenny mixed the lemonade to sell at the fair. The instructions say to mix 4 cans of water with each can of concentrate. To make a large batch, they mixed 25 cans of water with 7 cans of concentrate.
   (a) Did they mix it in the correct ratio?
   (b) How many cans of water or concentrate should be added to make a correct mixture?

C

6. Here are 4 gears.

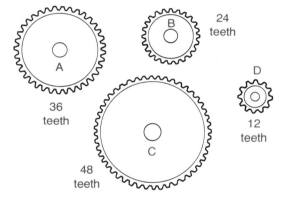

Which two gears would you choose to have a ratio of 3 to 1?

MICRO MATH

NEW

```
100 REM MESSAGE ON THE SCREEN
110 PRINT"YOUR NAME ACROSS THE SCREEN"
120 INPUT"TYPE YOUR NAME ";A$
130 X=LEN(A$)
140 FOR Y=X+1 TO 39
150 A$=A$+" "
160 NEXT Y
170 PRINT"";A$
180 A$=RIGHT$(A$,38)+LEFT$(A$,1)
190 PRINT"";A$
200 GOTO 180
210 END
```

RUN

6.3 PROPORTIONS

A statement such as $\frac{2}{3} = \frac{4}{6}$ or $2:3 = 4:6$ is called a proportion.

> A proportion is the statement of the equality of two ratios.
>
> $$\frac{a}{b} = \frac{c}{d} \qquad \text{or} \qquad a:b = c:d$$

A nut mixture contains 150 g of peanuts, and 75 g of cashews. The ratio by mass of peanuts to cashews is $150:75$. We can reduce the ratio to $2:1$.

We read the proportion $150:75 = 2:1$ as "one hundred fifty is to seventy-five as two is to one."

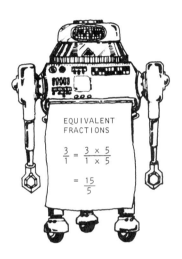

EQUIVALENT
FRACTIONS

$\frac{3}{1} = \frac{3 \times 5}{1 \times 5}$

$= \frac{15}{5}$

Example 1. Find the value of x in the proportion $\frac{3}{1} = \frac{x}{5}$.

Solution: $\frac{3}{1} = \frac{x}{5}$

$\frac{3}{1} = \frac{x}{5}$

$\times 5$

Since $1 \times 5 = 5$
then $3 \times 5 = x$
and $x = 15$

Example 2. Find the value of x in each proportion.

(a) $12:3 = x:1$ (b) $\frac{32}{x} = \frac{8}{3}$

Solution:

(a) $12:3 = x:1$

$\frac{12}{3} = \frac{x}{1}$

$\times 3$

Since $1 \times 3 = 3$
then $x \times 3 = 12$
and $x = 4$

(b) $\frac{32}{x} = \frac{8}{3}$

$\times 4$

$\frac{32}{x} = \frac{8}{3}$

Since $8 \times 4 = 32$
then $3 \times 4 = x$
and $x = 12$

Example 3. The ratio of hamburgers to hot dogs sold was $5:3$.
There were 275 hamburgers sold in one day.
How many hot dogs were sold?

Let the number of hot dogs be represented by x.

A proportion is
$$5:3 = 275:x$$

Solution 1:

$$\overset{\times\ 55}{\overbrace{\dfrac{5}{3} = \dfrac{275}{x}}}$$

Since $5 \times 55 = 275$
then $3 \times 55 = x$
and $x = 165$

Solution 2:

$$\dfrac{5}{3} = \dfrac{275}{x}$$

$$\dfrac{5}{3}\diagdown\dfrac{275}{x}$$

$$5 \times x = 275 \times 3$$
$$5x = 825$$
$$x = 165$$

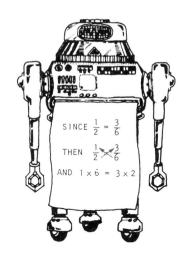

SINCE $\frac{1}{2} = \frac{3}{6}$

THEN $\frac{1}{2} \diagdown\diagup \frac{3}{6}$

AND $1 \times 6 = 3 \times 2$

∴ there were 165 hot dogs sold.

Example 4. Calculate the value of x to the nearest tenth.
$$x:5 = 7:24$$

Solution 1:

$$x:5 = 7:24$$
$$\dfrac{x}{5} = \dfrac{7}{24}$$

⎛ The LCD
⎜ of 5 and 24
⎝ is 120.

$$120\left(\dfrac{x}{5}\right) = \left(\dfrac{7}{24}\right)120$$

⎛ Multiply both
⎜ sides by the
⎝ LCD.

$$24x = 35$$
$$x = \dfrac{35}{24}$$
$$x \doteq 1.5$$

Solution 2:

$$x:5 = 7:24$$
$$\dfrac{x}{5} = \dfrac{7}{24}$$
$$\dfrac{x}{5}\diagdown\dfrac{7}{24}$$
$$24 \times x = 5 \times 7$$
$$24x = 35$$
$$x = \dfrac{35}{24}$$
$$x \doteq 1.5$$

EXERCISE

B

1. Solve for x in the following proportions.

(a) $\dfrac{x}{4} = \dfrac{6}{8}$ (b) $\dfrac{10}{x} = \dfrac{2}{1}$

(c) $x:3 = 5:15$ (d) $3:x = 9:12$

(e) $\dfrac{6}{12} = \dfrac{18}{x}$ (f) $5:4 = x:16$

2. Solve for x in the following proportions.

(a) $x:7 = 15:21$ (b) $\dfrac{3}{x} = \dfrac{12}{48}$

(c) $\dfrac{6}{9} = \dfrac{x}{6}$ (d) $\dfrac{2}{8} = \dfrac{x}{32}$

(e) $\dfrac{5}{x} = \dfrac{x}{20}$ (f) $4:x = \dfrac{12}{15}$

3. Solve for x to the nearest tenth in these proportions.

(a) $\dfrac{x}{5} = \dfrac{7}{12}$ (b) $\dfrac{2}{7} = \dfrac{x}{12}$

(c) $\dfrac{3}{21} = \dfrac{x}{7}$ (d) $\dfrac{x}{11} = \dfrac{5}{8}$

(e) $x:3 = 2:5$ (f) $\dfrac{7}{x} = \dfrac{8}{10}$

(g) $\dfrac{3}{7} = \dfrac{10}{x}$ (h) $5:x = 3:10$

4. The ratio of $\triangle$ to $\bigcirc$ is $1:5$.

$$? \quad \begin{array}{c} \triangle \; \triangle \; \triangle \\ \triangle \; \triangle \\ \triangle \end{array}$$

How many $\bigcirc$ are there?

APPLICATIONS

5. In a survey, 6 out of 30 people ate a sandwich for lunch. Solve for x in this proportion to find how many ate a sandwich in a school of 1120 students.

$$\dfrac{x}{1120} = \dfrac{6}{30}$$

6. The Southwood junior basketball team makes 11 of 20 field goal shots during a game.

(a) How many field goals are made in 100 shots?
(b) How many shots does the team take to make 77 field goals?

7. The maximum load per axle on large trucks is 9200 kg.
(a) What weight can be carried by a truck with 3 axles?
(b) How many axles are required by a truck with a load of 50 000 kg?

6.4 SCALE DRAWINGS: MAPS

A map is a scale drawing. The scale on a map is the ratio of the distance on the map to the distance on the earth. The scale on this map is the ratio

$$\frac{1}{40\ 000\ 000} \qquad \text{or} \qquad 1:40\ 000\ 000$$

$$40\ 000\ 000\ \text{cm} = 400\ 000\ \text{m}$$
$$= 400\ \text{km}$$

This means that 1 cm on the map represents 400 km on the earth.

Example. Find the distance from Edmonton to Winnipeg.

Solution: The distance on the map is 2.9 cm.
1 cm on the map represents 400 km on the earth.
2.9 cm on the map represents
$400 \times 2.9 = 1160$ km on the earth.
The distance from Edmonton to Winnipeg is approximately 1160 km.

EXERCISE

B
Use the map and the scale
1 cm to 400 km to complete
this distance chart.

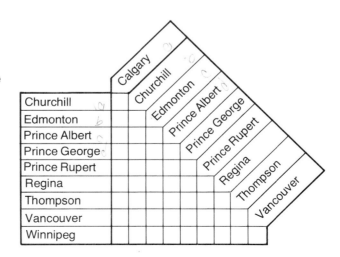

	Calgary	Churchill	Edmonton	Prince Albert	Prince George	Prince Rupert	Regina	Thompson	Vancouver
Churchill									
Edmonton									
Prince Albert									
Prince George									
Prince Rupert									
Regina									
Thompson									
Vancouver									
Winnipeg									

6.5 THREE-TERM RATIOS

In the previous sections, we compared two quantities in a two-term ratio. We can also compare three quantities in a three-term ratio.

Example 1. The school hockey team finished the season with 7 wins, 3 losses, and 2 ties. What is the ratio of wins to losses to ties?

Solution: The ratio of wins to losses to ties is
$$7:3:2$$
The ratio is read "seven to three to two."

Example 2. The ratio of large to medium to small sizes of T-shirts sold on a Saturday is $18:21:35$. Find the following ratios in lowest terms.
(a) large to medium
(b) medium to small
(c) large to small

Solution: (a) large to medium is: $\dfrac{18}{21}$ or $\dfrac{6}{7}$

(b) medium to small is: $\dfrac{21}{35}$ or $\dfrac{3}{5}$

(c) large to small is: $\dfrac{18}{35}$

ALWAYS
STATE RATIOS
IN LOWEST
TERMS.

Example 3. The ratio of Bill's mass to Jim's mass to Gord's mass is $10:15:18$. Bill's mass is 60 kg. What are the masses of Jim and Gord?

Solution:
Let x represent Jim's mass, and y represent Gord's mass.
Then $10:15:18 = 60:x:y$.

Find Jim's mass.

$$\frac{10}{15} = \frac{60}{x}$$

$\times 6$

$$\frac{10}{15} = \frac{60}{x}$$

Since $10 \times 6 = 60$
then $15 \times 6 = x$
and $x = 90$

Find Gord's mass.

$$\frac{10}{18} = \frac{60}{y}$$

$\times 6$

$$\frac{10}{18} = \frac{60}{y}$$

Since $10 \times 6 = 60$
then $18 \times 6 = y$
and $y = 108$

METHOD I	METHOD II
$\frac{10}{15} \times \frac{60}{x}$	$\frac{10}{18} \times \frac{60}{y}$
$10 \times x = 60 \times 15$	$10 \times y = 60 \times 18$
$10x = 900$	$10y = 1080$
$x = 90$	$y = 108$

∴ Jim's mass is 90 kg and Gord's mass is 108 kg.

EXERCISE

A

1. Compare these quantities using ratios.
   (a) 12 wins to 4 losses to 3 ties
   (b) 8 m to 5 m to 2 m
   (c) 2 m to 8 m to 15 m
   (d) 8 boys to 13 girls to 2 teachers
   (e) 3 parts flour to 1 part salt to 1 part water

2.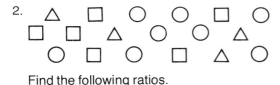

   Find the following ratios.
   (a) ○ to △ to □
   (b) △ to ○ to □
   (c) □ to △ to ○

B

3. Find the value of x and y.
   (a) $1:2:3 = 17:x:y$
   (b) $1:1:3 = 12:x:y$
   (c) $3:4:5 = 3:y:x$
   (d) $2:4:7 = x:8:y$
   (e) $3:6:9 = y:x:225$

APPLICATIONS

4. The ratio of adults to students to children attending the class play was $81:48:51$. Express these ratios in lowest terms.
   (a) adults to children
   (b) children to students
   (c) adults to students
   (d) students to children

5. The ratio of highest speeds for rowing, sailing, and water skiing is $1:3:10$. The highest speed for rowing is 20 km/h.
   (a) What is the highest speed for sailing?
   (b) What is the highest speed for water skiing?

6. The profits from a concert were divided among a minor soccer team, the Boy Scouts, and the Girl Guides in the ratio $3:5:4$. The soccer team received $1250.
   (a) How much did the Boy Scouts receive?
   (b) How much did the Girl Guides receive?

7. The numbers $9:6:5$ on a bag of fertilizer gives the ratio of nitrogen to potassium to potash. In a large bag of fertilizer there are 15 kg of potash.
   (a) What is the mass of nitrogen in the bag?
   (b) What is the mass of potassium in the bag?

C

8.

   Write a three-term ratio to compare these values.
   (a) a penny to a nickel to a dime
   (b) a nickel to a dime to a quarter
   (c) 2 nickels to a dime to 2 quarters
   (d) 5 nickels to 5 dimes to 2 quarters

6.6 PROBLEMS INVOLVING RATIO

In this section we shall look at problems that are solved using proportions. You will have to [READ] carefully to set up the proportion.

Example 1.

The Drama Club and the Camera Club raised $1400 at a school dance.
How much does each receive if the money is divided in the ratio 5 : 2 with the Drama Club getting the larger part?

Solution:

Divide the $1400 into 5 + 2 = 7 parts.
$$\$1400 \div 7 = \$200$$
1 part is $200
The Drama Club receives 5 parts.
$$5 \times \$200 = \$1000$$
The Camera Club receives 2 parts.
$$2 \times \$200 = \$400$$
The total is $1000 + $400 = $1400.

The ratio is $\dfrac{1000}{400} = \dfrac{5}{2}$.

Example 2. A punch is made with lemonade, orange juice, and ginger ale in the ratio 3 : 2 : 10. How much lemonade, orange juice, and ginger ale are needed to make 30 L of punch?

Solution: Divide the 30 L into 3 + 2 + 10 = 15 equal parts.
$$30\,L \div 15 = 2\,L$$
1 part is 2 L
The amount of lemonade is:
$$3 \times 2\,L = 6\,L$$
The amount of orange juice is:
$$2 \times 2\,L = 4\,L$$
The amount of ginger ale is:
$$10 \times 2\,L = 20\,L$$
The total is 6 L + 4 L + 20 L = 30 L.

The ratio is 6 : 4 : 20 which is equivalent to 3 : 2 : 10.

EXERCISE

B

1. Joe and Eric share a $10 000 prize in the ratio of 2:3. Eric receives the larger share.
   How much does each receive?

2. A board 150 cm long is to be cut in the ratio 2:3.
   How long is each piece?

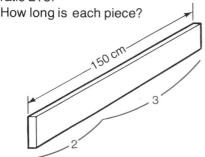

3. A pipe 246 cm long is to be cut into 3 pieces in the ratio 4:3:1.
   How long is each piece?

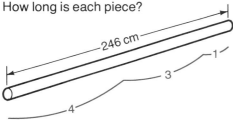

4. Three people invest in a business in the ratio 5:3:1. They share in a profit of $63 000 in the same ratio.
   Find each person's share.

5. The school store orders jackets sized small, medium, and large in the ratio 5:7:2.
   How many of each size are in a shipment of 322 jackets?

6. Two people ran for president of the student council. The votes were split in the ratio 5:2. There were 861 votes cast in the election.
   How many votes did each candidate get?

Ballot Box

C

7. Jane and Harry invest in a pizza stand at the fair. Jane invests $100 and Harry invests $40.
   (a) In what ratio should the profits be shared?
   (b) How much does each receive if the profit was $112?

8. Three people invest in a small business with $8000, $12 000, and $10 000, respectively. They plan to share the profits in the ratio of the amounts invested.
   (a) In what ratio should profits be shared?
   (b) How much does each receive if the profit was $75 000?

CHALLENGE

In how many ways can you spell PYRAMID? You can move to the right or up.

A	M	I	D
R	A	M	I
Y	R	A	M
P	Y	R	A

6.7 RATE PROBLEMS: WORKING TOGETHER

In this section we solve problems that involve doing things together. The following example illustrates an important concept in solving rate problems — using the reciprocal.

Example. It takes Mark 6 h to paint a boat. It takes Steve 3 h to paint a boat the same size.
How long will it take them to paint a boat, working together?

Solution: Mark takes 6 h to paint a boat.

In 1 h, Mark paints $\frac{1}{6}$ of a boat.

Steve takes 3 h to paint a boat.

In 1 h, Steve paints $\frac{1}{3}$ of a boat.

Working together, in 1 h, they paint

$$\frac{1}{6} + \frac{1}{3} = \frac{1}{6} + \frac{2}{6}$$
$$= \frac{3}{6}$$
$$= \frac{1}{2}.$$

If they paint $\frac{1}{2}$ of a boat in 1 h,

they can paint a whole boat in 2 h.

∴ Mark and Steve can paint a boat in 2 h, working together.

Step 1.

Find the reciprocals.

Step 2.

Add the reciprocals.

Step 3.

Find the reciprocal of the sum.

Step 4.

State the answer.

EXERCISE

A

1. Joan and Peter, working together, can wash $\frac{1}{3}$ of the windows in 1 h.

   How long will it take to wash all of the windows?

2. Theresa and Harry, working together, can pick $\frac{1}{4}$ of the strawberries in 1 d.

   How long will it take them to pick all the strawberries?

B

3. Sheila can cut the lawn in 3 h. Jill can cut the same lawn in 2 h.
   How long will it take them to cut the lawn by working together?

4. It takes Bob 4 h to clean the dolphins' tank. Scottie can do the same job in 6 h.
   How long will it take them to clean the tank by working together?

5. Adam and Chris work on a large sailboat. It takes Adam 4 h to scrub the deck. Chris does the same job in 3 h.
   How long will it take them to scrub the deck by working together?

6. It takes Martha 2 h to line the field for a soccer game. It takes Heather 4 h to do the same job.
   How long will it take them to line the field by working together?

7. Mary takes 8 h to paint the apartment. Gerry can paint the apartment in 6 h.
   How long does it take Mary and Gerry to paint the apartment, working together?

8. Bob washes a car in 10 min and Tony washes a car in 5 min.
   How long will it take Bob and Tony to wash a car by working together?

9. Drain A will empty the tank in 4 h. Drain B will empty the tank in 6 h.
   How long will it take to empty the tank using both drains?

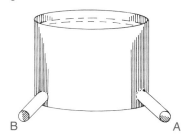

10. Pipe A will fill the tank in 5 h. Pipe B will fill the tank in 2 h.
    How long will it take to fill the tank using both pipes?

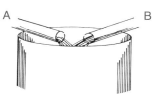

6.8 PERCENT

A percent is a fraction with a denominator of 100. Ratios are often expressed as percentages.

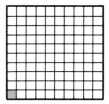 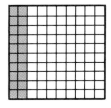 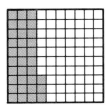

The shaded part is
$$\frac{1}{100}$$
$$\frac{1}{100} = 1\%$$

The shaded part is
$$\frac{20}{100}$$
$$\frac{20}{100} = 20\%$$

The shaded part is
$$\frac{33}{100}$$
$$\frac{33}{100} = 33\%$$

In the figures above, we compare quantities using percent.

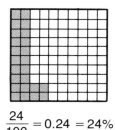

$$\frac{24}{100} = 0.24 = 24\%$$

24 of the 100 squares are shaded. This can be written in several forms:

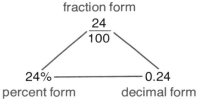

fraction form
$$\frac{24}{100}$$
24% ——————— 0.24
percent form   decimal form

To write a fraction as a percent, we use an equivalent fraction with 100 as a denominator.

Example 1. Write 48% as a fraction in lowest terms.

Solution: As a fraction:
$$48\% = \frac{48}{100}$$
$$= \frac{12}{25}$$

Example 2. Write $\frac{3}{5}$ as a percent.

Solution: $\frac{3}{5} = \frac{3 \times 20}{5 \times 20}$
$$= \frac{60}{100}$$
$$= 60\%$$

EXERCISE

A

1. Express the shaded portion of each figure as a percent.

   (a)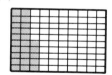

   (b)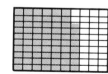

2. Express the unshaded portion of each figure as a percent.

   (a)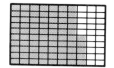

   (b)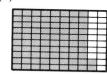

3. What percent of each figure is shaded?

   (a)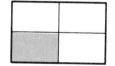

   (b)

   (c)

   (d)

   (e)

   (f)

4. Complete the following:

   (a) $\dfrac{1}{4} = \dfrac{\square}{100}$

   (b) $\dfrac{3}{50} = \dfrac{\square}{100}$

   (c) $\dfrac{3}{5} = \dfrac{\square}{100}$

   (d) $\dfrac{9}{25} = \dfrac{\square}{100}$

B

5. Write as percents.

   (a) $\dfrac{19}{100}$

   (b) $\dfrac{7}{100}$

   (c) $\dfrac{21}{100}$

   (d) $\dfrac{7}{20}$

   (e) $\dfrac{9}{50}$

   (f) $\dfrac{7}{10}$

   (g) $\dfrac{3}{4}$

   (h) $\dfrac{4}{5}$

   (i) $\dfrac{3}{25}$

6. Write as percents.

   (a) 0.21
   (b) 0.35
   (c) 0.75
   (d) 0.62
   (e) 0.5
   (f) 0.3
   (g) 0.23
   (h) 0.17
   (i) 0.07

7. Write as fractions in lowest terms.

   (a) 12%
   (b) 35%
   (c) 47%
   (d) 65%
   (e) 25%
   (f) 18%
   (g) 68%
   (h) 37%
   (i) 75%

8. Northern Tech won 12 of the 25 regular season games.
   What percent of the games did it win?

MICRO MATH

This program calculates your percent on a test.

NEW

```
10 PRINT"WHAT IS YOUR PERCENT?"
20 INPUT"TOTAL TEST SCORE";A
30 INPUT"MY TEST SCORE IS";B
40 LET C=100*B/A
50 PRINT"YOUR PERCENT IS";C;"%"
60 END
```

RUN

6.9 PERCENTS AND DECIMALS

When we use a percent we are comparing a quantity to 100.

Example 1. Express as decimals.
   (a) 6%   (b) 20.5%

Solution: (a) 6% $= \dfrac{6}{100}$

     $= 0.06$

  (b) 20.5% $= \dfrac{20.5}{100}$

      $= 0.205$

Example 2. Write as percents.
   (a) 0.35   (b) 0.075   (c) 1.25

Solution: (a) $0.35 = 0.35 \times 100\%$ or $0.35 = \dfrac{35}{100}$

      $= 35\%$ $= 35\%$

   (b) $0.075 = 0.075 \times 100\%$ or $0.075 = \dfrac{7.5}{100}$

       $= 7.5\%$ $= 7.5\%$

   (c) $1.25 = 1.25 \times 100\%$ or $1.25 = \dfrac{125}{100}$

      $= 125\%$ $= 125\%$

Example 3. A sailfish can swim at 60 km/h.
A honeybee flies at
20% of this speed.
How fast does the bee fly?

Solution: What is 20% of 60 km/h?
20% of 60 $= 0.20 \times 60$
      $= 12$
The honeybee flies at 12 km/h.

EXERCISE

A

1. Express the following percents as decimals.
   (a) 17%   (b) 38%
   (c) 25%   (d) 63%
   (e) 76%   (f) 12.5%
   (g) 37.5%   (h) 18.7%
   (i) 125%   (j) 258%
   (k) 312%   (l) 1225%

2. Express the following decimals as percents.
   (a) 0.37   (b) 0.68
   (c) 0.05   (d) 0.53
   (e) 0.01   (f) 0.8
   (g) 1.5   (h) 3.75
   (i) 6.08   (j) 0.75
   (k) 2.5   (l) 3.05

B

3. Find the following quantities.
   (a) 20% of 625
   (b) 35% of 520
   (c) 50% of 818
   (d) 75% of 324
   (e) 12.5% of 4576
   (f) 37.5% of 5232
   (g) 125% of 4100
   (h) 250% of 6320

4. Find to the nearest tenth.
   (a) 20% of 650
   (b) 25% of 206
   (c) 53% of 813
   (d) 72% of 705
   (e) 85% of 6321
   (f) 62.5% of 8115
   (g) 87.5% of 2065
   (h) 150% of 6507
   (i) 175% of 183
   (j) 250% of 2516

APPLICATIONS

5. Jim LaPorte is a car salesman who earns 2% of his total sales. In one month he had $48 234 in sales.
   How much did he earn?

6. When a house is sold, the owner pays 6% to the real estate company that sells the house. The agent who sells the house is paid a commission of 1.5%. If a house sold for $92 000,
   (a) what is the selling cost to the owner?
   (b) what is the commission for the agent?

7. In an election, 74% of the eligible voters turned out to vote. There were 32 674 eligible voters in town.
   How many people voted?

MICRO MATH

NEW

```
10 PRINT"FINDING A PERCENT OF A NUMBER"
20 INPUT"WHAT IS THE PERCENT?";P;"%"
30 INPUT"WHAT IS THE QUANTITY?";Q
40 LET N=0.01*P*Q
50 PRINT"THE ANSWER IS";N
60 END
```

RUN

6.10 PERCENTS AND FRACTIONS

Many schools have spirit days to cheer teams on to victory. The success of these days is often determined by the number of students who wear the school colours.

$\frac{4}{5}$ of the students in grade nine wore their school colours on a spirit day.

We can express this fraction as a percent. We would say "80% of the students in grade nine wore their school colours on a spirit day."

> We can express fractions as percents by changing the fraction to a decimal first.

Example 1. Express these fractions as percents.

(a) $\frac{1}{4}$ (b) $\frac{7}{8}$ (c) $\frac{2}{3}$

Solution:

(a) For $\frac{1}{4}$, we divide:

1 ÷ 4.

$$\begin{array}{r} 0.25 \\ 4)\overline{1.00} \end{array}$$

$\frac{1}{4} = 0.25$
$\phantom{\frac{1}{4}} = 0.25 \times 100\%$
$\phantom{\frac{1}{4}} = 25\%$

(b) For $\frac{7}{8}$, we divide:

7 ÷ 8.

$$\begin{array}{r} 0.875 \\ 8)\overline{7.000} \end{array}$$

$\frac{7}{8} = 0.875$
$\phantom{\frac{7}{8}} = 0.875 \times 100\%$
$\phantom{\frac{7}{8}} = 87.5\%$

(c) For $\frac{2}{3}$, we divide:

2 ÷ 3.

$$\begin{array}{r} 0.666\ldots \\ 3)\overline{2.000} \end{array}$$

$\frac{2}{3} \doteq 0.667$
$\phantom{\frac{2}{3}} \doteq 0.667 \times 100\%$
$\phantom{\frac{2}{3}} \doteq 66.7\%$
to the nearest tenth

> To express a percent as a fraction, we write the percent as a fraction with a denominator of 100.

Example 2.
Express these percents as fractions in simplest form.

(a) 28%   (b) 37.5%   (c) $112\frac{1}{2}\%$

Solution:

(a) $28\% = \dfrac{28}{100}$

$= \dfrac{7}{25}$

(b) $37.5\% = \dfrac{37.5}{100}$

$= \dfrac{375}{1000}$

$= \dfrac{3}{8}$

(c) $112\frac{1}{2}\% = 112.5\%$

$= \dfrac{112.5}{100}$

$= \dfrac{1125}{1000}$

$= \dfrac{9}{8}$

$= 1\frac{1}{8}$

EXERCISE

A

1. Express the following fractions as percents.

   (a) $\dfrac{1}{2}$ (b) $\dfrac{3}{4}$

   (c) $\dfrac{1}{10}$ (d) $\dfrac{2}{5}$

   (e) $\dfrac{4}{5}$ (f) $\dfrac{7}{10}$

   (g) $\dfrac{3}{10}$ (h) $\dfrac{3}{20}$

2. Express the following percents as fractions.

   (a) 21% (b) 35%
   (c) 60% (d) 15%
   (e) 45% (f) 30%
   (g) 75% (h) 70%

B

3. Write these fractions as percents to the nearest tenth.

   (a) $\dfrac{4}{7}$ (b) $\dfrac{15}{35}$

   (c) $\dfrac{19}{27}$ (d) $\dfrac{4}{35}$

   (e) $\dfrac{1}{3}$ (f) $\dfrac{14}{25}$

   (g) $\dfrac{8}{11}$ (h) $\dfrac{8}{13}$

4. Write these percents as fractions.

   (a) 48% (b) 125%
   (c) 20% (d) 150%
   (e) 7.5% (f) 0.5%

APPLICATIONS

5. In mixing lemonade, you get 5 cans if you mix 1 can of concentrate with 4 cans of water.

What percent of the lemonade is concentrate?

6. In voting to accept a pay increase, 385 of the 420 workers voted "yes." What percent of the workers voted "yes"?

7. In a shipment of 2500 light bulbs, 75 did not work.

What percent of the light bulbs did not work?

8. The police department investigated 247 traffic accidents. 112 of these were caused by impaired drivers. What percent of the accidents were caused by impaired drivers?

9. Find.

   (a) 20% of 25 (b) 50% of 4.8
   (c) 60% of 80 (d) 35% of 70
   (e) 15% of 150 (f) 7% of 200

6.11 PERCENTS AND PROPORTIONS

We can solve many percent problems using proportions. These problems can be solved by either of the methods shown.

Example 1. A full grown blue whale is about 30 m long. The length of a crocodile is about 21% of this length. How long is a crocodile?

Solution:

METHOD I

21% of 30 $= 0.21 \times 30$

$= 6.3$

METHOD II

$$\frac{21}{100} \diagdown \frac{x}{30}$$

$21 \times 30 = x \times 100$

$630 = 100x$

$x = 6.3$

A crocodile is about 6.3 m long.

Example 2. A blue whale has a mass of 140 000 kg. An African elephant has a mass of 7000 kg. What percent of 140 000 is 7000?

Solution:

METHOD I

$$\frac{7000}{140\,000} = 7 \div 140$$

$= 0.05$

$= 0.05 \times 100\%$

$= 5\%$

7000 is 5% of 140 000.

METHOD II

$$\frac{7000}{140\,000} = \frac{x}{100}$$

$$\frac{7}{140} \diagdown \frac{x}{100}$$

$7 \times 100 = x \times 140$

$700 = 140x$

$x = 5$

EXERCISE

B

1. (a) What is 20% of 120?
   (b) What is 60% of 30?
   (c) What is 65% of 19?
   (d) What is 7% of 85?
   (e) What is 30% of 53?
   (f) What is 12% of 455?

2. (a) What percent of 200 is 40?
   (b) What percent of 450 is 90?
   (c) What percent of 100 is 10?
   (d) What percent of 50 is 40?
   (e) What percent of 75 is 30?

APPLICATIONS

3. Jan scores 18 baskets in 40 shots during a basketball game.
   On what percent of her shots does Jan score a basket?

4. On a written driver's test, you need 75% to pass. There are 60 questions on the test.
   How many questions must you answer correctly to pass?

What do these signs mean?

5. Adam got 60% on a test at cadet camp. Each question is worth 1 mark, and he answered 18 questions correctly.
   How many questions were on the test?

6. The Apollo 10 command module reached a speed of 39 000 km/h. The Pioneer 10 reached a speed of 52 000 km/h.
   What percent of 52 000 is 39 000?

7. In a recent election, 2131 of the 8574 eligible voters cast ballots.
   What percent of the voters turned out to vote?

8. The population of Central School is 1250. There is an 10% increase in the number of students.
   (a) How many more students are there?
   (b) What is the new population of Central School?

9. Partly skimmed milk contains 2% butterfat.
   What is the volume of butterfat in 1000 mL of milk?

10. Gerry bought a jacket on sale for $32. The regular price was $40.
    (a) What was the discount?
    (b) Express the discount as a percent.

6.12 APPLICATIONS OF PERCENT: SALES TAX

Tax rates are usually expressed as percents.

The amount of sales tax depends on
    i) the rate of tax.
    ii) the cost of the item.

Example. Sally sells an electric drill for $69.95.
       (a) Find the amount of sales tax at 7%.
       (b) Find the total cost of the drill.

Solution:
  (a) 7% of $69.95 = 0.07 × $69.95
                       = $4.90   (to the nearest cent)
    The sales tax is $4.90.
  (b) $69.95 + $4.90 = $74.85
    The total cost is $74.95.

EXERCISE

B
Round all answers to the nearest cent.
1. Find 5% of
   (a) $4.50   (b) $25.60   (c) $32.80
   (d) $18.95   (e) $7.75   (f) $1.50
   (g) $76.95   (h) $65.80   (i) $14.50

2. Find 7% of
   (a) $45.00   (b) $63.00   (c) $125
   (d) $8.65   (e) $4.95   (f) $17.89
   (g) $0.50   (h) $65.60   (i) $1.77

3. Find 6% of
   (a) $4.75   (b) $8.95   (c) $15.00
   (d) $29.50   (e) $65.00   (f) $89.95
   (g) $119.50   (h) $329.95   (i) $775

4. Find the following amounts of tax.
   (a) 7% of $14 000   (b) 7% of $23 500
   (c) 5% of $18 800   (d) 8% of $69 700
   (e) 6% of $93 700   (f) 6% of $62 500
   (g) 8% of $83 500   (h) 5% of $64 500
   (i) 7% of $14 700   (j) 7% of $28 750

5. A record album costs $12.95, and the sales tax is 7%.
How much would you pay for the album?

6. A waterbed costs $1750.00, and the sales tax is 6%.
How much would you pay for the bed?

7. A bicycle costs $249.95, and the sales tax is 8%.

   (a) How much is the sales tax?
   (b) What is the total cost?

8. A store sold $150 000 of taxable goods in one month.
How much sales tax was collected at 7%?

6.13 APPLICATIONS OF PERCENT: DISCOUNT

A discount is a reduction in price. The rate of reduction is expressed as a percent. Some stores offer a discount to promote sales.

Example. A jacket that sells regularly for $69.95 is reduced 20%.
  (a) Calculate the discount.
  (b) Find the sale price.

Solution:
  (a) 20% of $69.95 = 0.20 × $69.95
            = $13.99
      The discount is $13.99.

  (b) Sale price = regular price − discount
      Sale price = $69.95 − $13.99
            = $55.96
      The sale price is $55.96.

EXERCISE

B
Round all answers to the nearest cent.
1. There is a 15% discount on a backgammon set that sells for $19.95. What is the discount?

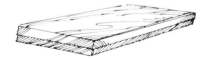

2. A tent costs $129.50. There is a 24% discount. How much is the discount?

3. The Ajax Wholesale Company gives a 2% discount for prompt payment. What is the discount on the following amounts?
   (a) $35.00   (b) $6537
   (c) $28 650   (d) $13 207
   (e) $40 603   (f) $2117

4. A car sells for $12 500. There is a 12% discount.
   (a) How much is the discount?
   (b) What is the sale price?

5. There is a storewide sale where everything is discounted 15%. Find the discount and the sale price. The regular prices are:
   (a) Skates: $129.50
   (b) Album: $11.95
   (c) Stereo: $3250.00
   (d) Radio: $324.50

6.14 APPLICATIONS OF PERCENT: SIMPLE INTEREST

Interest is the money you receive when you deposit your money in a savings account. Interest may also be the money you have to pay when you borrow someone else's money.

The formula to determine simple interest is:

$$I = Prt$$

where

I represents the interest
P represents the principal (the amount invested)
r represents the rate per year
t represents the time in years.

Example 1. Find the simple interest on $2500 invested for 3 a at 14% per annum.

Solution: P = $2500   r = 14%   t = 3
$\qquad\qquad\qquad\qquad$ = 0.14

$\quad$ I $\ = Prt$
$\quad$ I $\ = 2500 \times 0.14 \times 3$
$\qquad = 1050$

∴ the interest is $1050.00.

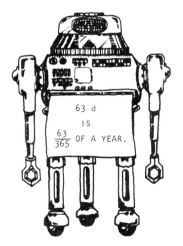

63 d
I S
$\frac{63}{365}$ OF A YEAR.

Example 2. Find the simple interest on $1150 borrowed for 63 days at $18\frac{1}{4}$% per annum.

Solution: P = 1150   r = $18\frac{1}{4}$%   t = $\dfrac{63}{365}$
$\qquad\qquad\qquad\qquad$ = 0.1825

$\quad$ I $\ = Prt$

$\quad$ I $\ = 1150 \times 0.1825 \times \dfrac{63}{365}$

$\qquad \doteq 36.23$

∴ the interest is $36.23.

EXERCISE

A

1. Express the following percents as decimals.
   - (a) 7%
   - (b) 12%
   - (c) 5%
   - (d) 18%
   - (e) $8\frac{1}{2}$%
   - (f) $11\frac{1}{4}$%
   - (g) $15\frac{3}{4}$%
   - (h) $20\frac{1}{2}$%

B

2. Express as fractions of a year.
   - (a) 30 d
   - (b) 60 d
   - (c) 90 d
   - (d) 5 weeks
   - (e) 27 weeks
   - (f) 69 d
   - (g) 157 d
   - (h) 244 d

3. Find the simple interest earned on each of the following investments.
   - (a) $200 invested for 3 a at 12% per annum
   - (b) $500 invested for 5 a at 14% per annum
   - (c) $2500 invested for 4 a at 18% per annum
   - (d) $2000 invested for 3 a at 13% per annum

4. Find the simple interest charged on each of the following loans.
   - (a) $500 borrowed for 90 d at 18% per annum
   - (b) $2500 borrowed for 72 d at 12.5% per annum
   - (c) $850 borrowed for 400 d at 15.25% per annum
   - (d) $1500 borrowed for 65 d at 16% per annum
   - (e) $750 borrowed for 30 days at 18.75% per annum

5. John invested $500 for 2 a at 16% per annum.
   - (a) Calculate the simple interest.
   - (b) What amount does John have after 2 a?

   Amount = $500 + interest

6. Edna borrowed $129 for 30 d at 22% per annum.
   - (a) Calculate the simple interest she will have to pay.
   - (b) What amount will Edna have to pay in 30 d?

7. Mark borrowed $6000 from his father to buy a used car. He agreed to repay the money in 2 a at 8% per annum.
   - (a) How much interest will Mark pay?
   - (b) How much will he have to pay his father in 2 a?

8. The student council invested $6000 for 90 d. The council invested $2000 at 12% and the remainder at 15%.
   - (a) What was the interest on the money invested at 12%?
   - (b) What was the interest on the money invested at 15%?
   - (c) What was the total interest?

ᴍɪᴄʀᴏ ᴍᴀᴛʜ

NEW

```
10 PRINT"FINDING SIMPLE INTEREST"
20 INPUT"PRINCIPAL";P
30 INPUT"RATE";R
40 INPUT"TIME";T
50 LET I=P*R*T
60 PRINT"THE INTEREST IS",I
70 END
```

RUN

INTERNATIONAL STANDARD BOOK NUMBERS

An International Standard Book Number (ISBN) is a 10-digit identification number that is assigned by publishers to their books. ISBN's provide an easy way to order and store books.

An ISBN is divided into four groups. The following is a typical ISBN.

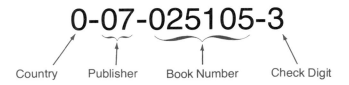

$$0\text{-}07\text{-}025105\text{-}3$$

Country   Publisher   Book Number   Check Digit

The 0 in this ISBN tells us that the book was published in an English-speaking country.

The publisher's number tells you who the publisher is. The publisher's number must be at least 2 digits long. The number 07 in our example means that the book was published by McGraw-Hill.

The third group of digits is a number chosen by the publisher to identify the particular book. The number 025105 identifies a book called "A Mathematical Journey" by Stanley Gudder.

The final digit in the ISBN is the check digit. The check digit is either 0, 1, 2, 3, 4, 5, 6, 7, 8, 9, or X. The X stands for 10. The check digit confirms that the other 9 digits have been recorded correctly. The check digit is calculated after the first 9 digits have been determined. Suppose the first 9 digits of an ISBN are:

$$0\text{-}07\text{-}082734\text{-}\blacksquare$$

To determine the check digit we multiply the first 9 digits by 10, 9, 8, 7, 6, 5, 4, 3, and 2 respectively and add the products.

$$10(0) + 9(0) + 8(7) + 7(0) + 6(8) + 5(2) + 4(7) + 3(3) + 2(4)$$
$$= \quad 0 \quad + \quad 0 \quad + 56 \quad + \quad 0 \quad + 48 \quad + 10 \quad + 28 \quad + \quad 9 \quad + \quad 8 = 159$$

The check digit is chosen so that when it is added to the sum (159), the new sum is evenly divisible by 11. By adding 6 to 159 we get 165, which is evenly divisible by 11. The check digit is 6. The complete ISBN is

0-07-082734-6

Once a book order is received, a computer evaluates the ISBN in the following manner. Suppose the ISBN is 0-446-30292-9. Then

$$10(0) + 9(4) + 8(4) + 7(6) + 6(3) + 5(0) + 4(2) + 3(9) + 2(2) + 9 \quad \text{Check Digit}$$
$$= \quad 0 \quad + 36 \quad + 32 \quad + 42 \quad + 18 \quad + \quad 0 \quad + \quad 8 \quad + 27 \quad + 4 \quad + 9$$
$$= 176$$

And $176 \div 11 = 16$

Since the sum is evenly divisible by 11, the ISBN is a correct one. If the sum was not evenly divisible by 11 the ISBN would not be correct. The computer would notify the operator of the error.

EXERCISE

B

1. Which of the following ISBN's are correct?
    (a) 0-07-005776-1
    (b) 0-7730-1496-3
    (c) 0-8359-0398-2
    (d) 0-395-25061-6

2. Determine the check digit for each of the following.
    (a) 0-395-29188-▨
    (b) 0-201-05420-▨
    (c) 0-03-920038-▨
    (d) 0-07-082733-▨

6.15 CHAPTER 6 REVIEW EXERCISE

1.

Find these ratios.

(a) △ to ◯

(b) ◯ to □

(c) □ to △

2. In one hour, 32 cars, 18 trucks, and 6 buses went past the school.
Express the ratio of buses to cars to trucks in lowest terms.

3. Which of these are equivalent ratios?

(a) $\frac{3}{4}$ and $\frac{4}{5}$ (b) $\frac{3}{8}$ and $\frac{9}{24}$

(c) $4:8$ and $3:6$ (d) $6:9$ and $4:6$

(e) $\frac{2}{3}$, and $\frac{4}{9}$ (f) $3:2$ and $9:6$

4. Solve the x in the following proportions.

(a) $\frac{x}{10} = \frac{4}{5}$ (b) $\frac{x}{3} = \frac{3}{9}$

(c) $\frac{x}{12} = \frac{6}{4}$ (d) $\frac{x}{5} = \frac{21}{15}$

(e) $\frac{x}{15} = \frac{3}{5}$ (f) $\frac{x}{12} = \frac{3}{4}$

5. Solve for x in the following proportions.

(a) $x:3 = 4:6$ (b) $x:5 = 8:10$

(c) $\frac{5}{10} = \frac{x}{2}$ (d) $\frac{12}{5} = \frac{x}{10}$

(e) $\frac{8}{12} = \frac{4}{x}$ (f) $\frac{15}{10} = \frac{3}{x}$

6. A punch recipe calls for orange juice, pink lemonade, and ginger ale in the ratio $2:3:5$.
How much lemonade and ginger ale are needed to mix with 10 mL of orange juice?

7. Express the shaded portion of each figure as a percent.

(a)   (b)

(c) 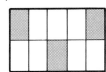   (d)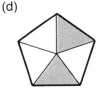

8. Express the following fractions and decimals as percents.

(a) $\frac{3}{100}$ (b) $\frac{3}{10}$ (c) $\frac{3}{50}$

(d) 0.25   (e) 0.45   (f) 0.63

(g) 0.07   (h) 0.36   (i) 0.05

(j) $\frac{8}{25}$ (k) $\frac{7}{20}$ (l) $\frac{11}{50}$

9. Express the following percents as decimals.

(a) 20%   (b) 50%   (c) 8%

(d) 45%   (e) 15%   (f) 48%

(g) 75%   (h) 60%   (i) 80%

10. Express the following percents as fractions.

(a) 25%   (b) 40%   (c) 60%

(d) 51%   (e) 7%   (f) 75%

(g) 27%   (h) 72%   (i) 20%

11. Find the following quantities.

(a) 25% of 60

(b) 15% of 40

(c) 50% of 80

(d) 75% of 160

(e) 80% of 500

(f) 7% of 118

(g) 12% of 65

(h) 30% of 418

12. (a) What percent of 100 is 50?
    (b) What percent of 60 is 15?
    (c) What percent of 80 is 20?
    (d) What percent of 65 is 13?
    (e) What percent of 48 is 12?
    (f) What percent of 144 is 72?
    (g) What percent of 32 is 8?
    (h) What percent of 50 is 7?
    (i) What percent of 100 is 7?

13. Find a ratio in lowest terms to compare the value of 4 nickels to 2 quarters.

14. Jesse got 45 hits in 180 times at bat during the regular season.
    What percent of the times at bat did Jesse get a hit?

15. In a survey, 3 out of 10 students said they would attend the school dance.
    How many people would attend the school dance if there are 800 students in the school?

16. Paul and Joe received $50 for painting a garage. Paul worked 6 h and Joe worked 4 h.
    (a) In what ratio should they share the money?
    (b) How much of the $50 should each receive?

17. Hose A will fill a tank in 6 h. Hose B will fill the same tank in 4 h.
    How long will it take to fill the tank using both hoses?

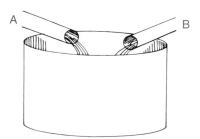

18. At a service station, 1 out of 12 customers orders grease and oil.
    How many of the 288 customers ordered grease and oil?

19. The owner of a house pays 6% of the selling price of a house to the real estate company.
    How much is paid in real estate fees for houses that sell for the following prices?
    (a) $95 000   (b) $68 500
    (c) $108 000   (d) $147 500

20. In a batch of 945 silicon chips for microcomputers, 45 were found to be defective.
    What percent of the chips were defective?

21. Andrea ran for vice-president in the student council elections. 508 of the 635 students in the school voted for her.
    What percent of the students voted for Andrea?

22. Terry bought new skates on sale at 15% off the regular price. The regular price was $149.50.
    How much did Terry pay for the skates?

23. The formula for simple interest is
    $$I = Prt$$
    Find the interest on $4500, for 60 d at 18% per annum.

CHAPTER 6 TEST

1.

$$\overset{\mid\quad+\quad+\quad+\quad+\quad+\quad+\quad+\mid}{\text{A}\quad\text{B}\quad\text{C}\quad\text{D}\quad\text{E}\quad\text{F}\quad\text{G}\quad\text{H}}$$

Find the ratios of these lengths.
(a) $\overline{AC}$ to $\overline{BE}$ (b) $\overline{BF} : \overline{FG}$ (c) $\overline{AH} : \overline{HD}$

2. Which of these pairs of ratios are equivalent ratios?

    (a) $12 : 3$ and $20 : 5$ (b) $\dfrac{2}{4}$ and $\dfrac{8}{10}$

3. Solve for x in the following proportion. $\dfrac{x}{8} = \dfrac{5}{4}$

4. A map has a scale 1 cm to 150 km.
How far apart are two cities that are 3.5 cm apart on the map?

5. A rope 27 m long is to be cut into 2 pieces in the ratio $4 : 5$. How long is each piece of rope?

6. Write as percents.

    (a) $\dfrac{35}{100}$ (b) 0.63 (c) $\dfrac{1}{4}$

7. (a) Write 20% as a fraction in lowest terms.
   (b) Write 37.5% as a decimal.

8. Find 20% of 550.

9. On a computer quiz, you need 80% to go to the next level.
There are 60 questions in the quiz.
How many questions must you answer correctly to go to the next level?

10. In Maplegrove School, 72% of the students are under 16.
There are 900 students at Maplegrove School.
How many students are under 16?

11. A jacket sells for $49.95. There is a discount of 20%.
What is the cost of the jacket?

12. The formula for simple interest is I = Prt.
Find the simple interest to the nearest cent on $500 invested for 90 d at 12%.

7

STATISTICS AND PROBABILITY

REVIEW AND PREVIEW TO CHAPTER 7

PERCENT

EXERCISE 1

Express each of the following percents as decimals.

1.	25%	2.	37%	3.	54%
4.	15%	5.	6%	6.	9%
7.	100%	8.	135%	9.	12.5%
10.	23.6%	11.	86.9%	12.	6.3%

EXERCISE 2

Express each of the following decimals as percents.

1.	0.45	2.	0.37	3.	0.5
4.	0.67	5.	0.8	6.	0.04
7.	0.09	8.	0.235	9.	0.486
10.	0.046	11.	0.307	12.	1.25

EXERCISE 3

Express each of the following fractions as percents.

1. $\frac{1}{2}$ 2. $\frac{1}{4}$ 3. $\frac{3}{4}$

4. $\frac{3}{10}$ 5. $\frac{2}{5}$ 6. $\frac{3}{5}$

7. $\frac{7}{10}$ 8. $\frac{7}{20}$ 9. $\frac{17}{50}$

EXERCISE 4

Express each of the following percents as fractions.

1.	25%	2.	50%	3.	75%
4.	35%	5.	42%	6.	20%
7.	80%	8.	6%	9.	3%

EXERCISE 5

Evaluate the following.

1. 10% of 200
2. 20% of 60
3. 50% of 80
4. 75% of 40
5. 40% of 324
6. 21% of 3200
7. 5% of 600
8. 2% of 550
9. 100% of 456
10. 18% of 260

EXERCISE 6

Write these fractions as percents to the nearest tenth.

1. $\dfrac{1}{8}$
2. $\dfrac{5}{8}$
3. $\dfrac{1}{3}$

4. $\dfrac{2}{7}$
5. $\dfrac{1}{6}$
6. $\dfrac{1}{9}$

EXERCISE 7

1. What percent of 200 is 100?

2. What percent of 80 is 60?

3. What percent of 32 is 8?

4. What percent of 50 is 7?

5. What percent of 100 is 21?

EXERCISE 8

1. A radio costs $230.00 and the rate of sales tax is 7%.
   (a) What is the sales tax?
   (b) What is the total cost?

2. There are 920 students at Highview School. Eighty-five percent of them attended a concert.
   How many attended the concert?

3. The Pineland School basketball team won 18 of the 25 games that they played.
   (a) What percent of their games did they win?
   (b) What percent of their games did they lose?

7.1 COLLECTING DATA

Statistics is the science of collecting and interpreting data.
You can collect data in many ways.
One way is to take a survey.

Jan took a survey in her school.

She used the survey sheet shown at the right to collect the data.

First she completed the Tally column by asking the question,
"What sport do you like to watch most?"

Then Jan completed the Frequency column by adding the tallies.

Frequency tells you how often something happens.

SURVEY SHEET

Sport	Tally	Frequency
Baseball	⊬⊬ IIII	9
Basketball	IIII	4
Football	⊬⊬ ⊬⊬ II	12
Hockey	⊬⊬ ⊬⊬ IIII	14
Skiing	II	2
Tennis	III	3
Other	⊬⊬ I	6
Total		50

To help her interpret the data, Jan completed the summary sheet at the right.

9 students out of 50 chose baseball.

The ratio of students choosing baseball to the total is $\frac{9}{50}$.

We change $\frac{9}{50}$ to a percent as follows:

$$\frac{9}{50} \times 100\% = 18\%.$$

What was the most popular sport?

What was the least popular sport?

What sports might have been counted as "other"?

SUMMARY SHEET

Sport	Frequency	Ratio	Percent
Baseball	9	$\frac{9}{50}$	18%
Basketball	4	$\frac{4}{50}$	8%
Football	12	$\frac{12}{50}$	24%
Hockey	14	$\frac{14}{50}$	28%
Skiing	2	$\frac{2}{50}$	4%
Tennis	3	$\frac{3}{50}$	6%
Other	6	$\frac{6}{50}$	12%
Total	50		100%

EXERCISE

B

1. The following list gives the number of goals scored by Wayne Gretzky in each game during the 1981–82 NHL season.

1	0	2	4	1	0	0	1	3	0
0	3	1	1	2	0	1	0	1	0
2	0	0	1	2	1	0	1	0	1
4	1	1	1	0	3	2	2	1	2
0	0	2	3	1	0	1	1	5	0
1	2	0	1	0	1	2	1	3	0
2	0	2	0	2	1	1	0	0	1
3	1	0	0	1	0	1	2	4	1

Complete the table.

Goals in a game	Tally	Frequency
0		
1		
2		
3		
4		
5		
Total	✕	

2. Frank surveyed the members of his class. He asked them to name their favourite type of movie. Complete Frank's summary sheet.

Type of Movie	Frequency	Ratio	Percent
Adventure	7		
Comedy	6		
Crime	2		
Drama	3		
Romance	4		
Other	3		
Totals	25	✕	

3. Terry Andrews decided to open a seafood restaurant in a resort town on the ocean. To help her decide on what food to put on the menu, she took a seafood survey. Complete Terry's summary sheet.

Seafood	Frequency	Ratio	Percent
Fish	20		
Clams	12		
Lobster	28		
Oysters	8		
Scallops	4		
Shrimp	8		
Totals		✕	

CHALLENGE

Arrange 10 coins to form a triangle.

Move only 3 coins to form this new triangle.

7.2 SAMPLING A POPULATION

There are 3 radio stations in the town of Logan. There are about 60 000 potential radio listeners in the town. Peter was hired by a polling company to determine the approximate number of listeners each station had.

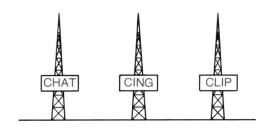

Peter couldn't ask everyone in town. It would take too long and cost too much. He decided to survey 200 people. These 200 people are called a sample of the population. The results of his survey are shown at the right.

Radio Station	Frequency	Ratio	Percent
CHAT	64	$\frac{64}{200}$	32%
CING	48	$\frac{48}{200}$	24%
CLIP	72	$\frac{72}{200}$	36%
None	16	$\frac{16}{200}$	8%
Totals	200		100%

Peter then applied the percents he found from the sample to the population. His results are shown at the right.

Peter has used a sample to make a prediction about an entire group.

Who would be interested in the results of Peter's survey?

Why are the results only "approximate"?

Radio Station	Percent	Calculations	Listeners
CHAT	32%	$0.32 \times 60\,000$ = 19 200	19 200
CING	24%	$0.24 \times 60\,000$ = 14 400	14 400
CLIP	36%	$0.36 \times 60\,000$ = 21 600	21 600
None	8%	$0.08 \times 60\,000$ = 4800	4800
Totals	100%		60 000

EXERCISE

B

1. The school cafeteria sells hamburgers, hot dogs, pizza, and sandwiches. To determine how much of each item to order, a survey was taken. Students were asked what type of food they prefer.
   (a) Complete the survey sheet. The first one has been done for you.

Food	Frequency	Ratio	Percent
Hamburgers	7	$\frac{7}{50}$	14%
Hot dogs	9		
Pizza	21		
Sandwiches	13		
Totals	50		

   (b) 400 students buy lunch at school each day. Use the percents from the summary sheet to calculate the approximate number of servings required each day.

Food	%	Calculations	Number of Servings
Hamburgers	14%	0.14×400 = 56	56
Hot dogs			
Pizza			
Sandwiches			
Totals			

2. Judy was hired by an advertising agency. Her job was to determine what method of advertising people liked the best. She surveyed 300 people.
   (a) Complete her summary sheet.

Type	Frequency	Ratio	Percent
Billboards	24	$\frac{24}{300}$	8%
Catalogues	66		
Magazines	15		
Newspapers	96		
Radio	39		
Television	60		
Totals	300		

   (b) There are about 150 000 people who use advertising in the city where Judy works. Use the percents calculated from the summary sheet to find out how many prefer each type.

Type	%	Calculations	Number of People
Billboards	8%	$0.08 \times 150\,000$ = 12 000	12 000
Catalogues			
Magazines			
Newspapers			
Radio			
Television			
Totals			

CHALLENGE

A hunter walked 2 km due south, then 2 km due west, and finally 2 km due north. He ended up right back where he started from. Where did he start from?

7.3 READING BAR GRAPHS AND BROKEN LINE GRAPHS

Graphs are used to display information in an eye appealing way.

BAR GRAPHS

The graph at the right is a bar graph. Bar graphs are used to compare similar things.

This bar graph shows the number of games won during one season by the teams in the Western Conference of the C.F.L.

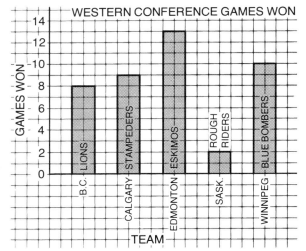

i) How many games did B.C. win?
ii) Which team won the most games?
iii) Which team won the fewest games?
iv) What was the total number of games won?

BROKEN LINE GRAPHS

The graph at the right is a broken line graph. Broken line graphs are used to show how something changes.

This graph shows the temperature, on the hour, at Spur City for several hours.

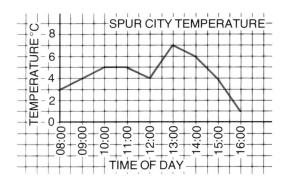

i) What was the temperature at 12:00?
ii) At what time was the highest temperature recorded?
iii) At what time was the lowest temperature recorded?

EXERCISE

B

1. The following graph shows the daily circulation, in millions of papers, for the world's largest newspapers.

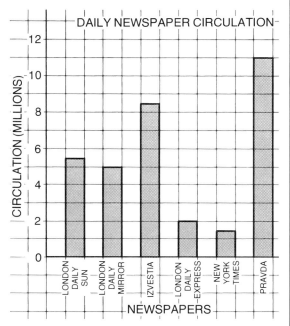

   (a) Which newspaper has the highest circulation?
   (b) Which newspaper has the lowest?
   (c) What is the approximate circulation of each paper?

2. The graph shows the number of sports cars sold by Magnum Sports Cars for one year.

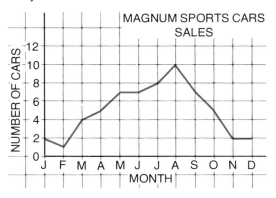

   (a) What month had the most sales?
   (b) How many cars were sold in May?
   (c) What month had the fewest sales?
   (d) What were the total sales for the year?

3. The graph shows the maximum depth of each of the Great Lakes.

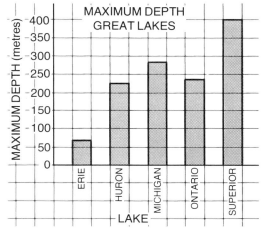

   (a) Which lake is the shallowest?
   (b) Which lake is the deepest?
   (c) What lakes are about the same depth?
   (d) What is the approximate depth of each lake?

4. The graph shows Mark's entertainment expenses for one year.

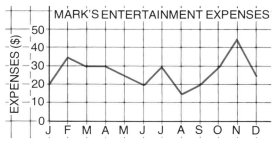

   (a) In what month were his expenses the highest?
   (b) What were his expenses in March?
   (c) What were his total expenses for the year?

7.4 DRAWING BAR GRAPHS

The table at the right gives the number of record albums that have sold over one million copies, for several artists.

To make a bar graph showing this information we use these steps.

Step 1. Draw and label the horizontal axis. Space the names of the artists evenly.

Step 2. Draw and label the vertical axis. Make sure that the last number is large enough so that every number in the table can be graphed.

Step 3. Draw the bars to show the number of albums. Give the graph a title.

Artist	Albums
Beach Boys	12
Beatles	20
Bob Dylan	15
Elton John	11
Elvis Presley	21
Three Dog Night	14

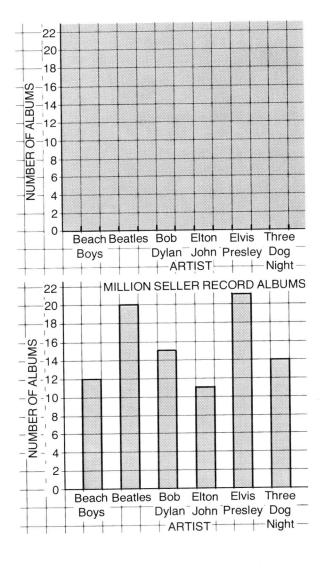

EXERCISE

B

1. The table gives the number of moons that the planets have.
   (a) Display this information on a bar graph.

Planet	Number of Moons
Earth	1
Jupiter	16*
Mars	2
Neptune	3
Pluto	1
Saturn	21*
Uranus	5

   (b) Which of our sun's planets have no moons?

   *Reports of other moons are presently being investigated.

2. The table gives the typical life spans for several animals. Display this information on a bar graph.

Animal	Life Span (in years)
Horse	30
Rabbit	12
Cat	15
Lion	25
Hippopotamus	40
Elephant	60

3. The table gives the approximate number of flights during one year for several airports. Display this information on a bar graph.

Airport	Flights
Calgary	55 000
Edmonton	35 000
Halifax	25 000
Montreal	75 000
Ottawa	35 000
Toronto	130 000
Vancouver	70 000
Winnipeg	40 000

4. The table gives the lengths of several rivers in eastern Canada. Display this information on a bar graph.

River	Length (km)
Ottawa	1120
Saguenay	760
St. John	670
St. Lawrence	3050

7.5 DRAWING BROKEN LINE GRAPHS

The table at right gives Dale Brown's winnings (to the nearest $1000) while driving in stock car races for nine months.

To make a broken line graph showing this information we follow these steps.

Month	Winnings
January	$4000
February	$2000
March	$3000
April	$6000
May	$7000
June	$4000
July	$3000
August	$3000
September	$1000

Step 1. Draw and label the horizontal axis. Space the names of the months evenly.

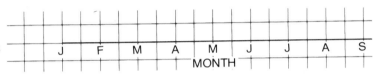

Step 2. Draw and label the vertical axis. Make sure that the last number is large enough so that every number in the table can be graphed.

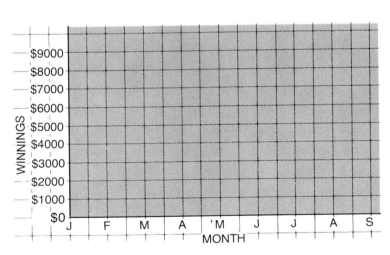

Step 3. Plot the ordered pairs from the table. For example, the first ordered pair is (J,$4000).

Step 4. Connect each pair of points with a line.
Give the graph a title.

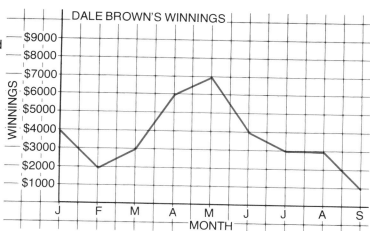

EXERCISE

B

1. Jennifer works as a weather forecaster on a large ocean liner. The table gives the temperature for several hours. Display this information on a broken line graph.

Time	Temp(°C)
09:00	9
10:00	12
11:00	14
12:00	15
13:00	16
14:00	16
15:00	13
16:00	11

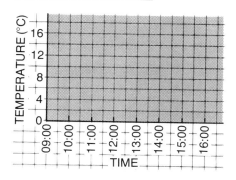

2. The table gives the new car sales of Apple Automotive for one week. Display this information on a broken line graph.

Day	Cars Sold
Monday	3
Tuesday	4
Wednesday	6
Thursday	7
Friday	3
Saturday	5

3. The table gives the number of home computers sold by the Atlantic Computer Company during one year. Display this information on a broken line graph.

Month	J	F	M	A	M	J	J	A	S	O	N	D
Computers	15	10	16	20	24	24	21	28	30	17	19	35

7.6 READING AND DRAWING CIRCLE GRAPHS

Circle graphs show how something is divided. The circle graph at right shows the results of the Bears' hockey season when they played 70 games.

BEARS' HOCKEY SEASON

WON 50%

LOST 30%

TIED 20%

The team lost 21 games, since 30% of 70 = 21.

i) How many games did they win?
ii) How many games did they tie?

CIRCLE GRAPHS ARE ALSO CALLED PIE GRAPHS.

The table shows how Sandra uses the $200.00 she earns each month at her part-time job. To make a circle graph to show this information, we can use these steps.

Item	Cost
Movies	$20.00
Lunches	$30.00
Buses	$20.00
Clothes	$90.00
Savings	$40.00
Total	$200.00

Step 1. Express each item as a percent of the total income.

Movies: $\frac{20}{200} \times 100\% = 10\%$

Lunches: $\frac{30}{200} \times 100\% = 15\%$

Buses: $\frac{20}{200} \times 100\% = 10\%$

Clothes: $\frac{90}{200} \times 100\% = 45\%$

Savings: $\frac{40}{200} \times 100\% = 20\%$

Step 2. Find the angle size by converting to a decimal and multiplying by 360°. (There are 360° in a circle.)

Movies: $0.10 \times 360° = 36°$

Lunches: $0.15 \times 360° = 54°$

Buses: $0.10 \times 360° = 36°$

Clothes: $0.45 \times 360° = 162°$

Savings: $0.20 \times 360° = 72°$

Step 3. Draw a circle and the required angles. Label each sector. Give the graph a title.

SANDRA'S MONTHLY SPENDING

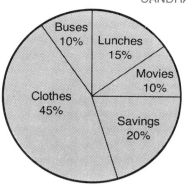

EXERCISE

B

1. The circle graph shows how the student council spent the money they earned selling T-shirts.

STUDENT COUNCIL SPENDING

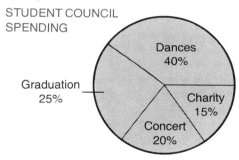

The student council spent $3000. How much did they spend in each category?

2. The circle graph shows how one hour of a radio station's time is divided.

ONE HOUR OF RADIO

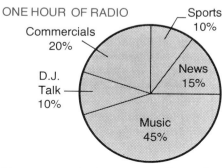

How many minutes are used in each category?

3. It has been estimated that the buried pirate treasure in North America is divided as follows.

Atlantic Coast	65%
Pacific Coast	20%
Thousand Islands	15%
TOTAL	100%

Display this information in a circle graph.

4. The Blue Sox baseball team had the following expenses.

Uniforms	$1200
Equipment	$ 600
Travel	$ 300
Other	$ 900
TOTAL	$3000

Display this information on a circle graph.

5. Julie had the following car expenses for one year.

Payments	$3600
Gasoline	$1200
Insurance	$ 900
Maintenance	$ 300
TOTAL	$6000

Display this information on a circle graph.

7.7 READING AND DRAWING PICTOGRAPHS

The graph at the right is called a pictograph. On a pictograph, picture symbols are used to represent the data.

Sometimes the data have been rounded.

This pictograph shows the album sales of the Sound City Record Store for one week.

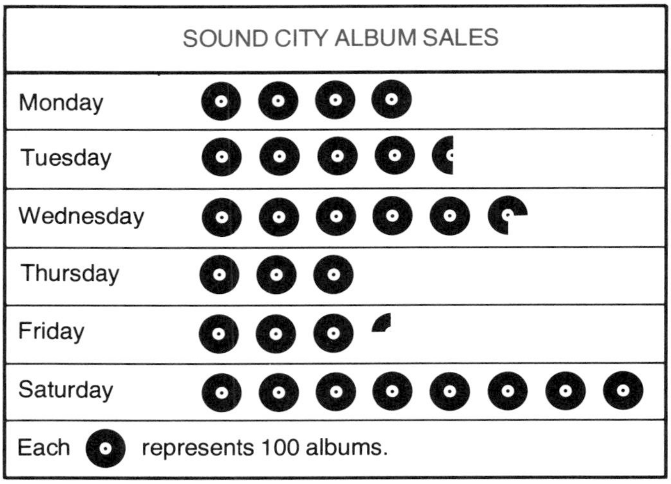

How many albums were sold on Thursday?

On what day were the most albums sold?

On what day were the fewest albums sold?

Estimate the number of albums sold during the week.

SOUND CITY ALBUM SALES	
Monday	● ● ● ●
Tuesday	● ● ● ● ◖
Wednesday	● ● ● ● ● ◖
Thursday	● ● ●
Friday	● ● ● ◢
Saturday	● ● ● ● ● ● ● ●
Each ● represents 100 albums.	

Example. The table gives the number of cars sold for 6 months by Adams Auto. Display this information on a pictograph.

Car Sales	
Jan.	10
Feb.	15
Mar.	25
April	17
May	13
June	20

Solution:

Step 1. Select an appropriate symbol to represent car sales, such as 🚗 .

Step 2. Decide on an appropriate scale. For example, let each 🚗 represent 5 cars.

Step 3. Draw the graph.

Step 4. Give the graph a title.

ADAMS AUTO CAR SALES	
January	🚗 🚗
February	🚗 🚗 🚗
March	🚗 🚗 🚗 🚗 🚗
April	🚗 🚗 🚗 🚗
May	🚗 🚗 🚗
June	🚗 🚗 🚗 🚗
Each 🚗 represents 5 cars.	

EXERCISE

B

1. The pictograph shows the number of hot dogs sold in the cafeteria during one week.

HOT DOG SALES	
Monday	🌭 🌭 🌭
Tuesday	🌭 🌭 🌭 🌭
Wednesday	🌭 🌭 🌭 🌭 🌭
Thursday	🌭 🌭
Friday	🌭 🌭 🌭
Each 🌭 represents 10 hot dogs.	

(a) How many hot dogs were sold on Monday?
(b) On what day were the most hot dogs sold?
(c) On what day were the fewest hot dogs sold?
(d) What were the total sales for the week?

2. The table gives the points scored by five members of the Raiders basketball team in one season.

Player	Points Scored
Adams	80
Lentini	40
Thompson	55
Palmer	90
Monaco	65

Let one ⊖ represent 10 points and display this information on a pictograph.

3. The table gives the attendance at the Cinema II theatre during one week.

Day	Attendance
Monday	300
Tuesday	350
Wednesday	225
Thursday	275
Friday	318
Saturday	423
Sunday	307

Let one 🧍 represent 50 people and display this information on a pictograph.

7.8 THE MEAN OR AVERAGE

Sometimes it is useful to know where the "centre" of a group of numbers is. The mean or average is one of the numbers that locates the centre.

Example 1. Find the mean of 10, 12, 14, and 16.

Solution:
Step 1. Add the numbers. $10 + 12 + 14 + 16 = 52$

Step 2. Divide by 4. $\dfrac{52}{4} = 13$

The mean is 13.

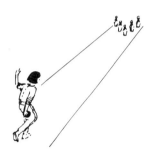

Example 2. Melissa bowled three games. Her scores were 212, 215, and 230. What was her average?

Solution:
Step 1.   Add the scores. $212 + 215 + 230 = 657$

Step 2.   Divide by 3. $\dfrac{657}{3} = 219$

Her average was 219.

> The mean or average of a set of numbers
> is found by adding the numbers and then
> dividing by the number of numbers in the set.

Example 3. During one week of the monsoon season, the following amounts of rain fell on Mt. Waiateal, Hawaii.
Monday, 5.1 cm; Tuesday, 6.3 cm; Wednesday, 4.9 cm; Thursday, 3.4 cm; Friday, 2.7 cm; Saturday, 5.6 cm; Sunday, 6.1 cm.
What was the average daily amount of rainfall (to the nearest tenth)?

Solution:
Step 1. $5.1 + 6.3 + 4.9 + 3.4 + 2.7 + 5.6 + 6.1 = 34.1$

Step 2. $\dfrac{34.1}{7} \doteq 4.87$

The average amount of rainfall was 4.9 cm.

EXERCISE

B

1. Find the mean of each set of numbers.
   (a) 25, 30, 35
   (b) 16, 17, 18, 17
   (c) 84, 82, 71, 95
   (d) 12, 47, 66, 19, 71
   (e) 121, 136, 156, 129, 168

2. Find the mean of each set of numbers.
   Round answers to the nearest tenth.
   (a) 18, 24, 31
   (b) 21, 29, 36, 19
   (c) 66, 73, 75, 57
   (d) 123, 141, 251, 304, 213

3. Find the mean of each set of numbers.
   Round answers to the nearest tenth.
   (a) 9.7, 8.4, 7.6
   (b) 21.4, 36.5, 29.7, 34.9
   (c) 91.6, 103.7, 121.2, 87.6

APPLICATIONS

4. Francine made three long distance phone calls. The costs were $3.56, $4.12, and $4.83.
   What was the average cost?

5. Five students received the following marks for a safe driving course.
   81, 84, 93, 76, 91
   What is the average of the marks?

6. Justine had the following times for the 100 m dash.
   11.8 s, 11.4 s, 11.5 s, 12.1 s
   What was her average time?

7. The precipitation for each month during one year in Windsor, Ontario, is given in the chart below.

Month	J	F	M	A	M	J	J	A	S	O	N	D
Precip.(cm)	13	14	18	23	27	28	31	27	24	22	24	16

   Calculate the average amount of precipitation.

8. Linda bowls every week in a league. Calculate her average at the end of three weeks.

Week	Game 1	Game 2	Game 3	Average
1	212	204	217	
2	211	225	221	
3	187	201	194	

9. The number of fire alarms answered each day for one month were recorded on the following chart.

Fire Station No. 9		
Calls	Tally	Frequency
1	IIII	
2	III	
3	HHH III	
4	HHH HHH	
5	HHH	

   (a) Complete the frequency column.
   (b) Calculate the average number of calls per day.

MICRO MATH

NEW

```
100 PRINT"FIND THE AVERAGE"
110 PRINT"HOW MANY NUMBERS?"
120 INPUT N
130 PRINT"ENTER THE NUMBERS"
140 PRINT"ONE AT A TIME"
150 LET S=0
160 FOR I=1 TO N
170 INPUT X
180 LET S=S+X
190 NEXT I
200 LET A=S/N
210 PRINT"THE AVERAGE IS";A
220 END
```

RUN

7.9 THE MEDIAN

Another number that locates the centre of a set of numbers is the median.

> When a set of numbers is arranged in order from smallest to largest, or largest to smallest, the median is the middle number.

There are just as many values above the median as there are below it.

Example 1. Find the median of 16, 13, 17, 15, and 19.

Solution:

Step 1.   Arrange the numbers in order: 13, 15, 16, 17, 19

Step 2.   Find the middle number.   16

The median is 16.

If there are two middle numbers, the median is the average of the two.

Example 2. Find the median of 21, 19, 26, 18, 27, and 14.

Solution:

Step 1.   Arrange the numbers in order: 14, 18, 19, 21, 26, 27

Step 2.   The two middle numbers are 19 and 21.
$$\frac{19 + 21}{2} = \frac{40}{2}$$
$$= 20$$

The median is 20.

EXERCISE

1. Find the median of each set.
   (a) 10, 12, 17, 13, 9
   (b) 79, 81, 99, 91, 79, 87, 86
   (c) 35, 26, 28, 30
   (d) 7, 11, 6, 11, 8, 4
   (e) 10.4, 8.7, 9.6, 8.4, 7.9
   (f) 164, 134, 142, 165, 153, 171

2. Find the median of these golf scores.
   78, 72, 70, 75, 77, 72, 70

7.10 THE MODE

In the set of numbers

$$3, 4, 4, 5, 5, 5, 6, 7,$$

5 occurs most often.

5 is called the mode of the data.

> The mode of a set of numbers is the number that occurs most often. There may be more than one mode.

Finding the mode is made simpler if you arrange the numbers in order.

For the set of numbers $\quad$ 5, 6, 6, 6, 7, 7, 8, $\quad$ the mode is 6.
For the set of numbers $\quad$ 4, 5, 5, 6, 7, 7, 8, $\quad$ the modes are 5 and 7.
For the set of numbers $\quad$ 7, 9, 10, 11, 15, $\quad$ there is no mode.

Example. Michael works part time at a shoe store. On Saturday he sold shoes of the following sizes.

$$8, 10, 9, 9\frac{1}{2}, 7, 7, 8, 9, 8\frac{1}{2}, 11, 9, 9\frac{1}{2}$$

Find the mode of the sizes.

Solution: Arrange the numbers in order.

$$7, 7, 8, 8, 8\frac{1}{2}, 9, 9, 9, 9\frac{1}{2}, 9\frac{1}{2}, 10, 11$$

The mode is 9.

EXERCISE

1. Find the mode of each set.
   (a) 2, 3, 4, 2, 3, 5, 3
   (b) 9, 8, 7, 9, 8, 8, 9, 7, 9
   (c) 21, 22, 23, 22, 22, 23, 21, 23
   (d) 5, 7, 8, 9, 10, 11, 6, 4
   (e) 84, 93, 91, 82, 81, 84
   (f) 8, $8\frac{1}{2}$, 9, 9, 8, $8\frac{1}{2}$, $8\frac{1}{2}$, 9

2. The following list gives the number of scoops put on twelve ice cream cones in one hour.

   $$3, 2, 1, 1, 2, 3, 3, 2, 1, 2, 3, 2$$

   Find the mode of this data.

7.11 MEAN, MEDIAN, OR MODE?

The mean, median, and mode are all used to locate the "centre" of data. In most cases, one of them will be more meaningful than the other two.

The following are the test marks that 10 students received on a sailing test.

Sandra	100
Marco	100
Judy	90
Dennis	60
Tyson	60
Nicole	50
Sheila	50
Rudy	50
Mike	50
Glen	40

The mean of the marks is 65.
The median of the marks is 55.
The mode of the marks is 50.

Which is the best indicator of the "centre" of this data?

 The mean is 65. Three students scored higher than 65. Seven scored lower. The 3 high marks have raised the mean.

 The median is 55. It is in the middle of the data. Five students scored higher than 55. Five students scored lower.

 The mode is 50. Five students scored higher than 50. One scored lower.

In this example, the median is the best indicator of the "centre" of the data.

EXERCISE

B

1. Find the mean, median, and mode.
   (a) 5, 6, 7
   (b) 10, 10, 10
   (c) 3, 3, 5, 9
   (d) 1, 1, 1, 3, 4

2. Find the mean, median, and mode.
   (a) 9, 13, 14, 9, 15
   (b) 10, 9, 3, 8, 10
   (c) 15, 18, 16, 17
   (d) 9, 10, 11, 9, 8, 13
   (e) 2, 4, 3, 3, 2
   (f) 2, 9, 8, 10, 5, 6, 9
   (g) 18, 10, 9, 8, 10, 11

3. Find the mean, median, and mode.
   (a) 68, 70, 85, 67, 70
   (b) 12.8, 6.3, 5.4, 9.3, 8.2
   (c) 90, 95, 90, 105, 215

4. (a) Find the mean, median, and mode of 20, 20, 30, 35, 40.
   (b) We now replace 40 by 100. Find the mean, median, and mode of 20, 20, 30, 35, 100.
   (c) By how much does the mean change when we replace 40 by 100?
   (d) Does the median change when we replace 40 by 100?
   (e) Does the mode change when we replace 40 by 100?

5. The following is a list of salaries paid to 9 employees of a company.
   $200 000
   $160 000
   $ 50 000
   $ 50 000
   $ 50 000
   $ 30 000
   $ 30 000
   $ 30 000
   $ 30 000
   (a) Calculate the mean, median, and mode of these salaries.
   (b) Which is the best indicator of the centre of this data?

6. The precipitation for each month during one year in Smithville is given in the chart.

Month	J	F	M	A	M	J	J	A	S	O	N	D
Precip.(cm)	8	17	18	18	19	7	5	7	5	5	6	23

   (a) Calculate the mean, median, and mode.
   (b) Which one describes the data best?

C

7. On one Saturday, Susan sold shoes of the following sizes:

   $9, 10, 9, 10\frac{1}{2}, 11, 11\frac{1}{2}, 9, 9, 12, 9$

   (a) Find the mean, median, and mode.
   (b) Which of these numbers is most important to Susan when she reorders shoes? Why?

8. Adam is a hockey goalie. The following list gives the number of goals scored on him in ten games.
   6, 1, 0, 2, 1, 5, 0, 1, 6, 1
   (a) Find the mean, median, and mode.
   (b) Which of these numbers is the best indicator of Adam's goal tending?

7.12 POSSIBLE OUTCOMES OF EXPERIMENTS

Probability is the branch of mathematics that helps you determine the chances of something happening. The following are some probability statements.

"There is a 25% chance that it will snow tonight."

"You have a fifty-fifty chance of winning the game."

"You will probably pass the math test."

Before we can predict the chances of something happening, we have to be able to list the possible outcomes of events.

When you toss a coin there are two possible outcomes.

A head   A tail

Each outcome is "equally likely."

When you roll a die there are six possible outcomes.

Each outcome is "equally likely."

When you toss a coin and roll a die at the same time, there are twelve possible outcomes. A tree diagram helps show these outcomes.

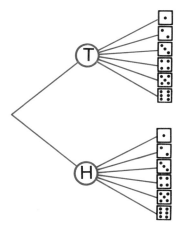 

EXERCISE

B

1. The following tree diagram shows the possible outcomes when a nickel and a dime are tossed at the same time. List all the possible outcomes.

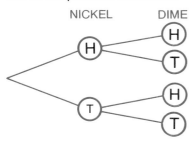

2. A box contains a red marble, a blue marble, and a white marble. You remove two marbles from the box. What are the possible outcomes of this experiment?

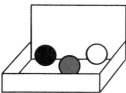

3. A box contains four balls—one red, one blue, one green, and one orange.
   (a) List the possible outcomes if you remove one ball.
   (b) List the possible outcomes if you remove two balls.
   (c) List the possible outcomes if you remove three balls.
   (d) List the possible outcomes if you remove four balls.

4. When a thumbtack is tossed, it can land in two ways—point up or point down.

POINT UP   POINT DOWN

List the possible outcomes when a coin and a thumbtack are tossed at the same time.

5. List the possible outcomes when a die is rolled and a thumbtack is tossed at the same time.

6. When a paper cup is tossed it can land in one of the following three ways.

On the side   Top up   Bottom up

List the possible outcomes when a coin and a paper cup are tossed at the same time.

7. A penny, a nickel, and a dime are tossed at the same time. List the possible outcomes of this experiment.

8. A penny, a nickel, a dime, and a quarter are tossed at the same time. List the possible outcomes of this experiment.

CHALLENGE

The numbers 1, 3, 6, 10 . . . are called triangular numbers because they can be shown as equilateral triangles

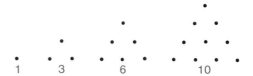

What are the next four triangular numbers?

7.13 THE PROBABILITY FORMULA

When a coin is tossed and you call "heads," for you there is one favourable outcome—a head.

There are two possible outcomes to this event—a head and a tail. Both these outcomes are equally likely—they each have the same chance of happening.

When you call "heads," you have 1 chance out of 2 of being correct. We say that the probability of a head is

$$P(head) = \frac{1}{2}$$

number of ways to get a head

number of equally likely ways the coin can land

We define probability as follows:

$$\frac{\text{Probability of}}{\text{an event}} = \frac{\text{number of favourable outcomes}}{\text{total number of possible outcomes}}$$

Example 1. A bag contains 3 pennies, 4 nickels, and 3 dimes. What is the probability of choosing a nickel from the bag?

Solution: There are 10 coins in the bag. There are 4 nickels.

$$P(nickel) = \frac{\text{number of favourable outcomes}}{\text{total number of possible outcomes}}$$

$$= \frac{4}{10}$$

$$= \frac{2}{5}$$

Example 2. Suppose you spin the spinner and toss a coin at the same time.

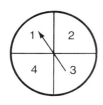

What is the probability of getting a 3 on the spinner and a head on the coin?

Solution: A tree diagram shows the possible outcomes.

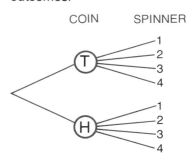

There are eight possible outcomes.

$$P(3 \text{ and head}) = \frac{1}{8}$$

EXERCISE

B

1. A bag contains 4 dimes and 3 quarters. If you select one coin from the bag, what is the probability that
   (a) the coin is a dime?
   (b) the coin is a quarter?

2. When a die is rolled, what is the probability of getting
   (a) a 4?
   (b) an odd number?
   (c) a number less than 3?
   (d) a number divisible by 3?

3. A bag contains 20 red balls, 25 yellow balls, and 30 green balls. If you select one ball from the bag, what is the probability that
   (a) the ball is green?
   (b) the ball is red?
   (c) the ball is yellow?

4. The tree diagram shows the possible ways in which a family can have two children (no twins).

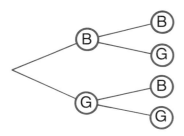

   (a) What is the probability of having a family of two boys?
   (b) What is the probability that the oldest child is a girl?

5. (a) Draw a tree diagram to show the possible outcomes when a nickel and a dime are tossed at the same time.
   (b) What is the probability of getting 2 tails?
   (c) What is the probability of getting a tail and a head?

6. A nickel, a dime, and a quarter are tossed at the same time.
   (a) Draw a tree diagram to show the possible outcomes.
   (b) What is the probability of getting 3 heads?
   (c) What is the probability of getting 2 tails and 1 head?

7. A coin is tossed and a die is rolled at the same time.
   (a) Draw a tree diagram to show the possible outcomes.
   (b) What is the probability of getting a head and a 6?
   (c) What is the probability of getting a tail and an odd number?

C

8. A card is drawn from a deck of 52 playing cards. What is the probability of drawing
   (a) a black card?
   (b) a diamond?
   (c) a 10?
   (d) the three of clubs?

ΜΙΣΚΟ ΜΑΤΗ

NEW

```
100 REM THIS PROGRAM ROLLS TWO DICE
110 PRINT "TYPE NUMBER OF ROLLS"
120 PRINT "TO BE MADE"
125 INPUT N
130 PRINT
140 FOR A =1 TO N
150 D1=INT(6*RND(1))+1
160 D2=INT(6*RND(1))+1
170 T=D1+D2
180 PRINT " FIRST DIE=" D1
190 PRINT "SECOND DIE=" D2
200 PRINT"        TOTAL=" T
210 PRINT"     "
220 NEXT A
```

RUN

EXTRAEXTRA EXTRA EXTRA EXTRA

The Mystery of Marie Rogêt

The Purloined Letter

The Fall of the House of Usher

The Gold Bug

STYLOMETRY

Stylometry is the science that measures "spoken" or "written" words. Stylometry is used to show that one particular person is responsible for saying or writing something, rather than any other person.

Studies have shown that approximately the same percentage of three-letter words will be used by a person when writing something this year as when writing something last year. The same is true for words of any length. But the percentage of three-letter words used by one author will very likely be different from the percentage of three-letter words used by another author.

The frequency of word length used by an author is best shown on a graph. The graph gives a "picture" of how someone writes or speaks. This "picture" is as personal as a person's fingerprints.

The following table gives the word lengths in a 500-word passage written by Edgar Allan Poe. The percent column has also been calculated.

Word Length in letters	Frequency Number of Words	Percent
1	20	4
2	58	11.6
3	132	26.4
4	98	19.6
5	48	9.6
6	48	9.6
7	46	9.2
8	20	4
9	8	1.6
10	8	1.6
11	6	1.2
12	5	1
13+	3	0.6

The graph of the frequency (as a percent) versus word length is shown below.

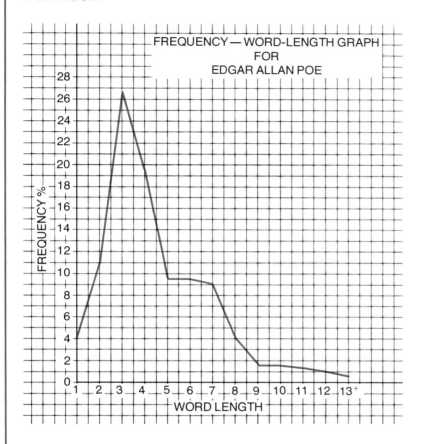

FREQUENCY — WORD-LENGTH GRAPH
FOR
EDGAR ALLAN POE

Suppose you had an essay that you suspected was written by Edgar Allan Poe. To decide whether it was or not, you could draw a frequency/word-length graph for the essay. You would then compare the graph to a frequency/word-length of something you know Edgar Allan Poe has written. Graphs can be compared by placing one on top of the other.

EXERCISE

1. Construct a frequency/word-length graph for a magazine or newspaper article.

2. Construct a frequency/word-length for a sample of your writing.

3. Compare your graph to the one made using the article.

7.14 CHAPTER 7 REVIEW EXERCISE

1. Susan surveyed the members of her class. She asked them to name their favourite type of T.V. show. Complete Susan's summary sheet.

Type of Show	Frequency	Ratio	Percent
Comedy	8		
Mystery	6		
Drama	3		
Police	5		
Western	2		
Other	1		
Total	25		

2. The bar graph shows the average daily high temperature in January for 5 cities.

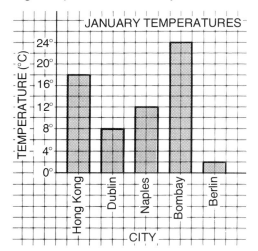

(a) What city has the highest temperature?
(b) What city has the lowest temperature?
(c) What is the difference in temperature between Naples and Dublin?
(d) How much warmer than Berlin is Hong Kong?

3. The table gives the length of each of the Great Lakes.
Display this information on a bar graph.

Lake	Length (km)
Erie	388
Huron	397
Michigan	517
Ontario	311
Superior	616

4. The table gives Babe Ruth's home run totals while playing for the New York Yankees. Display this information on a broken line graph.

Year	Home runs	Year	Home runs
1920	54	1928	54
1921	59	1929	46
1922	35	1930	49
1923	41	1931	46
1924	46	1932	41
1925	25	1933	34
1926	47	1934	22
1927	60		

5. The circle graph shows the make-up of the human body.

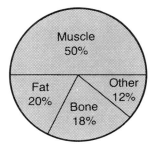

Peter has a mass of 50 kg. What is the mass of each component of Peter's body?

6. The table gives the attendance at Westside's five school dances. Display this information on a pictograph.

Dance	Attendance
Hallowe'en	200
Christmas	250
Valentine	100
Spring Prom	150
Graduation	300

7. Find the mean of each set of numbers.
   (a) 30, 40, 20, 25, 35
   (b) 29, 15, 37, 42, 28, 41
   (c) 128, 115, 144

8. Find the median of each set of numbers.
   (a) 46, 35, 18, 21, 22
   (b) 15, 12, 9, 10, 11, 19, 13, 12, 10
   (c) 75, 79, 72, 70, 74, 80

9. Find the mode of each set of numbers.
   (a) 1, 6, 4, 9, 6, 8, 7, 5
   (b) 14, 13, 12, 13, 14, 15, 14, 13
   (c) 20, 21, 23, 21, 20, 22, 21, 20

10. Find the mean, median, and mode for the following sets of numbers.
    (a) 11, 6, 12, 13, 15, 6, 7
    (b) 14, 17, 27, 21, 19, 16
    (c) 54, 42, 54, 51, 53, 52, 54, 52

11. Draw a tree diagram to show the possible outcomes when a nickel, dime, and quarter are tossed at the same time.

12. A box contains 5 red cubes and 6 blue cubes. If you select one cube from the box, what is the probability that
    (a) the cube is red?
    (b) the cube is blue?

13. Twenty-nine students wrote a math test. The median mark was 81. Paula was the only student to get 81.
    (a) How many students scored higher than Paula?
    (b) How many students scored lower than Paula?

CHAPTER 7 TEST

1. The table gives the number of radios owned by five families. Display this information on a bar graph.

Family	Radios
Miller	3
Wong	5
McDade	6
Florio	4
Adams	7

2. The table gives the temperature in Winnipeg on one spring morning. Display this information on a broken line graph.

Time	Temp.
06:00	8°C
07:00	10°C
08:00	13°C
09:00	13°C
10:00	14°C
11:00	15°C
12:00	14°C

3. The circle graph shows how Melissa McVittie's college expenses for one year are divided. If her expenses for one year are $6000.00, how much does she spend in each category?

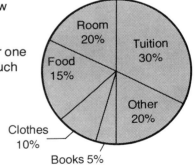

4. Find the mean of the set of numbers.
   26, 35, 42, 39, 73

5. Find the median of the set of numbers.
   26, 34, 41, 31, 52, 43, 36

6. Find the mode of the set of numbers.
   7, 6, 8, 6, 8, 7, 5, 7

7. A bag contains 5 red cubes, 4 blue cubes, and 6 white cubes. If you select one cube from the bag, what is the probability that the cube is blue?

8

ALGEBRA

REVIEW AND PREVIEW TO CHAPTER 8

EXERCISE 1

Simplify.

1. $3 + 5 - 2$
2. $5 \times 3 + 5$
3. $8 \div 2 + 9$
4. $6 + 7 \times 4$
5. $12 - 6 \div 3$
6. $6 \times 3 \div 9$
7. $36 \div 9 \times 2$
8. $0 \times 2 + 5$
9. $4 + 20 \div 5$
10. $18 - 36 \div 9 + 2$
11. $24 - 16 \div 8 - 7$
12. $2 \times 7 - 15 \div 3$

EXERCISE 2

Simplify.

1. $4^2 - 3$
2. $\frac{1}{2}$ of 10
3. $3^2 + 2^3$
4. $\frac{1}{3}$ of 27
5. $4^2 - 2 \times 3$
6. $6 + 5 - 2^2 \times 1$
7. $2^3 + 5 - 1$
8. $8 \div 2^2 - 1 \times 1$
9. $2^2 + 3^2 - 1^3$
10. $6 \times 2^3 - 8 \div 2$
11. $3^2 - 1^3 + 2^3$
12. $4^2 \div 8 - 1$

EXERCISE 3

Simplify.

1. $(5 + 3) \times 2$
2. $20 \div (6 - 1)$
3. $6 \times 3 \div (8 + 1)$
4. $3^2 - (5 - 2)$
5. $24 - 8 \times 2 + 3$
6. $(3 - 1)^2 - 1 + 4$
7. $(8 - 3) + (5 + 4)$
8. $(8 + 4) \div 3 - 1 + 2$
9. $(5 - 4) \times 6 \times 2 \div 4$
10. $(4 - 2)^2 + 5 - 7$

EXERCISE 4

Simplify.

1. $3.3 \times 2 + 4.1$
2. $5(6 + 7)$
3. $\frac{1}{2} \times 4 \times 6$
4. $\frac{1}{2} \times 5.6 \times 4$
5. $6.1(5 - 3)$
6. $8(11 + 13)$
7. $8.4 \div 4 + 5$
8. $5 \times 3.1 - 4 \times 2$
9. $\frac{1}{2} \times 6.8 - 2 - 3$
10. $10 \times 13.4 - 10^2 + 11$

EXERCISE 5

To find the area of a rectangle we use the formula

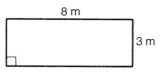

ℓ

w $A = \ell \times w$

Calculate the area of each of the rectangles.

1.

8 m
3 m

2.
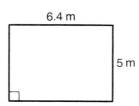
6.4 m
5 m

3.
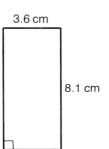
3.6 cm
8.1 cm

4.
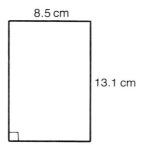
8.5 cm
13.1 cm

EXERCISE 6

Calculate the area of each of the figures.

1.
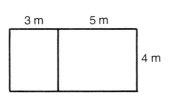
3 m   5 m
4 m

2.
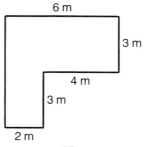
6 m
3 m
4 m
3 m
2 m

3.
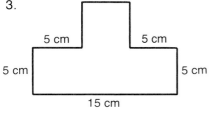
5 cm
5 cm   5 cm
5 cm   5 cm
15 cm

4.
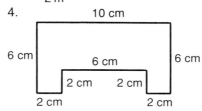
10 cm
6 cm   6 cm   6 cm
2 cm   2 cm
2 cm   2 cm

8.1 VARIABLES AND EXPRESSIONS

Algebra is a branch of mathematics. It uses letters and numbers to solve problems.

Imagine a machine that adds 7 to every number you put into it.

Suppose you put in 8.

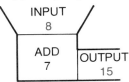

Suppose you put in 20.

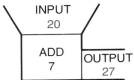

For every Input there is an Output. We can draw one picture for all the possibilities. We will use a letter for the INPUT.

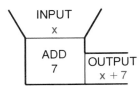

INPUT	OUTPUT
8	15
20	27
31	38
x	x + 7

When we use a letter to represent a number we call the letter a variable.

We call x + 7 an algebraic expression.

An algebraic expression is some combination of variables and numbers.

We often have to evaluate algebraic expressions.

Example 1. Evaluate $5n + 4$ for $n = 3$.

5n means the same as 5 × n

Solution: $5n + 4 = 5(3) + 4$
$$= 15 + 4$$
$$= 19$$

Example 2. Evaluate $7x - 1$ for $x \in \{2, 3, 4\}$.

Solution: When $x = 2$, $\quad 7x - 1 = 7(2) - 1$
$$= 14 - 1$$
$$= 13$$

When $x = 3$, $\quad 7x - 1 = 7(3) - 1$
$$= 21 - 1$$
$$= 20$$

When $x = 4$, $\quad 7x - 1 = 7(4) - 1$
$$= 28 - 1$$
$$= 27$$

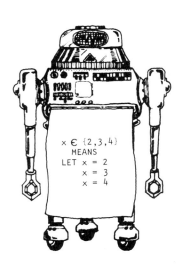

$x \in \{2,3,4\}$
MEANS
LET x = 2
x = 3
x = 4

EXERCISE

A

1. If x = 8, find the value of each expression.
   - (a) x + 9
   - (b) x − 3
   - (c) 15 − x
   - (d) 3x
   - (e) x ÷ 2
   - (f) 4x − 1

B

2. Complete the table for the machine shown.

(a)

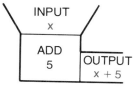

INPUT x	OUTPUT x + 5
3	
9	
15	
21	

(b)

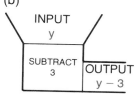

INPUT y	OUTPUT y − 3
7	
12	
16	
31	

(c)

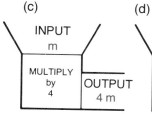

INPUT m	OUTPUT 4m
3	
7	
8	
0	

(d)

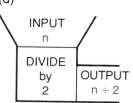

INPUT n	OUTPUT n ÷ 2
6	
14	
18	
30	

3. If m = 15, find the value of each expression.
   - (a) m − 12
   - (b) 24 − m
   - (c) 2m
   - (d) m ÷ 5
   - (e) 2m − 7
   - (f) 1 + 3m

4. If k = 6, find the value of each expression.
   - (a) 7k
   - (b) 30 ÷ k
   - (c) k + 14
   - (d) 4k + 5
   - (e) 3k − 4
   - (f) 18 − k

5. If y = 20, find the value of each expression.
   - (a) y − 7
   - (b) y ÷ 10
   - (c) 15 + y
   - (d) 3y + 14
   - (e) 2y − 7
   - (f) 10y

6. If x = 5 and y = 7, find the value of each expression.
   - (a) x + y
   - (b) y − x
   - (c) 2x + 3y
   - (d) 5y − 1 − 24
   - (e) 3x + 1
   - (f) 45 ÷ x

7. Evaluate 4x for x ∈ {1, 2, 3, 4}.

8. Evaluate 3y + 4 for y ∈ {2, 5, 7, 9}.

9. Evaluate 5m − 3 for m ∈ {1, 6, 9, 11}.

10. Evaluate 20 − n for n ∈ {0, 3, 8, 20}.

11. Evaluate 5 + 6x for x ∈ {9, 13, 24}.

12. Complete the following tables.

(a)

INPUT x	OUTPUT x + 9
21	
	18
	23
	34

(b)

INPUT y	OUTPUT y − 3
9	
	6
	11
	14

(c)

INPUT m	OUTPUT 3m
5	
	18
	24
	36

(d)

INPUT n	OUTPUT n ÷ 3
6	
	4
	1
	3

8.2 FACTORS AND EXPONENTS

When two or more numbers are multiplied, each of the numbers is a factor of the product.

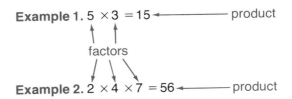

Example 1. $5 \times 3 = 15 \longleftarrow$ product

factors

Example 2. $2 \times 4 \times 7 = 56 \longleftarrow$ product

Exponents are used to write the product of factors that are the same.

$$9 = 3 \times 3 = 3^2 \longleftarrow \left(\begin{array}{l}\text{The 2 tells us that there} \\ \text{are 2 equal factors.}\end{array}\right.$$

$$125 = 5 \times 5 \times 5 = 5^3 \longleftarrow \left(\begin{array}{l}\text{The 3 tells us that there} \\ \text{are 3 equal factors.}\end{array}\right.$$

Exponent
$$5^3 = 125$$
Base

125 and 5^3 are both called the third power of 3.

The following illustrates the first three powers of 4.

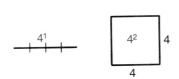

First Power: $4 = 4^1$
Second Power: $16 = 4^2$
Third Power: $64 = 4^3$

Exponents can also be used with variables.

Exponential Form
$$x^3 = x \times x \times x$$
$$2y^2 = 2 \times y \times y$$
$$m^3n^2 = m \times m \times m \times n \times n$$
Factored Form

Example 1. If $x = 4$, evaluate $3x^2$.

Solution: $3x^2 = 3(4)^2$
$= 3 \times 4 \times 4$
$= 48$

Example 2. If m $= 2$, evaluate $2m^3 + 7$.

Solution: $2m^3 + 7 = 2(2)^3 + 7$
$\qquad\qquad\quad = 2(8) + 7$
$\qquad\qquad\quad = 16 + 7$
$\qquad\qquad\quad = 23$

EXERCISE

A

1. Find the value of each.
   (a) 3^2 (b) 5^2
   (c) 6^2 (d) 7^1
   (e) 2^3 (f) 5^3
   (g) 10^2 (h) 2^4
   (i) 5^3 (j) 10^3
   (k) 3^4 (l) 3^5

2. Write in exponential form.

   $2 \times 2 \times 2 \times 2 = 2^4$

   (a) $3 \times 3 \times 3$
   (b) $4 \times 4 \times 4 \times 4 \times 4$
   (c) $y \times y \times y \times y$
   (d) $m \times m$
   (e) $2 \times x \times x \times x$
   (f) $r \times r \times s \times s \times s$
   (g) $6 \times y \times y \times y \times y \times z \times z$

B

3. Evaluate.
   (a) $2^2 + 5$ (b) $3^2 + 9$
   (c) $5^2 - 1^3$ (d) $2^5 + 6$
   (e) $3^3 + 2^2$ (f) $4^3 - 5^2$

4. Write each in factored form.

   $m^3 = m \times m \times m$

   (a) 2^3 (b) x^2
   (c) y^4 (d) x^3y^2
   (e) $2n^4$ (f) $3xy^4$
   (g) $5m^3n^3$ (h) $8a^3b^2c$

5. If $x = 2$, evaluate each expression.
   (a) x^4 (b) x^5
   (c) $4x^2$ (d) $5x^3$
   (e) $x^2 + 3$ (f) $x^3 - 1$
   (g) $2x^2 + 4$ (h) $3x^2 - 4$
   (i) $x^2 + x$ (j) $x^3 - x$

6. Evaluate $x^2 + 1$ for $x \in \{1, 2, 3, 4\}$.

7. Evaluate $2x^3 - 1$ for $x \in \{1, 2, 3\}$.

8. If $x = 3$ and $y = 2$, evaluate each expression.
   (a) $2x + 3y$ (b) $x^2 + y^2$
   (c) $x^2 - y^2$ (d) $x^3 - y$
   (e) $2x^2 + 3y^2$ (f) $4xy - 1$
   (g) $2x^2y - xy$ (h) $x^2y^2 - 4$

9. Complete the following tables.

   (a)

INPUT x	OUTPUT $x^2 + 1$
2	
3	
5	
8	

   (b)

INPUT y	OUTPUT $y^2 - 2$
3	
4	
6	
7	

10. Draw a diagram to illustrate 3^2.

11. Draw a diagram to illustrate 5^3.

12. $(2x)^2$ means $2x \times 2x$. Write each of these in factored form.
    (a) $(3x)^2$ (b) $(4y)^2$
    (c) $(2xy)^2$ (d) $(5x^2y)^2$

CHALLENGE

What does the following say?

8.3 FLOW CHARTS AND EXPRESSIONS

Flow charts with loops help evaluate expressions. The following flow chart evaluates $3x + 4$ for $x \in \{1, 2, 3\}$.

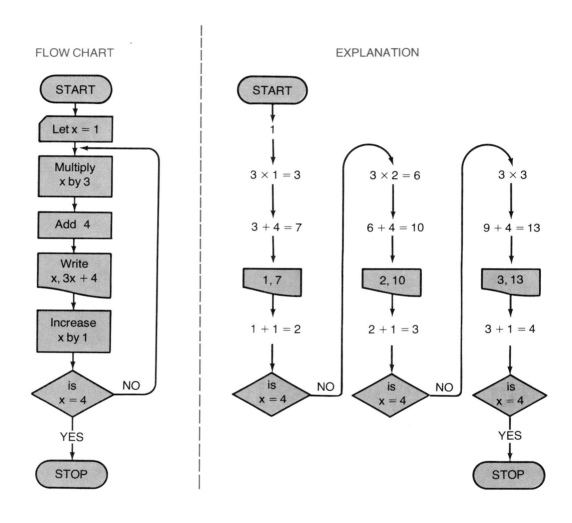

FLOW CHART

EXPLANATION

The output for this flow chart is:

1, 7
2, 10
3, 13

EXERCISE

B

1. Determine the output of each of the
   following flow charts.

(a)

(b)

(c)

(d)

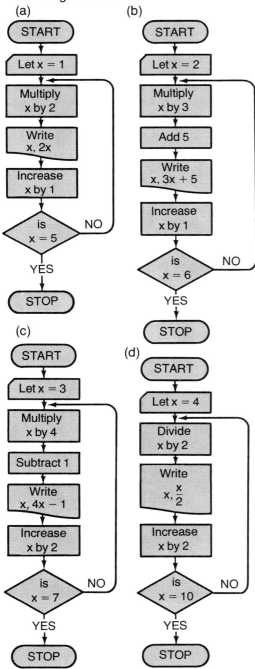

2. Determine the output of each of the
   following flow charts.

(a)

(b)

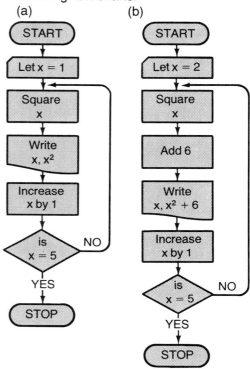

CHALLENGE

Place the numbers from 1 to 11 in the
circles so that each line adds to 18.

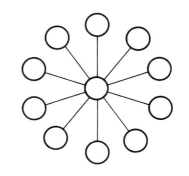

8.4 INTEGERS IN ALGEBRA

In many algebraic expressions, integers are substituted for variables

Example 1. If $x = -2$, evaluate $3x + 7$.

Solution: $3x + 7 = 3(-2) + 7$
$$= -6 + 7$$
$$= 1$$

Example 2. If $y = -3$, evaluate $7 - y$.

Solution: $7 - y = 7 - (-3)$
$$= 7 + 3$$
$$= 10$$

Example 3. If $m = -4$, evaluate $3m^2 - 1$.

Solution: $3m^2 - 1 = 3(-4)^2 - 1$
$$= 3(16) - 1$$
$$= 48 - 1$$
$$= 47$$

Example 4. If $x = -2$ and $y = 3$, evaluate $2xy - x$.

Solution: $2xy - x = 2(-2)(3) - (-2)$
$$= -12 + 2$$
$$= -10$$

Example 5. If $m = -2$ and $n = -1$, evaluate $2m^3 - n^2$.

Solution: $2m^3 - n^2 = 2(-2)^3 - (-1)^2$
$$= 2(-8) - (+1)$$
$$= -16 - 1$$
$$= -17$$

EXERCISE

A

1. If $x = -1$, evaluate
   - (a) $3x$
   - (b) $4x$
   - (c) $-2x$
   - (d) $-6x$
   - (e) $-x$
   - (f) $10x$

B

2. If $x = -3$, evaluate
   - (a) $3x + 1$
   - (b) $4x + 5$
   - (c) $2x - 3$
   - (d) $6x - 7$
   - (e) $4 + 5x$
   - (f) $1 + 3x$
   - (g) $7 - 2x$
   - (h) $8 - x$

3. If $m = -2$, evaluate
   - (a) m^2
   - (b) $2m^2$
   - (c) m^3
   - (d) $3m^2$
   - (e) $-m^2$
   - (f) $-2m^3$

4. If $y = -3$, evaluate
   - (a) $y^2 + 1$
   - (b) $y^2 - 4$
   - (c) $2y^2 + 3$
   - (d) $2y^3 + 6$
   - (e) $4 - 2y^2$
   - (f) $5 - y^3$

5. If $m = -1$ and $n = -2$, evaluate
   - (a) $3mn$
   - (b) $4mn$
   - (c) $2m + 3n$
   - (d) $m + n$
   - (e) $m - n$
   - (f) $n - m$
   - (g) $2m - 3n + 6$
   - (h) $2mn - 3$

6. If $x = -2$ and $y = 2$, evaluate
   - (a) $x + y$
   - (b) $x - y$
   - (c) $y - x$
   - (d) $2xy + 1$
   - (e) $x^2 + y^2$
   - (f) $3xy - 4$
   - (g) $2x^2 + 4$
   - (h) $3y^2 - x$

ΠΙΙCRO ΠΙΑΤΗ

This program evaluates expressions in one variable.

Type in the integer values of X for which you wish to evaluate the expression in statement 20 using BASIC computer language.

Type in the expression you want to evaluate in place of $3*X*(X+2)$ in statement 30 using BASIC computer language.

NEW

```
10 PRINT" X","EXPRESSION"
20 FOR X = a TO b
30 LET Y=(expression)
40 PRINT X,Y
50 NEXT X
60 END
```

RUN

Example. Evaluate $3X(X + 2)$, for
$$X \in \{-3, -2, -1, 0, 1, 2, 3, 4\}$$

Solution: In BASIC, $3X(X + 2)$ is
$$3*X*(X+2)$$

NEW

```
10 PRINT" X","EXPRESSION"
20 FOR X = -3 TO 4
30 LET Y=3*X*(X+2)
40 PRINT X,Y
50 NEXT X
60 END
```

RUN

X	EXPRESSION
-3	9
-2	0
-1	-3
0	0
1	9
2	24
3	45
4	72

Evaluate these expressions for the given values of X.

1. $X + 3$, for $X \in \{1, 2, 3, 4, 5\}$

2. $3(5X + 1)$ for $X \in \{1, 2, 3, 4, 5\}$

3. $X^2 - 5$ for $X \in \{-2, -1, 0, 1, 2, 3\}$

4. $X^2 + 3X + 9$ for
   $X \in \{-4, -3, -2, -1, 0, 1, 2, 3\}$

8.5 ADDING LIKE TERMS

A term is a mathematical expression using numbers, or variables, or both, to indicate a product or a quotient. The following are examples of terms.

$$2x \qquad 4xy \qquad 2x^2y$$

In expressions, terms are separated by $+$ and $-$ signs. Some expressions are given special names.

For example,

one term:	$3x \longleftarrow$	a monomial
two terms:	$2x^2 + 5 \longleftarrow$	a binomial
three terms:	$3xy + 7x - 5y \longleftarrow$	a trinomial

Polynomial is the general name for such mathematical expressions.

> A term is made up of two parts:
> a numerical coefficient and a literal coefficient.
>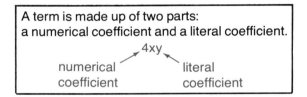
> numerical coefficient   literal coefficient

The expression $4x + 3x$ can be simplified as follows:

4x means x + x + x + x
3x means x + x + x

$$4x + 3x = \overbrace{x + x + x + x}^{4x} + \overbrace{x + x + x}^{3x}$$
$$\underbrace{\qquad\qquad\qquad\qquad}_{7x}$$
$$= 7x$$

Terms such as 4x and 3x are called like terms. Like terms have the same literal coefficients.

The expression $3m + 2x$ cannot be simplified because the literal coefficients are different. The terms are unlike.

$$3m + 2x = \overbrace{m + m + m}^{3m} + \overbrace{x + x}^{2x}$$
$$= 3m + 2x$$

Example. Simplify $5x - 3y + 4x - y + 5$

Solution: $5x - 3y + 4x - y + 5 = 5x + 4x - 3y - y + 5$
$$= 9x - 4y + 5$$

You can also add polynomials in a vertical form.

$$\begin{array}{r} 3x^2 - 4x - 7 \\ + 4x^2 + 3x - 3 \\ \hline 7x^2 - x - 10 \end{array}$$

EXERCISE

A

1. Is the expression a monomial, binomial, or trinomial?
   (a) $2x + 3y$
   (b) $6x$
   (c) $x + y + 4$
   (d) 8
   (e) $2x^2 + 3y^2$
   (f) $x^2 + 2x + 1$

2. State whether the terms are like or unlike.
   (a) $3x, 4x$
   (b) $3y, 5x$
   (c) $9, 2a$
   (d) $3x^2, -4x^2$
   (e) $-9m, -3m$
   (f) $2x^2, 3x$
   (g) $-2y^3, -3y^2$
   (h) $5xy, xy$
   (i) $2x^2, 3$
   (j) $x, -6x$

3. Add.
   (a) $4x$
      $7x$
   (b) $6ab$
      $3ab$

   (c) $-5a$
      $6a$
   (d) $3x^2$
      $-7x^2$

   (e) $-7y$
      $-5y$
   (f) $-4xy$
      $-8xy$

B

4. Simplify.
   (a) $3x + 5x$
   (b) $7a + 9a$
   (c) $9m + 6m$
   (d) $8y + y$
   (e) $13x + 8x$
   (f) $2y + 4y + 5y$
   (g) $6a + a + 8a$
   (h) $2x^2 + 3x^2 + 5x^2$
   (i) $2y^2 + y^2 + 4y^2$
   (j) $3t + 9t + t$

5. Simplify.
   (a) $5x - 3x$
   (b) $4a - a$
   (c) $10y - 6y$
   (d) $13t - 8t$
   (e) $9x^2 - 2x^2$
   (f) $15y^2 - y^2$

6. Simplify.
   (a) $6x + 3x - 2x$
   (b) $9y + 4y - 7y$
   (c) $8t - 5t + 3t$
   (d) $11a - 6a + 3a$
   (e) $9x^2 - 4x^2 + 3x^2$
   (f) $15y^2 + 2y^2 - 7y^2$

7. Simplify.
   (a) $-2x + 3x$
   (b) $-7t + 3t$
   (c) $9a - 4a$
   (d) $3y - 5y$
   (e) $6x - 9x$
   (f) $x - 8x$
   (g) $-2x - 6x$
   (h) $-9b - 7b$
   (i) $-3x^2 - 8x^2$
   (j) $5x - 4x - 3x$
   (k) $-2y - 3y - y$
   (l) $4a - 8a + a$

8. Simplify.
   (a) $3x + 2x + 6y$
   (b) $4a + 3a + 7b + 2b$
   (c) $6s + 5s + 7t - 2t$
   (d) $9x - 3x + 4y - y$

9. Simplify.
   (a) $4x - 6x + 2y - 3y$
   (b) $6a - 7a - 2b + 4b$
   (c) $7s - 4s - 3t - 2t$
   (d) $-2x + 3y - 4x + 6y$
   (e) $-4x^2 + 5 + 3x^2 + 2$

10. Simplify.
    (a) $2x^2 + 3x - 4 + 5x^2 + 6x + 7$
    (b) $y^2 - 3y + 4y - 6y^2 + 7 - 2$
    (c) $4a - 3b - 4 - 6a - 8b + 1$
    (d) $-x - y - 1 - x - y - 3$
    (e) $5t - 4 - s + 3s - 6t - 4s$
    (f) $-2x - 3x + 7 - 4x - 11$
    (g) $-3 + 6a - 2b - 8a - 4b - 6b$

11. Add.
    (a) $3x + 2y$
       $4x + 5y$
    (b) $3a + 2b + 6$
       $4a - 5b + 7$

    (c) $x^2 - 3x + 4$
       $-2x^2 - 4x - 6$
    (d) $-6s - 4t - 8$
       $-3s - 8t - 3$

    (e) $-2y^2 - 3y - 5$
       $4y^2 - 6y + 6$
    (f) $3a - 2b - 1$
       $-a - b - 3$

8.6 VERTICAL SUBTRACTION

When you subtract, you add the opposite.

$$6 - (-9) = 6 + 9$$
$$= 15$$

The same rule applies when subtracting expressions.

Example 1. Subtract. $3x + 7$
                            $x - 2$

Solution:

$3x + 7$ Rewrite $3x + 7$
$x - 2$ and add. $-x + 2$
                       $2x + 9$

Example 2. Subtract. $4a^2 - 3a - 1$
                           $6a^2 - 5a + 3$

Solution: $4a^2 - 3a - 1$ Rewrite $4a^2 - 3a - 1$
             $6a^2 - 5a + 3$ and add. $-6a^2 + 5a - 3$
                                           $-2a^2 + 2a - 4$

EXERCISE

A

1. Name the opposite.

(a) 6   (b) 11
(c) −5   (d) −14
(e) 9   (f) −16
(g) 2x   (h) −3b
(i) $4x^2$ (j) $-7y^2$
(k) −3xy   (l) 2t
(m) 2x + 2y   (n) x + 7
(o) x − 9   (p) $2x^2 - 1$
(q) −3x − 4   (r) $-2x^2 - 3x - 1$
(s) 5x − 2y − 7   (t) 2m + 3n − 5

B

2. Subtract.

(a) 4x + 7y   (b) 5a + 3b
    2x + 3y   2a + b

(c) 7s + 5t   (d) $5x^2 + 7$
    6s + t $3x^2 + 7$

(e) $6x^2 + 5x + 7$ (f) 4a + 3b + 6
    $2x^2 + 5x + 6$ 2a + 2b + 2

3. Subtract.

(a) $\begin{array}{r} 3x + 5y \\ 2x - 2y \\ \hline \end{array}$

(b) $\begin{array}{r} 9x^2 + 6 \\ 3x^2 - 4 \\ \hline \end{array}$

(c) $\begin{array}{r} 6a + 3b \\ 4a - 4b \\ \hline \end{array}$

(d) $\begin{array}{r} 2x^2 + 7 \\ x^2 - 8 \\ \hline \end{array}$

(e) $\begin{array}{r} 9s + 6t \\ 9s - \ \ t \\ \hline \end{array}$

(f) $\begin{array}{r} 2x^2 + 7x + 6 \\ x^2 - 3x - 4 \\ \hline \end{array}$

(g) $\begin{array}{r} 3a + 4b \\ -2a - 3b \\ \hline \end{array}$

(h) $\begin{array}{r} 2x + 7y + 4 \\ -3x - 6y + 4 \\ \hline \end{array}$

4. Subtract.

(a) $\begin{array}{r} 7x - 3y \\ 4x + 2y \\ \hline \end{array}$

(b) $\begin{array}{r} 8a - 2b \\ 6a + 3b \\ \hline \end{array}$

(c) $\begin{array}{r} 6x^2 - 2 \\ 3x^2 + 5 \\ \hline \end{array}$

(d) $\begin{array}{r} 7s - 4t \\ -9s - 4t \\ \hline \end{array}$

(e) $\begin{array}{r} 5x - \ \ y \\ 6x - 7y \\ \hline \end{array}$

(f) $\begin{array}{r} 3x^2 - \ \ x - 5 \\ 2x^2 - 4x + 7 \\ \hline \end{array}$

(g) $\begin{array}{r} -4a - 3b \\ 6a - 5b \\ \hline \end{array}$

(h) $\begin{array}{r} -y^2 - 3y + 4 \\ 2y^2 - 6y - 2 \\ \hline \end{array}$

(i) $\begin{array}{r} -x^2 - 7x + 6 \\ -3x^2 + 2x - 5 \\ \hline \end{array}$

(j) $\begin{array}{r} -2a - 3b - 7 \\ a - 4b + 6 \\ \hline \end{array}$

(k) $\begin{array}{r} -3x - 3y - 4 \\ -7x - 5y - 2 \\ \hline \end{array}$

(l) $\begin{array}{r} x^2 + 2xy + y^2 \\ -x^2 - xy - 2y^2 \\ \hline \end{array}$

(m) $\begin{array}{r} -3a - 4b - 9 \\ 2a + 5b + 4 \\ \hline \end{array}$

(n) $\begin{array}{r} s + t - 1 \\ -s + t + 1 \\ \hline \end{array}$

(o) $\begin{array}{r} -x - y - 1 \\ -x - y - 1 \\ \hline \end{array}$

(p) $\begin{array}{r} a - 2b - c \\ 4a - 2b + c \\ \hline \end{array}$

5. Subtract.

(a) $\begin{array}{r} 3a + 2b \\ 4a \\ \hline \end{array}$

(b) $\begin{array}{r} 5x \\ 6x - 2y \\ \hline \end{array}$

(c) $\begin{array}{r} 5x^2 \\ -2x^2 - x + 3 \\ \hline \end{array}$

(d) $\begin{array}{r} -2x^2 \ \ \ \ \ \ -2 \\ x^2 - 3x + 4 \\ \hline \end{array}$

(e) $\begin{array}{r} 0 \\ 5a - 3b \\ \hline \end{array}$

(f) $\begin{array}{r} 0 \\ -x^2 - 3x + 7 \\ \hline \end{array}$

CHALLENGE

The triangular numbers are
$1, 3, 6, 10, \ldots$

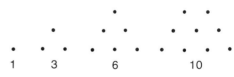

The square numbers are $1, 4, 9, 16, \ldots$

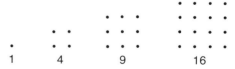

3 and 6 are consecutive triangular numbers. When you add them you get a square number.

$$3 + 6 = 9$$

Find eight other square numbers that can be written as the sum of two consecutive triangular numbers.

8.7 THE DISTRIBUTIVE PROPERTY

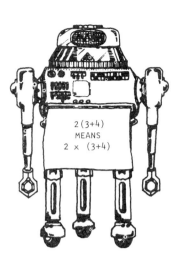

The expression $2(3+4)$ can be simplified as follows.

$$2(3+4) = 2(7)$$
$$= 14$$

We can also simplify by expanding.

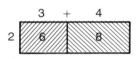

$$2(3+4) = 2(3+4)$$
$$= 2 \times 3 + 2 \times 4$$
$$= 6 + 8$$
$$= 14$$

The above illustrates the distributive property.
$$2(3+4) = 2 \times 3 + 2 \times 4$$

We use the distributive property to simplify expressions with brackets.

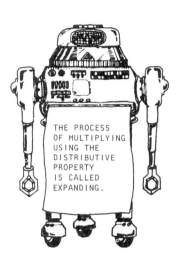

Example 1. Expand. $2(x+3)$

Solution: "Expand" means "remove the brackets and simplify."

$$2(x+3) = 2(x+3)$$
$$= 2 \times x + 2 \times 3$$
$$= 2x + 6$$

Example 2. Expand. $3(2a - 3b - 4)$

Solution: $3(2a - 3b - 4) = 3(2a - 3b - 4)$
$$= 3 \times 2a - 3 \times 3b - 3 \times 4$$
$$= 6a - 9b - 12$$

Example 3. Expand and simplify. $-3(x+4) - (x-7)$

Solution: $-3(x+4) - (x-7) = -3(x+4) - 1(x-7)$
$$= -3(x+4) - 1(x-7)$$
$$= -3x - 12 - x + 7$$
$$= -4x - 5$$

EXERCISE

A

1. Expand.
    (a) $2(x + 4)$
    (b) $3(y + 5)$
    (c) $5(t + 3)$
    (d) $4(m + 6)$
    (e) $3(x - 4)$
    (f) $2(t - 5)$

2. Expand.
    (a) $3(2x + 3)$
    (b) $4(3y + 5)$
    (c) $5(2a + 4b)$
    (d) $2(3x - 2y)$
    (e) $4(6a - b)$
    (f) $1(2a + 3b - 4)$
    (g) $5(2x - 3y - 1)$
    (h) $7(x^2 - 2x - 1)$

B

3. Expand.
    (a) $-2(x + 3)$
    (b) $-3(a + 4)$
    (c) $-4(y - 2)$
    (d) $-2(x - 7)$
    (e) $-(t - 4)$
    (f) $-7(x - 3)$

4. Expand.
    (a) $-2(2a + 3)$
    (b) $-3(3x - 4)$
    (c) $-(2x - 3y)$
    (d) $-4(5a - 2b)$
    (e) $-2(x^2 + 3x - 1)$
    (f) $-(y^2 - 2y + 4)$
    (g) $-4(1 - 2a + a^2)$
    (h) $-(x - y - 5)$
    (i) $-10(1 - 2x - x^2)$

5. Expand and simplify.
    (a) $2(x + 3) + 3(x + 2)$
    (b) $4(a + 2) + 5(a + 1)$
    (c) $3(t - 1) + 4(t - 2)$
    (d) $2(x - y) + 3(x + y)$
    (e) $3(b - 4) - (b + 2)$
    (f) $-2(x + 6) - (x - 4)$

6. Expand and simplify.
    (a) $2(2x - 1) + 3(3x - 2)$
    (b) $4(2t + 3) + 2(t - 3)$
    (c) $6(2y - 3) - (4y - 2)$
    (d) $2(x + y - 2) - 2(x - y)$

7. Expand and simplify.
    (a) $2(x^2 - 2x - 1) - (x^2 - 2)$
    (b) $3(t^2 + t + 4) - 3t + 5$
    (c) $4(y^2 - 3) - (y - 4) + 2$
    (d) $-(2a - 3b) - 3a + 4$
    (e) $-3(2x - y) - 4x - 6y$
    (f) $-(x - y) - (y + x) - 4$

C

8. Expand and simplify.
    (a) $2(2a - b - 1) - 3(3a + 2b - 5)$
    (b) $3(x^2 - x - 4) - (2x^2 - x + 4)$
    (c) $-2(x^2 - y^2) - x^2 - 2(x^2 - y^2)$
    (d) $-(t^2 - 4t + 1) - (3t^2 - t - 4)$
    (e) $2(x^2 + x - 5) - 2x^2 - 3$
    (f) $4 - 2(x - 3y) - 4x$

9. Expand.
    (a) $P = 2(\ell + w)$

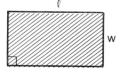

    (b) $A = \pi(R^2 - r^2)$

8.8 MULTIPLICATION OF MONOMIALS

When we add two unlike terms such as x and y, we write the sum as

$$x + y \quad \text{or} \quad y + x$$

The product of these two terms, $x \times y$, is written as

$$x \times y = xy \quad \text{or} \quad yx$$

Monomials are multiplied in the following manner.

$$3x \times 2y = 3 \times x \times 2 \times y$$
$$= 3 \times 2 \times x \times y$$
$$= 6xy$$

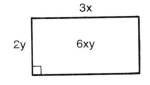

$$A = 3x \times 2y$$
$$= 6xy$$

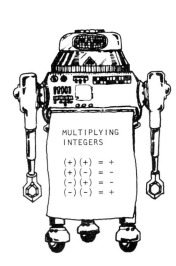

MULTIPLYING INTEGERS

(+) (+) = +
(+) (−) = −
(−) (+) = −
(−) (−) = +

Example 1. Multiply. $4a^2b \times 3c$

Solution: $4a^2b \times 3c = 4 \times a^2 \times b \times 3 \times c$
$$= 4 \times 3 \times a^2 \times b \times c$$
$$= 12a^2bc$$

Example 2. Multiply. $(-2x^2)(5y^2z)$

Solution: $(-2x^2)(5y^2z) = (-2x^2) \times (5y^2z)$
$$= -2 \times x^2 \times 5 \times y^2 \times z$$
$$= -2 \times 5 \times x^2 \times y^2 \times z$$
$$= -10x^2y^2z$$

Example 3. Multiply. $-4a^2(-6bc)$

Solution: $-4a^2(-6bc) = -4a^2 \times (-6bc)$
$$= -4 \times -6 \times a^2 \times b \times c$$
$$= 24a^2bc$$

EXERCISE

A

1. Multiply.
   (a) $2x \times 4y$
   (b) $4a \times 3b$
   (c) $6r \times 2s$
   (d) $7 \times 3m$
   (e) $8r \times 6t$
   (f) $2a^2 \times 5b^2$
   (g) $2m^2 \times 2n$
   (h) $3 \times 4r^2$
   (i) $5a^2b \times 4c$
   (j) $8 \times 9b$
   (k) $7a \times 3b$

B

2. Multiply.
   (a) $(4x)(3y)$
   (b) $(2a)(6b)$
   (c) $(3x^2)(2y^2)$
   (d) $(10ab)(4c)$
   (e) $(-3x)(2y)$
   (f) $(-5a)(4b)$
   (g) $(-7x^2)(-2y^2)$
   (h) $(4a)(-4b)$
   (i) $(6xy)(-3z)$
   (j) $(-2m)(-7n)$

3. Multiply.
   (a) $(-2x^2)(-4y^2)$
   (b) $(-5t^2)(-3s)$
   (c) $(3ab)(-6c^2)$
   (d) $(-6x^2)(5y^2)$
   (e) $(4xy)(4z)$
   (f) $(-10a^2)(3b^2)$
   (g) $(7rst)(-2y)$

4. Multiply.
   (a) $2a^2(2b)$
   (b) $3xy(-4z)$
   (c) $-3x(-5y)$
   (d) $-5t^2(-2s)$
   (e) $9s^2(-3t)$
   (f) $-4ab(5c^2)$

5. Multiply.
   (a) $(2a)(3b)(4c)$
   (b) $(4x)(-2y)(5z)$
   (c) $(-2m)(3n)(-2t)$
   (d) $(-3a^2)(-b^2)(-2c^2)$
   (e) $(-2xy)(-3z)(-4t)$
   (f) $(5a)(-2b)(-2c)$
   (g) $(-6r)(-2s)(2t)$

CHALLENGE

How many different combinations of coins have a value of $0.28? Complete this table to find out.

COIN	$0.25	$0.10	$0.05	$0.01
Combinations	1	0	0	3
	0	1	2	8
and so on				

8.9 EXPONENT RULE FOR MULTIPLICATION

To simplify $x^2 \times x^3$ we proceed as follows.

$$x^2 = x \times x$$
$$x^3 = x \times x \times x$$

Therefore,

$$x^2 \times x^3 = \overbrace{x \times x}^{\text{2 factors}} \times \overbrace{x \times x \times x}^{\text{3 factors}}$$
$$\underbrace{}_{\text{5 factors}}$$
$$= x \times x \times x \times x \times x$$
$$= x^5$$

Similarly, $w^5 \times w^3 = \overbrace{w \times w \times w \times w \times w}^{\text{5 factors}} \times \overbrace{w \times w \times w}^{\text{3 factors}}$
$$\underbrace{}_{\text{8 factors}}$$
$$= w^{5+3}$$
$$= w^8$$

When multiplying, if the bases are the same, add the exponents.

Exponent Rule for Multiplication

$$x^a \times x^b = x^{a+b}$$

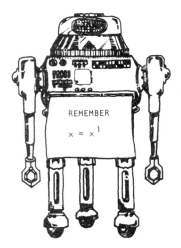

REMEMBER

$x = x^1$

Example 1. Multiply. $7w^3 \times 2w^2$

Solution: $7w^3 \times 2w^2 = 7 \times w^3 \times 2 \times w^2$
$$= 7 \times 2 \times w^3 \times w^2$$
$$= 14 \times w^{3+2}$$
$$= 14w^5$$

Example 2. Simplify. $(-3x^2y^3)(4xy^2)$

Solution: $(-3x^2y^3)(4xy^2) = (-3x^2y^3) \times 4xy^2$
$$= (-3) \times 4 \times x^2 \times x \times y^3 \times y^2$$
$$= -12x^3y^5$$

Example 3. Simplify. $(-5abc)(-3a^2b)$

Solution: $(-5abc)(-3a^2b) = -5abc \times (-3a^2b)$
$$= -5 \times (-3) \times a \times a^2 \times b \times b \times c$$
$$= 15a^3b^2c$$

Example 4. Simplify. $(2x^3)(5x^2)(-4x)$

Solution: $(2x^3)(5x^2)(-4x) = 2x^3 \times 5x^2 \times (-4x)$
$$= 2 \times 5 \times (-4) \times x^3 \times x^2 \times x$$
$$= -40x^6$$

EXERCISE

A

1. Multiply.
   (a) $x^5 \times x^2$
   (b) $a^3 \times a^3$
   (c) $b^2 \times b$
   (d) $y \times y^4$
   (e) $m^6 \times m^7$
   (f) $r \times r^4$
   (g) $t^3 \times t^4$
   (h) $c^2 \times c^2$

2. Multiply.
   (a) $x^2 \times x^3 \times x^2$
   (b) $a^2 \times a^3 \times a^3$
   (c) $t^2 \times t \times t^4$
   (d) $m \times m \times m$
   (e) $y \times y^2 \times y$
   (f) $w^2 \times w^3 \times w^4$
   (g) $b^2 \times b \times b^2$
   (h) $s \times s^2 \times s^4$

B

3. Multiply.
   (a) $x^2 \times x^3 \times y^2$
   (b) $m^2 \times m^3 \times n \times n^2$
   (c) $w^3 \times x \times w^4 \times x^3$
   (d) $a^3 \times b^2 \times b \times a^4$
   (e) $r^2 \times s \times s \times r^2$
   (f) $x \times x^2 \times x \times y^2$
   (g) $s^2 \times s^4 \times t \times t^5$
   (h) $x^3 \times y \times y \times y^4$

4. Multiply.
   (a) $7x^2 \times 2x^3$
   (b) $5t^3 \times 3t^4$
   (c) $6a^2 \times 5a$
   (d) $4m \times m^3 \times 3$
   (e) $8y^2 \times 3y^3 \times 2$
   (f) $2t \times 4t^3 \times t$
   (g) $3x^2 \times 2x^2 \times x^3$
   (h) $5m^2 \times 6m^3 \times 2m$

5. Multiply.
   (a) $6x^2 \times 2x \times 3y^2$
   (b) $2a^2 \times b^3 \times 3b^3$
   (c) $4r^2 \times 3s \times 2r^3$
   (d) $5t \times 4s \times s^4$
   (e) $6 \times x^2 \times x^3 \times 3$

6. Multiply.
   (a) $(-2x^2)(3x)$
   (b) $(-5t^3)(-2t)$
   (c) $(4y^4)(-3y^2)$
   (d) $(-2m)(-6m^5)$
   (e) $(-5a)(-3a^3)$
   (f) $(-7y^5)(2y^2)$

7. Multiply.
   (a) $(2a^2b^2)(3a^3b^3)$
   (b) $(-4x^2y)(-2xy^2)$
   (c) $(5rs^3)(-3r^2s^4)$
   (d) $(-8a^2b^3)(2a^3b^2)$
   (e) $(-6abc^2)(abc)$
   (f) $(-2rst^2)(3r^2s)$
   (g) $(7a^2b^2c^2)(-2a^3)$
   (h) $(-10x^2)(-10xy^2)$

8. Multiply.
   (a) $(2x)(-3x)(-3x^2)$
   (b) $(2a^2b)(2ab)(-3ab)$
   (c) $(-4st)(-2t^2)(-3s^2)$
   (d) $(5xy)(-2x^2)(-3y^2)$
   (e) $(2t^2)(-3s)(4st)$
   (f) $(6x^2y)(-x^2)(-y^2)$
   (g) $(-3xy)(-xy)(xy)$

8.10 DIVISION OF MONOMIALS

Division is often shown as a fraction. We can simplify as follows.

$$12 \div 8 = \frac{\overset{3}{\cancel{12}}}{\cancel{8}_2}$$
$$= \frac{3}{2}$$

Both 12 and 8 are divided by 4.

The same procedure applies to algebra.

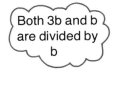

Both 3b and b are divided by b

BOTH 6x AND 3 ARE DIVIDED BY 3.

$$6x \div 3 = \frac{6x}{3}$$
$$= \frac{\overset{2}{\cancel{6}} \times x}{\cancel{3}_1}$$
$$= 2x$$

$$3b \div b = \frac{3b}{b}$$
$$= \frac{3 \times \cancel{b}}{\cancel{b}_1}$$
$$= 3$$

In this example, b cannot have a value of 0. Why?

Example 1. Divide. $\dfrac{10ab}{5}$

Solution: $\dfrac{10ab}{5} = \dfrac{\overset{2}{\cancel{10}} \times a \times b}{\cancel{5}_1}$
$$= 2ab$$

Example 2. Divide. $(-7ab) \div (ab)$

Solution: $(-7ab) \div (ab) = \dfrac{-7ab}{ab}$
$$= \frac{-7 \times \cancel{a} \times \cancel{b}}{\cancel{a} \times \cancel{b}}$$
$$= -7$$

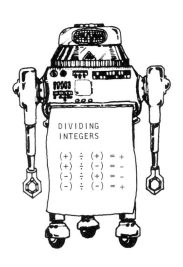

DIVIDING INTEGERS

(+) ÷ (+) = +
(+) ÷ (−) = −
(−) ÷ (+) = −
(−) ÷ (−) = +

Example 3. Divide. $(-20rst) \div (-5rs)$

Solution: $(-20rst) \div (-5rs) = \dfrac{-20rst}{-5rs}$
$$= \frac{\overset{4}{-\cancel{20}} \times \cancel{r} \times \cancel{s} \times t}{-\cancel{5} \times \cancel{r} \times \cancel{s}}$$
$$= 4t$$

EXERCISE

A

1. Divide.

(a) $\dfrac{4x}{2}$ (b) $\dfrac{21b}{7}$

(c) $\dfrac{32t}{8}$ (d) $\dfrac{48r}{6}$

(e) $\dfrac{20m}{5}$ (f) $\dfrac{16abc}{4}$

(g) $\dfrac{5t}{5}$ (h) $\dfrac{36xy}{6}$

2. Divide.

(a) $\dfrac{4a}{a}$ (b) $\dfrac{5x}{x}$

(c) $\dfrac{3abc}{ab}$ (d) $\dfrac{2rs}{r}$

(e) $30a \div 6$ (f) $42x \div 7$

(g) $7m \div m$ (h) $9t \div t$

B

3. Divide.

(a) $\dfrac{12abc}{3abc}$ (b) $\dfrac{16xy}{4y}$

(c) $\dfrac{18rst}{9rs}$ (d) $\dfrac{45xy}{9xy}$

(e) $\dfrac{24mn}{12mn}$ (f) $\dfrac{14abc}{7a}$

(g) $32rs \div 8rs$ (h) $9xyz \div 9xy$

(i) $30ab \div 6b$ (j) $6rst \div 6rst$

4. Divide.

(a) $\dfrac{-10a}{2}$ (b) $\dfrac{14x}{-7}$

(c) $\dfrac{-36w}{-6}$ (d) $\dfrac{-5t}{-5}$

(e) $\dfrac{60x}{-10}$ (f) $\dfrac{-15ab}{-3}$

(g) $\dfrac{-28t}{4}$ (h) $\dfrac{8s}{-8}$

5. Divide.

(a) $\dfrac{-6a}{a}$ (b) $\dfrac{-5x}{-x}$

(c) $\dfrac{9t}{-t}$ (d) $\dfrac{11a}{-a}$

(e) $\dfrac{-4xy}{x}$ (f) $\dfrac{-6rs}{-r}$

6. Divide.

(a) $\dfrac{-36ab}{6a}$ (b) $\dfrac{12xyz}{-4x}$

(c) $\dfrac{-15ab}{-5ab}$ (d) $\dfrac{-10xy}{2x}$

(e) $(-24ab) \div (6a)$

(f) $(28rst) \div (-7r)$

(g) $(-32xy) \div (-4xy)$

(h) $(-40abc) \div (4ab)$

(i) $(-9xy) \div (9xy)$

(j) $(-6abc) \div (-6a)$

(k) $(48mn) \div (-8mn)$

(l) $(-6xy) \div (-3xy)$

(m) $(-2a) \div (-1)$

(n) $(12rs) \div (-4s)$

CHALLENGE

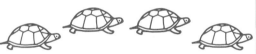

Four turtles, named Peggy, Donna, Frank, and John, were entered in a turtle race. Each came from a different side of town. Use the following clues to determine which side of town each turtle is from and in which order each finished.

1. The turtle from the east side of town won the race. Donna came in second.
2. Peggy is not from the east or west side of town.
3. Frank finished last; just behind the turtle from the north.
4. Donna and John are from opposite sides of town.

8.11 DIVISION AND EXPONENTS

We can simplify $x^5 \div x^3$ as follows.

$$x^5 = x \times x \times x \times x \times x \times x \times x \times x$$
$$x^3 = x \times x \times x \times x \times x$$

$$x^5 \div x^3 = \frac{x^5}{x^3}$$
$$= \frac{x \times x \times x \times x \times x \times x \times x \times x}{x \times x \times x \times x \times x}$$
$$= x \times x \times x$$
$$= x^2$$

Similarly, $w^6 \div w^2 = \frac{w^6}{w^2}$
$$= \frac{w \times w \times w \times w \times w \times w}{w \times w}$$
$$= w^4$$

We can also get this result by subtracting exponents.

$$w^6 \div w^2 = w^{6-2}$$
$$= w^4$$

When dividing, if the bases are the same, subtract the exponents.

Exponent Rule for Division
$x^a \div x^b = x^{a-b}$

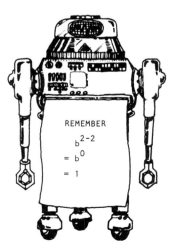

REMEMBER

b^{2-2}

$= b^0$

$= 1$

Example 1. Divide. $\dfrac{30x^5}{5x^2}$

Solution: $\dfrac{30x^5}{5x^2} = 6x^{5-2}$
$$= 6x^3$$

Example 2. Divide. $(-18a^5b^2) \div (-6a^3b^2)$

Solution: $(-18a^5b^2) \div (-6a^3b^2) = \dfrac{-18a^5b^2}{-6a^3b^2}$
$$= 3a^{5-3}b^{2-2}$$
$$= 3a^2$$

EXERCISE

A

1. Divide.

(a) $\dfrac{x^4}{x^3}$ (b) $\dfrac{a^7}{a^4}$

(c) $\dfrac{m^6}{m^2}$ (d) $\dfrac{t^3}{t^3}$

(e) $\dfrac{w^5}{w^2}$ (f) $\dfrac{x^3}{x}$

2. Divide.

(a) $m^8 \div m^3$
(b) $y^6 \div y$
(c) $x^4 \div x^4$
(d) $t^5 \div t^4$
(e) $c^7 \div c^3$

B

3. Divide.

(a) $\dfrac{24x^5}{6x^3}$ (b) $\dfrac{32m^3}{8m^2}$

(c) $\dfrac{18t^2}{9t}$ (d) $\dfrac{40a^6}{10a^4}$

(e) $(27x^3) \div (9x^2)$
(f) $(15t^2) \div (15t)$
(g) $(42m^4) \div (7m^2)$
(h) $(16x^5) \div (4x^4)$
(i) $(50y^3) \div (5y)$
(j) $(22a^4) \div (11a^2)$
(k) $(6m^2) \div (6m)$

4. Divide.

(a) $\dfrac{24a^2b}{6a}$ (b) $\dfrac{32x^4y^3}{8x^2}$

(c) $\dfrac{18m^5n^4}{9m^3n^4}$ (d) $\dfrac{20s^5t^5}{4s^3t^5}$

(e) $(10a^3b) \div (5ab)$
(f) $(14x^3y^5) \div (7x^3y)$
(g) $(12m^4n^3) \div (4mn)$
(h) $(30s^2t^5) \div (10s^2t^3)$
(i) $(27a^3b^2) \div (9ab^2)$

5. Divide.

(a) $\dfrac{-8a^3}{2a}$ (b) $\dfrac{-9x^3}{-3x^2}$

(c) $\dfrac{20m^4}{-4m^2}$ (d) $\dfrac{-15m^3n^2}{3mn}$

(e) $(-6a^4) \div (3a^2)$
(f) $(28x^5) \div (-7x^4)$
(g) $(-35m^7) \div (5m^2)$
(h) $(12a^3b^2) \div (-4ab)$
(i) $(-20m^4n^2) \div (5m^3n)$
(j) $(18x^4y^6) \div (-2xy^3)$
(k) $(-24s^4t^3) \div (-4s^4t^2)$
(l) $(8a^3b^2) \div (-8a^2b^2)$
(m) $(-x^2y^4) \div (xy^2)$

6. Simplify.

$$\dfrac{a^2 \times a^5}{a^3} = \dfrac{a^7}{a^3} = a^4$$

(a) $\dfrac{x^6 \times x^4}{x^3}$ (b) $\dfrac{t^3 \times t^5}{t^2}$

(c) $\dfrac{m \times m^3}{m^4}$ (d) $\dfrac{c^3 \times c^3}{c^5}$

(e) $\dfrac{x^2 \times x^4}{x^3 \times x}$ (f) $\dfrac{m^5 \times m^7}{m^4 \times m^4}$

CHALLENGE

Place the numbers from 1 to 7 in the circles so that each line adds to 12.

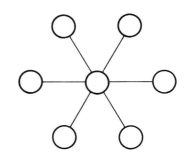

8.12 POWER RULE FOR EXPONENTS

An expression such as $(x^2)^3$ can be simplified using the exponent rule for multiplication.

$$(x^2)^3 = x^2 \times x^2 \times x^2$$
$$= x^{2+2+2}$$
$$= x^6$$

We see that
$$(x^2)^3 = x^{2 \times 3}$$
$$= x^6$$

Now, $(w^4)^3 = w^4 \times w^4 \times w^4$
$$= w^{4 \times 3}$$
$$= w^{12}$$

Checking this result,
$$w^4 \times w^4 \times w^4$$
$$= w^{4+4+4}$$
$$= w^{12}$$

Power Rule for Exponents
$$(x^a)^b = x^{a \times b}$$

Example 1. Simplify. $(w^2x^3)^2$

Solution: $(w^2x^3)^2 = w^{2 \times 2} \times x^{3 \times 2}$
$$= w^4x^6$$

Example 2. Simplify. $(2ab^2)^3$

Solution: $(2ab^2)^3 = (2^1a^1b^2)^3$
$$= 2^{1 \times 3}a^{1 \times 3}b^{2 \times 3}$$
$$= 2^3a^3b^6$$
$$= 8a^3b^6$$

Example 3. Simplify. $(-3x^2y^3)^4$

Solution: $(-3x^2y^3)^4 = (-3)^4x^8y^{12}$
$$= 81x^8y^{12}$$

EXERCISE

A

1. Simplify.
   (a) $(x^3)^2$
   (b) $(a^4)^3$
   (c) $(w^2)^3$
   (d) $(a^3)^3$
   (e) $(t^4)^2$
   (f) $(m^2)^5$

2. Simplify.

   $$(2^3)^2 = 2^{3 \times 2} = 2^6$$

   (a) $(3^2)^2$
   (b) $(2^4)^3$
   (c) $(5^3)^2$
   (d) $(4^3)^4$

B

3. Simplify.
   (a) $(a^2b^3)^2$
   (b) $(m^3n^3)^2$
   (c) $(s^4t^2)^3$
   (d) $(x^5y)^4$
   (e) $(ab^4)^3$
   (f) $(m^2n^4)^5$

4. Simplify.
   (a) $(2x^2)^3$
   (b) $(3m^3)^2$
   (c) $(4a^4)^2$
   (d) $(3y^5)^3$
   (e) $(2m)^2$
   (f) $(10x^4)^4$
   (g) $(3t^3)^4$
   (h) $(2s^6)^5$

5. Simplify.
   (a) $(2a^2b^2)^3$
   (b) $(3x^3y^2)^2$
   (c) $(2m^4n)^4$
   (d) $(4x^2y^4)^2$
   (e) $(5a^3b)^3$
   (f) $(3x^4y^2)^3$

6. Simplify.
   (a) $(-2x^2)^3$
   (b) $(-3a^4)^2$
   (c) $(-4t^5)^2$
   (d) $(-2m^3)^3$
   (e) $(-1y^4)^5$
   (f) $(-1b^6)^7$

7. Simplify.
   (a) $(-2x^2y^3)^2$
   (b) $(-3a^3b)^3$
   (c) $(-m^5n^3)^4$
   (d) $(4r^3t^2)^2$
   (e) $(-x^4y)^5$
   (f) $(-2a^3b^2)^4$
   (g) $(5r^2t)^3$
   (h) $(-10st)^3$
   (i) $(-2r^2st^3)^5$
   (j) $(-x^3y)^6$

8. Evaluate for $x = 2$.
   (a) $x^2 \times x^3$
   (b) $x^4 \div x^2$
   (c) $(x^2)^2$
   (d) $(x^3)^2$

9. Evaluate for $x = -1$.
   (a) $x^5 \times x^2$
   (b) $x^6 \div x^3$
   (c) $(x^3)^2$
   (d) $(x^2)^4$

CHALLENGE

In how many ways can you make change for a quarter using standard Canadian coins?

8.13 PICTURING MULTIPLICATION

The formulas for the area of a square and a rectangle can be used to illustrate the distributive property.

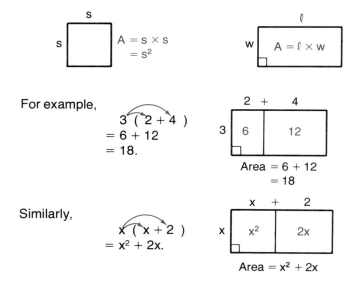

For example,

$$3 (2 + 4)$$
$$= 6 + 12$$
$$= 18.$$

Area $= 6 + 12$
$= 18$

Similarly,

$$x (x + 2)$$
$$= x^2 + 2x.$$

Area $= x^2 + 2x$

We can also illustrate the product of two binomials, such as $(x + 3)(x + 2)$, using the formulas for area.

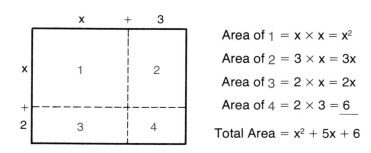

Area of 1 $= x \times x = x^2$
Area of 2 $= 3 \times x = 3x$
Area of 3 $= 2 \times x = 2x$
Area of 4 $= 2 \times 3 = 6$

Total Area $= x^2 + 5x + 6$

The total area of the figure is $x^2 + 5x + 6$.

$$\therefore (x + 2)(x + 3) = x^2 + 5x + 6.$$

EXERCISE

B

1. Complete the following.

```
        x  +        3
    ┌─────────┬──────────┐
  x │    1    │    2     │
    └─────────┴──────────┘
```

Area of 1 =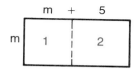
Area of 2 =

Total Area =

x(x + 3) =

2. (a) Complete.

```
        m  +     5
    ┌───────┬────────┐
  m │   1   │   2    │
    └───────┴────────┘
```

Area of 1 =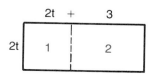
Area of 2 =
Total Area =

m(m + 5) =

(b) Find the area when m = 7.

3. (a) Complete.

```
        2t  +      3
    ┌────────┬──────────┐
 2t │   1    │    2     │
    └────────┴──────────┘
```

Area of 1 =
Area of 2 =
Total Area =

2t(2t + 3) =

(b) Find the area when t = 4.

4. Complete the following.

```
        x  +      2
    ┌──────┬───────┐
  x │  1   │   2   │
  + ├──────┼───────┤
  1 │  3   │   4   │
    └──────┴───────┘
```

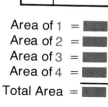

Area of 1 =
Area of 2 =
Area of 3 =
Area of 4 =
Total Area =

(x + 1)(x + 2) =

5. (a) Complete.

```
        m  +       3
    ┌──────┬─────────┐
  m │  1   │    2    │
  + ├──────┼─────────┤
  4 │  3   │    4    │
    └──────┴─────────┘
```

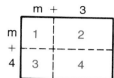

Area of 1 =
Area of 2 =
Area of 3 =
Area of 4 =
Total Area =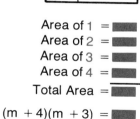

(m + 4)(m + 3) =

(b) Find the area when m = 6.

6. (a) Complete.

```
        t  +      5
    ┌──────┬────────┐
  t │  1   │   2    │
  + ├──────┼────────┤
  2 │  3   │   4    │
    └──────┴────────┘
```

Area of 1 =
Area of 2 =
Area of 3 =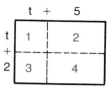
Area of 4 =
Total Area =

(t + 2)(t + 5) =

(b) Find the area when t = 6.

8.14 MULTIPLYING A POLYNOMIAL BY A MONOMIAL

We use the distributive property to multiply a polynomial by a monomial.

Example 1. Expand. $2x(x + 3)$

	x	+	3
2x	$2x^2$		6x

Solution: $2x(x + 3) = 2x(x + 3)$
$$= 2x \times x + 2x \times 3$$
$$= 2x^2 + 6x$$

We can check the multiplication by substituting any number for x.

Using x = 2

$$2x(x + 3) = 2 \times 2(2 + 3)$$
$$= 2 \times 10$$
$$= 20 \checkmark$$

$$2x^2 + 6 \times 2 = 2(2)^2 + 6 \times 2$$
$$= 2 \times 4 + 12$$
$$= 20 \checkmark$$

Example 2. Expand and simplify.
$$3x(x - 1) - 3(x + 4)$$

Solution:
$$3x(x - 1) - 3(x + 4) = 3x(x - 1) - 3(x + 4)$$
$$= 3x^2 - 3x - 3x - 12$$
$$= 3x^2 - 6x - 12$$

Example 3. Expand and simplify.
$$3(x^2 - 2x - 2) - x(x - 1)$$

Solution:
$$3(x^2 - 2x - 2) - x(x - 1) = 3(x^2 - 2x - 2) - x(x - 1)$$
$$= 3x^2 - 6x - 6 - x^2 + x$$
$$= 2x^2 - 5x - 6$$

EXERCISE

A

1. Expand.
   (a) 3x(x + 1)
   (b) 2a(a + 4)
   (c) 4t(t − 3)
   (d) 5m(m − 2)
   (e) y(y − 4)

2. Expand.
   (a) −2x(x + 3)
   (b) −3m(m + 4)
   (c) −2t(t − 3)
   (d) −5m(m − 1)
   (e) −x(x + 2)
   (f) −x(x − 3)

B

3. Expand.
   (a) 2x(2x − 3)
   (b) 3a(2a − 1)
   (c) −2t(3t + 3)
   (d) −4m(3m − 5)
   (e) 5y(1 + 3y)
   (f) 3x(1 + 4x)
   (g) −2m(1 − 3m)
   (h) −t(1 − 2t)

4. Expand and simplify.
   (a) 2x(x + 1) + 3(x + 2)
   (b) 3t(t + 2) + 4(t + 3)
   (c) m(m + 4) + m(m + 5)
   (d) 4x(x + 3) + 2x(x + 1)
   (e) 2w(w − 1) + 3(w − 4)
   (f) 3y(y − 5) − 2(y + 6)
   (g) x(x − 3) − 3x(x − 2)
   (h) −3m(m − 4) − 3(m − 5)
   (i) −a(a + 7) − 4a(a − 2)
   (j) 2x(1 + x) + 3x(1 + 2x)
   (k) −m(1 − m) − m(1 − m)

5. Expand and simplify.
   (a) 2x(2x + 1) + 3(3x + 2)
   (b) 3y(y − 4) + 2y(y − 1)
   (c) 3t(2t + 5) − 2t(t − 1)
   (d) 6(3w − 7) − 4w(3w − 2)
   (e) −2a(2a + 1) − a(a − 3)
   (f) 2m(1 + 3m) − m(1 − 2m)
   (g) −3x(4x − 5) + 2x(1 − 3x)

6. Expand and simplify.
   (a) 2(x² + 2x + 1) + x(x + 2)
   (b) 2m(m − 3) − 2(m² − m − 7)
   (c) t(2t + 3) − (t² − 5t − 4)
   (d) −3(w² − 3w − 1) − w(w − 5)
   (e) 6(2r² − 2r − 3) − (r² − 3r − 7)
   (f) 2a(2a − 1) − 2(2a² − a − 1)

CHALLENGE

Here are 17 toothpicks.

Move 3 toothpicks to make 5 squares that are the same size.

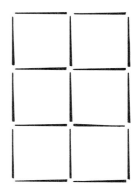

8.15 MULTIPLYING TWO BINOMIALS

In section 8.13 we found the product of two binomials using areas. We will now find the product using the distributive property.

Example 1. Expand. $(x + 3)(x + 4)$

$$Solution: (x + 3)(x + 4) = (x + 3)(x + 4)$$
$$= (x + 3)x + (x + 3)4$$
$$= x^2 + 3x + 4x + 12$$
$$= x^2 + 7x + 12$$

OR, we can find the product by multiplying each term in the first bracket by each term in the second bracket.

$$(x + 3)(x + 4) = (x + 3)(x + 4)$$

$$= x^2 + 4x + 3x + 12$$
$$= x^2 + 7x + 12$$

Area $= x^2 + 7x + 12$

The word FOIL will help you remember the procedure.

$(x + 3)(x + 4)$	=	x^2	+	$4x$	+	$3x$	+	12
		F		O		I		L
		Product of First terms		Product of Outside terms		Product of Inside terms		Product of Last terms

Example 2. Expand. $(2x - 7)(3x + 1)$

$$Solution: (2x - 7)(3x + 1) = (2x - 7)(3x + 1)$$

$$= 6x^2 + 2x - 21x - 7$$
$$= 6x^2 - 19x - 7$$

$$\overset{F}{\underset{L}{\overset{O}{(x + 3)}}\ \overset{I}{(x + 4)}}$$

EXERCISE

B

1. Complete the following.

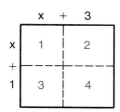

Area of 1 = ▇▇

Area of 2 = ▇▇

Area of 3 = ▇▇

Area of 4 = ▇▇

Total area = ▇▇

$(x + 1)(x + 3)$ = ▇▇

2. Expand.
   (a) $(x + 1)(x + 2)$
   (b) $(t + 3)(t + 4)$
   (c) $(m + 5)(m + 5)$
   (d) $(y + 2)(y + 7)$
   (e) $(x + 8)(x + 2)$

3. Expand.
   (a) $(x - 4)(x - 3)$
   (b) $(m - 2)(m - 1)$
   (c) $(t - 1)(t - 1)$
   (d) $(y - 6)(y - 7)$
   (e) $(r - 3)(r - 3)$

4. Expand.
   (a) $(x - 2)(x + 3)$
   (b) $(m + 4)(m - 5)$
   (c) $(y - 4)(y + 1)$
   (d) $(a - 5)(a + 5)$
   (e) $(x + 1)(x - 1)$

5. Expand.
   (a) $(x + 6)(x - 5)$
   (b) $(y - 2)(y - 3)$
   (c) $(m - 4)(m + 7)$
   (d) $(t + 7)(t + 8)$
   (e) $(x + 6)(x + 10)$
   (f) $(w - 3)(w + 3)$
   (g) $(r - 9)(r + 6)$
   (h) $(3 - t)(2 - t)$

6. Expand.
   (a) $(2x + 1)(x + 3)$
   (b) $(t - 2)(3t + 2)$
   (c) $(3m + 1)(m + 2)$
   (d) $(4x - 3)(x - 1)$
   (e) $(3a + 2)(2a - 1)$
   (f) $(2y - 1)(3y - 4)$
   (g) $(1 + 2x)(1 - 2x)$

7. Expand.

$$(x + 2)^2 = (x + 2)(x + 2)$$

   (a) $(x + 3)^2$
   (b) $(y - 2)^2$
   (c) $(m + 4)^2$
   (d) $(t - 3)^2$

8. Expand.
   (a) $(x - 1)(x + 1)$
   (b) $(m + 3)(m - 3)$
   (c) $(y + 4)(y - 4)$
   (d) $(a - 5)(a + 5)$
   (e) $(t - 2)(t + 2)$
   (f) $(a - b)(a + b)$

C

9. Expand.
   (a) $(x + 2)(x^2 + 2x + 1)$
   (b) $(x - 1)(x^2 - 3x + 3)$
   (c) $(t^2 + 3t - 2)(t + 3)$

8.16 DIVISION OF A POLYNOMIAL BY A MONOMIAL

TERMS ARE SEPARATED BY + AND − SIGNS.

In arithmetic, we add fractions as follows.

$$\frac{3}{8} + \frac{2}{8} = \frac{3+2}{8} = \frac{5}{8}$$

This process can be reversed.

$$\frac{5}{8} = \frac{3+2}{8} = \frac{3}{8} + \frac{2}{8}$$

We use this reversed process to divide a polynomial by a monomial.

Example 1. Divide. $\dfrac{2a + 2b}{2}$

Solution: $\dfrac{2a + 2b}{2} = \dfrac{2a}{2} + \dfrac{2b}{2}$
$$= a + b$$

Every term in the numerator is divided by the denominator.

Example 2. Divide. $\dfrac{3x^2 + 6x - 9}{3}$

Solution: $\dfrac{3x^2 + 6x - 9}{3} = \dfrac{3x^2}{3} + \dfrac{6x}{3} - \dfrac{9}{3}$
$$= x^2 + 2x - 3$$

Example 3. Divide. $\dfrac{4x^2 - 2x}{2x}$

Solution: $\dfrac{4x^2 - 2x}{2x} = \dfrac{4x^2}{2x} - \dfrac{2x}{2x}$
$$= 2x - 1$$

EXERCISE

A

1. Divide.

(a) $\dfrac{3x + 3y}{3}$

(b) $\dfrac{4a + 2b}{2}$

(c) $\dfrac{6s + 12t}{6}$

(d) $\dfrac{8m + 4}{2}$

(e) $\dfrac{6x + 6}{6}$

(f) $\dfrac{2a - 4b}{2}$

(g) $\dfrac{4m - 8n}{4}$

(h) $\dfrac{9x - 6}{3}$

(i) $\dfrac{7a - 7}{7}$

B

2. Divide.

(a) $\dfrac{2x^2 + 4x + 6}{2}$

(b) $\dfrac{3t^2 + 6t + 9}{3}$

(c) $\dfrac{4m^2 - 8m + 12}{4}$

(d) $\dfrac{6a^2 - 9a - 3}{3}$

(e) $\dfrac{8r^2 - 4r + 4}{4}$

(f) $\dfrac{12x^2 - 12x + 18}{6}$

(g) $\dfrac{5a^2 - 5a + 15}{5}$

(h) $\dfrac{2r^2 - 2r - 2}{2}$

3. Divide.

(a) $\dfrac{2x^2 + 4x}{2x}$

(b) $\dfrac{6a^2 + 9a}{3a}$

(c) $\dfrac{4a^2 - 8a}{4a}$

(d) $\dfrac{6t^2 - 7t}{t}$

(e) $\dfrac{9w^2 + 3w}{3w}$

(f) $\dfrac{10x^2 - 5x}{5x}$

4. Divide.

(a) $\dfrac{2x^3 + 4x^2 + 6x}{2x}$

(b) $\dfrac{6m^3 - 9m^2 - 12m}{3m}$

(c) $\dfrac{8t^3 - 4t^2 + 16t}{4t}$

(d) $\dfrac{5a^3 + 15a^2 - 5a}{5a}$

CHALLENGE

In one of the bags, there are two oranges; in another, two apples. In the third, there is an apple and an orange. The bags are labelled incorrectly.

By taking one piece of fruit from one of the bags you can tell what is in each bag. How can you do this?

8.17 FACTORS OF A MONOMIAL

When we write
$$12 = 4 \times 3$$
we say that 4 and 3 are factors of 12.

Using whole numbers as factors we can factor 12 in three ways.

$$12 = 4 \ \times 3 \qquad \text{4 and 3 are factors of 12.}$$
$$12 = 6 \ \times 2 \qquad \text{6 and 2 are factors of 12.}$$
$$12 = 12 \times 1 \qquad \text{12 and 1 are factors of 12.}$$

We can also factor 12 using integers.
Some ways are:

$$12 = (-4)(-3)$$
$$12 = (+4)(+3)$$
$$12 = (-6)(-2)$$

We can factor monomials in the same way.

$$12x^2 = (2x)(6x) \qquad \text{2x and 6x are factors of } 12x^2.$$
$$12x^2 = (-4x)(-3x) \qquad \text{−4x and −3x are factors of } 12x^2.$$
$$12x^2 = (12)(x^2) \qquad \text{12 and } x^2 \text{ are factors of } 12x^2.$$

EXERCISE

Find the missing factor in each of the following.

A

1. (a) $6x = (3x) \times \square$
   (b) $4x = \square \times (2x)$
   (c) $15x^2 = (5x) \times \square$
   (d) $12xy = \square \times (3y)$
   (e) $12xy = (6xy) \times \square$

B

2. (a) $5y^2 = \square \times (5y^2)$
   (b) $20x^2y = (4y) \times \square$
   (c) $21x^3 = \square \times (7x)$
   (d) $30pqr = (6pq) \times \square$
   (e) $32x^4 = \square \times (4x^3)$
   (f) $18abc = (9ab) \times \square$
   (g) $24a^2b^2 = \square \times (8b^2)$

3. (a) $27x^2y^2 = (9x^2y) \times \square$
   (b) $16x^2y = \square \times (x^2y)$
   (c) $-8x = (-4x) \times \square$
   (d) $-12ab = \square \times (3a)$
   (e) $20xy = (-5x) \times \square$
   (f) $18x^2 = \square \times (-9x)$

4. (a) $28x^2y = (4x^2) \times \square$
   (b) $30abc = \square \times (-6ab)$
   (c) $-9x^2y^2 = (-3x^2) \times \square$
   (d) $-10a^2bc = \square \times (5a^2)$
   (e) $-14p^2q^2r = (-2p^2) \times \square$
   (f) $-6abc = \square \times (6abc)$

8.18 FACTORING

We can calculate the area of a rectangle using the formula

$$A = \ell w$$

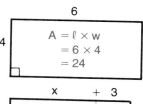

$$A = \ell \times w$$
$$= 6 \times 4$$
$$= 24$$

The area of this rectangle is

$$A = x \times (x + 3)$$
$$= x(x + 3)$$
$$= x^2 + 3x.$$

| x | x² | 3x |

This process can be reversed. When we are given the area and the width we can find the length.

$$A = \ell w$$
$$x^2 + 4x = x \times (?)$$

Since $\quad x \times x = x^2$
and $\quad x \times 4 = 4x$
Then $\quad x^2 + 4 = x \times (x + 4)$

The length is $x + 4$.

(rectangle with width x, area $x^2 + 4x$, length ?)

EXERCISE

B

1. Find the missing dimension in each.

   (a)

   $A = x^2 + 3x$ $\qquad$ x $\qquad$ $\ell = \blacksquare$

   (b)

   $A = x^2 - 5x$ $\qquad$ x $\qquad$ $\ell = \blacksquare$

2. Complete the chart for the rectangles.

	Area	Width	Length
(a)	$x^2 + 3x$	x	
(b)	$x^2 + 7x$	x	
(c)	$x^2 - 2x$		x
(d)	$x^2 - 6x$		x

3. Complete the chart for the rectangles.

	Area	Width	Length
(a)	$x^2 + 5x$	x	
(b)	$x^2 + 2x$		x + 2
(c)	$x^2 - 3x$		x
(d)	$x^2 - 4x$	x - 4	
(e)	$2x^2 - 4x$		2x
(f)	$3x^2 + 9x$		3x
(g)	$5a + 5b$	5	
(h)	$6a + 3b$	3	

8.19 COMMON MONOMIAL FACTORS

We can factor 5x and 5y as follows.

$$5x = 5 \times x$$
$$\text{and } 5y = 5 \times y$$

Both 5x and 5y have one factor that is the same, 5.
5 is called the common (same) factor of 5x and 5y.

We use this idea and the distributive property to factor polynomials.

$$5x + 5y = 5 \times x + 5 \times y$$
$$= 5(x + y)$$

5 is the common factor of 5x and 5y.

We check using the distributive property.

$$5(x + y) = 5(x + y)$$
$$= 5x + 5y$$

Example 1. Factor. $2x^2 + 6y$

Solution: By inspection, 2 is the common factor. We can find the other factor by division.

$$2x^2 + 6y = 2\left(\frac{2x^2 + 6y}{2}\right) = 2(x^2 + 3y)$$

Check: $2(x^2 + 3y) = 2(x^2 + 3y)$
$$= 2x^2 + 6y$$

Common Factoring
1. Find the common factor by inspection.
2. Find the other factor by division.

Example 2. Factor. $3x^2 - 6x$

Solution: $3x^2 - 6x = 3x\left(\frac{3x^2 - 6x}{3x}\right) = 3x(x - 2)$

Check: $3x(x - 2) = 3x(x - 2)$
$$= 3x^2 - 6x$$

EXERCISE

A

1. Find the greatest common factor of each pair.
   - (a) 2x, 4y
   - (b) 14a, 7b
   - (c) 12x, 18y
   - (d) 3x, 5x
   - (e) 4ab, 3ac
   - (f) $5x^2$, 10x
   - (g) 8abc, 12ab
   - (h) 4xy, 5xy

B

2. Complete.
   - (a) $2x + 4 = 2(x + \blacksquare)$
   - (b) $3a + 9 = 3(a + \blacksquare)$
   - (c) $x^2 - 4x = x(x - \blacksquare)$
   - (d) $a^2 + 6a = a(a + \blacksquare)$
   - (e) $3a - 6b = 3(a - \blacksquare)$
   - (f) $2x^2 - 8x = 2x(x - \blacksquare)$

3. Complete.
   - (a) $5a + 5b = 5(\blacksquare)$
   - (b) $7x - 7y = 7(\blacksquare)$
   - (c) $3x + 6 = 3(\blacksquare)$
   - (d) $4a - 12 = 4(\blacksquare)$
   - (e) $2a + 4b + 6c = 2(\blacksquare)$
   - (f) $3x^2 - 6x = 3x(\blacksquare)$
   - (g) $6x^3 + 4x^2 + 2x = 2x(\blacksquare)$

4. Complete.
   - (a) $\blacksquare(x + y) = 3x + 3y$
   - (b) $\blacksquare(a - b) = 2a - 2b$
   - (c) $\blacksquare(x + 2) = x^2 + 2x$
   - (d) $\blacksquare(a - 4) = a^2 - 4a$
   - (e) $\blacksquare(2x + 1) = 2x^2 + x$
   - (f) $\blacksquare(x - 1) = x^3 - x^2$
   - (g) $\blacksquare(3a + 4) = 3a^2 + 4a$

5. Factor.
   - (a) $4a + 4b$
   - (b) $2x - 2y$
   - (c) $3x + 6$
   - (d) $5b - 10$
   - (e) $8y - 4$
   - (f) $2a + 6b - 8c$
   - (g) $4x^2 + 2y$
   - (h) $7x^2 - 14x + 21$
   - (i) $20a + 5b - 15$
   - (j) $6t^2 - 6t + 12$

6. Factor.
   - (a) $x^2 + 3x$
   - (b) $a^2 - 2a$
   - (c) $5ax + 6ay$
   - (d) $4xy - 7ax$
   - (e) $2ax + 2ay$
   - (f) $3mx - 6my$
   - (g) $10tx - 5ty$
   - (h) $3x^2 + 12x$
   - (i) $5a^2 - 15a$
   - (j) $8x^3 - 4x^2$

C

7. Factor.
   - (a) $6x^2y - 3xy^2$
   - (b) $4a^2b + 6ab - 8ab^2$
   - (c) $14x^2y^2 - 7xy^2 + 7xy$
   - (d) $6abc - 2abx + 10aby$
   - (e) $7a^3 + 14a^2 - 7a$
   - (f) $8mx - 4nx + 6x$
   - (g) $6x^3 - 10x^2y - 8x^2y^2$

CHALLENGE

Sandra painted a cube red.
She then cut the cube into 27 smaller cubes as shown.

How many of the small cubes have

   - (a) just 3 red sides?
   - (b) just 2 red sides?
   - (c) just 1 red side?
   - (d) no red sides?

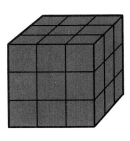

8.20 FACTORING THE DIFFERENCE OF SQUARES

Expanding $(x + 5)(x + 5)$ gives 3 terms in the product.

$$(x + 5)(x + 5) = (x + 5)(x + 5)$$
$$= x^2 + 5x + 5x + 25$$
$$= x^2 + 10x + 25$$

Expanding $(x - 5)(x - 5)$ gives 3 terms in the product.

$$(x - 5)(x - 5) = (x - 5)(x - 5)$$
$$= x^2 - 5x - 5x + 25$$
$$= x^2 - 10x + 25$$

Expanding $(x - 5)(x + 5)$ gives 2 terms in the product.

$$(x - 5)(x + 5) = (x - 5)(x + 5)$$
$$= x^2 + 5x - 5x - 25$$
$$= x^2 - 25$$
$$\text{or } x^2 - 5^2$$

The polynomial $x^2 - 25$ is called a difference of squares.

To factor a difference of squares we write the expression as a product of 2 binomials.

$$x^2 - 25 = (x - 5)(x + 5)$$

In general,

$$\boxed{a^2 - b^2 = (a - b)(a + b)}$$

Example 1. Factor. $t^2 - 36$

Solution: $t^2 - 36 = t^2 - 6^2$
$$= (t - 6)(t + 6)$$

Example 2. Factor. $16x^2 - 9$

Solution: $16x^2 - 9 = (4x)^2 - 3^2$
$$= (4x - 3)(4x + 3)$$

EXERCISE

A

1. Complete the following.
   (a) $x^2 - 16 = (x - 4)(x + \square)$

   (b) $m^2 - 4 = (m - \square)(m + 2)$

   (c) $t^2 - 9 = (t - \square)(t + \square)$

   (d) $x^2 - 1 = (x - 1)(\square + 1)$

   (e) $a^2 - 49 = (\square - 7)(\square + 7)$

2. State the missing factor.
   (a) $x^2 - 9 = (x - 3)(\blacksquare)$

   (b) $a^2 - 100 = (\blacksquare)(a + 10)$

   (c) $m^2 - 25 = (m - 5)(\blacksquare)$

   (d) $r^2 - 36 = (\blacksquare)(r + 6)$

   (e) $9x^2 - 4 = (3x - 2)(\blacksquare)$

   (f) $25m^2 - 1 = (\blacksquare)(5m + 1)$

B

3. Factor.
   (a) $x^2 - 16$

   (b) $n^2 - 9$

   (c) $t^2 - 1$

   (d) $r^2 - 121$

   (e) $y^2 - 49$

   (f) $s^2 - 81$

   (g) $x^2 - 64$

   (h) $b^2 - 144$

4. Factor.
   (a) $4x^2 - 25$

   (b) $9m^2 - 1$

   (c) $16t^2 - 49$

   (d) $25n^2 - 121$

   (e) $64x^2 - 9$

   (f) $100a^2 - 1$

   (g) $4s^2 - 81$

C

5. Factor.
   (a) $16 - x^2$

   (b) $36 - y^2$

   (c) $81 - m^2$

   (d) $100 - t^2$

   (e) $9 - 4x^2$

   (f) $121 - 16m^2$

   (g) $81 - 25t^2$

   (h) $64 - 9x^2$

CHALLENGE

Find the length of the longest stick that can be placed in this box.

3 cm

4 cm

12 cm

8.21 FACTORING A TRINOMIAL

Some trinomials can be factored into the product of two binomials. We can see how this is done by studying the expansion of two binomials.

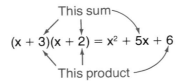

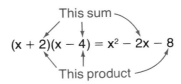

Expanding two general binomials gives the following.

$$(x + m)(x + n) = x^2 + nx + mx + mn$$
$$= x^2 + mx + nx + mn$$
$$= x^2 + (mx + nx) + mn$$

$$\boxed{(x + m)(x + n) = x^2 + (m + n)x + mn}$$

To factor $x^2 + 7x + 12$ we compare it to $x + (m + n)x + mn$.

x^2	$+$	$7x$ $+ 12$	$m + n = 7$
x^2	$+$	$(m + n)x + mn$	$m \times n = 12$

Since $m + n = 7$ and $mn = 12$, then m and n are 3 and 4.

The factors of $x^2 + 7x + 12$ are $(x + 3)$ and $(x + 4)$.

So $x^2 + 7x + 12 = (x + 3)(x + 4)$.

Example. Factor. $x^2 - 2x - 15$

Solution: Comparing to $x^2 + (m + n)x + mn$, we have

x^2	$-$	$2x$ $- 15$	$m + n = -2$
x^2	$+$	$(m + n)x + mn$	$m \times n = -15$

Since $m + n = -2$ and $mn = -15$,
then m and n are -5 and $+3$.
So $x^2 - 2x - 15 = (x - 5)(x + 3)$.

EXERCISE

A

1. State the values of m and n.

	m + n	mn	m	n
(a)	5	6		
(b)	6	8		
(c)	3	2		
(d)	−4	3		
(e)	−2	1		
(f)	−7	12		
(g)	−7	10		
(h)	−1	−12		
(i)	2	−8		
(j)	1	−12		
(k)	3	−10		

B

2. Find the missing factor.
   (a) $x^2 + 5x + 6 = (x + 3)(\blacksquare)$

   (b) $m^2 + 9x + 8 = (\blacksquare)(m + 8)$

   (c) $t^2 + 7x + 12 = (t + 4)(\blacksquare)$

   (d) $y^2 − 4x + 3 = (y − 1)(\blacksquare)$

   (e) $a^2 − 6a + 9 = (\blacksquare)(a − 3)$

   (f) $z^2 − 10z + 16 = (z − 2)(\blacksquare)$

   (g) $x^2 + 4x − 5 = (x − 1)(\blacksquare)$

   (h) $t^2 − 2x − 24 = (\blacksquare)(t + 4)$

   (i) $r^2 + 5r − 14 = (r + 7)(\blacksquare)$

   (j) $n^2 − n − 20 = (\blacksquare)(n + 4)$

3. Factor.
   (a) $x^2 + 6x + 5$

   (b) $t^2 + 9t + 14$

   (c) $m^2 + 9m + 20$

   (d) $n^2 + 4n + 4$

   (e) $y^2 − 3y + 2$

   (f) $k^2 − 5k + 6$

   (g) $a^2 − 7a + 12$

   (h) $b^2 − 8b + 12$

   (i) $x^2 − 2x − 24$

   (j) $m^2 + m − 12$

   (k) $x^2 − 2x − 35$

   (l) $n^2 + 5n − 24$

   (m) $y^2 − 4y − 21$

   (n) $a^2 − 6a + 9$

   (o) $x^2 − 2x + 1$

CHALLENGE

A penny, a nickel, a dime, and a quarter are all in a row. The quarter is not first. The nickel is between the dime and the penny. The penny is between the quarter and the nickel. Find their order.

WHAT DAY WAS IT?

Did you ever wonder what day of the week an important event occurred on? The following formula will tell you the day of the week if you know the date of the event.

$$w = d + 2m + \left[\frac{3(m + 1)}{5}\right] + y + \left[\frac{y}{4}\right] - \left[\frac{y}{100}\right] + \left[\frac{y}{400}\right] + 2$$

where d = day of the month
          y = year
          m = number of the month

Note: January is regarded as the 13th month of the previous year.
February is regarded as the 14th month of the previous year.
All other months are regular month numbers.

For example, February 3, 1983 would be substituted in the formula as:

$$d = 3$$
$$m = 14$$
$$y = 1982$$

For each calculation in the brackets, use only the number to the left of the decimal.

For example, $\dfrac{3(13)}{5} = 7.8$

Just use the 7.

Once you have found w, divide this number by 7.

The remainder is the day of the week.

Remainder	Day
0	Saturday
1	Sunday
2	Monday
3	Tuesday
4	Wednesday
5	Thursday
6	Friday

Example.

Neil Armstrong was the first person to step on the moon.
It happened on July 20, 1969.
What day of the week was it?

Solution:

$d = 20$
$y = 1969$
$m = 7$

$$w = d + 2m + \left[\frac{3(m+1)}{5}\right] + y + \left[\frac{y}{4}\right] - \left[\frac{y}{100}\right] + \left[\frac{y}{400}\right] + 2$$

$$= 20 + 2 \times 7 + \left[\frac{3(7+1)}{5}\right] + 1969 + \left[\frac{1969}{4}\right] - \left[\frac{1969}{100}\right] + \left[\frac{1969}{400}\right] + 2$$

$$= 20 + 14 + [4.8] + 1969 + [492.25] - [19.69] + [4.9225] + 2$$

$$= 20 + 14 + 4 + 1969 + 492 - 19 + 4 + 2$$

$$= 2486$$

Dividing by 7:

```
      355
7)2486
   21
   ‾‾
    38
    35
    ‾‾
     36
     35
     ‾‾
      1
```

Remainder is 1.
The day of the week was Sunday.

EXERCISE

1. The space shuttle Columbia was first launched on
   April 12, 1981.
   What day of the week was it?

2. On August 17, 1974, Cindy Nicholas, a 16-year-old
   Toronto high school student, swam 51.5 km across
   Lake Ontario.
   What day of the week was it?

3. On what day of the week were you born?

8.22 CHAPTER 8 REVIEW EXERCISE

1. Find the value of each expression.
   (a) 2^2 (b) 3^2
   (c) 5^3 (d) 6^2
   (e) 4^3 (f) 10^4

2. If $x = 3$, evaluate each of the following.
   (a) $x + 9$ (b) $8 - x$
   (c) $4x - 1$ (d) $x^2 + 1$

3. If $x = -2$, evaluate each of the following.
   (a) $x + 7$ (b) $9 - x$
   (c) $2x + 8$ (d) $x^2 + 1$
   (e) $8 - x^2$ (f) $7 + 6x$

4. Simplify.
   (a) $3x + 5x$ (b) $4m - 2m$
   (c) $4t + 5t + t$ (d) $2x^2 + 3x^2 - x^2$
   (e) $5x - 3x - 2x$ (f) $3y - 5y$
   (g) $-2x - 4x$ (h) $6m - 8m + m$
   (i) $6y - 9y$ (j) $5t - 3t - 6t$
   (k) $7y + 3y - y$ (l) $9t - 8t - 3t$

5. Expand.
   (a) $3(x + 4)$ (b) $7(y - 2)$
   (c) $5(3x + 2y)$ (d) $4(3x - 2y + 4)$

6. Simplify.
   (a) $3x \times 2y$ (b) $(4x^2)(2y^2)$
   (c) $x^3 \times x^4$ (d) $t^2 \times t^4 \times t^2$
   (e) $5m^3 \times 2m^2$ (f) $(3n^4)(2n)$
   (g) $x^8 \div x^3$ (h) $(10t^5) \div (2t)$
   (i) $(m^4)^3$ (j) $m \times m^2 \times m^4$

7. Expand.
   (a) $2x(x + 3)$ (b) $5t(t - 1)$
   (c) $-3x(x - 4)$ (d) $-4m(m + 3)$
   (e) $y(y + 5)$ (f) $-x(x + 3)$

8. Determine the output of each of the following flow charts.
   (a)   (b)

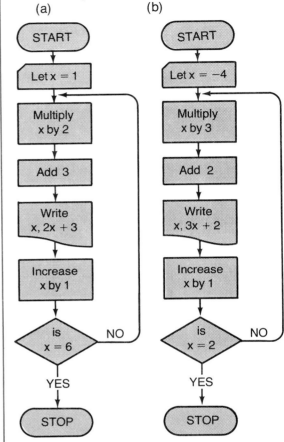

9. If $x = 2$ and $y = 3$, evaluate each of the following.
   (a) $x + y$ (b) $2xy - 4$
   (c) $x - y$ (d) $x^2 + y^2$
   (e) $3x^2 - 2xy$ (f) $2y^2 - xy$

10. If $m = -1$, and $n = -2$, evaluate each of the following.
    (a) $m - n$ (b) $n - m$
    (c) $3mn - 7$ (d) $m^2 + n^2$
    (e) $2m^2 - 3n$ (f) $12 - 2mn + n$

11. Simplify.
   (a) $3x + 5x + 4y + 3y$
   (b) $x + 2x + 4y - 2y$
   (c) $4m - 3t + 7m - 6t$
   (d) $-6x - x + 5y - 2y$
   (e) $6 + 3m - 4n + 6m - n + 1$
   (f) $9 - 3x - 7y + 5t - 6t + y + x$
   (g) $-x - y - 4 - x - y - 5$

12. Expand.
   (a) $-2(x - 5)$
   (b) $4(2a - 3b - 7)$
   (c) $-2(2x^2 + x - 3)$
   (d) $-(x - y - 6)$
   (e) $3(x - 4) + 4(x + 6)$
   (f) $-3(x - 1) - (x + 5)$
   (g) $9 - 3(t + 8) - 2(t + 1)$
   (h) $3(x + y) - 2(x + y) + 9$
   (i) $-4(x + 5) - (x - 5) - 5$

13. Multiply.
   (a) $5x^2 \times 3x^3$
   (b) $7a^3 \times 2a$
   (c) $5n^2 \times n^3 \times n$
   (d) $2y^2 \times 4y \times y^3$
   (e) $(-4x^2)(3x)$
   (f) $(-3m^4)(-2m)$
   (g) $(8a^2b^2)(-2ab^2)$
   (h) $(3rst)(-2r^2s^2)$
   (i) $(-4a^2b^2c)(-5abc)$
   (j) $(-7x^3y^2)(-3xy)$

14. Divide.
   (a) $(15x^3) \div (5x)$
   (b) $(20t^4) \div (4t^2)$
   (c) $(-12b^5) \div (3b^2)$
   (d) $(35s^6) \div (-5s^3)$
   (e) $(-10x^3y^2) \div (-2xy)$
   (f) $(-16a^3b^2) \div (4ab)$
   (g) $\dfrac{30a^4}{6a}$
   (h) $\dfrac{27x^3y^2}{3xy}$
   (i) $\dfrac{-24m^3n^2}{-6m^2}$
   (j) $\dfrac{18r^4s^2}{-3r^2s}$

15. Simplify.
   (a) $(a^2b^3)^2$
   (b) $(2x^3y^2)^3$
   (c) $(-3r^2s)^3$
   (d) $(-m^4n^2)^4$
   (e) $(-4x^3y^3)^2$
   (f) $(-3ab^2c^3)^4$

16. Expand.
   (a) $2x(x + 4)$
   (b) $4y(3y - 1)$
   (c) $3x(2x + 1) + 3(x - 6)$
   (d) $2w(w - 4) - 3w(w + 5)$
   (e) $2(x^2 + 2x - 1) + 3(2x^2 - 3x - 1)$
   (f) $3m(2m - n) - 2n(m + 2n)$

17. Expand.
   (a) $(x + 2)(x + 3)$
   (b) $(t - 4)(t + 2)$
   (c) $(t + 6)(t + 9)$
   (d) $(x - 4)(x - 5)$
   (e) $(m - 4)(m + 4)$
   (f) $(y - 5)(y - 3)$
   (g) $(2x - 1)(x + 5)$
   (h) $(1 - 3x)(1 + 3x)$

18. Divide.
   (a) $\dfrac{4x^2 + 8x}{4}$
   (b) $\dfrac{6a^2 - 9a - 9}{3}$
   (c) $\dfrac{4x^2 - 7x}{x}$
   (d) $\dfrac{8r^2 - 12r}{4r}$
   (e) $\dfrac{5x^3 + 10x^2 - 15x}{5x}$
   (f) $\dfrac{10t^3 - 4t^2 + 16t}{2t}$

19. Factor.
   (a) $3a + 3b$
   (b) $2x - 10$
   (c) $3ax + 2ay$
   (d) $14rt - 21rs$

20. Factor.
   (a) $x^2 - 9$
   (b) $t^2 - 25$
   (c) $x^2 + 4x + 3$
   (d) $m^2 - 2m - 8$
   (e) $y^2 + 3y - 10$
   (f) $a^2 + 4a + 4$

CHAPTER 8 TEST

1. If $x = -3$, evaluate each of the following.
    (a) $x + 4$ (b) $x^2 - 2$ (c) $7 - x^2$

2. Simplify.
    (a) $3x + 5x - 2x$
    (b) $-2x + 3x - 4y - 5y$
    (c) $9 - 3x - x - 2y + 4y$

3. Multiply.
    (a) $2x^3 \times 3x^2$
    (b) $(-5a^2) \times (2a^3)$
    (c) $(-4y) \times (-6y^4)$
    (d) $(-7x^2y) \times (3x^3y^2)$

4. Divide.
    (a) $(12x^4) \div (3x^2)$
    (b) $(-10a^3) \div (5a)$
    (c) $(20x^5) \div (-4x^2)$
    (d) $\dfrac{-24m^3n^2}{6mn}$

5. Expand.
    (a) $3(x + 2)$
    (b) $-2(2x + y - 3)$
    (c) $4(2x + 1) - 3(3x - 4)$

6. Simplify.
    (a) $(a^3b^2)^2$ (b) $(-3x^4)^3$ (c) $(-2x^3y^2)^4$

7. Expand.
    (a) $2x(x + 1)$
    (b) $3m(2m + n) - 2n(m - 2n)$
    (c) $(x + 4)(x + 2)$
    (d) $(y - 3)(y + 3)$
    (e) $(2x + 1)(3x - 4)$

8. Divide.
    (a) $\dfrac{5x^2 + 10x}{5}$ (b) $\dfrac{12x^3 - 4x^2}{2x}$

9. Factor.
    (a) $2x + 8$
    (b) $10ax - 5ay$
    (c) $x^2 - 4$
    (d) $x^2 - 8x + 15$

9

EQUATIONS

REVIEW AND PREVIEW TO CHAPTER 9

EXERCISE 1

Simplify.

1. $3x + 5x$
2. $2y + 5y + 7y$
3. $4a + 7a + a$
4. $7x - 6x$
5. $7b - 3b + 4b$
6. $4t + 3t - 5t$
7. $6x + 7x + 3y - y$
8. $4x^2 + 6x^2 - x^2$
9. $3xy + 7xy - 4xy$
10. $4a + 6b - 2a + 5b$

EXERCISE 2

Simplify.

1. $5x + x - 4x$
2. $4a - 6a$
3. $-3x + 4x - 2x$
4. $-4t - 5t - 2t$
5. $3m - 5m - 2n - 4n$
6. $5s - 6s - t - 6t$
7. $3x^2 - 8x^2 + x^2$
8. $5 - 5m - 7n - 2m$
9. $3xy - 7xy - xy$
10. $-y - 3y - x + 4x$

EXERCISE 3

Expand.

1. $2(x + 4)$
2. $4(3y - 5)$
3. $5(2a + 3b)$
4. $6(4x - 7)$
5. $-2(x - 3)$
6. $-3(2t + 6)$
7. $-(5x + 7)$
8. $8(3m + 5n)$
9. $-3(3s - 2t)$
10. $-7(2m + 9)$

EXERCISE 4

1. If $x = 2$, evaluate each of the following.
   - (a) $3x$
   - (b) $7x + 4$
   - (c) $5x - 1$
   - (d) $x + 3$
   - (e) $21 - x$
   - (f) $18 - 7x$

2. If x = 4 and y = 3, evaluate each of the following.
(a) x + y
(b) x − y
(c) 6xy
(d) 4x + 5y
(e) 4y − 2x
(f) x + 2y
(g) 7x − 3xy + 6
(h) 7 − 2x − y

3. If r = −1, s = 2, and t = −2, evaluate each of the following.
(a) 3r + 6
(b) 6s + 3t + 1
(c) 3rs − 5
(d) 4rs + 2st − 3rt
(e) r + s + t
(f) 6t − 4 − s − r
(g) 4rst + 2
(h) 9 − rs − st

EXERCISE 5

Find the value of 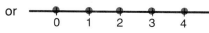 in each of the following.
1. ☐ + 3 = 5
2. ☐ + 6 = 9
3. ☐ + 4 = 13
4. ☐ − 3 = 7
5. ☐ − 2 = 4
6. ☐ − 5 = 6
7. 7 + ☐ = 10
8. 2 + ☐ = 13
9. 8 − ☐ = 6
10. 6 − ☐ = 2

EXERCISE 6

The set of natural numbers is

$$N = \{1, 2, 3, 4, \ldots\}$$

or

The set of whole numbers is

$$W = \{0, 1, 2, 3, 4, \ldots\}$$

or

The set of integers is

$$I = \{\ldots -3, -2, -1, 0, 1, 2, 3, \ldots\}$$

or

Graph each of the following.
1. x < 5, x∈ N
2. x > 3, x∈ N
3. x < 4, x∈ W
4. x > 2, x∈ W
5. x > 4, x∈ I
6. x < 3, x∈ I
7. x < −2, x∈ I
8. x > −4, x∈ I
9. x > 0, x∈ I
10. x < −1, x∈ I

x ∈ N
MEANS
THAT x
BELONGS TO
THE NATURAL
NUMBERS.

9.1 ROOTS OF EQUATIONS

Are the following statements true or false?

Alexander Graham Bell invented the telephone. ←————————true

John Glenn discovered America. ←————————false

He has red hair. ←————————may be true, may be false
(It depends on who "he" is.)

The sentences below are like the ones above.

$5 + 4 = 9$ ←————————————true

$5 + 2 = 8$ ←————————————false

$x + 3 = 7$ ←————————may be true, may be false
(It depends on what "x" is.)

Number sentences that contain an $=$ sign are called equations. As you have seen, equations are not always true.

Is x + 3 = 5 true, if x = 4?	Is x + 3 = 5 true, if x = 2?
$x + 3 = 5$	$x + 3 = 5$
$\overline{4 + 3} \mid 5$	$\overline{2 + 3} \mid 5$
$= 7$	$= 5$
NO!	Yes!

We call 2 the root or solution of the equation $x + 3 = 5$ because it is a value for x that makes the equation true.

Is 5 a root of $9 - x = 3$?

Check 5. $9 - x = 3$
$\overline{9 - 5} \mid 3$
$= 4$
NO!

Is 6 a root of $9 - x = 3$?

Check 6. $9 - x = 3$
$\overline{9 - 6} \mid 3$
$= 3$
YES!

EXERCISE

A

1. Which number shown in colour is a solution?
   - (a) $x + 3 = 7$ 5   or   4?
   - (b) $5 + b = 8$ 3   or   2?
   - (c) $y - 3 = 5$ 2   or   8?
   - (d) $3m = 12$ 9   or   4?
   - (e) $x - 2 = 4$ 6   or   4?
   - (f) $5 + b = 7$ 2   or   3?
   - (g) $2x = 6$ 4   or   3?
   - (h) $m - 9 = 25$ 34   or   16?

2. Is $x + 4 = 7$ true for $x = 3$?

3. Is $b - 2 = 6$ true for $b = 4$?

4. Is $3x = 12$ true for $x = 4$?

5. Is $y + 5 = 12$ true for $y = 7$?

6. Is 3 a root of $2x = 6$?

7. Is 5 a root of $b - 2 = 4$?

8. Is 3 a root of $2x = 6$?

9. Is 4 a root of $7 - x = 2$?

B

10. Write an equation that has 2 as a root.

11. Write an equation that has 4 as a root.

12. Which number shown is a root of the equation?
    - (a) $x + 5 = 8$ 3   or   4?
    - (b) $b - 2 = 5$ 3   or   7?
    - (c) $6 = 4 + m$ 2   or   5?
    - (d) $2y = 8$ 4   or   6?
    - (e) $b + 7 = 13$ 6   or   20?
    - (f) $4m = 20$ 16   or   5?
    - (g) $5 - x = 3$ 4   or   2?
    - (h) $12 = x + 7$ 5   or   7?
    - (i) $15 = 5t$ 3   or   10?

13. One way to find a root of an equation is by systematic trial. The following flow chart shows this procedure.

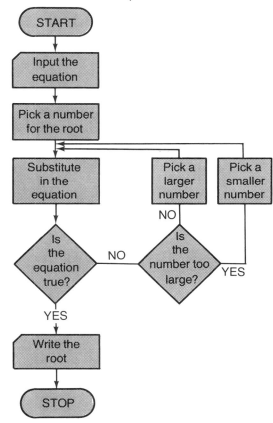

Solve the following equations using the flow chart above.
- (a) $x + 9 = 17$
- (b) $b - 4 = 11$
- (c) $3t = 24$
- (d) $5 + m = 21$
- (e) $23 = b + 4$
- (f) $18 = x - 3$
- (g) $2x + 1 = 7$
- (h) $2m - 1 = 9$
- (i) $3t + 2 = 11$
- (j) $b + 3 = 0$

9.2 SOLVING EQUATIONS BY ADDITION

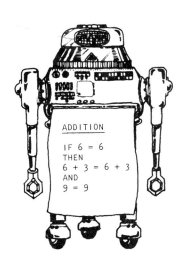

The scale at the right is balanced.

When the same mass is added to both sides of the scale, the scale remains balanced.

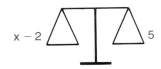

The equation
   $x - 2 = 5$
is like a balanced scale.

$x - 2$ $\qquad$ 5

ADDITION
IF 6 = 6
THEN
6 + 3 = 6 + 3
AND
9 = 9

When you add 2 to both sides, the equation still balances.

$x - 2 + 2$ $\qquad$ $5 + 2$

| Addition Rule |
| When you add the same number to both sides of an equation, the equality does not change. |

$$x - 2 = 5$$
$$x - 2 + 2 = 5 + 2$$
$$x + 0 = 7$$
$$x = 7$$

$\therefore$ the root of the equation is 7.

When solving equations we try to get the variable by itself on one side of the equation.

EXERCISE

A

1. Solve.
   (a) $x - 1 = 7$ (b) $m - 3 = 4$
   (c) $w - 5 = 6$ (d) $t - 8 = 2$
   (e) $y - 2 = 3$ (f) $m - 4 = 6$

B

2. Solve.
   (a) $x - 10 = 32$ (b) $t - 12 = 15$
   (c) $w - 11 = 3$ (d) $m - 14 = 21$
   (e) $y - 5 = 6$ (f) $x - 4 = 0$

3. Solve.
   (a) $x - 21 = 32$ (b) $y - 51 = 23$
   (c) $m - 16 = 49$ (d) $t - 18 = 56$
   (e) $w - 58 = 22$ (f) $r - 30 = 40$

4. Solve.
   (a) $8 = x - 1$ (b) $4 = m - 5$
   (c) $3 = t - 2$ (d) $13 = s - 3$
   (e) $9 = r - 6$ (f) $1 = x - 6$

5. Solve.
   (a) $x - 3 = 4.3$ (b) $x - 1 = 5.6$
   (c) $t - 2.1 = 7$ (d) $m - 3.4 = 6$
   (e) $w - 0.6 = 1.2$ (f) $s - 5.3 = 0.9$

6. Solve.
   (a) $x - 7 = 9 - 4$
   (b) $t - 1 = 13 + 3$
   (c) $m - 1 = 8 - 8$
   (d) $y - 5 = 21 - 7$
   (e) $w - 11 = 15 + 15$
   (f) $13 + 3 = x - 3$

9.3 SOLVING EQUATIONS BY SUBTRACTION

When the same mass is subtracted from both sides of a balanced scale, the scale remains balanced.

The equation
$$x + 3 = 8$$
is like a balanced scale.

$x + 3$ 8

When you subtract 3 from both sides, the equation still balances.

$x + 3 - 3$ $8 - 3$

$$x + 3 = 8$$
$$x + 3 - 3 = 8 - 3$$
$$x = 5$$

∴ the root of the equation is 5.

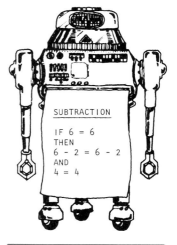

SUBTRACTION

IF 6 = 6
THEN
6 - 2 = 6 - 2
AND
4 = 4

Subtraction Rule
When you subtract the same number from both sides of an equation, the equality does not change.

EXERCISE

A

1. Solve.
   (a) $x + 2 = 3$
   (b) $m + 4 = 7$
   (c) $w + 1 = 6$
   (d) $t + 3 = 9$
   (e) $r + 6 = 8$
   (f) $y + 5 = 6$

B

2. Solve.
   (a) $x + 9 = 14$
   (b) $t + 21 = 32$
   (c) $r + 14 = 23$
   (d) $y + 35 = 42$
   (e) $s + 8 = 41$
   (f) $m + 7 = 31$

3. Solve.
   (a) $8 + x = 18$
   (b) $13 + y = 21$
   (c) $17 + m = 51$
   (d) $27 + r = 53$
   (e) $21 + t = 30$
   (f) $43 + w = 71$

4. Solve.
   (a) $21 = x + 7$
   (b) $14 = m + 13$
   (c) $18 = 5 + w$
   (d) $24 = 17 + r$
   (e) $51 = 23 + s$
   (f) $78 = x + 59$

5. Solve.
   (a) $x + 5 = 9.7$
   (b) $y + 3.3 = 6.8$
   (c) $w + 0.9 = 1.4$
   (d) $5.7 + s = 13.1$
   (e) $16.5 + r = 19.7$
   (f) $19.1 = t + 14.6$

6. Solve.
   (a) $x + 57 = 146$
   (b) $m + 283 = 545$
   (c) $276 + t = 384$
   (d) $356 = x + 45$
   (e) $401 = 53 + m$
   (f) $764 = 503 + m$
   (g) $x + 29 = 36 + 14$
   (h) $m + 68 = 107 - 13$
   (i) $13 + t = 84 + 6$
   (j) $36 + 84 = m + 2$

9.4 SOLVING EQUATIONS BY DIVISION

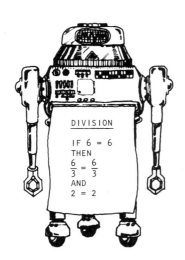

The equation
$$4x = 12$$
is like a balanced scale.

When we divide both sides by 4 the equation still balances.

$$4x = 12$$
$$\frac{4x}{4} = \frac{12}{4}$$
$$x = 3$$

∴ the root of the equation is 3.

Division Rule

When you divide both sides of an equation by the same number, the equality does not change.

EXERCISE

A

1. Solve.
   (a) $2x = 6$ (b) $5m = 10$
   (c) $3t = 6$ (d) $4y = 16$
   (e) $6n = 18$ (f) $2x = 8$
   (g) $5y = 20$ (h) $7t = 21$
   (i) $3r = 12$ (j) $4m = 24$
   (k) $8r = 16$ (l) $7x = 28$

B

2. Solve.
   (a) $5x = 25$ (b) $8m = 72$
   (c) $7t = 49$ (d) $9y = 54$
   (e) $2r = 18$ (f) $3w = 33$
   (g) $6n = 24$ (h) $4x = 44$
   (i) $4r = 48$ (j) $7m = 7$

3. Solve.
   (a) $10 = 2x$ (b) $8 = 4y$
   (c) $18 = 3m$ (d) $12 = 4r$

   (e) $30 = 5t$ (f) $16 = 8z$
   (g) $72 = 9w$ (h) $48 = 8x$
   (i) $24 = 6z$ (j) $4x = 0$

4. Solve.
   (a) $2x = 8.4$ (b) $3y = 36.9$
   (c) $0.2m = 8$ (d) $7t = 1.4$
   (e) $0.3n = 9.3$ (f) $0.5x = 3.5$
   (g) $5.2y = 26$ (h) $0.4t = 16$

5. Solve.
   (a) $9m = 324$ (b) $14m = 686$
   (c) $330 = 22t$ (d) $35w = 280$
   (e) $36x = 504$ (f) $33r = 1023$

6. Solve.
   (a) $2x = 15 + 5$ (b) $3m = 19 - 1$
   (c) $17 + 3 = 5t$ (d) $27 - 7 = 10s$
   (e) $4r = 18 + 6$ (f) $33 - 3 = 6w$

9.5 SOLVING EQUATIONS BY MULTIPLICATION

The equation

$$\frac{x}{3} = 4$$

is like a balanced scale.

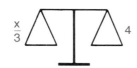

When we multiply both
sides by 3, the equation
still balances.

$$\frac{x}{3} = 4$$

$$3 \times \frac{x}{3} = 3 \times 4$$

$$x = 12$$

∴ the root of the equation is 12.

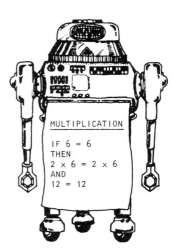

MULTIPLICATION

IF 6 = 6
THEN
2 × 6 = 2 × 6
AND
12 = 12

Multiplication Rule

When you multiply both sides of an equation by
the same number, the equality does not change.

EXERCISE

A

1. Solve.

   (a) $\frac{x}{2} = 3$ (b) $\frac{m}{3} = 5$ (c) $\frac{w}{6} = 1$

   (d) $\frac{t}{5} = 9$ (e) $\frac{n}{4} = 6$ (f) $\frac{s}{7} = 2$

   (g) $\frac{x}{10} = 4$ (h) $\frac{t}{9} = 8$ (i) $\frac{w}{8} = 7$

B

2. Solve.

   (a) $\frac{x}{9} = 13$ (b) $\frac{m}{5} = 14$ (c) $\frac{w}{2} = 21$

   (d) $\frac{r}{6} = 10$ (e) $\frac{t}{3} = 21$ (f) $\frac{s}{11} = 6$

   (g) $\frac{x}{8} = 40$ (h) $\frac{n}{6} = 31$ (i) $\frac{w}{12} = 9$

3. Solve.

   (a) $\frac{x}{3} = 2$ (b) $\frac{m}{2} = 1$ (c) $\frac{t}{4} = 4$

   (d) $\frac{w}{7} = 0$ (e) $\frac{s}{5} = 6$ (f) $\frac{r}{6} = 3$

   (g) $\frac{n}{9} = 5$ (h) $\frac{x}{8} = 7$ (i) $\frac{t}{10} = 6$

4. Solve.

   (a) $\frac{x}{3} = 1.3$ (b) $\frac{m}{2} = 0.5$

   (c) $\frac{n}{10} = 2.6$ (d) $\frac{t}{20} = 3.1$

9.6 SOLVING EQUATIONS USING FLOW DIAGRAMS

To build the Left Side of the equation,

$$2x + 1 = 9$$

we can use the following flow diagram.

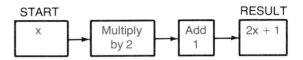

To solve the equation $2x + 1 = 9$, we get x by itself on the Left Side. To do this, we reverse the steps in the flow diagram used to build the Left Side.

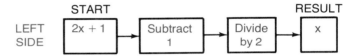

We now apply these reversed steps to the Right Side of the equation.

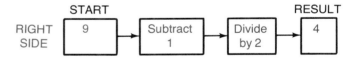

Comparing the results of the two reversed flow diagrams, we see that

$$x = 4$$

The root of $2x + 1 = 9$ is 4.

EXERCISE

B

1. Find the result of each flow diagram.
   (a)

   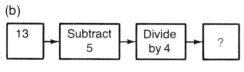

   (b)

   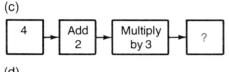

   (c)

   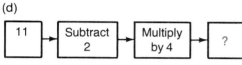

   (d)

   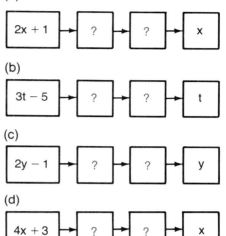

2. Find the result of each flow diagram.
   (a)

   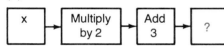

   (b)

   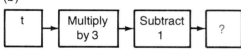

   (c)

   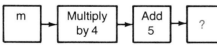

   (d)

   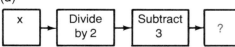

   (e)

   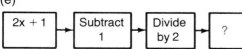

3. Complete the following flow diagrams.
   (a)

   (b)

   (c)

   (d)

4. Solve the following equations using flow diagrams.
   (a) $2x + 3 = 5$
   (b) $2x - 1 = 7$
   (c) $3t - 4 = 8$
   (d) $5m + 2 = 12$
   (e) $4x - 3 = 13$
   (f) $5y - 7 = 23$

5. Solve the following equations using flow diagrams.
   (a) $\dfrac{x}{2} - 1 = 2$

   (b) $\dfrac{x}{3} - 2 = 3$

   (c) $\dfrac{m}{4} + 2 = 5$

   (d) $\dfrac{t}{2} - 3 = 1$

9.7 SOLVING EQUATIONS

BUILDING AN EQUATION

To build an equation, we could proceed as follows.

$$x = 2 \longleftarrow \text{Solution}$$
$$3x = 6 \longleftarrow \text{Multiply both sides by 3.}$$
$$3x + 2 = 6 + 2 \longleftarrow \text{Add 2 to both sides.}$$
$$3x + 2 = 8 \longleftarrow \text{Equation}$$

SOLVING AN EQUATION

To solve $3x + 2 = 8$, we reverse the above procedure.

$$3x + 2 = 8 \longleftarrow \text{Equation}$$
$$3x + 2 - 2 = 8 - 2 \longleftarrow \text{Subtract 2 from both sides.}$$
$$3x = 6 \longleftarrow \text{Simplify.}$$
$$\frac{3x}{3} = \frac{6}{3} \longleftarrow \text{Divide both sides by 3.}$$
$$x = 2 \longleftarrow \text{Solution}$$

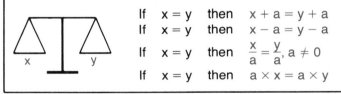

RULES FOR SOLVING EQUATIONS

If	$x = y$	then	$x + a = y + a$
If	$x = y$	then	$x - a = y - a$
If	$x = y$	then	$\dfrac{x}{a} = \dfrac{y}{a}, a \neq 0$
If	$x = y$	then	$a \times x = a \times y$

Example. Solve. $5x - 3x - 1 = 11 - 6$

Solution:

$$5x - 3x - 1 = 11 - 6$$
$$2x - 1 = 5 \longleftarrow \text{Simplify.}$$
$$2x - 1 + 1 = 5 + 1 \longleftarrow \text{Add 1 to both sides.}$$
$$2x = 6 \longleftarrow \text{Simplify.}$$
$$\frac{2x}{2} = \frac{6}{2} \longleftarrow \text{Divide both sides by 2.}$$
$$x = 3 \longleftarrow \text{Solution}$$

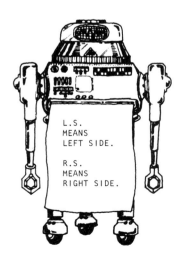

L.S.
MEANS
LEFT SIDE.

R.S.
MEANS
RIGHT SIDE.

Check   L.S. $= 5x - 3x - 1$ | R.S. $= 11 - 6$
$= 5(3) - 3(3) - 1$ | $= 5 \checkmark$
$= 15 - 9 - 1$
$= 5 \checkmark$
∴ the root is 3.

EXERCISE

B

1. Solve.
   (a) $x = 15 - 4$
   (b) $m = 13 + 6$
   (c) $t + 3 = 17 + 1$
   (d) $n - 3 = 9 - 2$
   (e) $r + 5 - 1 = 14$
   (f) $s + 6 - 3 = 8 + 4$
   (g) $y + 8 - 3 = 15 + 3$
   (h) $x + 5 = 13 - 1$

2. Solve and check.
   (a) $2x = 11 - 1$ (b) $3t = 14 + 4$
   (c) $2m + 1 = 9$ (d) $4n + 3 = 11$
   (e) $5y - 2 = 13$ (f) $2t - 3 = 7$
   (g) $6x - 4 = 14$ (h) $5w + 6 = 16$

3. Solve.
   (a) $5x - 3x = 8$ (b) $4w + w = 20$
   (c) $7t - 4t = 15$ (d) $2m + m = 24$
   (e) $3n + 2n = 25$ (f) $7x - 3x = 16$
   (g) $4t + 3t = 14$ (h) $8w - 3w = 35$

4. Solve.
   (a) $3x - x = 8 - 2$
   (b) $4w + 2w = 15 + 3$
   (c) $5t - 2t = 13 + 2$
   (d) $4m + 3m = 18 - 4$
   (e) $7n - 6n = 8 - 5$
   (f) $x + 2x = 11 - 2$
   (g) $5w - 3w = 9 + 1$
   (h) $2t + 4t = 15 - 3$

5. Solve and check.
   (a) $5x - 3x + 4 = 12$
   (b) $2w + w - 1 = 8$
   (c) $4t + 2t + 2 = 15 - 1$
   (d) $7m - 5m - 3 = 7 + 6$
   (e) $3n + 2n + 4 = 16 - 2$
   (f) $9x - 7x - 6 = 18 + 2$
   (g) $5w + 2w + 4 = 3 + 15$
   (h) $8t - 5t - 3 = 7 - 1$

6. Solve.
   (a) $\dfrac{x}{2} = 3 + 1$ (b) $\dfrac{m}{3} = 4 - 1$
   (c) $\dfrac{t}{4} = 5 + 2$ (d) $\dfrac{n}{5} = 6 - 4$
   (e) $\dfrac{x}{2} + 1 = 5$ (f) $\dfrac{t}{3} - 1 = 4$
   (g) $\dfrac{m}{4} + 1 = 6 - 2$ (h) $\dfrac{n}{5} - 2 = 8 - 5$

CHALLENGE

PICK A LETTER

1. Pick any letter from A to Z and write it on a piece of paper.

2. Write down the letter at the top of each column that contains your letter. Use the code A = 1, B = 2, C = 3, and so on, to convert these top letters to numbers. Find the sum of these numbers. Use the code to convert the sum back to a letter. This letter should be the same as the one you picked. Can you explain why?

A	H	P	D	B
C	I	Q	E	C
E	J	R	F	F
G	K	S	G	G
I	L	T	L	J
K	M	U	M	K
M	N	V	N	N
O	O	W	O	O
Q	X	X	T	R
S	Y	Y	U	S
U	Z	Z	V	V
W			W	W
Y				Z

9.8 EQUATIONS WITH INTEGERS

In some equations the roots are integers.

-2 is a root of $x + 5 = 3$
because $-2 + 5 = 3$.

To solve equations with integers, we proceed the same way as before.

Example 1. Solve. $2x - 1 = -9$

Solution:

$$
\begin{aligned}
2x - 1 &= -9 &&\longleftarrow \text{Equation} \\
2x - 1 + 1 &= -9 + 1 &&\longleftarrow \text{Add 1 to both sides.} \\
2x &= -8 &&\longleftarrow \text{Simplify.} \\
\frac{2x}{2} &= \frac{-8}{2} &&\longleftarrow \text{Divide both sides by 2.} \\
x &= -4 &&\longleftarrow \text{Simplify.}
\end{aligned}
$$

$\therefore$ the root is -4.

Example 2. Solve. $3x - 2 = 5 - 10$

Solution:

$$
\begin{aligned}
3x - 2 &= 5 - 10 &&\longleftarrow \text{Equation} \\
3x - 2 &= -5 &&\longleftarrow \text{Simplify.} \\
3x - 2 + 2 &= -5 + 2 &&\longleftarrow \text{Add 2 to both sides.} \\
3x &= -3 &&\longleftarrow \text{Simplify.} \\
\frac{3x}{3} &= \frac{-3}{3} &&\longleftarrow \text{Divide both sides by 3.} \\
x &= -1 &&\longleftarrow \text{Simplify.}
\end{aligned}
$$

$\therefore$ the root is -1.

Example 3. Solve and check. $4t - 5t + 6 = -3 + 8$

Solution:

$$
\begin{aligned}
4t - 5t + 6 &= -3 + 8 &&\longleftarrow \text{Equation} \\
-t + 6 &= 5 &&\longleftarrow \text{Simplify.} \\
-t + 6 - 6 &= 5 - 6 &&\longleftarrow \text{Subtract 6 from both sides.} \\
-t &= -1 &&\longleftarrow \text{Simplify.} \\
\frac{-t}{-1} &= \frac{-1}{-1} &&\longleftarrow \text{Divide both sides by } -1. \\
t &= 1 &&\longleftarrow \text{Simplify.}
\end{aligned}
$$

Check　L.S. $= 4t - 5t + 6$　　R.S. $= -3 + 8$
　　　　　　$= 4(1) - 5(1) + 6$　　　$= 5\checkmark$
　　　　　　$= 4 - 5 + 6$
　　　　　　$= -1 + 6$
　　　　　　$= 5\checkmark$
　　　　$\therefore$ the root is 1.

EXERCISE

A

1. Solve.
   (a) $x + 2 = 5$
   (b) $t - 2 = 7$
   (c) $m - 1 = -2$
   (d) $y + 3 = -1$
   (e) $x - 4 = 0$
   (f) $b + 4 = -2$
   (g) $3x = 6$
   (h) $2x = -10$
   (i) $y - 3 = 2$
   (j) $m + 4 = -1$
   (k) $x + 2 = -6$
   (l) $m - 1 = -2$
   (m) $3x = -12$
   (n) $-2x = 4$
   (o) $-x = 7$
   (p) $-t = -3$

B

2. Solve and check.
   (a) $2x + 1 = -7$
   (b) $2t - 3 = -9$
   (c) $3m + 4 = 10$
   (d) $4y + 1 = -11$
   (e) $5 - 2x = 7$
   (f) $7 - m = -2$
   (g) $-x + 3 = 4$
   (h) $3x + 1 = -2$
   (i) $1 - 2x = 5$
   (j) $-4m + 3 = -1$

3. Solve.
   (a) $2t - 1 = 3 - 6$
   (b) $3m - 2 = 1 - 9$
   (c) $4x + 5 = -5 + 2$
   (d) $2 - 3x = -6 - 1$
   (e) $1 - 2m = 3 - 8$
   (f) $5t - 4 = 1 - 10$

4. Solve.
   (a) $2x - 3x = 4$
   (b) $4t - 6t = -6$
   (c) $m - 4m = -9$
   (d) $3y - 6y + 1 = 7$
   (e) $1 - 3t + t = -8 + 11$
   (f) $2x - 6x + 1 = 9$
   (g) $5 - 5t + 2t = -13$
   (h) $1 - 2y + 3y = -9 + 2$
   (i) $2m - 3 - 4m = 7 - 12$
   (j) $7 - 3x + 6x = -2$

CHALLENGE

PALINDROMES
The word NOON is a palindrome since it reads the same forwards as backwards.
The number 252 is a palindrome.

The number 163 is not a palindrome.

To change 163 to a number that is a palindrome, we proceed as follows.

Write.	163
Reverse and add.	+ 361
524 is not a palindrome,	524
so we reverse and add.	+ 425
949 is a palindrome.	949

Use the above method to change the following numbers to palindromes.

1. 429　　　　6. 1235
2. 381　　　　7. 7138
3. 724　　　　8. 8436
4. 836　　　　9. 7817
5. 907　　　　10. 6917

9.9 VARIABLES ON BOTH SIDES OF THE EQUATION

Sometimes the variable is on both sides of the equation. To solve these equations you get the variable alone on one side of the equation.

Example 1. Solve. $5x = 8 + 3x$

Solution:

$$5x = 8 + 3x \longleftarrow \text{Equation}$$
$$5x - 3x = 8 + 3x - 3x \longleftarrow \text{Subtract 3x from both sides.}$$
$$2x = 8 \longleftarrow \text{Simplify.}$$
$$\frac{2x}{2} = \frac{8}{2} \longleftarrow \text{Divide both sides by 2.}$$
$$x = 4 \longleftarrow \text{Simplify.}$$

For some equations it is easier to get the variable alone on the Right Side of the equation.

Example 2. Solve. $4x - 6 = 7x$

Solution:

$$4x - 6 = 7x \longleftarrow \text{Equation}$$
$$4x - 6 - 4x = 7x - 4x \longleftarrow \text{Subtract 4x from both sides.}$$
$$-6 = 3x \longleftarrow \text{Simplify.}$$
$$\frac{-6}{3} = \frac{3x}{3} \longleftarrow \text{Divide both sides by 3.}$$
$$-2 = x \longleftarrow \text{Simplify.}$$

When you are able to solve equations easily, you can try doing some of the steps mentally.

Example 3. Solve. $5t + 9 = t - 7$

Solution:

All steps shown	Some steps done mentally
$5t + 9 = t - 7$	$5t + 9 = t - 7$
$5t + 9 - 9 = t - 7 - 9$	$5t = t - 16$
$5t = t - 16$	$4t = -16$
$5t - t = t - 16 - t$	$t = -4$
$4t = -16$	
$\dfrac{4t}{4} = \dfrac{-16}{4}$	
$t = -4$	

EXERCISE

B

1. Solve.
   (a) $3x = 4 + 2x$
   (b) $5m = 2m + 9$
   (c) $5t = 3t + 8$
   (d) $6y = 5y + 1$
   (e) $4x - 7 = 3x + 2$
   (f) $3m - 2 = m + 10$
   (g) $8y - 3 = 3y + 7$
   (h) $3x - 4 = 11 - 2x$
   (i) $m + 3 = 19 - 3m$
   (j) $2t - 7 = 11 - 4t$

2. Solve.
   (a) $3x + 16 = 7x$
   (b) $2m + 15 = 5m$
   (c) $4y + 8 = 6y$
   (d) $2t + 9 = 5t$
   (e) $5m = 7m - 14$
   (f) $3t = 7t - 20$
   (g) $4x = 13x - 27$
   (h) $2m = 9m - 35$

3. Solve.
   (a) $3x = 5x + 8$
   (b) $2t + 9 = 5t + 12$
   (c) $3m - 7 = 6m + 5$
   (d) $5y + 6 = y - 14$
   (e) $7x - 3 = 4x + 6$
   (f) $m + 5 = 6m - 5$
   (g) $3t + 14 = 2 - 3t$
   (h) $3y + 8 = 23 + 8y$
   (i) $m - 7 = 6m + 3$
   (j) $11 - 3x = 19 - x$
   (k) $21 - 2t = 3t - 4$
   (l) $17 + 3m = 23 - 3m$

4. Solve.
   (a) $5x + 2x = 3x + 16$
   (b) $4t - t = t + 6$
   (c) $7m + 5 = 4m - 3m + 17$
   (d) $3x - 5x - 1 = x + 8$
   (e) $2y - 7y + 4 = y - 20$
   (f) $3t - 5t - 6 = 8$
   (g) $13 = 3m - 6m + 4$
   (h) $11x = 2x - 81$
   (i) $2m - 13 = 17 - 3m$
   (j) $1 - 8t = t - 26$

5. Solve the equations.
   Take the corresponding letter from the table at the right to find the word.
   (a) $5x = 3x + 8$
   (b) $2x = 7x + 30$
   (c) $6x - 2 = x - 17$
   (d) $2x - 1 = 5x + 17$
   (e) $7x - 9 = 2x + 16$
   (f) $9x + 4 = 7x + 18$
   (g) $3x + 26 = 2 - x$
   (h) $4x - 5 = 10x + 13$

$-6 =$	A
$-3 =$	N
$7 =$	I
$4 =$	C
$5 =$	D

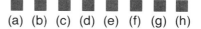

(a) (b) (c) (d) (e) (f) (g) (h)

Chemists work from formulas.

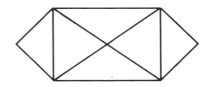

9.10 EQUATIONS WITH BRACKETS

Some equations have brackets. To solve these equations, we first remove the brackets and simplify.

Example 1. Solve. $2(x + 3) = 10$

Solution:
$$2(x + 3) = 10$$
$$2x + 6 = 10$$
$$2x + 6 - 6 = 10 - 6$$
$$2x = 4$$
$$\frac{2x}{2} = \frac{4}{2}$$
$$x = 2$$

∴ the root of the equation is 2.

Example 2. Solve and check. $4(x - 3) = 2x$

Solution:
$$4(x - 3) = 2x$$
$$4x - 12 = 2x$$
$$4x - 12 + 12 = 2x + 12$$
$$4x = 2x + 12$$
$$4x - 2x = 2x + 12 - 2x$$
$$2x = 12$$
$$\frac{2x}{2} = \frac{12}{2}$$
$$x = 6$$

Check   L.S. $= 4(x - 3)$ | R.S. $= 2x$
$= 4(6 - 3)$ | $= 2(6)$
$= 4(3)$ | $= 12 \checkmark$
$= 12 \checkmark$ |

∴ the root of the equation is 6.

EXERCISE

B

1. Solve.
   (a) $2(x + 1) = 4$
   (b) $3(m - 1) = 6$
   (c) $4(t - 2) = 2t$
   (d) $5(y + 1) = 4y$
   (e) $3(x - 3) = 0$
   (f) $4(m + 3) = 4$

2. Solve.
   (a) $6 = 2(x - 1)$
   (b) $15 = 3(m + 4)$
   (c) $-15 = 5(y - 3)$
   (d) $3t = 4(t + 2)$
   (e) $m = 3(m - 2)$

3. Solve and check.
   - (a) $2(x - 1) + 7 = 9$
   - (b) $3(m - 4) + 7 = 10$
   - (c) $4(m + 2) - 13 = 3$
   - (d) $5(t + 3) - 1 = 4$
   - (e) $2(y - 5) - 1 = 13$

4. Solve.
   - (a) $3(y + 6) = 2y + 14$
   - (b) $4(x - 2) = x + 4$
   - (c) $5(m - 1) = 2m - 8$
   - (d) $2(t + 3) = 3 - t$
   - (e) $3(x + 5) = 1 - 4x$

5. Solve and check.
   - (a) $3(x - 1) = 2(x + 2)$
   - (b) $5(t + 3) = 3(t + 1)$
   - (c) $7(m + 2) = 2(m - 3)$
   - (d) $3(x + 2) = 5(x - 4)$

6. Solve.
   - (a) $3(x - 1) + 2 = 2(x + 1)$
   - (b) $4(m + 1) + 8 = 2(m - 1)$
   - (c) $5(t - 3) - 1 = 2(t + 4)$
   - (d) $7(y - 1) + 6 = 2(y - 3)$
   - (e) $5(x - 2) - 1 = 2(x + 2)$

7. Solve.
   - (a) $2(x - 2) = 7 - 2(x + 3)$
   - (b) $11 - 3(m - 1) = 2(m + 2)$
   - (c) $6 - (x - 1) = 3(x + 5)$
   - (d) $7 - (y - 1) = 5 - 2(y - 2)$
   - (e) $6 - 3(y - 2) = 0$

8. Solve.
   - (a) $2(2x - 1) + 3 = 9$
   - (b) $3(3x - 1) + 6 = -15$
   - (c) $2(2x - 1) = 3(x - 4)$
   - (d) $3(1 - 2x) + 11 = 2(3x + 1)$
   - (e) $6 - (2x - 1) = 3(2x + 5)$

C

9. The equation $9(x + 1) = 27$ represents the area of a rectangle. Solve the equation and then find the value of $(x + 1)$, the width of the rectangle.

10. The equation $7(x + 3) = 28$ represents the area of a rectangle. Solve the equation and then find the value of $(x + 3)$, the width of the rectangle.

ⅢICRD ⅢRTH

This program solves equations.

Type in the left side of your equation in place of (left side) in statement 20 using BASIC computer language.

Type in the right side of your equation in place of (right side) in statement 30 using BASIC computer language.

NEW

```
10 FOR X = Ø TO 1
20 LET L = (left side)
30 LET R = (right side)
40 LET F(X) = L-R
50 NEXT X
60 LET A = F(Ø)/(F(Ø)-F(1))
70 PRINT"X = ";A
80 END
```

RUN

Example Solve for x.
$$3(X - 2) = 2(X + 3) - 5$$

Solution:

NEW

```
10 FOR X = Ø TO 1
20 LET L = 3*(X-2)
30 LET R = 2*(X+3)-5
40 LET F(X) = L-R
50 NEXT X
60 LET A = F(Ø)/(F(Ø)-F(1))
70 PRINT"X = ";A
80 END
```

RUN

x = 7
∴ the root is 7.

Solve the following equations.
   1. $5(2x + 3) + 4 = 3x + 8$
   2. $3 - 2(x + 4) = 4 - 5x$
   3. $2x - 5(x + 2) = 4x + 7$
   4. $4(2x - 1) - 3x = 6x - (3x + 1)$

9.11 SOLVING EQUATIONS WITH DECIMALS

Many equations contain decimals. There are two ways to solve them.

In Method I the decimals are carried throughout the solution. In Method II the first step is to clear the decimals.

Example 1. Solve. $1.2x + 0.4 = 2.8$

Solution:

METHOD I	*METHOD II*
Carrying Decimals	Clearing Decimals

METHOD I

$$1.2x + 0.4 = 2.8$$
$$1.2x + 0.4 - 0.4 = 2.8 - 0.4$$
$$1.2x = 2.4$$
$$\frac{1.2x}{1.2} = \frac{2.4}{1.2}$$
$$x = 2$$

METHOD II

$$1.2x + 0.4 = 2.8$$
$$10 \times 1.2x + 10 \times 0.4 = 10 \times 2.8 \leftarrow \text{Multiply by 10.}$$
$$12x + 4 = 28$$
$$12x + 4 - 4 = 28 - 4$$
$$12x = 24$$
$$\frac{12x}{12} = \frac{24}{12}$$
$$x = 2$$

Example 2. Solve and check. $3x - 0.5 = 0.1$

Solution and check:

METHOD I

$$3x - 0.5 = 0.1$$
$$3x - 0.5 + 0.5 = 0.1 + 0.5$$
$$3x = 0.6$$
$$\frac{3x}{3} = \frac{0.6}{3}$$
$$x = 0.2$$

METHOD II

$$3x - 0.5 = 0.1$$
$$10 \times 3x - 10 \times 0.5 = 10 \times 0.1$$
$$30x - 5 = 1$$
$$30x - 5 + 5 = 1 + 5$$
$$30x = 6$$
$$\frac{30x}{30} = \frac{6}{30}$$
$$x = 0.2$$

Check   L.S. $= 3x - 0.5$ R.S. $= 0.1 \checkmark$
$$= 3(0.2) - 0.5$$
$$= 0.6 - 0.5$$
$$= 0.1 \checkmark$$

EXERCISE

B

1. Solve.
   (a) $x + 0.5 = 0.7$
   (b) $m - 0.3 = 0.5$
   (c) $t + 5.7 = 4.3$
   (d) $y - 3.6 = 1.4$
   (e) $m + 7.3 = 3.5$

2. Solve.
   (a) $0.2x = 2$
   (b) $0.3x = 15$
   (c) $1.5m = 4.5$
   (d) $0.4y = 1.6$
   (e) $0.5t = -1.5$

3. Solve and check.
   (a) $2x - 0.5 = 0.7$
   (b) $3t + 0.1 = 1.3$
   (c) $4m - 0.4 = 2$
   (d) $3y + 1.6 = 4.6$
   (e) $5x - 1.7 = 1.8$

4. Solve.
   (a) $3m - 2.6 = 7.9$
   (b) $2t + 5.8 = 1.2$
   (c) $4y - 1.8 = -3.8$
   (d) $5x + 1.3 = -2.2$
   (e) $2x - 5.4 = -8.6$

5. Solve.
   (a) $1.3x + 0.7 = 3.3$
   (b) $0.4t + 3 = 4.2$
   (c) $0.6m + 5.6 = 2$
   (d) $1.1y - 3.2 = -8.7$
   (e) $2.7x - 5.5 = -10.9$

6. Solve.
   (a) $1.2x + 0.7 = 0.4x + 2.3$
   (b) $3.5t - 0.4 = 1.5t + 0.6$
   (c) $2.3m - 1.47 = 6.85 + 0.7m$
   (d) $1.8y + 2.63 = 2.4y - 1.33$
   (e) $2.4x - 3.57 = 1.2x - 5.01$

CALCULATOR MATH

SOLVING EQUATIONS USING A CALCULATOR.

Example. Solve.
$$5.6x + 1.023 = 1.4x + 4.089$$

 Step 1. Collect the x's on the left side and store the number of x's in the memory.

PRESS: 5 . 6 − 1 . 4 =
 M+ or STO or M

 Step 2. Collect the numerical terms on the right side.

PRESS: 4 . 0 8 9 − 1 . 0 2 3 =

 Step 3. Divide the number in the display by the number in the memory.

PRESS: ÷ MR = or RCL

The display gives the root 0.73 or .73.

Solve these equations using a calculator.
1. $2.9x + 2.3x = 10.61 + 8.11$
2. $4.31x - 2.89x = 7.304 + 3.914$
3. $8.71x - 7.354 = 9.195$
4. $6.3x + 2.843 = 3.6 + 4.355$
5. $3.2x + 1.96 = 9.38 - 2.1x$
6. $8.2x - 58.139 = 73.666 - 6.3x$

9.12 EQUATIONS WITH FRACTIONS

Some equations contain more than one fraction. To solve these equations, we first clear the denominators.

To do this, multiply each term by the Lowest Common Denominator (L.C.D.) of the denominators.

THE LOWEST COMMON DENOMINATOR OF 3 AND 2 IS 6.

Example 1. Solve. $\dfrac{x}{3} = \dfrac{1}{2}$

Solution:
The Lowest Common Denominator of 3 and 2 is 6.

$$\dfrac{x}{3} = \dfrac{1}{2} \longleftarrow \text{Equation}$$

$$6 \times \dfrac{x}{3} = 6 \times \dfrac{1}{2} \longleftarrow \text{Multiply both sides by 6.}$$

$$2x = 3 \longleftarrow \text{Simplify.}$$

$$\dfrac{2x}{2} = \dfrac{3}{2} \longleftarrow \text{Divide both sides by 2.}$$

$$x = \dfrac{3}{2} \text{ or } 1\dfrac{1}{2} \longleftarrow \text{Simplify.}$$

> To clear fractions, multiply both sides by the L.C.D.

Example 2. Solve and check. $\dfrac{x}{3} = \dfrac{x}{4} + 1$

Solution:
The Lowest Common Denominator of 3 and 4 is 12.

$$\dfrac{x}{3} = \dfrac{x}{4} + 1 \longleftarrow \text{Equation}$$

$$12 \times \dfrac{x}{3} = 12\left(\dfrac{x}{4} + 1\right) \longleftarrow \text{Multiply both sides by 12.}$$

$$4x = 3x + 12 \longleftarrow \text{Simplify.}$$

$$4x - 3x = 3x + 12 - 3x \longleftarrow \text{Subtract 3x from both sides.}$$

$$x = 12 \longleftarrow \text{Simplify.}$$

Check   L.S. $= \dfrac{x}{3}$ $\qquad$ R.S. $= \dfrac{x}{4} + 1$

$\qquad\qquad\quad = \dfrac{12}{3}$ $\qquad\qquad\quad = \dfrac{12}{4} + 1$

$\qquad\qquad\quad = 4 \ \checkmark$ $\qquad\qquad\quad = 3 + 1$

$\qquad\qquad\qquad\qquad\qquad\qquad\quad = 4 \ \checkmark$

$\therefore$ the root of the equation is 12.

EXERCISE

B

1. Solve and check.

(a) $\dfrac{x}{3} = 6$

(b) $\dfrac{m}{4} = 2$

(c) $\dfrac{t}{3} = -1$

(d) $\dfrac{x}{2} - 1 = 3$

(e) $\dfrac{m}{5} + 1 = -2$

(f) $\dfrac{t}{6} - 2 = -4$

(g) $\dfrac{m}{2} - 3 = -7$

(h) $\dfrac{x}{3} - 5 = -8$

2. Solve.

(a) $\dfrac{x}{2} = \dfrac{1}{4}$

(b) $\dfrac{m}{4} = \dfrac{1}{3}$

(c) $\dfrac{t}{5} = \dfrac{1}{4}$

(d) $\dfrac{m}{6} = \dfrac{1}{3}$

(e) $\dfrac{x}{8} = \dfrac{1}{2}$

(f) $\dfrac{m}{5} = \dfrac{2}{3}$

(g) $\dfrac{t}{4} = \dfrac{4}{5}$

(h) $\dfrac{m}{3} = \dfrac{5}{6}$

(i) $\dfrac{x}{4} = \dfrac{7}{8}$

3. Solve and check.

(a) $\dfrac{x}{2} = \dfrac{x}{3} + 1$

(b) $\dfrac{x}{3} = \dfrac{x}{4} - 1$

(c) $\dfrac{x}{2} = \dfrac{x}{4} - 2$

(d) $\dfrac{x}{5} - \dfrac{x}{3} = 2$

(e) $\dfrac{x}{6} - \dfrac{x}{3} = 4$

(f) $\dfrac{x}{4} + \dfrac{x}{6} = 10$

4. Solve.

(a) $\dfrac{x}{2} = \dfrac{x}{3} + \dfrac{1}{2}$

(b) $\dfrac{x}{4} = \dfrac{x}{3} - \dfrac{1}{6}$

(c) $\dfrac{x}{4} - \dfrac{x}{2} = \dfrac{1}{2}$

(d) $\dfrac{x}{3} - \dfrac{x}{5} = \dfrac{2}{5}$

(e) $\dfrac{x}{2} + \dfrac{x}{3} = \dfrac{2}{3}$

CHALLENGE

What letters go with each number on a telephone dial?

9.13 INEQUALITIES — I (BY INSPECTION)

WE READ INEQUALITIES FROM LEFT TO RIGHT.

Number sentences that contain the signs $>$ or $<$ are called inequalities.

Examples of inequalities are:

$9 > 8$	(9 "is greater than" 8)
$6 < 7$	(6 "is less than" 7)

When an inequality contains a variable such as

$$x + 1 > 4, x \in W$$

it is either "true" or "false," depending on the value we assign to x.

When x is a whole number greater than 3, then $x + 1 > 4$ is true.

$$4 + 1 > 4$$
$$5 + 1 > 4$$
$$6 + 1 > 4$$

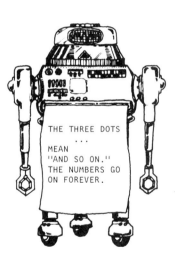

THE THREE DOTS
...
MEAN "AND SO ON." THE NUMBERS GO ON FOREVER.

The solution for $x + 1 > 4, x \in W$ is written as

$$\{4, 5, 6, \ldots\}$$
or $\quad x > 3$

The solution can also be graphed on a whole number line.

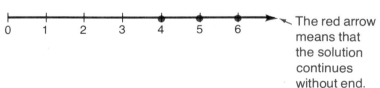

The red arrow means that the solution continues without end.

Example. Solve. $x + 3 < 6, x \in W$

Solution: We must find the whole number values for x so that when we add 3 to x, the result will be less than 6.

Since $0 + 3 < 6$, 0 is part of the solution.
Since $1 + 3 < 6$, 1 is part of the solution.
Since $2 + 3 < 6$, 2 is part of the solution.

The solution set is $\{0, 1, 2\}$.

EXERCISE

A

1. Replace the ▨ by either < or >.
   (a) 7 ▨ 9
   (b) 16 ▨ 13
   (c) 11 ▨ 12
   (d) 63 ▨ 64
   (e) 193 ▨ 191
   (f) 84 ▨ 85

2. State whether the following are true or false.
   (a) 16 < 17
   (b) 7 > 9
   (c) 21 < 24
   (d) 29 > 28
   (e) 33 < 32

3. Replace the ▨ by either < or >.
   (a) 8 ▨ 7
   (b) 0 ▨ 5
   (c) −4 ▨ 2
   (d) 3 ▨ −1
   (e) −5 ▨ −3
   (f) 0 ▨ −2

B

4. The graphs show the solutions of inequalities. Write the solution using symbols.
   (a)

   (b)

   (c)

5. Solve. $x \in W$
   (a) $x > 5$
   (b) $x < 3$
   (c) $x > 7$
   (d) $x < 6$

6. Solve. $x \in W$
   (a) $x + 1 < 4$
   (b) $x - 2 > 3$
   (c) $x + 3 > 5$
   (d) $x - 3 < 6$

7. Solve. Graph the solution.
   (a) $x + 1 < 5, x \in W$
   (b) $x - 1 > 4, x \in W$
   (c) $x + 2 > 6, x \in W$
   (d) $x - 3 < 8, x \in W$

CHALLENGE

Move 4 toothpicks to form 5 identical squares.

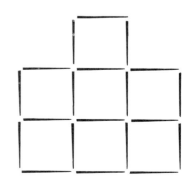

9.14 INEQUALITIES — II (BY INSPECTION)

There are three other inequality signs. If we read from left to right, they are:

$\leq$ is less than or equal to
$\geq$ is greater than or equal to
$\neq$ is not equal to

Inequalities containing these signs are solved as before.

Example 1. Solve. $x + 2 \leq 5, x \in W$

Solution: We must find the whole number values for x so that when we add 2 to x the result is less than or equal to 5.

Since $0 + 2 \leq 5$, 0 belongs to the solution.
Since $1 + 2 \leq 5$, 1 belongs to the solution.
Since $2 + 2 \leq 5$, 2 belongs to the solution.
Since $3 + 2 \leq 5$, 3 belongs to the solution.

The solution for $x + 2 \leq 5, x \in W$ is written as:
$\{0, 1, 2, 3\}$
or $x < 4, x \in W$
or $x \leq 3, x \in W$

The solution can also be graphed on a whole number line.

Example 2. Solve. $x + 1 \neq 3, x \in W$

Solution: We must find the whole number values for x so that when we add 1 to x, the result is not equal to 3.

Since $0 + 1 \neq 3$, 0 is part of the solution.
Since $1 + 1 \neq 3$, 1 is part of the solution.
Since $3 + 1 \neq 3$, 3 is part of the solution.

The solution set is $\{0, 1, 3, 4 \ldots\}$
The graph is the solution set is

EXERCISE

A

1. State whether the following are true or false.
   (a) $6 \neq 7$
   (b) $8 \geqslant 9$
   (c) $7 \leqslant 6$
   (d) $5 \geqslant 5$
   (e) $7 \leqslant 10$
   (f) $4 \neq 4$
   (g) $9 \geqslant 10$

B

2. Match each graph with two inequalities at the right.
   (a)

   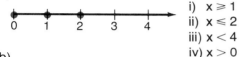

   (b)

   i) $x \geqslant 1$
   ii) $x \leqslant 2$
   iii) $x < 4$
   iv) $x > 0$
   v) $x \leqslant 3$
   vi) $x < 3$

   (c)

3. Solve. $x \in W$
   (a) $x > 3$ (b) $x \geqslant 5$
   (c) $x < 4$ (d) $x \leqslant 6$
   (e) $x \neq 5$ (f) $x \neq 2$

4. Solve. $x \in W$
   (a) $x + 1 \leqslant 5$
   (b) $x - 2 \geqslant 7$
   (c) $x + 3 \neq 6$
   (d) $x - 5 \leqslant 3$
   (e) $x + 2 \geqslant 6$

5. Solve. Graph the solution.
   (a) $x + 3 \leqslant 6$, $x \in W$
   (b) $x - 2 \geqslant 4$, $x \in W$
   (c) $x + 2 \neq 5$, $x \in W$
   (d) $x - 1 \leqslant 5$, $x \in W$
   (e) $x + 4 \geqslant 9$, $x \in W$
   (f) $x - 1 \neq 6$, $x \in W$
   (g) $x + 3 < 7$, $x \in W$
   (h) $x - 4 > 8$, $x \in W$

CHALLENGE

The following shows the first five rows of Pascal's Triangle.

$$
\begin{array}{ccccccccc}
 & & & & 1 & & & & \\
 & & & 1 & & 1 & & & \\
 & & 1 & & 2 & & 1 & & \\
 & 1 & & 3 & & 3 & & 1 & \\
1 & & 4 & & 6 & & 4 & & 1 \\
\end{array}
$$

What is the pattern?
What are the next two rows?

How are the following powers contained in Pascal's Triangle?
$$11^1 = 11$$
$$11^2 = 121$$
$$11^3 = 1331$$
$$11^4 = 14\ 641$$
$$11^5 = 161\ 051$$
$$11^6 = 1\ 771\ 561$$
$$11^7 = 19\ 487\ 171$$

9.15 SOLVING INEQUALITIES BY ADDITION

We can think of inequalities as objects on an unbalanced scale. For the diagram at the right,
$$3 > 2$$

For the diagram at the right,
$$x - 2 > 5$$

When the same mass is added to both sides of the scale, the scale remains unbalanced in the same direction.

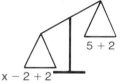

Example. Solve. $x - 2 > 5$, $x \in W$

Solution:
$$x - 2 > 5$$
$$x - 2 + 2 > 5 + 2$$
$$x > 7$$

This tells us that all the numbers greater than 7 are solutions of $x - 2 > 5$.
The graph of the solution is:

EXERCISE

B

1. Solve, $x \in I$.
   (a) $x - 3 > 4$
   (b) $x - 2 > 6$
   (c) $x - 3 < 5$
   (d) $x - 1 \geqslant 2$
   (e) $x - 1 \leqslant 3$
   (f) $x - 5 > -2$
   (g) $x - 4 \geqslant -6$
   (h) $x - 2 < -1$
   (i) $x - 7 \leqslant -9$
   (j) $x - 2 > 0$

2. Solve. Graph the solution.
   (a) $x - 3 > 2$, $x \in W$
   (b) $x - 5 < 6$, $x \in W$
   (c) $x - 4 \geqslant 1$, $x \in W$
   (d) $x - 2 \leqslant 3$, $x \in W$
   (e) $x - 4 < -1$, $x \in I$
   (f) $x - 2 \geqslant -6$, $x \in I$
   (g) $x - 1 < -3$, $x \in I$
   (h) $x - 5 \leqslant -6$, $x \in I$
   (i) $x - 1 \geqslant -3$, $x \in I$
   (j) $x - 2 < 0$, $x \in I$

9.16 SOLVING INEQUALITIES BY SUBTRACTION

For the diagram at the right.
    x + 2 > 5

When the same mass is subtracted from both sides of the scale, the scale remains unbalanced in the same direction.

Example. Solve.   x + 2 > 5, x ∈ W

Solution: x + 2 > 5
            x + 2 − 2 > 5 − 2
                    x > 3

This tells us that all numbers greater than 3 are solutions of
    x + 2 > 5.
The graph of the solution is:

EXERCISE

B

1. Solve, x ∈ I.
    (a) x + 3 > 6
    (b) x + 2 > 7
    (c) x + 4 < 8
    (d) x + 1 ⩾ 2
    (e) x + 5 ⩽ 7
    (f) x + 6 < 3
    (g) x + 1 > −2
    (h) x + 4 < −3
    (i) x + 3 ⩾ −5
    (j) x + 2 ⩽ 0

2. Solve. Graph the solution.
    (a) x + 2 > 6, x ∈ W
    (b) x + 1 < 4, x ∈ W
    (c) x + 3 ⩾ 5, x ∈ W
    (d) x + 4 ⩽ 7, x ∈ W
    (e) x + 6 > 2, x ∈ I
    (f) x + 5 < 3, x ∈ I
    (g) x + 4 > −1, x ∈ I
    (h) x + 7 ⩽ −2, x ∈ I
    (i) x + 5 ⩾ −3, x ∈ I
    (j) x + 1 > 0, x ∈ I

9.17 SOLVING INEQUALITIES BY DIVISION

When both sides of an inequality are divided by the same positive number, the scale remains unbalanced in the same direction.

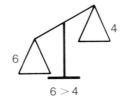

$$6 > 4$$

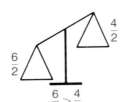

$$\frac{6}{2} > \frac{4}{2}$$

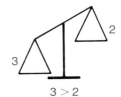

$$3 > 2$$

Example 1.

Solve, $3x > 12$, $x \in W$

Solution:

$$3x > 12$$
$$\frac{3x}{3} > \frac{12}{3}$$
$$x > 4$$

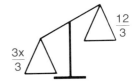

When both sides of an inequality are divided by the same negative number, the scale becomes unbalanced in the opposite direction

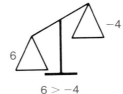

$$6 > -4$$

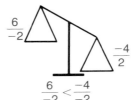

$$\frac{6}{-2} < \frac{-4}{-2}$$

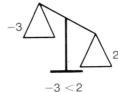

$$-3 < 2$$

Example 2.

Solve. $-3x > 12$, $x \in I$

Solution:

$$-3x > 12$$
$$\frac{-3x}{-3} < \frac{12}{-3}$$
$$x < -4$$

EXERCISE

A

1. Replace ▧ by $<$ or $>$ to make the statements true.

   (a) Since $3 < 12$, then $\dfrac{3}{-3}$ ▧ $\dfrac{12}{-3}$

   (b) Since $3 > -12$, then $\dfrac{3}{-3}$ ▧ $\dfrac{-12}{-3}$

   (c) Since $4 < 6$, then $\dfrac{4}{2}$ ▧ $\dfrac{6}{2}$

   (d) Since $-15 < -5$, then $\dfrac{-15}{-5}$ ▧ $\dfrac{-5}{-5}$

   (e) Since $-8 > -12$, then $\dfrac{-8}{4}$ ▧ $\dfrac{-12}{4}$

B

2. Solve, $x \in I$.
   (a) $2x > 6$
   (b) $3x < 12$
   (c) $4x \geqslant -8$
   (d) $5x \leqslant -10$
   (e) $-2x > 4$
   (f) $-3x < 3$
   (g) $-4x \geqslant -12$

3. Solve. Graph the solution.
   (a) $3x > 6$, $x \in I$
   (b) $4t < -12$, $t \in I$
   (c) $-2x < 6$, $x \in I$
   (d) $-x \geqslant -3$, $x \in I$

9.18 SOLVING INEQUALITIES BY MULTIPLICATION

When both sides of an inequality are multiplied by the same positive number, the scale remains unbalanced in the same direction.

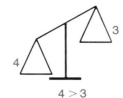

$4 > 3$

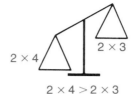

$2 \times 4 > 2 \times 3$

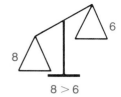

$8 > 6$

Example 1.

Solve. $\dfrac{x}{2} > 3$, $x \in W$

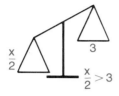

$\dfrac{x}{2} > 3$

Solution: $\dfrac{x}{2} > 3$

$$2 \times \dfrac{x}{2} > 2 \times 3$$

$$x > 6$$

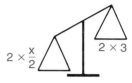

When both sides of an inequality are multiplied by the same negative number, the scale becomes unbalanced in the opposite direction.

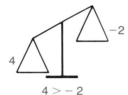

$4 > -2$

$-2 \times 4 < -2 \times -2$

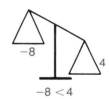

$-8 < 4$

Example 2.

Solve. $\dfrac{x}{-2} > 3$, $x \in I$

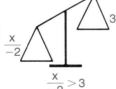

$\dfrac{x}{-2} > 3$

Solution: $\dfrac{x}{-2} > 3$

$$-2 \times \dfrac{x}{-2} < -2 \times 3$$

$$x < -6$$

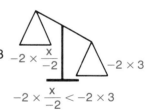

$-2 \times \dfrac{x}{-2} < -2 \times 3$

EXERCISE

B

1. Solve, $x \in I$.

 (a) $\dfrac{x}{2} > 4$ (b) $\dfrac{x}{3} < 2$

 (c) $\dfrac{x}{4} \geqslant -2$ (d) $\dfrac{x}{2} \leqslant -3$

 (e) $\dfrac{x}{-2} > 1$ (f) $\dfrac{x}{-3} < 4$

 (g) $\dfrac{x}{-4} \geqslant -2$ (h) $\dfrac{x}{-2} \leqslant -1$

 (i) $\dfrac{x}{3} \leqslant 0$ (j) $\dfrac{x}{-2} > 0$

2. Solve. Graph the solution.

 (a) $\dfrac{x}{2} < 3$, $x \in I$

 (b) $\dfrac{t}{4} \geqslant 2$, $t \in I$

 (c) $\dfrac{x}{-2} < 2$, $x \in I$

 (d) $\dfrac{x}{-4} \geqslant -1$, $x \in I$

 (e) $\dfrac{x}{2} \leqslant 0$, $x \in I$

9.19 SOLVING INEQUALITIES

In this section we combine the operations studied in the previous four sections to solve inequalities.

Example 1. Solve and graph the solution.
$$2x + 1 > 7, x \in I$$

Solution:

$2x + 1 > 7$	Inequality
$2x + 1 - 1 > 7 - 1$	Subtract 1 from both sides.
$2x > 6$	Simplify.
$\dfrac{2x}{2} > \dfrac{6}{2}$	Divide both sides by 2.
$x > 3$	Simplify.

Example 2. Solve. $\dfrac{x}{-2} - 4 \geqslant 1, x \in I$

Solution:

$\dfrac{x}{-2} - 4 \geqslant 1$	Inequality
$\dfrac{x}{-2} - 4 + 4 \geqslant 1 + 4$	Add 4 to both sides.
$\dfrac{x}{-2} \geqslant 5$	Simplify.
$-2 \times \dfrac{x}{-2} \leqslant -2 \times 5$	Multiply both sides by -2.
$x \leqslant -10$	Simplify.

Example 3. Solve. Graph the solution.
$$4x - 3 \leqslant x + 9, x \in I$$

Solution:

$4x - 3 \leqslant x + 9$	Inequality
$4x - 3 - x \leqslant x + 9 - x$	Subtract x from both sides.
$3x - 3 \leqslant 9$	Simplify.
$3x - 3 + 3 \leqslant 9 + 3$	Add 3 to both sides.
$3x \leqslant 12$	Simplify.
$\dfrac{3x}{3} \leqslant \dfrac{12}{3}$	Divide both sides by 3.
$x \leqslant 4$	Simplify.

EXERCISE

B

1. Solve, $x \in I$
   (a) $2x - 1 < 5$
   (b) $3x + 1 > 10$
   (c) $4x - 3 \leqslant 9$
   (d) $5x + 2 \geqslant 12$
   (e) $3x - 4 > -13$
   (f) $2x + 5 < -7$
   (g) $4x + 7 \geqslant -9$
   (h) $5x - 3 \leqslant -23$

2. Solve. Graph the solution.
   (a) $2x + 1 > 5$, $x \in I$
   (b) $3x - 1 < 11$, $x \in I$
   (c) $4x + 5 \geqslant 13$, $x \in I$
   (d) $5x - 4 \leqslant 16$, $x \in I$
   (e) $2x + 5 < -1$, $x \in I$
   (f) $3x - 4 > -7$, $x \in I$
   (g) $5x + 1 \leqslant -4$, $x \in I$
   (h) $2x - 7 \geqslant -11$, $x \in I$

3. Solve, $x \in I$
   (a) $\dfrac{x}{2} + 1 > 3$

   (b) $\dfrac{x}{3} - 2 < 1$

   (c) $\dfrac{x}{2} + 3 \geqslant 4$

   (d) $\dfrac{x}{4} - 5 \leqslant 2$

   (e) $\dfrac{x}{3} + 1 > -2$

   (f) $\dfrac{x}{4} - 2 < -3$

   (g) $\dfrac{x}{-5} - 3 \geqslant -6$

   (h) $\dfrac{x}{-2} + 1 > 2$

   (i) $\dfrac{x}{-3} - 4 \leqslant -3$

4. Solve. Graph the solution.
   (a) $\dfrac{x}{2} - 1 > 3$, $x \in I$

   (b) $\dfrac{x}{3} + 1 < 2$, $x \in I$

   (c) $\dfrac{x}{4} - 2 \geqslant -1$, $x \in I$

   (d) $\dfrac{x}{5} + 2 \leqslant -1$, $x \in I$

   (e) $\dfrac{x}{-2} + 1 > 2$, $x \in I$

   (f) $\dfrac{x}{-3} - 2 < -4$, $x \in I$

   (g) $\dfrac{x}{-4} + 3 \geqslant 2$, $x \in I$

   (h) $\dfrac{x}{-5} - 5 \leqslant -4$, $x \in I$

C

5. Solve, $x \in I$
   (a) $3x + 1 < 2x + 3$
   (b) $4x - 3 > 2x + 5$
   (c) $5x - 1 \leqslant 2x + 8$
   (d) $2x + 7 \geqslant 3x + 9$
   (e) $3x - 4 < 4x - 5$
   (f) $2x + 3 > 4x - 1$

6. Solve, $x \in I$
   (a) $2(x - 1) > 4$
   (b) $3(x + 2) < 9$
   (c) $4(x - 3) \geqslant 0$
   (d) $5(x + 1) \leqslant -15$

YOUR BLIND SPOT

Sometimes when we are unable to see an object right in front of us, we say that it is in our "blind spot." You can perform a simple test to find your blind spot using a sheet of blank paper. Place two black dots about 5 cm apart on the sheet of blank paper.

Hold the paper in front of you with your arm extended. Cover your left eye with one hand and stare at the left dot on the paper with your right eye. Slowly move the paper toward you until the right dot disappears. This area is called your blind spot. While the right dot is in your blind spot, have a classmate measure the distance from your eye to the paper.

Repeat the above procedure by covering your right eye and staring at the right dot with your left eye.

1. Are your two blind spot distances the same for both eyes?

2. What is the average blind spot distance for your class?

PERIPHERAL VISION

The angle within which we see is called the angle of peripheral vision. Although we all have peripheral vision, it varies from person to person. We can find the angle of peripheral vision with the following experiment.

Lightly mark on the floor, with chalk, a circle that has a one metre (1 m) radius. Have the subject stand at the centre of the circle, and the examiner stand directly in front, on the circle, holding a card with a 1 cm black dot on it. Another examiner holds a blank card just beside the card with the black dot.

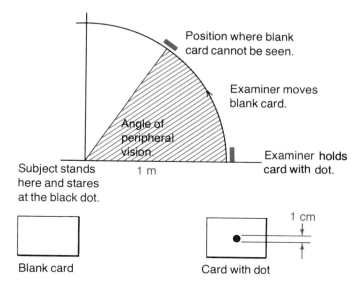

Position where blank card cannot be seen.

Examiner moves blank card.

Angle of peripheral vision.

Subject stands here and stares at the black dot.

1 m

Examiner holds card with dot.

Blank card

Card with dot

1 cm

While the subject stares at the black dot, the examiner slowly moves the blank card along the circle. When the subject no longer sees the blank card while staring at the card with the dot, the movement is stopped and the angle of peripheral vision is measured.

Repeat this experiment for both left and right vision.

What is the average angle of peripheral vision for your class?

9.20 CHAPTER 9 REVIEW EXERCISE

All variables belong to the set of integers.

1. Solve.
   (a) $x - 3 = 2$ (b) $m - 2 = 4$
   (c) $t - 1 = 5$ (d) $y - 5 = 0$
   (e) $x + 3 = 7$ (f) $t + 4 = 10$
   (g) $m + 1 = 8$ (h) $y + 2 = 9$
   (i) $3x = 9$ (j) $6m = 30$
   (k) $5t = 20$ (l) $4t = 24$
   (m) $\dfrac{x}{2} = 4$ (n) $\dfrac{m}{5} = 1$

   (o) $\dfrac{t}{3} = 7$ (p) $\dfrac{w}{4} = 2$

2. Solve.
   (a) $x + 5 = 3$ (b) $y - 1 = -2$
   (c) $t - 2 = -4$ (d) $m + 3 = -6$
   (e) $n + 7 = 3$ (f) $x - 2 = 8$
   (g) $3x = -9$ (h) $-2t = 14$
   (i) $-5n = -20$ (j) $-n = 3$
   (k) $\dfrac{x}{2} = -3$ (l) $\dfrac{m}{4} = -5$

   (m) $\dfrac{t}{3} = 0$ (n) $\dfrac{r}{6} = -1$

3. Solve.
   (a) $x - 2 > 3$ (b) $y + 3 < 7$
   (c) $t + 1 \leqslant 7$ (d) $m - 4 \geqslant 2$
   (e) $x + 1 \geqslant 0$ (f) $n + 3 \leqslant 6$
   (g) $m - 3 \leqslant 2$ (h) $x + 2 \geqslant 3$
   (i) $-2x > 4$ (j) $3t > 12$
   (k) $5t < -25$ (l) $4m > -16$
   (m) $-2x \leqslant 8$ (n) $-6t \geqslant -18$

   (o) $\dfrac{x}{3} > 4$ (p) $\dfrac{m}{2} < -3$

   (q) $\dfrac{t}{5} \geqslant -1$ (r) $\dfrac{n}{4} \leqslant -2$

4. Solve.
   (a) $x - 35 = 56$ (b) $m - 46 = 19$
   (c) $t + 24 = 87$ (d) $y + 58 = 71$
   (e) $9 = x + 4$ (f) $79 = x + 58$
   (g) $m - 57 = 13$ (h) $432 = n - 67$
   (i) $78 + t = 83$ (j) $61 - m = 43$

   (k) $35x = 280$ (l) $7t = 133$
   (m) $6t = 108$ (n) $9x = 144$
   (o) $\dfrac{m}{4} = 23$ (p) $\dfrac{t}{7} = 14$

   (q) $\dfrac{x}{5} = 18$ (r) $\dfrac{n}{9} = 19$

5. Solve.
   (a) $x + 3.2 = 4.5$ (b) $y - 1.4 = 6.6$
   (c) $m - 9 = 34.9$ (d) $t + 6.8 = 21$
   (e) $2x = 4.8$ (f) $5n = 20.5$
   (g) $\dfrac{x}{2} = 4.1$ ·   (h) $\dfrac{t}{5} = 6.4$

   (i) $\dfrac{m}{3} = 0.8$ (j) $\dfrac{n}{4} = 5.3$

6. Solve.
   (a) $4x - x = 9$
   (b) $2t = 7 - 1$
   (c) $6t - t = 24 + 1$
   (d) $3m + 2m = 20$
   (e) $7n - 3n = 27 - 3$
   (f) $6y + y = 14$
   (g) $5x - 3x = 7 + 3$
   (h) $m + 2m = 31 - 4$
   (i) $2x + 7 = 31$
   (j) $3m + 2 = 11$
   (k) $\dfrac{x}{2} = 5 + 3$

   (l) $\dfrac{t}{3} = 2 - 1$

7. Solve.
   (a) $3x + 2 = -10$
   (b) $2t + 5 = -1$
   (c) $4m - 3 = -15$
   (d) $1 - 2x = 13$
   (e) $5m + 1 = 1 - 15$
   (f) $2 - m = 0$

8. Solve.
   (a) $3x - 23 = 7 - 9$
   (b) $3t - 5t = 3 - 11$
   (c) $2m - 7 - 3m = 2$
   (d) $3s - 6s = 9$
   (e) $5 - 2x = -7$
   (f) $2x - 5x - 3 = 1 - 10$
   (g) $7 - 5t - t = -5$
   (h) $4 + 2x - 7x = 6 - 2$

9. Solve.
   (a) $5m = 3m + 9$
   (b) $3x = 7x - 16$
   (c) $6t - 3 = 5t$
   (d) $4n - 1 = n + 5$
   (e) $5y + 2 = 4y - 9$
   (f) $5 - t = 2t + 1$
   (g) $13 - 2x = x + 1$
   (h) $3m + 4m = 7 - 3m + 13$

10. Solve.
    (a) $2(x - 1) = 4$
    (b) $3(m + 4) = 15$
    (c) $4(t - 2) = t + 1$
    (d) $2(x - 3) = 3(x + 1)$
    (e) $5 - 2(t + 1) = 3$
    (f) $3 - (2x - 3) = 0$
    (g) $3(m + 2) - 4 = -1$
    (h) $5(t + 1) - 5 = 20$

11. Solve.
    (a) $x + 0.4 = 0.9$
    (b) $m - 3.2 = 4.7$
    (c) $2x - 0.5 = 0.7$
    (d) $1.2m - 3 = 0.6$
    (e) $0.3t + 1.5 = 6$
    (f) $2x - 1.7 = 0.5x + 1.3$

12. Solve.
    (a) $\dfrac{x}{6} = \dfrac{1}{3}$ (b) $\dfrac{m}{8} = \dfrac{1}{2}$

    (c) $\dfrac{x}{2} - \dfrac{x}{3} = 1$ (d) $\dfrac{x}{4} + \dfrac{x}{3} = 7$

    (e) $\dfrac{x}{4} - \dfrac{x}{5} = 1$ (f) $\dfrac{x}{2} + \dfrac{x}{4} = 3$

13. Solve. Graph the solution.
    (a) $x + 4 < 6, x \in W$
    (b) $x - 3 > 2, x \in W$
    (c) $x + 1 \geqslant 8, x \in W$
    (d) $x - 2 \leqslant 9, x \in W$

14. Solve. Graph the solution.
    (a) $2x > 8, x \in I$
    (b) $-3x < 15, x \in I$
    (c) $5x \leqslant -5, x \in I$
    (d) $-4x \geqslant -8, x \in I$
    (e) $\dfrac{x}{2} > 4, x \in I$

    (f) $\dfrac{x}{3} < -1, x \in I$

    (g) $\dfrac{t}{-4} \geqslant 2, x \in I$

    (h) $\dfrac{w}{-2} \leqslant -3, x \in I$

15. Solve.
    (a) $2x - 3 > 5$
    (b) $3t + 4 < 19$
    (c) $4m - 5 \geqslant -9$
    (d) $5x - 6 \leqslant 3x - 10$
    (e) $\dfrac{x}{2} + 3 < 5$

    (f) $\dfrac{m}{3} - 1 \geqslant 4$

CHAPTER 9 TEST

1. Solve.
   (a) $x + 5 = 9$
   (b) $4x + 1 = 13$
   (c) $5y - 7 = 2y + 8$
   (d) $6m - 43 = 137$
   (e) $\dfrac{x}{3} = 5$

2. Solve.
   (a) $2x - 13 = -5$
   (b) $8 - 3a - a = -4$
   (c) $6y - 1 - 8y = -9$

3. Solve.
   (a) $5t - 7 = 3t + 5$
   (b) $6x + 11 = 7x - 4$
   (c) $2(x - 1) = 8$
   (d) $4 - 3(x + 2) = 1$

4. Solve.
   (a) $2x - 0.7 = 0.3$
   (b) $0.3m + 1.1 = -0.4$
   (c) $\dfrac{a}{6} = \dfrac{1}{3}$
   (d) $\dfrac{m}{3} - \dfrac{m}{4} = 1$

5. Solve. Graph the solution.
   (a) $x - 2 > 4, x \in I$
   (b) $x + 5 < -1, x \in I$
   (c) $-2x \geqslant 8, x \in I$
   (d) $3x - 4 \leqslant 11, x \in I$
   (e) $\dfrac{m}{2} - 1 = 3, x \in I$

PROBLEM SOLVING

REVIEW AND PREVIEW TO CHAPTER 10

EXERCISE 1

Solve.

1. $x - 4 = 9$
2. $y + 3 = 7$
3. $m - 5 = 11$
4. $n + 7 = 15$
5. $y + 8 = 23$
6. $t - 7 = 1$
7. $s + 5 = 5$
8. $n - 6 = 0$
9. $\dfrac{x}{4} = 2$
10. $\dfrac{x}{7} = 1$

EXERCISE 2

Solve.

1. $x + 3 = 2$
2. $m - 4 = -1$
3. $n + 3 = -4$
4. $t - 5 = -4$
5. $s - 6 = 7$
6. $x + 6 = 3$
7. $y - 3 = -4$
8. $s - 5 = -6$
9. $\dfrac{m}{2} = -3$
10. $\dfrac{n}{4} = -1$

EXERCISE 3

Solve.

1. $2x + 5 = 9$
2. $3m + 2 = 11$
3. $3n - 2 = -11$
4. $2y + 3 = -7$
5. $5t - 1 = -16$
6. $5 - 2t = -3$
7. $4 - 3t = 13$
8. $-2 - 3m = 10$
9. $7y - 6 = 8$
10. $8 - t = 7$

EXERCISE 4

Solve.

1. $5x - 3x = 8$
2. $7t - 4t = -12$
3. $t - 3t = 6$
4. $4s - 1 = 2s + 5$
5. $6m - m = 2 - 12$
6. $24 = 8x - 5x$
7. $2m + 11 = -4 - 3m$
8. $7 - 2m = -3m - 4$
9. $4x - 5 = -5$
10. $7t - 8t = 3 - 4$

EXERCISE 5

Solve.

1. Record albums cost $12.87 each.
   How much will you pay for 6 albums?

2. Eric paid $37.77 for a sweater.
   How much change did he receive from $50.00?

3. Melissa drives at 50 km/h.
   How long will it take her to drive 250 km?

4. Howard bowled 213 in his
   first game and 197 in his
   second game.
   How much will he have to
   bowl in his third game to
   have a total of 600?

10.1 CONVERTING WORDS INTO SYMBOLS

Many problems can be solved by writing the words as equations and then solving the equations. In this section we review the procedure for writing words as mathematical symbols.

The following are examples of writing words as symbols. We let n represent the number.

WORDS	SYMBOLS
two times a number	$2n$
a number increased by seven	$n + 7$
a number decreased by four	$n - 4$
the product of eight and a number	$8n$
the sum of ten and a number	$10 + n$
a number divided by three	$n \div 3$

EXERCISE

A

1. Match the words with the symbols.

	WORDS	SYMBOLS
(a)	a number increased by four	$5n$
(b)	a number decreased by six	$3n$
(c)	five times a number	$2 + n$
(d)	the sum of two and a number	$n + 4$
(e)	a number divided by seven	$n - 2$
(f)	the product of three and a number	$12 - n$
(g)	two subtracted from a number	$n - 6$
(h)	twelve decreased by a number	$n \div 7$

2. Represent each of the following by symbols.
   (a) five added to x
   (b) four subtracted from y
   (c) six times x

(d) y divided by three
(e) x increased by eight
(f) y decreased by four
(g) the product of x and seven
(h) y multiplied by nine
(i) the sum of x and y
(j) the product of x and y
(k) x increased by eight
(l) y decreased by one
(m) the sum of s and t
(n) the product of s and t
(o) six divided by x

3. Represent each of the following by symbols.
   (a) eight times a number
   (b) a number divided by two
   (c) three added to a number
   (d) four subtracted from a number
   (e) a number increased by seven
   (f) a number decreased by two
   (g) the product of three and a number
   (h) the sum of eight and a number

(i) nine more than a number
(j) a number multiplied by seven
(k) a number divided by eight
(l) eleven divided by a number
(m) six more than a number
(n) twelve added to a number
(o) sixteen subtracted from a number

B

4. Represent each of the following by symbols.
   (a) the length increased by two metres
   (b) the width multiplied by five
   (c) the cost divided by two
   (d) the number of days in x weeks
   (e) Pete's age two years from now
   (f) Pam's age three years ago
   (g) the number of cents in x dimes
   (h) the number of cents in y nickels
   (i) the number of eggs in x dozen
   (j) the cost increased by three dolars
   (k) the cost decreased by seven dollars

5. Complete the tables.
   (a) The length of the rectangle is three times the width.

WIDTH	5	7	16	x	7y	11z
LENGTH						

   (b) Sandra is three years older than Kathy.

KATHY'S AGE	6	8	19	x	4y
SANDRA'S AGE					

   (c) The cost price is one-half the selling price.

SELLING PRICE	36	94	128	x	6x
COST PRICE					

6. The following is from a nonsense poem by Lewis Carroll called "The Hunting of the Snark."

The Beaver brought paper, portfolio, pens,
And ink in unfailing supplies:
While strange creepy creatures came out of their dens,
And watched them with wondering eyes.

So engrossed was the Butcher, he heeded them not,
As he wrote with a pen in each hand,
And explained all the while in a popular style
Which the Beaver could well understand.

"Taking Three as the subject to reason about—
A convenient number to state—
We add Seven, and Ten, and then multiply out
By One Thousand diminished by Eight.

"The result we proceed to divide, as you see
By Nine Hundred and Ninety and Two:
Then subtract Seventeen, and the answer must be
Exactly and perfectly true"

"The method employed I would gladly explain,
While I have it so clear in my head,
If I had but the time and you had but the brain—
But so much remains to be said."

   (a) What is the answer to the problem?
   (b) What is the answer when you start with Five instead of Three?
   (c) Can you explain why?

10.2 WORDS TO EQUATIONS

We shall now write sentences as equations.

The following is an example of writing a sentence as an equation.

"When a certain number is increased by six the result is fifteen."

$$x \qquad +6 \qquad = \qquad 15$$

or $x + 6 = 15$

Here is another example.

"Three times a certain number is equal to twelve"

$$3 \times \qquad x \qquad = \qquad 12$$

or $3x = 12$

EXERCISE

A

1. Match the sentence with the equation.

SENTENCE	EQUATION
(a) Six times a certain number is equal to eighteen.	$n \div 2 = 7$
(b) A certain number increased by nine is fourteen.	$8 + n = 15$
(c) A number decreased by five is eleven.	$6n = 18$
(d) A number divided by two is seven.	$n - 5 = 11$
(e) The sum of eight and a number is fifteen.	$n + 9 = 14$

B

2. Write each sentence as an equation.
   (a) Four times a certain number is twenty.
   (b) When a certain number is divided by two, the result is five.
   (c) When a certain number is decreased by four, the result is nine.
   (d) When a certain number is increased by six, the result is fourteen.

3. Write each sentence as an equation.
   (a) When five is added to a number, the result is twelve.
   (b) When four is subtracted from a number, the result is eleven.
   (c) Two times Frank's age is twenty-eight.
   (d) Sally's age, divided by three, is six.
   (e) Kathy's age seven years from now will be twenty-two.
   (f) The length, increased by ten, is thirty-one.
   (g) The width, decreased by four, is eight.

MICRO MATH

NEW

```
10 PRINT"SQUARE ROOT OF A NUMBER"
20 INPUT"TYPE IN THE NUMBER";A
30 LET B=SQR(A)
40 PRINT"THE SQUARE ROOT OF";A;"IS";B
50 END
```

RUN

10.3 SOLVING WORD PROBLEMS

In this section we will solve problems using equations. There are six steps to follow when solving a problem. These steps are shown in the solution of the Example.

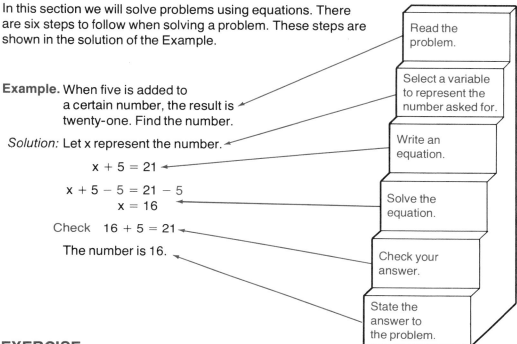

Example. When five is added to a certain number, the result is twenty-one. Find the number.

Solution: Let x represent the number.

$$x + 5 = 21$$

$$x + 5 - 5 = 21 - 5$$
$$x = 16$$

Check $16 + 5 = 21$

The number is 16.

Read the problem.

Select a variable to represent the number asked for.

Write an equation.

Solve the equation.

Check your answer.

State the answer to the problem.

EXERCISE

B

1. When twelve is added to a certain number, the result is forty-one. Find the number.

2. When sixteen is subtracted from a certain number, the result is twenty-two. Find the number.

3. When a certain number is multiplied by four, the result is sixty-eight. Find the number.

4. When a certain number is divided by six, the result is seventeen. Find the number.

5. The product of three and a number is eighty-four. Find the number.

6. Four times the depth of Lake Athabaska is four hundred ninety-six metres. How deep is the lake?

7. Seven times the length of the Welland Canal is three hundred eight kilometres. How long is the canal?

8. In nineteen years Sandra will be forty-two years old. How old is Sandra?

10.4 AIRCRAFT SPEEDS

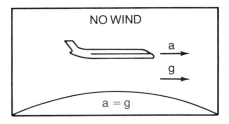

If an aircraft is flying and there is no wind, the ground speed is the same as the air speed.

ground speed = air speed

$$g = a$$

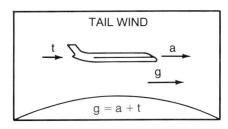

If an aircraft is flying and there is a tail wind, the wind pushes the aircraft. The ground speed is faster than the air speed.

ground speed = air speed + tail wind speed

$$g = a + t$$

Example 1. What is the ground speed of an aircraft if the air speed is 900 km/h and there is a tail wind of 80 km/h?

Solution: $g = a + t$
$g = 900 + 80$
$= 980$
The ground speed is 980 km/h.

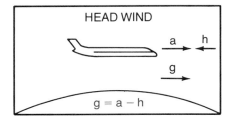

If an aircraft is flying and there is a head wind, the wind slows down the aircraft. The ground speed is slower than the air speed.

ground speed = air speed − head wind speed

$$g = a - h$$

Example 2. There is a head wind of 100 km/h. At what air speed should the pilot fly the aircraft to have a ground speed of 1000 km/h?

Solution:
$$g = a - h$$
$$1000 = a - 100$$
$$1000 + 100 = a - 100 + 100$$
$$1100 = a$$

The pilot should fly at an air speed of 1100 km/h.

EXERCISE

B

1. The air speed of an aircraft is 950 km/h. There is a tail wind of 100 km/h. What is the ground speed?

2. The air speed of an aircraft is 1100 km/h. There is a head wind of 150 km/h. What is the ground speed?

3. The ground speed of an aircraft is 1250 km/h. There is a tail wind of 125 km/h. What is the air speed?

4. The ground speed of an aircraft is 1050 km/h. There is a tail wind of 90 km/h. What is the air speed?

5. The air speed of an aircraft is 1250 km/h. The ground speed is 1175 km/h.
   (a) Is there a tail wind or a head wind?
   (b) What is the speed of the wind?

6. The ground speed of an aircraft is 930 km/h. The air speed is 880 km/h.
   (a) Is there a tail wind or a head wind?
   (b) What is the speed of the wind?

7. There is a head wind of 90 km/h. At what speed should the pilot fly to have a ground speed of 1100 km/h?

8. Complete the following table.

Ground Speed	Head Wind Speed	Tail Wind Speed	Air Speed
?	130		1250
?		160	1125
1225	145		?
1140		85	?
1260	?	?	1140
1030	?	?	1120

10.5 A BALANCING ACT

Seesaws can balance on a point, called the fulcrum.

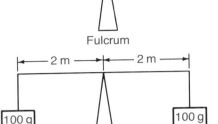

Fulcrum

When equal masses are placed on each end of the seesaw, it still balances.

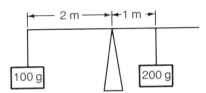

Suppose a larger mass is placed on one side of the seesaw. It must be placed closer to the fulcrum to keep the seesaw balanced.

For a seesaw to balance, the following must be true.

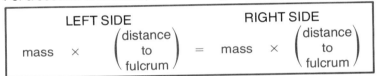

LEFT SIDE				RIGHT SIDE	
mass	×	$\begin{pmatrix} \text{distance} \\ \text{to} \\ \text{fulcrum} \end{pmatrix}$	= mass ×	$\begin{pmatrix} \text{distance} \\ \text{to} \\ \text{fulcrum} \end{pmatrix}$	

The seesaw at the right balances because

$$100 \times 2 = 200 \times 1$$

mass / mass \
distance   distance

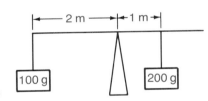

Example. Find the mass x so that the seesaw balances.

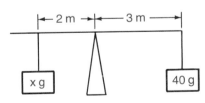

Solution:

mass × distance = mass × distance

$$x \times 2 = 40 \times 3$$
$$2x = 120$$
$$\frac{2x}{2} = \frac{120}{2}$$
$$x = 60$$

The mass which balances the seesaw is 60 g.

EXERCISE

B

1. State whether or not the following seesaws will balance.

(a)

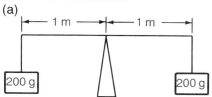

(b)

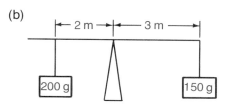

(c)

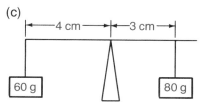

(d)

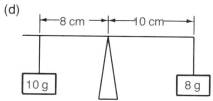

2. Find the mass x so that the seesaw balances.

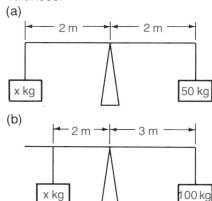

(c)

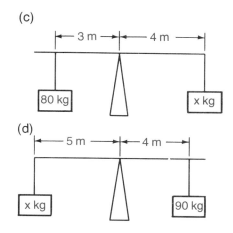

3. Find the length x so that the seesaw balances.

(a)

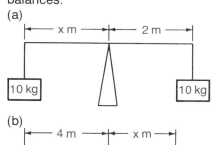

(b)

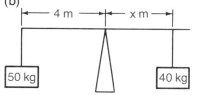

(c)

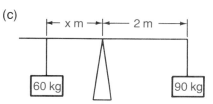

(d)

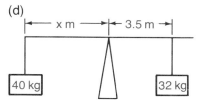

10.6 DISTANCE, RATE, TIME

An eagle can fly at a speed of 150 km/h.

Time Flying	Distance Travelled	
1 h	150 km	150×1
2 h	300 km	150×2
3 h	450 km	150×3
4 h	600 km	150×4

This means that in one hour an eagle can travel 150 km. In 3 h an eagle can travel
150×3 or 450 km

The table shows the distance an eagle can travel for different amounts of time.

When something travels at a constant speed (the same speed), the distance travelled can be found using this formula.

$$D = r \times t$$

distance   rate   time
(speed)

Example 1.
The Space Shuttle Orbiter lands at a speed of 350 km/h. How far will it travel in 3 h at this speed?

Solution:
$D = rt$
$D = 350 \times 3$
$\quad = 1050$
It will travel 1050 km.

Example 2.
The winner of a car race at Indianapolis travelled 800 km in 3.2 h (3 h, 12 min). What was the speed?

Solution:
$D = rt$
$800 = r \times 3.2$
$\dfrac{800}{3.2} = \dfrac{r \times 3.2}{3.2}$
$250 = r$
The speed was 250 km/h.

EXERCISE

B

1. Complete the table for a motorcycle travelling at 80 km/h.

	Time (h)	Distance (km)
(a)	1	
(b)	2	
(c)	4	
(d)	6	
(e)	3.5	

2. Complete the chart.

	Distance	Rate	Time
(a)		50 km/h	3 h
(b)		75 km/h	5 h
(c)	500 km		10 h
(d)	240 km	80 km/h	
(e)	420 km		6 h

3. Pony Express riders rode at 12 km/h.
   (a) How far did they travel in 6 h?
   (b) The Pony Express delivered mail between St. Joseph, Missouri, and Sacramento, California. The distance travelled was 2880 km.
   How many hours did it take to make the complete trip?

4. The Gossamer Albatross is a human-powered aircraft. When it flew across the English Channel, a distance of 39 km, it travelled at 13 km/h.
   (a) How far will it travel in 2.5 h at this rate of speed?
   (b) How long did it take to cross the Channel?

5. The balloon Double Eagle II was the first balloon to fly across the Atlantic Ocean. It travelled 4932 km in 137 h.
   At what speed did it travel?

6. Complete the chart.

	Distance	Rate	Time
(a)		23 km/h	13 h
(b)		45 km/h	5.5 h
(c)		72 km/h	8.5 h
(d)	90 km	60 km/h	
(e)	405 km	90 km/h	
(f)	96 km	80 km/h	

10.7 PERIMETER AND EQUATIONS

The perimeter of a figure is
the distance around the figure.

For geometric figures, the
perimeter is the sum of the
lengths of the sides.

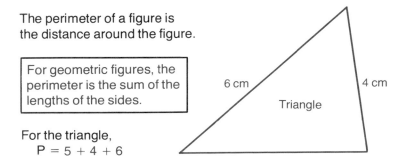

For the triangle,
$$P = 5 + 4 + 6$$
$$= 15$$
The perimeter of the triangle is 15 cm.

A rectangle is a four-sided figure.
The opposite sides are equal.
All angles are 90°.

A square is a four-sided figure.
All sides are equal.
All angles are 90°.

Example. The perimeter of the
rectangle is 26 cm. Find
the length and width.

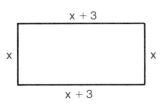

Solution:

METHOD I
$$(x + 3) + x + (x + 3) + x = 26$$
$$4x + 6 = 26$$
$$4x + 6 - 6 = 26 - 6$$
$$4x = 20$$
$$\frac{4x}{4} = \frac{20}{4}$$
$$x = 5$$

METHOD II
Since a rectangle has 2
lengths and 2 widths,
$$P = 2\ell + 2w$$
$$26 = 2(x + 3) + 2(x)$$
$$26 = 2x + 6 + 2x$$
$$26 = 4x + 6$$
$$26 - 6 = 4x + 6 - 6$$
$$20 = 4x$$
$$5 = x$$

The width is 5 cm.
The length is 8 cm.

EXERCISE

B

1. Use a ruler to find the perimeter of each figure. Measure each side, accurate to the nearest millimetre.

(a)

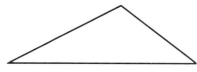

(b)

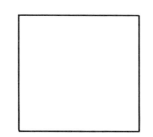

(c)

(d)

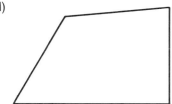

2. Find the length of each side of these squares.

(a)

The perimeter is 56 cm.

(b)

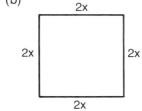

The perimeter is 72 cm.

3. Find the length and width of each rectangle.

(a)

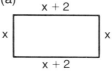

The perimeter is 24 cm.

(b)

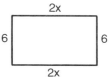

The perimeter is 40 cm.

(c)

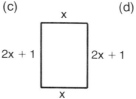

The perimeter is 50 cm.

(d)

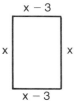

The perimeter is 26 cm.

4. Find the length of each side.

(a)

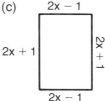

The perimeter is 29 cm.

(b)

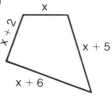

The perimeter is 18 cm.

(c)

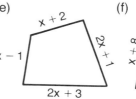

The perimeter is 56 cm.

(d)

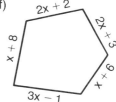

The perimeter is 73 cm.

(e)

The perimeter is 41 cm.

(f)

The perimeter is 36 cm.

10.8 AREA AND EQUATIONS

The area of a figure is the amount of surface the figure covers.

The square has sides of 1 cm and has an area of 1 cm^2.

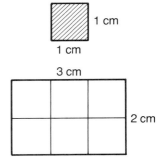

By counting squares, the area of the rectangle is 6 cm^2.
The length is 3 cm.
The width is 2 cm.
The area of the rectangle can also be calculated using the following formula.

$$A = \ell w$$

Example 1.
Calculate the area of the figure.

Solution:
The calculations can be simplified by dividing the figure into rectangles.

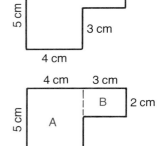

Area (rectangle A) = 5 cm × 4 cm
$\qquad\qquad$ = 20 cm^2
Area (rectangle B) = 3 cm × 2 cm
$\qquad\qquad$ = 6 cm^2
$\qquad$ Total area = 20 cm × 6 cm
$\qquad\qquad$ = 26 cm^2

Example 2.
The area of the rectangle is 72 cm^2. Find the length.

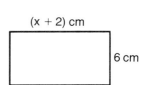

Solution:
$$A = \ell w$$
$$72 = (x + 2) \times 6$$
$$72 = 6(x + 2)$$
$$72 = 6x + 12$$
$$72 - 12 = 6x + 12 - 12$$
$$60 = 6x$$
$$\frac{60}{6} = \frac{6x}{6}$$
$$x = 10$$
The length is 10 + 2 or 12 cm.

EXERCISE

A

1. Determine the area of each of the following. (Each square is 1 cm².)

(a)

(b)

(c)

(d)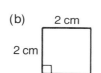

(e)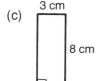

(f)

B

2. Calculate the area.

(a)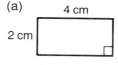
4 cm
2 cm

(b)
2 cm
2 cm

(c)
3 cm
8 cm

(d)
5 cm
5 cm

3. Calculate the area.

(a)
6 cm
3 cm
6 cm
3 cm

(b)
1 cm
2 cm
1 cm
3 cm
5 cm

(c)
2 cm
3 cm
2 cm
6 cm
2 cm
2 cm

(d)
4 cm
5 cm
8 cm
6 cm

4. The area is 35 cm².
Find the length.
(x + 1) cm
5 cm

5. The area is 45 cm².
Find the length.
(x − 6) cm
5 cm

6. The area is 90 cm².
Find the width.
15 cm
(x − 2) cm

CHALLENGE

The people at a party are forming equal teams to play a game. When they form groups of 2, 3, 4, 5, or 6, there is always one person left.
What is the smallest number of people that could be at the party?

10.9 PROBLEMS USING GEOMETRY FORMULAS

Many problems can be solved by using a formula. When using a formula, we substitute numbers for letters. This procedure gives us an equation.

Example 1.
The length of a rectangle is 6 m. The width is 4 m. Find the area.

Solution:
The formula for the area of a rectangle is:

$$A = \ell w$$
$$A = 6 \times 4$$
$$= 24$$

The area is 24 m².

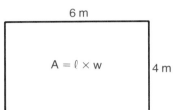

Example 2.
The perimeter of a rectangle is 26 cm. The length is 8 cm. Find the width.

Solution:
The formula for the perimeter of a rectangle is:

$$P = 2(\ell + w)$$
$$26 = 2(8 + w)$$
$$26 = 16 + 2w$$
$$26 - 16 = 16 + 2w - 16$$
$$10 = 2w$$
$$\frac{10}{2} = \frac{2w}{2}$$
$$5 = w$$

The width is 5 cm.

EXERCISE

B

1. The area of a rectangle is 108 cm². The width is 4 cm. Find the length.

2. A rectangle has a length of 17 m and a width of 14 m. Find the perimeter.

3. The formula for the area of a square is

   $A = s^2$.

   Find the area of the square that has sides 17 m long.

$A = s \times s$
$= s^2$

4. The formula for the area of a triangle is

   $A = \frac{1}{2}bh$, where b

   is the base and h is the height.
   Find the area of the triangle with a base of 16 cm and a height of 10 cm.

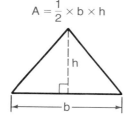

$A = \frac{1}{2} \times b \times h$

5. The area of a triangle is 12 cm². The base is 6 cm. Find the height.

6. The formula for the area of a parallelogram is $A = bh$.
   Find the area of a parallelogram with a base of 12 cm and a height of 9 cm.

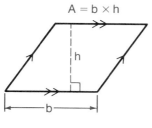

$A = b \times h$

7. The area of a parallelogram is 78 cm. The base is 13 cm. Find the height.

8. The formula for the circumference of a circle is $C = 2\pi r$, where $\pi = 3.14$ and r is the radius
   Find the circumference of a circle with radius of 6 cm.

$c = 2 \times \pi \times r$

9. The formula for the area of a circle is $A = \pi r^2$.
   Find the area of a circle with radius 4 cm.

$A = \pi \times r^2$

10. The formula for the volume of a box is $V = \ell wh$, where ℓ is the length, w is the width, and h is the height.
    Find the volume of a box with a length of 6 cm, a width of 4 cm, and a height of 3 cm.

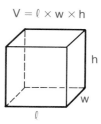

$V = \ell \times w \times h$

11. A box has a volume of 210 cm³. The length is 7 cm and the width is 5 cm. Find the height.

12. The formula for the volume of a cylinder is $V = \pi r^2 h$
    Find the volume of a cylinder with a radius of 3 cm and a height of 10 cm.

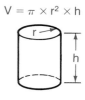

$V = \pi \times r^2 \times h$

13. The formula for the volume of a sphere is $V = \frac{4}{3}\pi r^3$.
    Find the volume of a sphere with a radius of 3 cm.

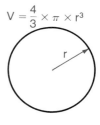

$V = \frac{4}{3} \times \pi \times r^3$

10.10 PROBLEMS USING FORMULAS

In this section we solve problems involving other formulas.

Example 1.

The formula relating the temperature (°C) and the number of chirps made by a cricket in one minute is

$$T = \frac{n}{7} + 4$$

where T is the temperature and n is the number of chirps per minute

What is the temperature if a cricket chirps 112 times in a minute?

Solution:

$$T = \frac{n}{7} + 4$$
$$= \frac{112}{7} + 4$$
$$= 16 + 4$$
$$= 20$$

The temperature is 20°C.

Example 2.

The formula relating the time between your seeing the lightning flash and hearing the thunderclap, and your distance from the storm is

$$t = 3d$$

where t is the time in seconds and d is the distance in kilometres. How far are you from a storm if the time between the flash and the thunderclap is 6 s?

Solution:

$$t = 3d$$
$$6 = 3d$$
$$\frac{6}{3} = \frac{3d}{3}$$
$$2 = d$$

You are 2 km from the storm.

EXERCISE

B

1. The following formula gives the number of hours of sleep a young person should have each day:

$$H = \frac{1}{2}(18 - n) + 8$$

where H is hours of sleep and n is the age in years.
   (a) How many hours of sleep should a 6-year-old have?
   (b) How many hours of sleep should a 14-year-old have?

2. The formula gives the distance an object will fall according to how long it falls.

$$D = 4.9 \times t^2$$

where D is the distance in metres and t is the time in seconds.
   (a) How far will an object fall in 3 s?
   (b) How far will an object fall in 10 s?

3. The following is a formula used by some companies to determine when an employee should retire:

$$a + y = 90$$

where a is the person's age and y is the number of years of employment.
   (a) Pete was 59 years old when he retired.
   How many years did he work for the company?
   (b) Susan retired after working for 33 years.
   How old was she?

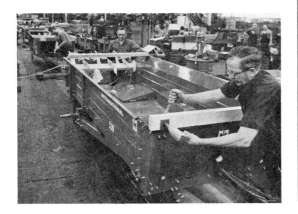

4. The following formula relates mass and height for young adults:

$$M = \frac{6(h - 90)}{7}$$

where M is the mass in kilograms and h is the height in centimetres.
What is the mass for a height of 160 cm?

5. Typing speed is calculated using the formula

$$S = \frac{w - 10e}{5}$$

where S is the typing speed in words per minute, w is the number of words typed in 5 min, and e is the number of errors.
Terry typed 300 words in 5 min and made 2 errors.
What is the typing speed?

6. The following formula gives the number of different connections that can be made through a telephone switchboard.

$$N = \frac{t(t - 1)}{2}$$

where N is the number of connections and t is the number of telephones.
   (a) How many connections can be made with 20 telephones?
   (b) How many connections can be made with 100 telephones?

10.11 DEVELOPING FORMULAS

In this section we shall develop formulas from practical situations.

Example 1.
Andrea earns sixteen dollars per hour training dolphins.
  (a) Determine a formula for her salary in terms of the number of hours worked.
  (b) How much does she earn in 39 h?

Solution:
  (a) Let S represent her salary. Let h, represent hours worked.
  Then the formula is
  $$S = 16 \times h.$$

  (b) For 39 h of work,
  $$S = 16 \times h$$
  $$= 16 \times 39$$
  $$= 624.$$
  She earns $624.

Example 2.
To determine what he should sell a new car for, a dealer multiplies his cost price by 1.3.
  (a) Determine a formula for selling price in terms of cost price.
  (b) A new car cost a dealer $16 000. What is the selling price?

Solution:
  (a) Let CP represent the cost price. Let SP represent the selling price. Then the formula is
  $$SP = 1.3 \times CP$$

  (b) $SP = 1.3 \times CP$
  $$= 1.3 \times 16\ 000$$
  $$= 20\ 800$$
  The selling price is $20 800.

EXERCISE

B

1. (a) Determine a formula for total cost in terms of number of tickets bought.

Number of Tickets	Total Cost
1	$6.50
2	$13.00
3	$19.50
4	$26.00

   (b) Use the formula to determine the cost of 19 tickets.

2.

Paul earns twelve dollars an hour as a tour guide in the Everglades.
   (a) Determine a formula for his salary in terms of the number of hours worked.
   (b) Find his earnings if he works the following hours.
      i) 17 h   ii) 26 h   iii) 42.5 h

3. Cynthia Evans owns a jewellery store. To determine the selling price of a diamond, she multiplies her cost by 1.8.
   (a) Determine a formula for selling price in terms of cost price.
   (b) Find the selling price for diamonds that have the following cost prices.
      i) $700
      ii) $1300
      iii) $3000

4. The elephants at the zoo eat fourteen bales of hay each day.
   (a) Determine a formula for the number of bales eaten in terms of days.
   (b) Find the number of bales eaten in
      i) 7 days;   ii) 13 days;   iii) 31 days.

5. Adam keeps the statistics for a hockey league. A team gets two points for a win and one point for a tie.
   (a) Determine a formula for points earned in terms of wins and ties.
   (b) How many points does a team have with
      i) 21 wins and 13 ties?
      ii) 42 wins and 9 ties?

6. A car rental agency charges $10/d plus $0.13/km to rent a car.
   (a) Determine a formula for the cost to rent in terms of days rented and kilometres driven.
   (b) Determine the cost to rent a car for 15 d if you drive 2000 km.
   (c) Determine the cost to rent a car for 7 d if you drive 1500 km.

SKID MARKS

When the police investigate a traffic accident, they measure the length of the skid marks and record the type of road surface. They use this information to estimate the speed of the car.

Depending on the surface, skid-resistance numbers are assigned to the conditions of the road surface. Dry, rough surfaces such as concrete or asphalt are assigned high numbers like 0.80. Surfaces that are slippery, such as ice, are assigned low skid-resistance numbers like 0.10.

If you know the skid-resistance number of the road and skidding distance, you can estimate the speed of a car, using a nomograph. We locate the skid-resistance number of the road surface on the right scale and the length of the skid on the left scale. Joining these points with a straight line, we read the speed of the car from the centre scale.

In the example, the speed of a car that skidded 15 m on wet asphalt is 42 km/h.

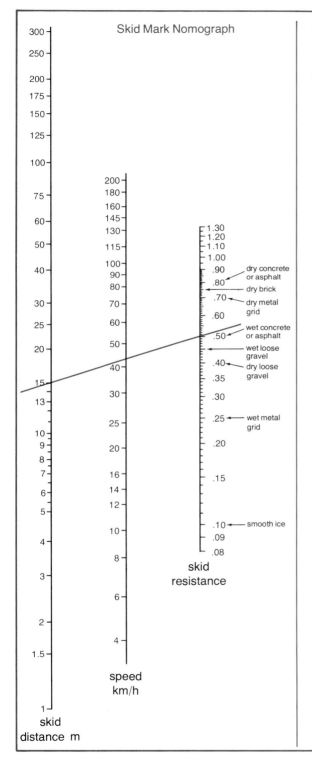

Skid Mark Nomograph

300
250
200
175
150
125
100
75
60
50
40
30
25
20
15
13
10
9
8
7
6
5
4
3
2
1.5
1

skid
distance m

200
180
160
145
130
115
100
90
80
70
60
50
40
30
25
20
16
14
12
10
8
6
4

speed
km/h

1.30
1.20
1.10
1.00
.90
.80
.70
.60
.50
.40
.35
.30
.25
.20
.15
.10
.09
.08

skid
resistance

dry concrete
or asphalt
dry brick
dry metal
grid
wet concrete
or asphalt
wet loose
gravel
dry loose
gravel
wet metal
grid
smooth ice

EXERCISE

Answer the following questions using the nomograph at left.

1. How fast would a car have to be going to skid 14 m on ice?

2. How fast would a car have to be going to skid 20 m on dry concrete?

3. A car skids on dry, loose gravel. What is the speed if the length of the skid marks is
   (a) 10 m?   (b) 20 m?

4. A car skids on wet concrete. What is the speed if the length of the skid marks is
   (a) 15 m?   (b) 45 m?

5. In order to check the nomograph, tests were taken to find the skid resistance for wet asphalt. Use the nomograph to complete the table.

Skid Distance m	Speed km/h	Skid Resistance
	50	0.5
8		0.5
	25	0.5
80	100	
5	25	

10.12 CHAPTER 10 REVIEW EXERCISE

1. Represent each of the following by symbols.
   (a) a number increased by eight
   (b) six times a number
   (c) a number decreased by three
   (d) a number divided by four
   (e) the product of five and a number
   (f) four added to a number
   (g) the sum of nine and a number
   (h) the length increased by three metres
   (i) five times the width
   (j) the number of cents in y dimes

2. When thirteen is added to a certain number the result is forty-one. Find the number.

3. When a certain number is multiplied by six the result is one hundred thirty-two. Find the number.

4. The air speed of an aircraft is 1200 km/h. There is a head wind of 225 km/h. What is the ground speed?

5. There is a tail wind of 145 km/h. At what air speed should the pilot fly to have a ground speed of 1100 km/h?

6. Find the mass of x so that the seesaw balances.

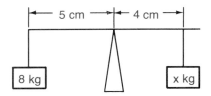

7. Find the length of x so that the seesaw balances.

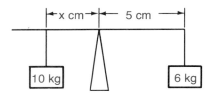

8. The spine-tailed swift is the fastest creature alive. It can fly at a speed of 170 km/h.
   How long will it take a spine-tailed swift to fly 255 km?

9. Find the length and width of the rectangle.

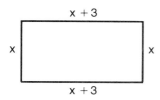

The perimeter is 30 cm.

10. Find the length of each side.

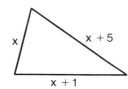

The perimeter is 33 cm.

11. The area is 54 cm². Find the value of x.

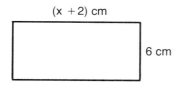

12. The area of a triangle is 42 cm².
The base is 7 cm.
Find the height.

13. The area of a parallelogram is 182 cm².
The height is 13 cm.
Find the length of the base.

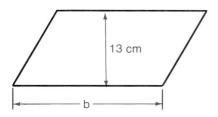

14. The distance a spaceship travels (in kilometres) in terms of the length of time it has been flying (in hours) is given by the following formula.

$$d = 40\ 200\ t$$

(a) How far will a spaceship travel in 23 h?

(b) How far will a spaceship travel in 17.5 h?

(c) How long will it take a spaceship to travel 140 700 km?

15. Sound travels at a speed of 330 m/s.
(a) Determine a formula for your distance from a storm in terms of the time interval between when you see the lightning flash and when you hear the thunderclap.
(b) How far are you from a storm if the time interval between the lightning flash and the thunderclap is 3 s?

CHAPTER 10 TEST

1. When thirty-nine is subtracted from a certain number, the result is eighty-four.
   Find the number.

2. The air speed of an aircraft is 1350 km/h. There is a tail wind of 250 km/h.
   What is the ground speed?

3. Find the mass of x so that the seesaw balances.

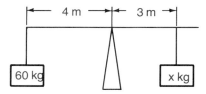

4. Find the length and width of the rectangle.

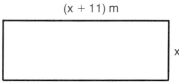

Perimeter is 106 m.

5. The formula gives the cost for a banquet:

$$C = 18n + 95$$

where C is the cost in dollars and n is the number of people attending the banquet.
What is the cost of a banquet for 87 people?

11

RELATIONS

REVIEW AND PREVIEW TO CHAPTER 11

MAPS

Many maps, such as the one shown below, use a different coordinate system to help you locate cities and towns. Coordinates containing numbers and letters are used to give you a small area in which to look for a place. The area defined by (B, 1) is shaded in red on the map.

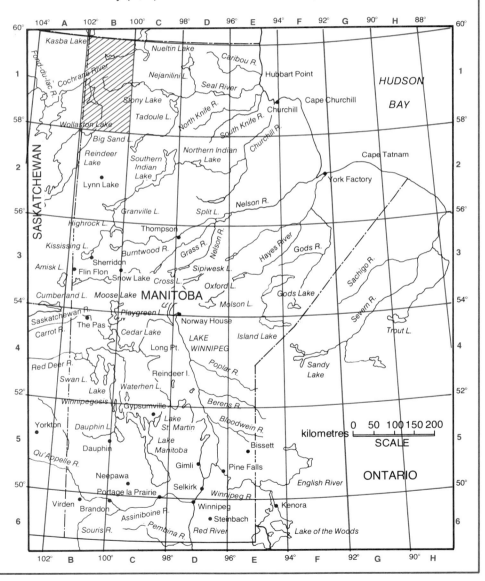

1. Given the coordinates, find the following places on the map.

    (a) Winnipeg, Manitoba, (D, 6)

    (b) Sandy Lake, Ontario, (F, 4)

    (c) Sherridon, Manitoba, (B, 3)

    (d) Churchill, Manitoba, (E, 1)

    (e) Gimli, Manitoba, (D, 5)

    (f) Amisk Lake, Saskatchewan (A, 3)

2. State the name of one place located in each of the following areas.

    (a) (G, 2)

    (b) (B, 5)

    (c) (D, 3)

    (d) (D, 5)

3. State the coordinates of the area in which the following places are located.

    (a) Steinbach, Manitoba

    (b) Flin Flon, Manitoba

    (c) The Pas, Manitoba

    (d) Berens River, Manitoba

    (e) Yorkton, Saskatchewan

    (f) Kenora, Ontario

    (g) York Factory, Manitoba

    (h) Lynn Lake, Manitoba

kilometres

0 50 100 150 200

SCALE

4. Using the above scale, find the distance from

    (a) Brandon to Pine Falls;

    (b) Winnipeg to York Factory;

    (c) Flin Flon to Churchill;

    (d) Thompson to Portage la Prairie.

11.1 TABLES OF VALUES

Sharon works at a discount grocery outlet. To simplify her calculations on a current sale of cases of pop, she keeps the following table of values taped to her cash register.

Cases	Cost
1	$ 6.82
2	$13.64
3	$20.46
4	$27.28
5	$34.10

Tables are also used to display results when we evaluate expressions.

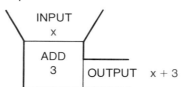

x	x + 3
2	5
4	7
9	12

Example. Evaluate $2x - 3$ for $x \epsilon \{4, 2, 0, -2\}$.
Display the results in a table of values.

Solution:

When $x = 4$, $\quad 2x - 3 = 2(4) - 3$
$$= 8 - 3$$
$$= 5$$

When $x = 2$, $\quad 2x - 3 = 2(2) - 3$
$$= 4 - 3$$
$$= 1$$

When $x = 0$, $\quad 2x - 3 = 2(0) - 3$
$$= 0 - 3$$
$$= -3$$

When $x = -2$, $\quad 2x - 3 = 2(-2) - 3$
$$= -4 - 3$$
$$= -7$$

x	2x − 3
4	5
2	1
0	−3
−2	−7

EXERCISE

B

1. Complete the tables for the machines shown.

(a)

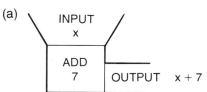

x	x + 7
5	
13	
−2	
−5	

(b)

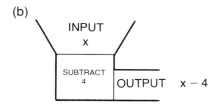

x	x − 4
5	
2	
−3	
−5	

2. Complete the following tables of values.

(a)

x	2x + 1
5	
2	
−2	
−3	

(b)

x	3x − 2
0	
−3	
−5	
−9	

(c)

x	4x − 7
1	
0	
−2	
−5	

3. Evaluate 2x − 5 for x∈{2, 0, −3, −6}. Display the results in a table of values.

4. Evaluate 5x + 2 for x∈{0, −2, −3, −5}. Display the results in a table of values.

5. School buttons cost $1.35 each.

Complete the following table of values.

Number of Buttons	Cost
1	
2	
3	
4	

C

6. Use your calculator to complete the following table of values.

x	2.5x − 1.75
4.7	
2.92	
1.44	
0.98	

11.2 ORDERED PAIRS

The equation $x + 2 = 5$ has one variable, x
There is one solution,
$$x = 3.$$

The equation $x + y = 5$ has two variables, x and y
This equation has many solutions.
These solutions can be shown in a table of values.

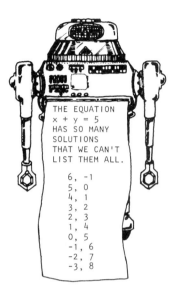

THE EQUATION
x + y = 5
HAS SO MANY
SOLUTIONS
THAT WE CAN'T
LIST THEM ALL.

6, -1
5, 0
4, 1
3, 2
2, 3
1, 4
0, 5
-1, 6
-2, 7
-3, 8

$$x + y = 5$$

When $x = 2$, $y = 3$,	since	$2 + 3 = 5$
When $x = 1$, $y = 4$,	since	$1 + 4 = 5$
When $x = 0$, $y = 5$,	since	$0 + 5 = 5$
When $x = -1$, $y = 6$,	since	$-1 + 6 = 5$
When $x = -2$, $y = 7$,	since	$-2 + 7 = 5$

x	y
2	3
1	4
0	5
-1	6
-2	7

We can also write these solutions as ordered pairs.

$$(2, 3), (1, 4), (0, 5), (-1, 6), (-2, 7)$$

The pairs of numbers are called ordered pairs because the order of the numbers is important. In the example, we have written the x value first, then the y value.

$$(x, y)$$

Equations containing two variables are often written with one of the variables on the left by itself.

For example, $y = 3x + 1$.

We can find many ordered pairs for equations in this form. We substitute values for the variable on the right side, then simplify.

$$y = 3x + 1$$

When $x = 1$, $\quad y = 3(1) + 1$
$\qquad\qquad = 3 + 1$
$\qquad\qquad = 4$

When $x = 0$, $\quad y = 3(0) + 1$
$\qquad\qquad = 0 + 1$
$\qquad\qquad = 1$

When $x = -1$, $\quad y = 3(-1) + 1$
$\qquad\qquad = -3 + 1$
$\qquad\qquad = -2$

Table of Values

x	y
1	4
0	1
-1	-2

ordered pairs

$(1, 4)$
$(0, 1)$
$(-1, -2)$

EXERCISE

1. Complete the following tables of values.

(a)

$x + y = 7$

x	y
3	
7	
-2	
-5	
0	

(b)

$x - y = 2$

x	y
3	
1	
0	
-4	

(c)

$y = x + 4$

x	y
5	
0	
-2	
-3	

(d)

$y = 3x - 5$

x	y
1	
0	
-3	
-7	

2. Find 5 ordered pairs for each of the following.

(a) $x + y = 4$ (b) $x - y = 3$

(c) $y = x + 4$ (d) $y = x - 5$

3. Find 5 ordered pairs for each of the following.

(a) $x + y = -3$

(b) $x - y = -2$

(c) $x + y = 0$

(d) $x - y = 0$

(e) $y = 2x + 1$

(f) $y = 3x - 4$

(g) $y = 4x + 7$

(h) $y = 2x - 2$

(i) $y = 3 + 4x$

(j) $y = 7 - 2x$

(k) $y = \dfrac{x + 1}{2}$

CHALLENGE

Complete the table to give the maximum number of pieces into which a pie can be divided with the number of cuts shown.

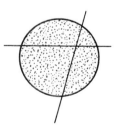

Number of Cuts	Maximum Number of Pieces
1	2
2	4
3	
4	

11.3 UNDERSTANDING RELATIONS

The following statements are examples of relations.

A relation tells us how one thing is related to another.

"Pete is shorter than Eric."
"Lake Ontario is deeper than Lake Erie."
"Summer is warmer than winter."

In mathematics, a set of ordered pairs is a relation.

An equation with two variables gives a set of ordered pairs.
These equations define relations.

Equations	Relations
x + y = 6	{(2, 4), (3, 3), (5, 1),...}
y = x + 4	{(1, 5), (2, 6), (3, 7),...}

Relations can also be shown as arrow diagrams.

For the relation x + y = 6, we have:

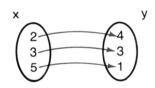

EXERCISE

A

1. State an equation that is represented by each table of values.

(a)

x	y
0	4
1	3
2	2
3	1

(b)

x	y
2	0
3	1
4	2
5	3

2. State an equation that is represented by the sets of ordered pairs.
   (a) (1, 4), (2, 3), (3, 2), (4, 1)
   (b) (0, 8), (3, 5), (4, 4), (10, −2)
   (c) (5, 4), (4, 3), (3, 2), (2, 1)
   (d) (8, 6), (7, 5), (6, 4), (4, 2)
   (e) (3, 4), (4, 5), (5, 6), (7, 8)

B

3. State an equation that is represented by the arrow diagrams.

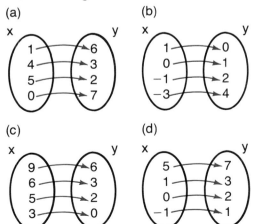

11.4 GRAPHING ORDERED PAIRS

We graph whole numbers on a whole number line.

We graph ordered pairs on a grid made up of two perpendicular number lines. The horizontal number line is called the x-axis. The vertical number line is called the y-axis. The lines intersect at the origin.

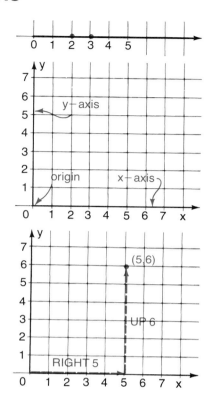

The ordered pair (5, 6) is shown on the grid. The 5 is the x-coordinate. It tells us how far to move horizontally from the origin. The 6 is the y-coordinate. It tells us how far to move vertically.

EXERCISE

A

1. Name the letter for each pair of coordinates.

   (a) (5, 6)   (b) (3, 3)   (c) (6, 4)
   (d) (10, 2)   (e) (4, 10)   (f) (2, 0)
   (g) (0, 8)   (h) (1, 5)   (i) (9, 9)
   (j) (0, 3)   (k) (0, 0)   (l) (7, 0)

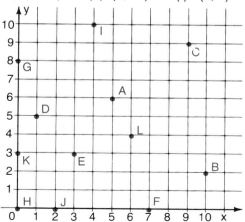

2. State the coordinates of each point on the graph.

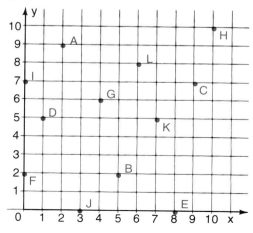

11.5 GRAPHING ON THE INTEGER GRID

We can extend the grid for graphing by using two intersecting integer lines. The lines make four quadrants. The names of the quadrants are shown at the right.

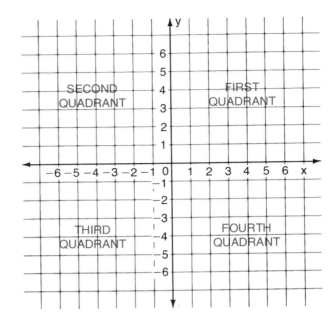

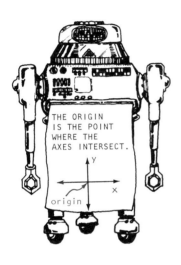

THE ORIGIN IS THE POINT WHERE THE AXES INTERSECT.

The ordered pair (−5, 4) is shown on the grid. The −5 in the ordered pair tells us to move five units to the left from the origin. The 4 in the ordered pair tells us to move up four units.

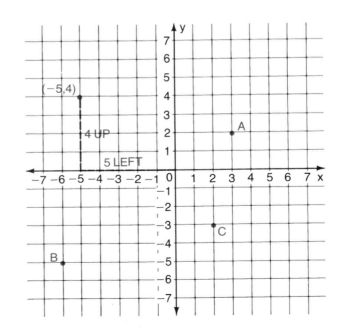

What are the coordinates of point A?

What are the coordinates of point B?

What are the coordinates of point C?

What are the coordinates of the origin?

EXERCISE

A

1. Name the letter for each pair of coordinates.

   (a) (6, 4)　　　　(b) (−4, 6)

   (c) (−6, −4)　　(d) (3, −3)

   (e) (2, 3)　　　　(f) (−3, −7)

   (g) (6, −5)　　　(h) (−8, 4)

   (i) (4, 0)　　　　(j) (−6, 0)

   (k) (0, 5)　　　　(l) (0, −7)

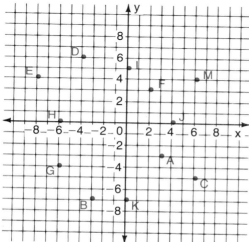

2. State the coordinates of each point on the graph.

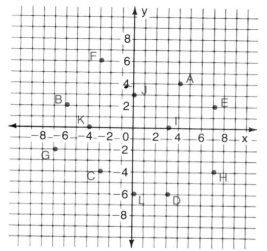

B

3. (a) Plot the points A(5, 3), B(5, 8), C(2, 8) and D(2, 3).
   (b) Join the points in the order A-B-C-D-A.
   (c) Name the figure.
   (d) Determine the area of the figure.

4. (a) Plot the points A(4, 2), B(−2, 2), C(−2, −4), and D(4, −4).
   (b) Join the points in the order A-B-C-D-A.
   (c) Name the figure.
   (d) Determine the area of the figure.

5. (a) Plot the points A(0, 1), B(−8, 1), and C(−8, −7).
   (b) Join the points in the order A-B-C-A.
   (c) Name the figure.
   (d) Determine the area of the figure.

6. Graph the following sets of points and join them. What is the pattern for each set?
   (a) (5, −2), (4, −1), (3, 0), (2, 1), (1, 2), (0, 3)
   (b) (−3, −5), (−2, −4), (−1, −3), (0, −2), (1, −1), (2, 0)
   (c) (5, 3), (3, 2), (1, 1), (−1, 0), (−3, −1), (−5, −2)

7. Graph a set of ordered pairs where the x-coordinate is always 2 greater than the y-coordinate.

8. Graph a set of ordered pairs where the y-coordinate is always 3.

CHALLENGE

Place 5 dots in the squares so that there is only one dot on each row, column, or diagonal.

11.6 GRAPHING RELATIONS

x	y
5	0
4	1
3	2
2	3
1	4
0	5

The equation $x + y = 5$ is a relation since its solutions are ordered pairs.

The graph shows some of the solutions of the equation $x + y = 5$. Since each solution is an ordered pair, we can plot it on a grid.

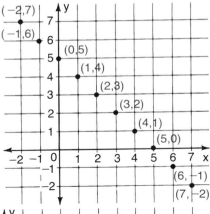

This graph shows more of the solutions of $x + y = 5$.

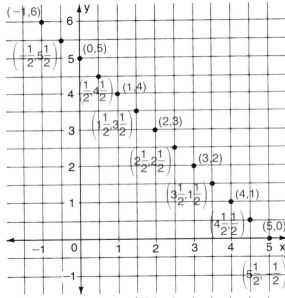

THE REAL NUMBERS, R, INCLUDE ALL THE WHOLE NUMBERS, INTEGERS, FRACTIONS, AND DECIMALS.

There are also other ordered pairs such as

$$\left(1\frac{2}{3}, 3\frac{1}{3}\right) \text{ and } (0.7, 4.3)$$

that are solutions to $x + y = 5$.

In order to show all the ordered pairs, we draw a straight line through the points.

This line is the graph of
$x + y = 5, \quad x, y \in R.$

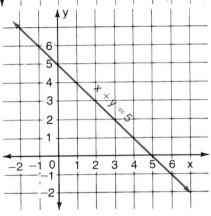

Example. Draw the graph of $y = 2x - 1$, $\quad x, y \in R$.

Solution: 1. Find four ordered pairs.
2. Plot them.
3. Join the points with a straight line.

When $x = 2$, $\quad y = 2(2) - 1$
$= 4 - 1$
$= 3$

When $x = 1$, $\quad y = 2(1) - 1$
$= 2 - 1$
$= 1$

When $x = 0$, $\quad y = 2(0) - 1$
$= 0 - 1$
$= -1$

When $x = -1$, $\quad y = 2(-1) - 1$
$= -2 - 1$
$= -3$

x	y
2	3
1	1
0	-1
-1	-3

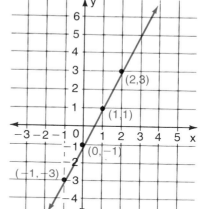

EXERCISE

B

1. Complete the following tables of values. Draw the graph of each equation.

(a) $x + y = 4$

x	y
4	
2	
0	
-2	

(b) $x - y = 2$

x	y
4	
3	
2	
1	

(c) $y = 2x + 1$

x	y
0	
1	
2	
3	

2. Draw the graph of each of the following equations.
   (a) $x + y = 6$ (b) $x + y = 3$
   (c) $x - y = 3$ (d) $x - y = 5$
   (e) $x - y = 0$ (f) $x + y = -1$

3. Draw the graph of each of the following equations.
   (a) $y = x + 4$ (b) $y = 2x + 3$
   (c) $y = x - 4$ (d) $y = 3x - 2$
   (e) $y = 6 - x$ (f) $y = 5 - 2x$

CHALLENGE

Place 6 dots in the squares so that there is only one dot in each row, column, or diagonal.

11.7 APPLICATIONS OF GRAPHING RELATIONS

The world's deepest mine is in Carletonville, South Africa. The mine extends almost 4 km below the earth's surface.

As you go deeper into the earth, the temperature of the air increases. The table at the right gives the air temperature for several depths. The graph of this relation is shown below.

Depth (km)	Temp. (°C)
0	20
1	30
2	40
3	50
4	60

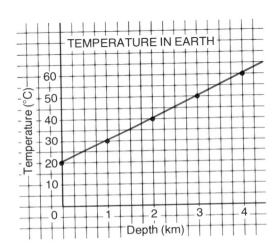

To determine the temperature 2.5 km below the earth's surface, we proceed as follows.

i) Locate 2.5 km on the horizontal axis.

ii) Move vertically until you meet the graph.

iii) Move horizontally until you meet the vertical axis.

iv) Read 45°C on the vertical axis.

The temperature 2.5 km below the earth's surface is 45°C.

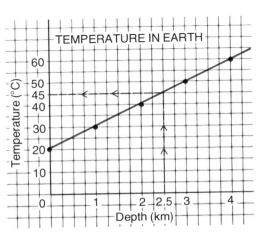

EXERCISE

B

1. The table gives the distance travelled versus time for a truck travelling at 80 km/h.

Time (h)	Distance (km)
0	0
1	80
2	160
3	240
4	320

(a) Graph this relation.

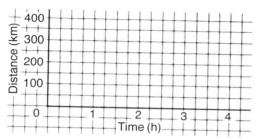

(b) Use your graph to determine the approximate distance travelled in
   i) 1.5 h   ii) 2.5 h

(c) Use your graph to determine the approximate time to travel
   i) 200 km   ii) 280 km

2. A car rental agency charges for the number of kilometres driven. The table gives the cost for various kilometres driven.

Kilometres Driven	Cost ($)
0	0
100	20
200	40
300	60
400	80
500	100

(a) Graph this relation.

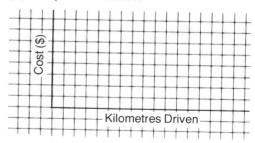

(b) Use your graph to determine the cost to drive
   i) 150 km   ii) 350 km   iii) 425 km

(c) Use your graph to determine how far you could drive for
   i) $50   ii) $90   iii) $35

3. Sandra has a small banquet room in her restaurant. The table below gives the cost of a banquet for various numbers of people.

Number of People	Cost $
10	300
20	500
30	700
40	900
50	1100

(a) Graph this relation.

(b) Use your graph to determine the approximate cost of a banquet for
   i) 25 people;   ii) 35 people;
   iii) 42 people.

(c) How many people could attend a banquet if you had $1000 to spend?

11.8 CROSSING POINT

The team bus left the school at 12:00. The bus travelled at 60 km/h. Pete was late for the bus. His father decided to drive and try to catch the bus. They left the school at 13:00. They drove at 100 km/h. When will Pete catch the bus?

The tables give the distance from the school for the bus and for Pete at several times.

BUS

Time	Distance from School (km)
12:00	0
13:00	60
14:00	120
15:00	180

PETE

Time	Distance from School (km)
12:00	—
13:00	0
14:00	100
15:00	200

We now graph these ordered pairs on the same grid.

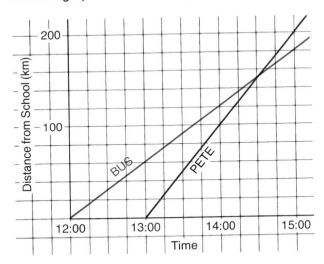

The two lines cross at (14:30, 150)

Pete caught the bus at 14:30. They were 150 km from the school.

EXERCISE

B

1. Susan left the camp, on a bicycle, at 09:00. She rode at a rate of 6 km/h. Holly left the camp at 10:00. Since she was trying to catch up with Susan, she rode at a rate of 10 km/h.

   (a) Complete the tables to show their distances from camp at several times.

   SUSAN

Time	Distance from Camp (km)
09:00	0
10:00	
11:00	
12:00	
13:00	

   HOLLY

Time	Distance from Camp (km)
09:00	—
10:00	0
11:00	
12:00	
13:00	

   (b) Graph the ordered pairs on the same grid.
   (c) At what point do the lines cross?
   (d) At what time did Holly catch Susan?
   (e) How far were they from camp when Holly caught Susan?

2. The suspects left the garage at 06:00. They travelled at 70 km/h. The police left the garage at 07:00, travelling at 90 km/h.

   (a) Complete the tables to show the distances from the garage at several times.

   SUSPECTS

Time	Distance from Garage (km)
06:00	0
07:00	
08:00	
09:00	
10:00	
11:00	

   POLICE

Time	Distance from Garage (km)
06:00	—
07:00	0
08:00	
09:00	
10:00	
11:00	

   (b) Graph the ordered pairs on the same grid.
   (c) At what point do the lines cross?
   (d) At what time did the police catch the suspects?
   (e) How far were they from the garage?

3. A spaceship left the earth's atmosphere for Mars at 15:00. It travelled at 14 000 km/h. At 16:00 the ship developed a leak in a fuel tank. At 17:00 a rescue ship left the earth's atmosphere travelling at 22 000 km/h.

   (a) Complete the tables to show the distances from the earth's atmosphere at several times.

   SPACESHIP

Time	Distance from Earth's Atmosphere (1000 km)
15:00	0
16:00	14
17:00	
18:00	
19:00	
20:00	
21:00	

   RESCUE SHIP

Time	Distance from Earth's Atmosphere (1000 km)
15:00	—
16:00	—
17:00	0
18:00	
19:00	
20:00	
21:00	

   (b) Graph the ordered pairs on the grid.
   (c) At what point do the lines cross?
   (d) At what time did the rescue ship reach the space ship?
   (e) How far were they from the earth's atmosphere?

11.9 SLOPE

Ski hills are sloped.

The roof of the house is sloped so that the snow will slide off.

In mathematics the slope of a line is the measure of the steepness of the line. Slope is defined by a ratio.

$$\text{slope} = \frac{\text{rise}}{\text{run}}$$

The following show examples of slopes of lines.

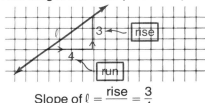

$$\text{Slope of } \ell = \frac{\text{rise}}{\text{run}} = \frac{3}{4}$$

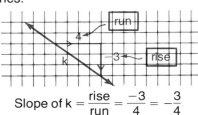

$$\text{Slope of } k = \frac{\text{rise}}{\text{run}} = \frac{-3}{4} = -\frac{3}{4}$$

Think of it as a negative rise.

By counting squares in the diagram at right, we see that the rise is 5, the run is 3, and the slope is $\frac{5}{3}$.

Instead of counting squares you can subtract coordinates as shown in the diagram.

When you know the coordinates of two points on a line, you can calculate the slope as follows.

$$\text{slope} = \frac{\text{rise}}{\text{run}} = \frac{7-2}{4-1} = \frac{5}{3}$$

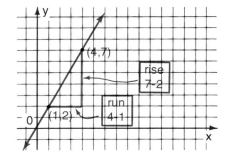

In general, the slope of the line that joins points (x_1, y_1) and (x_2, y_2) is:

$$\text{slope} = \frac{\text{rise}}{\text{run}}$$

$$= \frac{y_2 - y_1}{x_2 - x_1}$$

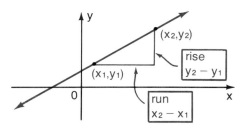

When a line rises from left to right, the slope is a positive number.

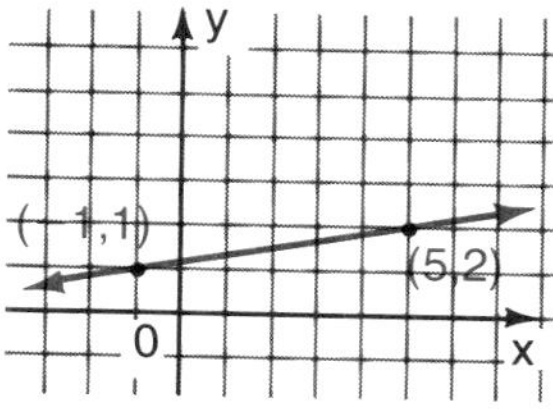

$\text{slope} = \frac{2-1}{5-(-1)} = \frac{1}{6}$

When a line falls from left to right, the slope is a negative number.

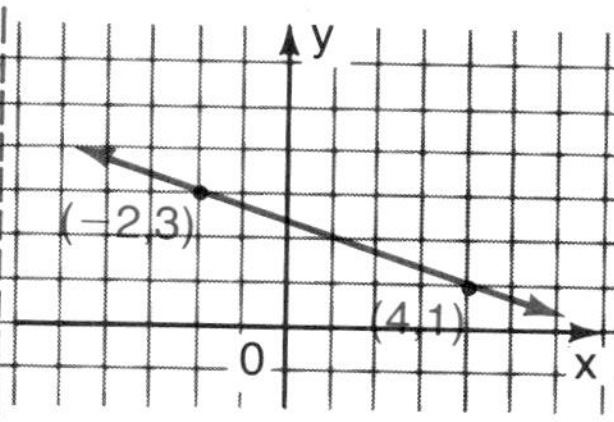

$\text{slope} = \frac{3-1}{-2-4} = \frac{2}{-6} = -\frac{1}{3}$

The slope of a horizontal line is zero.

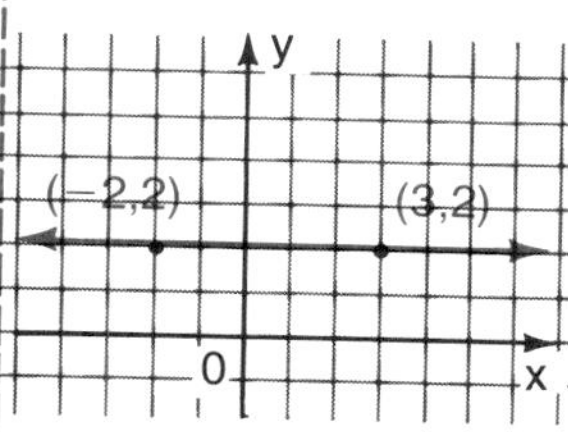

$\text{slope} = \frac{2-2}{-2-3} = \frac{0}{-5} = 0$

A vertical line does not have a slope.

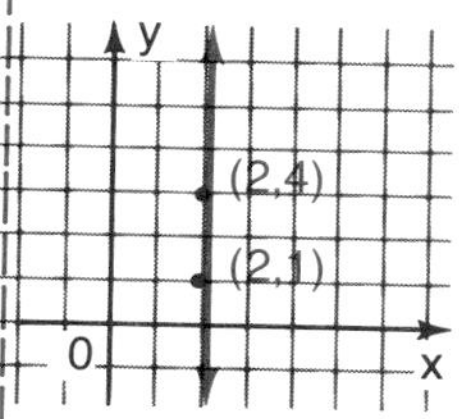

$\text{slope} = \frac{4-1}{2-2} = \frac{3}{0}$
(not defined)

EXERCISE

1. Calculate the rise, run, and slope for each.

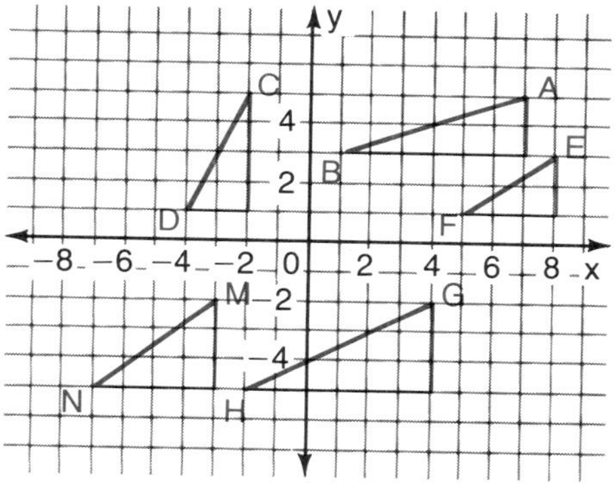

2. Calculate the rise, run, and slope for each.

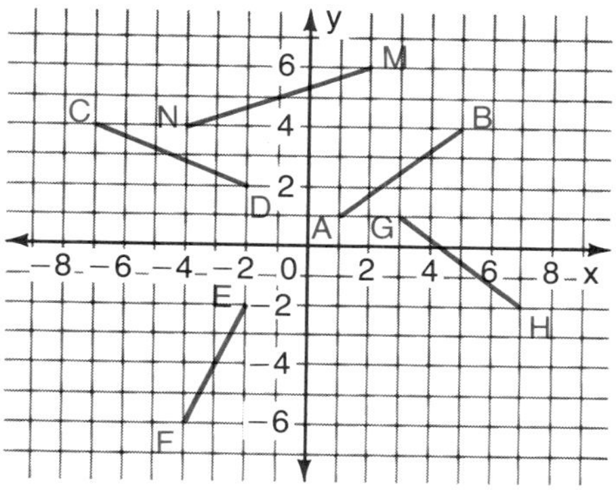

3. Determine the slope of the line passing through each pair of points.
   (a) A(6, 6), B(1, 2)
   (b) C(3, 4), D(9, 8)
   (c) M(9, 2), N(0, 1)
   (d) G(−2, 3), H(2, 2)
   (e) S(−2, −1), T(0, 5)
   (f) P(3, −2), Q(−4, 6)

4. Use the diagram to calculate the slope of each line segment.

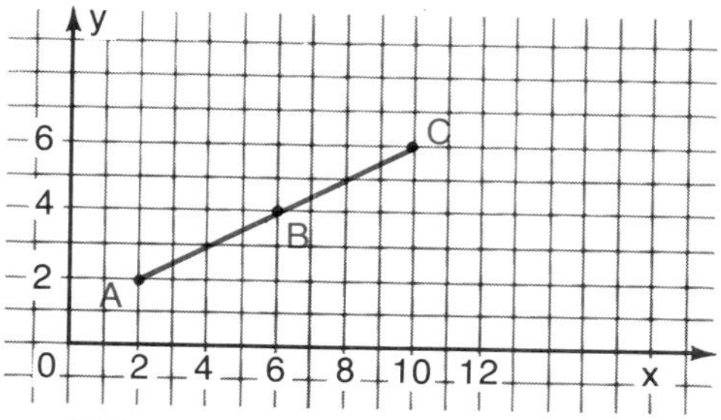

   (a) $\overline{AB}$ (b) $\overline{BC}$ (c) $\overline{AC}$
   What is true about the slopes? Why?

5. On grid paper, draw a line through (4, 2) with slope $\frac{2}{3}$.

6. On grid paper, draw a line through (−1, 3) with slope $\frac{-4}{5}$.

11.10 LENGTH OF A LINE SEGMENT

You have already used the Pythagorean Theorem to calculate distances on a right-angled triangle.

$$a^2 = b^2 + c^2$$
$$a^2 = 3^2 + 4^2$$
$$= 9 + 16$$
$$= 25$$
$$a = 5$$

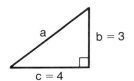

We can use this theorem to calculate distances on a grid.

Example 1. Calculate the distance between A(10, 7) and B(2, 1).

Solution: Plot A and B on a grid.
The diagram shows how the rise and run are used to form a right-angled triangle.

The rise $\overline{AC}$ is $7 - 1 = 6$.
The run $\overline{BC}$ is $10 - 2 = 8$.

Using the Pythagorean Theorem,

$$(\overline{AB})^2 = (\overline{AC})^2 + (\overline{BC})^2$$
$$= 6^2 + 8^2$$
$$= 36 + 64$$
$$(\overline{AB})^2 = 100$$
$$(\overline{AB}) = \sqrt{100}$$
$$(\overline{AB}) = 10$$

The length of $\overline{AB}$ is 10 units.

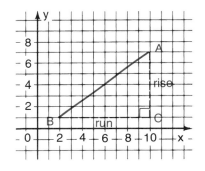

Example 2. Calculate the distance between P(−3, 5) and Q(2, −1).

Solution: The rise is $5 - (-1) = 6$.
The run is $-3 - 2 = -5$

$$(\overline{PQ})^2 = (\overline{PT})^2 + (\overline{QT})^2$$
$$= 6^2 + (-5)^2$$
$$= 36 + 25$$
$$= 61$$
$$\overline{PQ} = \sqrt{61}$$

The length of $\overline{PQ}$ is $\sqrt{61}$ units.

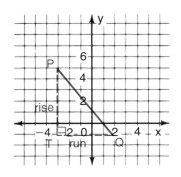

EXERCISE

A

1. Find the length of each line segment.

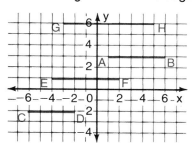

  (a) $\overline{AB}$ (b) $\overline{CD}$ (c) $\overline{EF}$ (d) $\overline{GH}$

2. Find the length of each line segment.

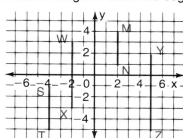

  (a) $\overline{MN}$ (b) $\overline{ST}$ (c) $\overline{WX}$ (d) $\overline{YZ}$

B

3. What is the length of $\overline{AC}$, $\overline{BC}$, and $\overline{AB}$?

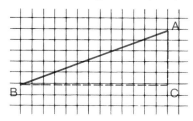

4. What is the length of $\overline{DF}$, $\overline{EF}$, and $\overline{DE}$?

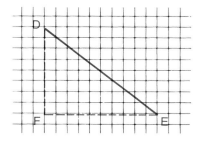

5. Calculate the length of each line segment.

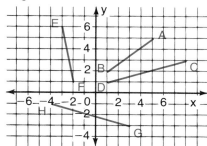

6. Calculate the length of each line segment.
     (a) A(7, 5), B(1, 1)
     (b) S(8, 6), T(−4, 1)
     (c) D(−3, −2), E(4, −5)
     (d) M(−5, 6), N(2, 1)

7. Find the length of each side of the triangle.

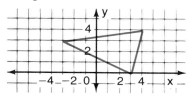

8. △ABC has vertices A(1, 1), B(1, 5), and C(−2, 1).
     (a) Calculate the length of each side.
     (b) Find the perimeter of the triangle.

ⅢⅠⅭⅡⅡ ⅢⅡⅠⅡⅪ

NEW

```
10 PRINT"LENGTH OF A LINE SEGMENT"
20 INPUT" FIRST POINT : (X,Y)";A,B
30 INPUT"SECOND POINT : (X,Y)";C,D
40 LET L=SQR((A-C)↑2+(B-D)↑2)
50 PRINT"THE LENGTH IS ";L
60 END
```

RUN

11.11 GRAPHING GENERAL RELATIONS

In this section we will graph relations without using equations. It will not be necessary to put a scale on the axes — the labels will be sufficient.

Example. Suppose you throw a ball straight up in the air. Sketch a graph of the height of the ball versus the amount of time since you threw it.

Solution:

Draw the axes and label them.

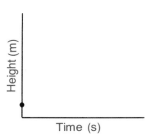

Before you throw the ball, the height of the ball will be the same as the height of your hand.

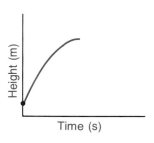

After you throw the ball, it will climb in the air to a certain height.

The ball will then fall back to the ground. Remember, it will take a little time for the ball to come back down. This is why the graph line does not come straight down.

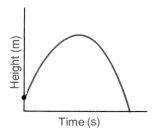

EXERCISE

B

1. Your height depends on your age.
   Sketch a graph of height versus age.

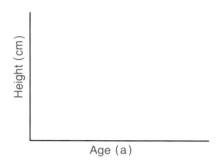

2. Andrea filled the tank in the test car with gasoline. She drove around the test track at a constant speed until the tank was empty.
   Sketch a graph of litres of gasoline left in the tank versus distance travelled.

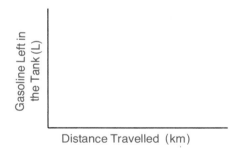

3. Dennis filled an ice-cube tray with warm water. He put the tray in the freezer.
   Sketch a graph of the temperature of the water in the tray versus the length of time in the freezer.

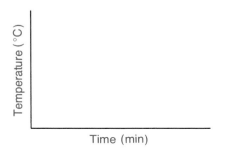

4. The number of minutes of daylight depends on the time of year.
   Sketch a graph of daylight minutes versus the month of the year.

5. Gino filled an electric kettle with cold water. He then plugged in the kettle.
   Sketch a graph of the water temperature versus the length of time the kettle has been plugged in.

6. Suppose that you are the last person to get on a ferris wheel. Your height above the ground depends on how long you have been riding.
   Sketch a graph of your height above the ground versus time.

11.12 ESTIMATING SQUARE ROOTS FROM A GRAPH

The square root of a number can be estimated using a graph.

The chart below gives the squares of the whole numbers from 0 to 5.

The coordinates for the graph are read from the table.

n	n^2		
0	0	$\rightarrow$	(0, 0)
1	1	$\rightarrow$	(1, 1)
2	4	$\rightarrow$	(2, 4)
3	9	$\rightarrow$	(3, 9)
4	16	$\rightarrow$	(4, 16)
5	25	$\rightarrow$	(5, 25)

These coordinates were plotted on the graph below. Then a smooth curve was drawn connecting the points.

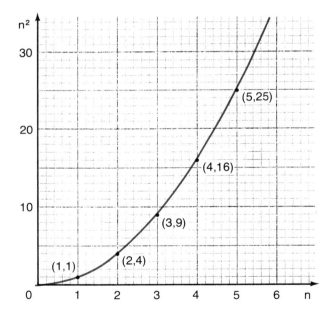

From this graph, two values can be estimated:
(1) the squares of numbers;
(2) the square roots of numbers.

Example. Use the graph to evaluate $\sqrt{12}$.

Solution:
i) Locate 12 on the vertical axis.

ii) Move horizontally to meet the graph.

iii) Move vertically to meet the horizontal axis.

iv) Read 3.4 on the horizontal axis.

$$\sqrt{12} \doteq 3.4$$

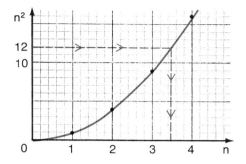

EXERCISE

B

1. Use the graph to estimate the following.
   (a) $\sqrt{20}$ (b) $\sqrt{6}$ (c) $\sqrt{15}$

2. Use the graph to estimate the following.
   (a) $(1.5)^2$ (b) $(3.5)^2$ (c) $(4.5)^2$

3. (a) Draw a graph for the squares of numbers from 1 to 7.
   (b) From your graph estimate:
      i) $\sqrt{38}$ ii) $\sqrt{47}$

4. Sometimes a plastic covering is used to protect tomatoes from frost at night. A square tomato plot measures 4.6 m by 4.6 m.
   Using your graph, estimate how many square metres of plastic will be required to protect the tomatoes on a cold night.

5. A square window pane was covered with 45 cm^2 of paper.
   Using your graph, estimate the dimensions of the window pane.

6. Copy the following table in your notebook and fill in the missing values.
   Use the graph to estimate the values.

n	n^2
▨	3
▨	11
0	▨
▨	17
2.5	▨
4.4	▨

MICRO MATH

NEW

```
10 PRINT"SLOPE"
20 INPUT" FIRST POINT : (X,Y)";A,B
30 INPUT"SECOND POINT : (X,Y)";C,D
40 LET M=(B-D)/(A-C)
50 PRINT"THE SLOPE IS ";M
60 END
```

RUN

LATITUDE AND LONGITUDE

LATITUDE

Every circle has 360°.
A semi-circle has 180°.

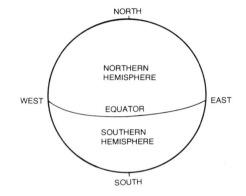

Around the middle of the earth is an imaginary line called the Equator. The Equator runs east and west. It divides the earth into a northern and a southern hemisphere. (A hemisphere is half a sphere.)

Other lines are drawn parallel to the Equator. They are called Parallels of Latitude. They are labelled using degrees. The N and S tell whether the latitude line is in the northern hemisphere or the southern hemisphere.

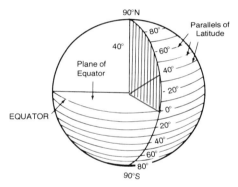

The degrees of latitude are determined by the angle at the interior centre of the earth. All places on the same parallel of latitude are an equal distance from the equator.

LONGITUDE

Longitude lines are drawn on the earth to complete the grid. They are drawn from the North Pole to the South Pole and are called Meridians of Longitude. The Meridians of Longitude are not parallel to each other.

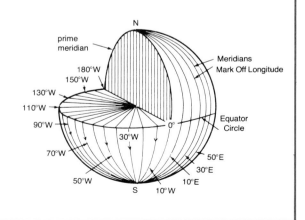

The prime meridian which runs through Greenwich, England is 0°. All other meridians are measured east and west from Greenwich and are measured up to 180°, the International Dateline.

Lines of latitude and longitude appear on most maps and globes as a network of lines on a grid.
Using these lines, we can locate any place on the earth.

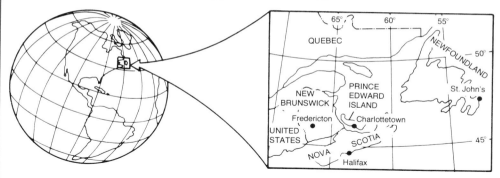

For example, Fredericton, New Brunswick, is close to 47°N Latitude and 67°W Longitude.
Halifax, Nova Scotia, is located near 44°N Latitude and 64°W Longitude.

EXERCISE

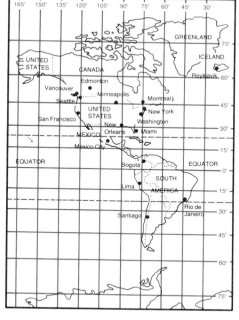

1. Use the map to find the approximate latitude and longitude of the following cities.
   - (a) Vancouver
   - (b) San Francisco
   - (c) Mexico City
   - (d) Lima
   - (e) Miami
   - (f) Santiago
   - (g) Edmonton
   - (h) New Orleans
   - (i) Montreal
   - (j) New York

2. Name the largest city located nearest the following latitudes and longitudes.
   - (a) 48°N, 122°W
   - (b) 45°N, 95°W
   - (c) 5°N, 75°W
   - (d) 20°N, 158°W
   - (e) 22°S, 44°W

3. Use an atlas or globe to find the approximate latitude and longitude of these cities.
   - (a) Moscow, U.S.S.R.
   - (b) Bombay, India
   - (c) Paris, France
   - (d) Warsaw, Poland
   - (e) Sydney, Australia
   - (f) London, England
   - (g) Peking, China
   - (h) Cape Town, South Africa
   - (i) Nome, Alaska
   - (j) Halifax, Nova Scotia

11.13 CHAPTER 11 REVIEW EXERCISE

1. Name the letter for each pair of coordinates.
   (a) (3, 2)   (b) (−6, −4)
   (c) (−5, 0)   (d) (0, −3)
   (e) (−2, 4)   (f) (7, 0)
   (g) (3, −5)   (h) (0, 2)
   (i) (−3, −3)

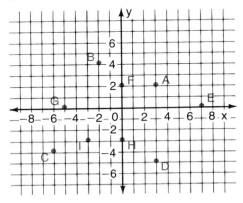

2. State the coordinates of each point on the graph.

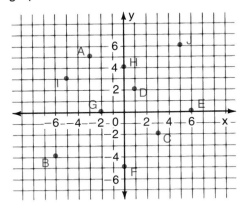

3. Complete the following table of values.

x	4x − 1
2	
0	
−2	
−4	

4. Complete the following table of values.

$x + y = 5$

x	y
3	
1	
0	
−2	
−5	

5. Find 5 ordered pairs for each of the following.
   (a) $x + y = 7$
   (b) $x − y = 1$
   (c) $y = 2x − 1$

6. (a) Plot the points A(4, 1), B(4, 7), and C(−2, 1).
   (b) Join the points and name the figure.
   (c) Calculate the area of the figure.

7. Complete the table of values.
   Draw the graph of the equation.

$x + y = 8$

x	y
4	
2	
0	
−1	
−3	

8. Draw the graphs of each of the following equations.
   (a) $x + y = 7$ (b) $x - y = 2$
   (c) $y = x + 2$ (d) $y = 2x - 1$

9. Calculate the slope of the line passing through each pair of points.
   (a) A(5, 6), B(2, 2)
   (b) D(8, 9), E(0, 2)
   (c) S(4, 7), T(−1, −3)
   (d) M(−2, 5), N(3, −2)
   (e) X(−1, −2), Y(−3, 4)
   (f) C(−3, 2), D(5, 2)
   (g) F(2, 2), G(2, 8)

10. Calculate the length of each line segment.
    (a) A(3, 4), B(9, 4)
    (b) C(4, 7), D(4, 1)
    (c) R(5, 4), S(0, 0)
    (d) X(4, 1), Y(−1, 2)
    (e) M(−2, 5), N(3, −1)
    (f) E(−1, −3), F(2, −6)

11. An underwater salvage team charges for the time spent working underwater. The table gives the cost for various times spent working underwater.

Time Underwater (hours)	Cost ($)
0	0
1	200
2	400
3	600
4	800

(a) Graph this relation.

(b) Use your graph to determine the cost for 1.75 h of underwater work.

(c) How much underwater work could be done for $300?

CHAPTER 11 TEST

1. Complete the following table of values.

x	3x − 4
3	
1	
−1	
−2	

2. Find 5 ordered pairs for each of the following.

   (a) $x + y = 4$

   (b) $x - y = -2$

3. Draw the graph of each of the following.

   (a) $x + y = 5$

   (b) $y = 2x - 3$

4. Calculate the slope of the line passing through each pair of points.

   (a) A(7, 9) and B(2, 1)

   (b) M(−2, 3) and N(−1, −5)

5. Calculate the length of each line segment.

   (a) S(6, 4), T(2, 1)

   (b) D(−2, 3), E(0, −1)

12

PERIMETER AND AREA

REVIEW AND PREVIEW TO CHAPTER 12

LINEAR UNITS OF MEASUREMENT

The following table shows a set of common metric units that are used frequently in the everyday world.

Quantity	Unit	Symbol	Relationship
length	kilometre	km	1 km = 1000 m
	metre	m	1 m = 10 dm = 100 cm
	decimetre	dm	1 dm = 10 cm
	centimetre	cm	1 cm = 10 mm
	millimetre	mm	

We can place the metric units on a place value chart.

kilometre	hectometre	decametre	metre	decimetre	centimetre	millimetre
km	hm	da	m	dm	cm	mm
1000 m	100 m	10 m	1 m	0.1 m	0.01 m	0.001 m

EXERCISE

1. Express in metres.
   - (a) 2.6 km
   - (b) 0.265 km
   - (c) 523 cm
   - (d) 4598 cm
   - (e) 4586 dm
   - (f) 256 dm
   - (g) 25 mm
   - (h) 564 mm

2. Express in centimetres.
   - (a) 2.6 m
   - (b) 0.56 m
   - (c) 36 mm
   - (d) 458 mm
   - (e) 45 dm
   - (f) 2.5 dm
   - (g) 0.025 m
   - (h) 75 000 mm

3. Select the best answer for each of the following.
   - (a) The length of a classroom is
     - i) 13 m
     - ii) 376 cm
     - iii) 3300 mm
     - iv) 3 m
   - (b) The height of a grade nine student is
     - i) 0.8 m
     - ii) 200 cm
     - iii) 125 m
     - iv) 0.5 km
   - (c) The length of a car is
     - i) 145 cm
     - ii) 2 m
     - iii) 3.8 m
     - iv) 2.6 m

AREA UNITS OF MEASUREMENT

The following table shows a set of common metric units that are used frequently in the everyday world.

Quantity	Unit	Symbol	Relationship
area	square kilometre	km²	1 km² = 100 ha
	hectare	ha	1 da² = 100 m²
	square decametre	da²	1 ha = 10 000 m²
	square metre	m²	1 m² = 10 000 cm²
	square centimetre	cm²	1 cm² = 100 mm²
	square millimetre	mm²	

We can place the metric units on a place value chart.

square kilometre	square hectometre or hectare	square decametre or are	square metre	square decimetre	square centimetre	square millimetre
km²	ha	da²	m²	dm²	cm²	mm²
1 000 000 m²	10 000 m²	100 m²	1 m²	0.01 m²	0.000 1 m²	0.000 001 m²

EXERCISE

1. Express in square metres.
   (a) 3.6 km²   (b) 0.165 km²
   (c) 0.025 km²   (d) 5 ha
   (e) 2.8 ha   (f) 0.5 ha
   (g) 75 000 cm²   (h) 3600 cm²

2. Express in hectares.
   (a) 36 000 m²   (b) 5000 m²
   (c) 25 km²   (d) 0.15 km²
   (e) 0.025 km²   (f) 250 000 m²

3. Express in square centimetres.
   (a) 3 m²   (b) 2.5 m²
   (c) 0.5 m²   (d) 0.05 m²
   (e) 0.005 m²   (f) 0.0005 m²
   (g) 0.025 m²   (h) 0.7 m²

4. Select the best answer for each of the following.
   (a) The area of one page of this book is
       i) 450 cm²   ii) 0.4 m²
       iii) 0.005 m²

   (b) The area of an LP jacket is
       i) 225 cm²   ii) 1.1 m²
       iii) 0.085 m²

   (c) The area of a television screen is
       i) 100 cm²   ii) 0.5 m²
       iii) 0.12 m²

   (d) The area of your class picture is
       i) 10 cm²   ii) 0.45 m²
       iii) 275 cm²

   (e) A credit card has an area of
       i) 53 cm²   ii) 0.0041 cm²
       iii) 210 cm²

VOLUME AND CAPACITY UNITS OF MEASUREMENT

The basic units for volume and capacity are the cubic metre (m^3) and the litre (L). An object that has a capacity of one litre (1 L) holds 1000 cm^3.

The following table shows the units for volume and capacity.

Quantity	Unit	Symbol	Relationship
volume	cubic metre	m^3	
	cubic decimetre	dm^3	$1\ m^3 = 1000\ dm^3$
	cubic centimetre	cm^3	$1\ dm^3 = 1000\ cm^3$
capacity	kilolitre	kL	
	litre	L	$1\ kL = 1000\ L$
	millilitre	mL	$1\ L = 1000\ mL$

We can place the metric units on a place value chart.

cubic metre or kilolitre	cubic decimetre or litre	cubic centimetre or millilitre
m^3 or kL	dm^3 or L	cm^3 or mL
1000 L	1 L	0.001 L

EXERCISE

1. Express in cubic centimetres.
   (a) 1 m^3
   (b) 0.25 m^3
   (c) 1.5 m^3
   (d) 0.05 m^3
   (e) 1.8 m^3
   (f) 0.0005 m^3
   (g) 25 m^3
   (h) 0.07 m^3

2. Express in cubic metres.
   (a) 25 000 000 cm^3
   (b) 15 000 cm^3
   (c) 25 cm^3
   (d) 1500 cm^3
   (e) 1 cm^3
   (f) 3 500 000 cm^3

3. Order the following volumes from smallest to largest.

   753 cm^3,   0.7 m^3,   8000 cm^3,
   0.004 m^3,   3.5 m^3

4. Express in litres.
   (a) 3 kL
   (b) 5.4 kL
   (c) 0.25 kL
   (d) 3500 kL
   (e) 25 000 mL
   (f) 0.1 kL
   (g) 275 mL
   (h) 0.005 kL

5. Express in millilitres.
   (a) 2.5 L
   (b) 0.25 L
   (c) 0.005 L
   (d) 0.375 L
   (e) 0.045 L
   (f) 5.8 L
   (g) 0.8 L
   (h) 10.5 L

6. Select the best value.
   739 mL of pop for 49¢
   or
   1.5 L of pop for 79¢
   or
   750 mL of pop for 50¢

MASS UNITS OF MEASUREMENT

The common units for mass are shown in the following table.

Quantity	Unit	Symbol	Relationship
mass	tonne	t	
	kilogram	kg	1 t = 1000 kg
	gram	g	1 kg = 1000 g
	milligram	mg	1 g = 1000 mg

We can relate the metric units to a place value chart.

kilogram	gram	milligram
kg	g	mg
1000 g	1 g	0.001 g

EXERCISE

1. Express in kilograms.
   (a) 5 t
   (b) 2.5 t
   (c) 1.5 t
   (d) 2500 t
   (e) 500 g
   (f) 0.005 t
   (g) 25 g
   (h) 25 000 g

2. Express in grams.
   (a) 2 kg
   (b) 15 kg
   (c) 0.5 kg
   (d) 150 kg
   (e) 0.125 kg
   (f) 3 500 000 mg
   (g) 500 mg
   (h) 125 000 mg

3. Express in milligrams.
   (a) 5 g
   (b) 2.5 g
   (c) 0.5 g
   (d) 0.035 g
   (e) 0.025 g
   (f) 0.15 g
   (g) 0.004 g
   (h) 1.125 g

4. Select the best answer for each of the following.
   (a) The mass of the meat portion for one meal is
      i) 1 kg
      ii) 400 g
      iii) 60 g
   (b) The average mass of a grade nine student is
      i) 40 kg
      ii) 60 kg
      iii) 90 kg
   (c) The mass of a paper clip is
      i) 500 mg
      ii) 10 mg
      iii) 1 kg

5. Select the best value.
   (a) 300 g of hamburger for 80¢
      or
      2 kg of hamburger for $4.00
      or
      750 g of hamburger for $1.75
   (b) 1.5 kg of flour for 79¢
      or
      750 g of flour for 50¢

12.1 PERIMETERS OF GEOMETRIC FIGURES

The distance around a figure is called the perimeter. When we need to find the length of material to frame a picture or to make a border, we use the perimeter. To find the perimeter, we add the lengths of the sides.

In order to find the amount of lumber required to build the corrals at the Calgary Stampede, you need to know the perimeter of each pen.

Example 1.

Find the amount of fence material required to enclose this lot.

Solution: The perimeter is
35 + 31 + 42 + 26 = 134.
The perimeter is 134 m.
It would take 134 m of material to fence the lot.

Example 2. Find the perimeter of these figures.

(a)
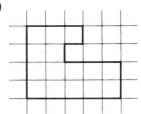

(b)
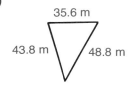

35.6 m
43.8 m   48.8 m

Solution: (a) When a figure lies on a grid, you can find the lengths of the sides by counting.

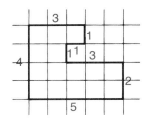

The perimeter is
3 + 1 + 1 + 1 + 3 + 2 + 5 + 4 = 20

(b) Adding the lengths of the sides, the perimeter is

     35.6
     43.8
     48.8
P = 128.2

The perimeter is 128.2 m.

EXERCISE

B

1. Find the perimeter of each figure. The length of the side of each small square is 1 unit.

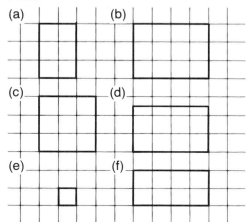

(a) (b)

(c) (d)

(e) (f)

2. Find the perimeter of each figure.

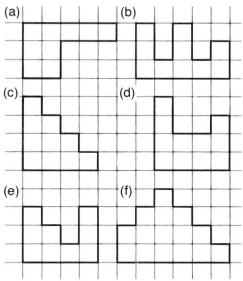

(a) (b)

(c) (d)

(e) (f)

3. Find the perimeter of each figure.

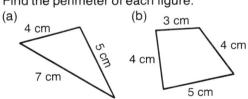

(a)

4 cm

5 cm

7 cm

(b)

3 cm

4 cm

4 cm

5 cm

(c)

7 cm

5 cm

8 cm

6 cm

(d)

2 cm 2 cm

3 cm 3 cm

3 cm

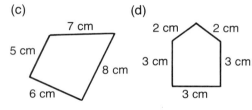

4. Use the lengths given at the right to find the perimeter of the following figures.

2   2.8   1

3

(a) (b)

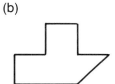

(c) (d)

5. Find the perimeter of this field.

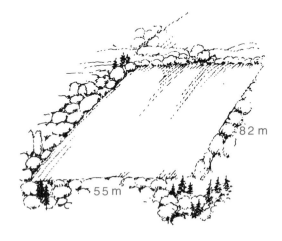

82 m

55 m

12.2 PERIMETERS OF SPECIAL FIGURES

1. REGULAR POLYGONS
In a regular polygon, all sides have the same length and all angles are equal.

Perimeter of regular polygon $= \left(\begin{array}{c}\text{number}\\ \text{of sides}\end{array}\right) \times \left(\begin{array}{c}\text{length of}\\ \text{each side}\end{array}\right)$

$$P = n \times s$$

Example 1. Find the perimeter of each of these regular polygons.

(a)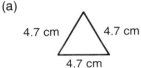

(b)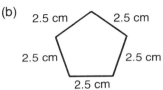

Solution: $P = n \times s$

(a) $P = 3 \times 4.7$
  $= 14.1$
  The perimeter is 14.1 cm.

(b) $P = 5 \times 2.5$
  $= 12.5$
  The perimeter is 12.5 cm.

2. RECTANGLES
We can find the perimeter by counting.

$P = 14$

We can also find the perimeter using patterns.

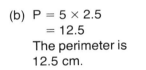

$P = 2(4 + 3)$
  $= 2 \times 7$
  $= 14$

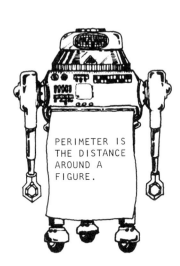

PERIMETER IS THE DISTANCE AROUND A FIGURE.

The formula for perimeter of a rectangle is

$P = \ell + w + \ell + w$
$P = 2(\ell + w)$

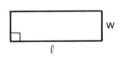

Example 2. Find the perimeter of these rectangles.

(a)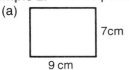
7cm

9 cm

(b)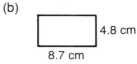
4.8 cm

8.7 cm

Solution:

(a) $P = 2(\ell + w)$
  $P = 2(9 + 7)$
  $= 2 \times 16$
  $= 32$
  The perimeter is 32 cm.

(b) $P = 2(\ell + w)$
  $P = 2(8.7 + 4.8)$
  $= 2 \times 13.5$
  $= 27$
  The perimeter is 27 cm.

EXERCISE

B

1. Find the perimeter of each regular polygon.

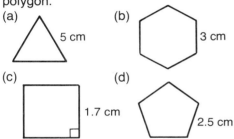

(a) 5 cm

(b) 3 cm

(c) 1.7 cm

(d) 2.5 cm

2. Find the perimeter of each rectangle.

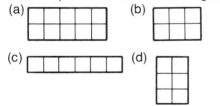

(a) (b) (c) (d)

3. Calculate the perimeter.

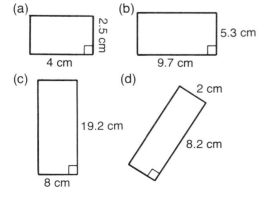

(a) 2.5 cm / 4 cm

(b) 5.3 cm / 9.7 cm

(c) 19.2 cm / 8 cm

(d) 2 cm / 8.2 cm

4. Find the perimeter of each figure.

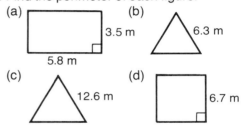

(a) 3.5 m / 5.8 m

(b) 6.3 m

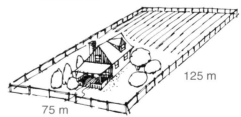

(c) 12.6 m

(d) 6.7 m

5. (a) Find the amount of fence material required.
   (b) What is the total cost of the fence at $12.75/m?

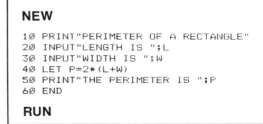

125 m

75 m

ⅢⅠⅭⓇ ⅢⅡⅡⅡ
MICRO MATH

NEW

```
10 PRINT"PERIMETER OF A RECTANGLE"
20 INPUT"LENGTH IS ";L
30 INPUT"WIDTH IS ";W
40 LET P=2*(L+W)
50 PRINT"THE PERIMETER IS ";P
60 END
```

RUN

12.3 AREAS OF SQUARES AND RECTANGLES

Area is the amount of surface covered. We use area of a surface when we do the following jobs.

Wallpapering

Planting grass

Mosaic

We can find the area of a figure by tracing it on a grid and counting the squares. **Notice how we count the partial squares.**

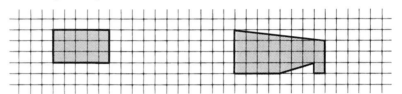

The number of squares is 15. If each square is 1 unit, then the area is 15 units.

The total number of squares is

(whole squares) $+ \frac{1}{2}$ (partial squares)

The area is

$$A = 21 + \frac{1}{2}(11)$$
$$= 26.5$$

The formula for area of a rectangle can be seen in the following examples. Each square is 1 cm by 1 cm and has an area of 1 cm².

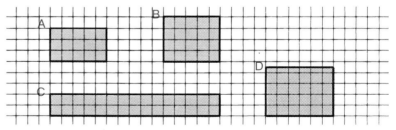

Rectangle	Area by Counting	Length	Width	Length × Width
A	15	5	3	5 × 3 = 15
B	20	5	4	5 × 4 = 20
C	30	15	2	15 × 2 = 30
D	27	6	4.5	6 × 4.5 = 27

Area of a rectangle = length × width

Area of a rectangle
$$A = \ell w$$

In the case of a square, all sides are equal.

Area of a square
$$A = s^2$$

EXERCISE

A

1. Find the area of each of the following.

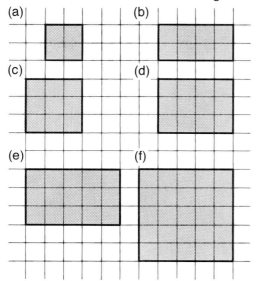

(a) (b) (c) (d) (e) (f)

2. Find the area of each figure.

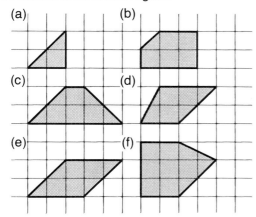

(a) (b) (c) (d) (e) (f)

B

3. Find the area of each of these squares.
   (a) 7 cm
   (b) 8 cm
   (c) 2.5 cm
   (d) 3.7 cm

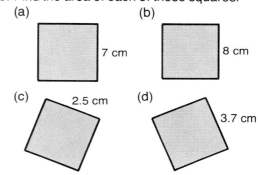

4. Find the area of each rectangle.
   (a) 4.8 cm, 3.6 cm
   (b) 2.5 cm, 3.1 cm
   (c) 4 cm, 8 cm
   (d) 11.4 cm, 6.2 cm

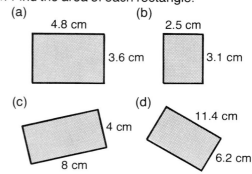

5. Find the area of each figure.
   (a) 1.8 cm, 4.6 cm
   (b) 4.2 cm

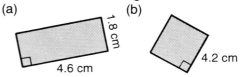

6. If the sides of a square are doubled in length, what happens to the surface area?

12.4 AREAS OF RECTANGULAR SHAPES

In our earlier work, we used the area formulas:

rectangle $A = \ell w$ square $A = s^2$

In this section we shall use the area formulas to find the area of rectangular shapes. The following figure is an L-shape.

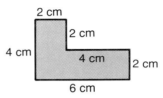

We can find the area of this shape by adding or subtracting areas. The method we use depends on the question.

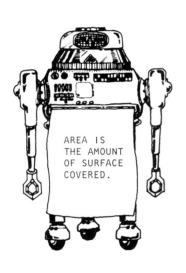

AREA IS THE AMOUNT OF SURFACE COVERED.

Adding Areas	Subtracting Areas

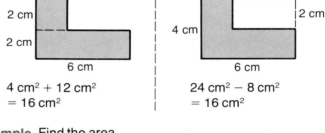

$4 \text{ cm}^2 + 12 \text{ cm}^2$
$= 16 \text{ cm}^2$

$24 \text{ cm}^2 - 8 \text{ cm}^2$
$= 16 \text{ cm}^2$

Example. Find the area.

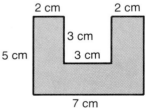

Solution:

Adding Areas   Subtracting Areas

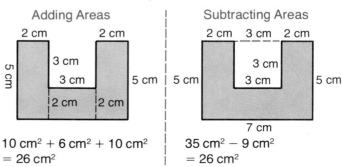

$10 \text{ cm}^2 + 6 \text{ cm}^2 + 10 \text{ cm}^2$
$= 26 \text{ cm}^2$

$35 \text{ cm}^2 - 9 \text{ cm}^2$
$= 26 \text{ cm}^2$

In the Example, the subtracting method required one less calculation than the adding method. However both methods produce the same result. We usually try to choose the method that requires the fewest calculations.

EXERCISE

B

1. Find the area of each of these rectangular shapes, by adding or subtracting.

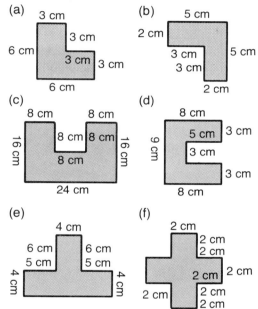

(a)

(b)

(c)

(d)

(e)

(f)

2. Find the area of each of the following rectangular shapes.

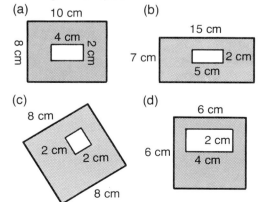

(a)

(b)

(c)

(d)

3. It costs $11.25/m² to pave a rectangular parking lot.
Find the cost to pave the following parking lots.

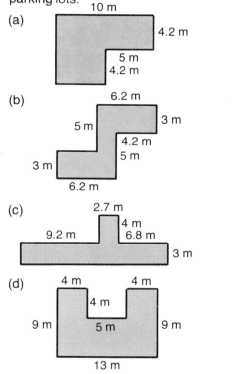

(a)

(b)

(c)

(d)

MICRO MATH

NEW

```
10 PRINT"AREA OF A RECTANGLE"
20 INPUT"LENGTH IS";L
30 INPUT"WIDTH IS";W
40 LET A=L*W
50 PRINT"THE AREA IS ";A
60 END
```

RUN

12.5 PARALLELOGRAMS, TRIANGLES, AND TRAPEZOIDS

PARALLELOGRAMS

A parallelogram has opposite sides equal and parallel. The formula for area of a parallelogram is found by relating the figure to a rectangle.

Slide triangle A to position B.

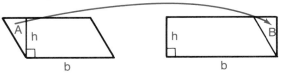

The areas of the two figures are equal. The height of the parallelogram, h, becomes the width of the new rectangle.

Area of a parallelogram
A = bh

TRIANGLES

A triangle has 3 sides. The formula for area of a triangle is found by relating the triangle to a parallelogram.

Rotate triangle A to position B so that a parallelogram is formed.

The area of the triangle is one-half the area of the parallelogram. The height of the triangle, h, is also the height of the parallelogram.

Area of a triangle

$A = \frac{1}{2}bh$

TRAPEZOIDS

A trapezoid has only one pair of sides parallel. The formula for area of a trapezoid is found by dividing it into two triangles.

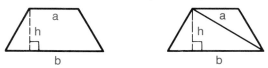

The height of the triangles, h, is the distance between the parallel lines.

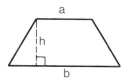

Area of a trapezoid

$$A = \frac{1}{2}ah + \frac{1}{2}bh$$

$$= \frac{1}{2}(a + b)h$$

EXERCISE

B

1. Find the area of each parallelogram.

(a)
(b)

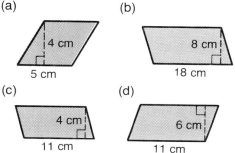

(a) 4 cm, 5 cm
(b) 8 cm, 18 cm

(c)
(d)

(c) 4 cm, 11 cm
(d) 6 cm, 11 cm

2. Find the area of each triangle.

(a)
(b)

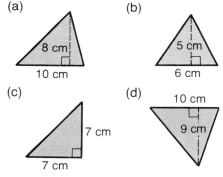

(a) 8 cm, 10 cm
(b) 5 cm, 6 cm

(c)
(d)

(c) 7 cm, 7 cm
(d) 10 cm, 9 cm

3. Find the area of each trapezoid.

(a)
(b)

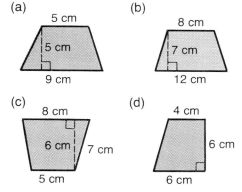

(a) 5 cm, 5 cm, 9 cm
(b) 8 cm, 7 cm, 12 cm

(c)
(d)

(c) 8 cm, 6 cm, 7 cm, 5 cm
(d) 4 cm, 6 cm, 6 cm

4. Find the area of each of the following.

(a)
(b)

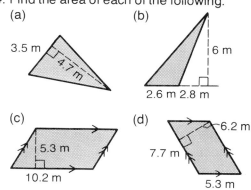

(a) 3.5 m, 4.7 m
(b) 6 m, 2.6 m, 2.8 m

(c)
(d)

(c) 5.3 m, 10.2 m
(d) 6.2 m, 7.7 m, 5.3 m

MICRO MATH

A program for finding area of a parallelogram can be found on page 381.

NEW

```
10 PRINT"AREA OF A TRIANGLE"
20 INPUT"BASE IS ";B
30 INPUT"HEIGHT IS ";H
40 LET A=0.5*B*H
50 PRINT"THE AREA IS ";A
60 END
```

RUN

NEW

```
10 PRINT"AREA OF A TRAPEZOID"
20 INPUT"BASE a is ";A
30 INPUT"BASE b is ";B
40 INPUT"HEIGHT h IS ";H
50 LET X=0.5*(A + B)*H
60 PRINT"THE AREA IS ";X
70 END
```

RUN

12.6 AREAS OF REGULAR POLYGONS

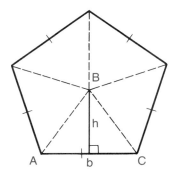

A regular polygon has all sides equal, and all angles equal.

A regular pentagon has 5 equal sides. The pentagon at the left has been divided into 5 congruent triangles. We can use this fact to find the areas of regular polygons.

> The area of triangle ABC $= \frac{1}{2}bh$

Since there are 5 congruent triangles in the pentagon, the area of the pentagon is $5 \times \frac{1}{2}bh$.

> The area of a regular polygon with n sides is
> $$A = \frac{nbh}{2}$$
> where n is the number of sides,
> b is the length of the side,
> (base of the triangle)
> h is the distance from the centre to one side,
> (height of the triangle)

Example 1.
Find the area of a regular hexagon with sides 8 cm, and distance from the centre to a side of approximately 7 cm.

Solution:
Area of triangle ABC is

$$A = \frac{1}{2}bh$$

$$\triangle ABC = \frac{1}{2} \times 8 \times 7$$

$$= 28$$

The area of triangle ABC is 28 cm². We multiply this value by 6, the number of sides, to find the area of the hexagon.

$$6 \times 28 = 168$$

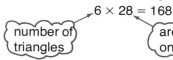 number of triangles area of one triangle

The area of the hexagon is 168 cm².

We can find the area directly, using the formula as in Example 2.

Example 2.
Find the area of a regular octagon with sides 10 cm, and distance from the centre to one side of approximately 12 cm.

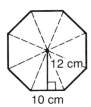

Solution:
Using the formula for area of a regular polygon:

$$A = \frac{nbh}{2}$$

n = 8, b = 10, and h = 12.

$$A = \frac{8 \times 10 \times 12}{2}$$

$$= 480$$

The area of the octagon is 480 cm².

EXERCISE

B

1. Calculate the area of each of the following regular polygons.

   (a)

   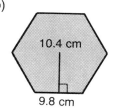

   2.8 cm

   5.6 cm

   (b)

   10.4 cm

   9.8 cm

2. A Crokinole board has sides 29 cm. The distance from the centre dot to the mid point of one side is about 33 cm. What is the surface area of the board?

   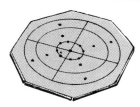

3. (a) State the formula for the area of a regular polygon with n sides.

   (b) What is the smallest possible value of n that you can substitute in this formula?

4. A patio stone is in the shape of a hexagon with sides 30 cm, and the distance from the centre to one side is about 26 cm. What total area would 10 patio stones cover?

MICRO MATH

NEW

```
10 PRINT"AREA OF A REGULAR POLYGON"
20 INPUT"b= ";B
30 INPUT"h= ";H
40 INPUT"n= ";N
50 LET A=N*B*H/2
60 PRINT"THE AREA IS";A
70 END
```

RUN

CHALLENGE

THE HAMPTON COURT MAZE

Mazes made out of shrubs were once very popular. The maze shown below is a diagram of the famous maze at Hampton Court, England. The goal is to get to the open area in the centre.

You can get to the centre using this rule:
Place one hand on any wall and *don't* take a path that requires you to lift your hand from the wall.

12.7 CIRCUMFERENCE OF A CIRCLE

The perimeter of a circle is called the circumference. A line segment through the centre of the circle is called the diameter.

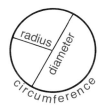

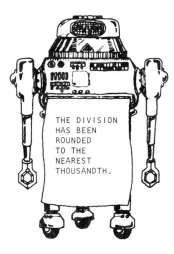

THE DIVISION
HAS BEEN
ROUNDED
TO THE
NEAREST
THOUSANDTH.

The following table shows the relationship between the circumference and the diameter of a circle.

Object	Circumference	Diameter	C ÷ d
Waste basket	110 cm	35 cm	3.143 cm
Soup tin	27.3 cm	8.7 cm	3.138 cm
Record album	95.7 cm	30.5 cm	3.138 cm
Glass	23.9 cm	7.6 cm	3.145 cm
Coin	56.5 mm	18 mm	3.139 mm

The average of the C ÷ d values above is about 3.14. In fact, C ÷ d = 3.14159....
This value is a constant called pi, and is written using the Greek letter π.
In this text, we use $\pi = 3.14$.

$$\pi = \frac{\text{circumference}}{\text{diameter}} = 3.14$$

The circumference of a circle is calculated using
$C = \pi d$ or $C = 2\pi r$, where $\pi = 3.14$

Example. Find the circumference of these circles.

(a)

4.7 cm

(b)

2.6 cm

Solution:

(a) $C = \pi d$
 $C = 3.14 \times 4.7$
   $= 14.758$
 The circumference is
 14.8 cm, to
 the nearest tenth.

(b) $C = 2\pi r$
 $C = 2 \times 3.14 \times 2.6$
   $= 16.328$
 The circumference is
 16.3 cm, to
 the nearest tenth.

EXERCISE

B

1. Find the circumference of each circle.

(a)

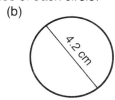
3 cm

(b)

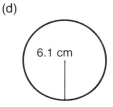
4.2 cm

(c)

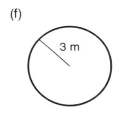
2.5 cm

(d)

6.1 cm

(e)

5.8 m

(f)

3 m

2. Find the circumference of each circle, to the nearest tenth.

(a) d = 3.5 cm   (b) d = 14.6 cm
(c) d = 25.5 cm   (d) r = 3.5 cm
(e) r = 16.5 cm   (f) d = 12.4 cm

APPLICATIONS

3. The diameter of a bicycle wheel is 63.5 cm.
   (a) Find the circumference of the back wheel of the bicycle.
   (b) How far will the bicycle go when the wheels make one complete turn?
   (c) How far will the bicycle travel when the wheels make 12 complete turns?
   (d) How many complete turns of the wheels are required to travel 1396 cm?

4. A natural gas pipeline has a diameter of 90 cm.
   What is the circumference of the pipe?

5. The diameter of the mirror in the Mount Palomar telescope is 5.08 m.

What is the circumference of the mirror?

6. The diameter of a circle can be found using the formula
   $$d \doteq C \div 3.14$$
   (a) Find the diameter of the circle whose circumference is 89.8 cm.
   (b) The circumference of a circular track is 377 m. What is the diameter of the track?

7. If the diameter of a circle is doubled what happens to the circumference?

ᗰIᑕᖇO ᗰᗩTᕼ

NEW

```
10 PRINT"CIRCUMFERENCE OF A CIRCLE"
20 INPUT"DIAMETER IS ";D
30 LET C=3.14*D
40 PRINT"THE CIRCUMFERENCE IS ";C
50 END
```

RUN

12.8 AREA OF A CIRCLE

We can transform a circle into a parallelogram to show how we find the area of a circle.

Divide the circle into sectors as shown.

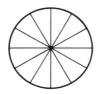

Separate the circle along any diameter to form two semi-circles.

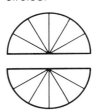

Open each semi-circle, and place the two sections together to form a parallelogram. The circle and the parallelogram have the same area.

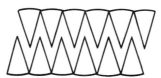

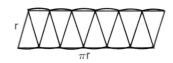

The base of the parallelogram is one-half of the circumference of the circle, and the height is approximately equal to the radius.

The area of the corresponding parallelogram is:

$A = bh$, where $b = \pi r$, and $h = r$

$$A = \pi r \times r$$
$$= \pi r^2$$

> The area of a circle is calculated using
> $A = \pi r^2$, where $\pi \doteq 3.14$.

Example. Find the area of these figures to the nearest tenth.

(a)

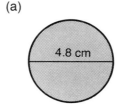

4.8 cm

(b)

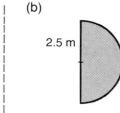

2.5 m

Solution:

(a) First, find the radius.

$d = 4.8$

$r = 2.4$

$A = \pi r^2$

$A = 3.14 \times 2.4^2$

$\quad = 3.14 \times 5.76$

$\quad = 18.086\ 4$

The area is 18.1 cm² to the nearest tenth

(b) The area of the semi-circle is one-half the area of the circle.

$r = 2.5$

$A = \pi r^2$

$A = 3.14 \times 2.5^2$

$\quad = 3.14 \times 6.25$

$\quad = 19.625$

The area of the semi-circle is $\frac{1}{2}$ of 19.625, which is 9.812 5 m².

The area is 9.8 cm² to the nearest tenth.

EXERCISE

B

1. Find the area of each of the following circles.

(a)

5 cm

(b)

8 cm

(c)

10 cm

(d)

3 cm

2. Find the area of each figure.

(a)

4 cm

(b)

3.1 cm

(c)

4 cm

(d)

10 cm

APPLICATIONS

3. A circular table top has a diameter of 1.3 m.
   What is the area of the table top?

4. The automatic lawn sprinklers at the park spray water a distance of 21 m.
   (a) What area is watered by one sprinkler?
   (b) How many sprinklers are required to water 11 000 m² of lawn?

5. Harry's CB radio can be received 8 km from his transmitter.
   Within what area can Harry broadcast on his CB radio?

6. If the radius of a circle is doubled, what is the effect on the surface area?

MICRO MATH

NEW

```
10 PRINT"AREA OF A CIRCLE"
20 INPUT"RADIUS IS ";R
30 LET A=3.14*R↑2
40 PRINT"THE AREA IS ";A
50 END
```

RUN

12.9 APPLICATIONS OF PERIMETER AND AREA

In this section we shall use the formulas developed in previous sections to solve problems.

Figure	Perimeter	Area
Rectangle	$P = 2(\ell + w)$	$A = \ell w$
Square	$P = 4s$	$A = s^2$
Circle	$C = 2\pi r$	$A = \pi r^2$
	$= \pi d$	
Triangle	add lengths of sides	$A = \frac{1}{2}bh$
Parallelogram	add lengths of sides	$A = bh$
Trapezoid	add lengths of sides	$A = \frac{1}{2}(a + b)h$

Example 1. Find the perimeter of this track.

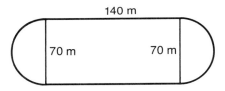

140 m

70 m   70 m

Solution: The track consists of two straight sides with circular ends.

The circular ends can be considered as a circle with diameter 70 m.

The sides are added to the distance around the ends.

70 m

140 m

140 m

$C = \pi d$
$C = 3.14 \times 70$
$= 219.8$

$140 + 140$

This is a 500 m track.

The perimeter is $140 + 140 + 219.8 = 499.8$.

Example 2. Find the area of this church window.

Solution: The window consists of a semi-circle above a rectangle.

Area of the semi-circle is one-half of:
$$A = \pi r^2$$
$$A = 3.14 \times 0.7^2$$
$$= 1.538\ 6$$
Area of the semi-circle is
$$1.538\ 6 \div 2 = 0.769\ 3$$
Area of the rectangle is
$$A = \ell w$$
$$A = 2.25 \times 1.4 = 3.15$$
Area of the window is
$$0.769\ 3 + 3.15 \doteq 3.9\ \text{m}^2$$
to the nearest tenth.

2.25 m

1.4 m

EXERCISE

B

1. Find the area of the shaded region.

(a)   (b)

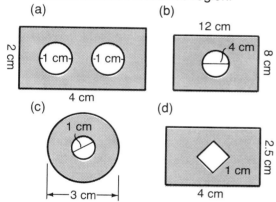

2 cm

-1 cm-   -1 cm-

4 cm

12 cm

4 cm

8 cm

(c)   (d)

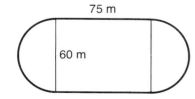

1 cm

←—3 cm—→

4 cm

1 cm

2.5 cm

2. Sod is to be laid in the interior of a running track as shown below.

75 m

60 m

(a) Find the area of the interior of the track.
(b) What is the total cost of the sod at $3.25/m²?

3. Calculate the area of the following highway signs, to the nearest tenth.

(a)   (b)

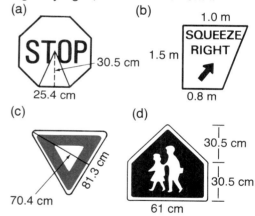

STOP

30.5 cm

25.4 cm

1.0 m

SQUEEZE RIGHT

1.5 m

0.8 m

(c)   (d)

81.3 cm

70.4 cm

30.5 cm

30.5 cm

61 cm

4. The radius of the earth at the equator is approximately 6380 km. A satellite circles the earth in an orbit 250 km above the earth.

(a) What is the circumference of the earth at the equator?
(b) What is the distance travelled by the satellite during 1 orbit?

5. A belt around two pulleys delivers power from a motor to a machine as shown in the diagram.
Both pulleys have a diameter of 7.5 cm. Their centres are 30 cm apart.
How long is the belt?

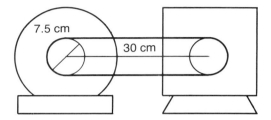

6. Two cylinders are held together by a steel band as shown.

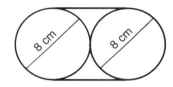

(a) What length of steel band is required to go just around the cylinders?
(b) How long should the steel band be if you require 2.8 cm for fastening?

7. The radius of the broadcast area of radio station CFRB is about 160 km.
Calculate the area that the station would call its broadcast area.

8. A bicycle wheel has a diameter of 66 cm.

(a) What is the circumference of the wheel?
(b) How far does the bicycle travel in one complete turn of the wheel?
(c) If the bicycle is geared so that one turn of the pedals results in three turns of the wheel, how far does the bicycle travel in one turn of the pedals?

9. A draw-string purse is made from two circles of cloth. Holes are punched around the outer edge of the large circle for the draw string.

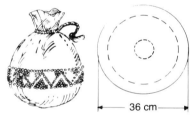

Heavy cardboard sewn between large and small circles of material

What is the area of the piece of material required for the large circle?

10. A garden, 30 m by 142 m, is surrounded by a gravel road 3 m wide.

(a) What is the perimeter of the inner edge of the road?
(b) What is the perimeter of the outer edge of the road?
(c) What is the area of the road surface?

11. A quilt is to be made from squares 30 cm by 30 cm. There are 54 squares in the quilt, arranged in a 6 by 9 pattern. Find the total length of the edges that must be stitched.

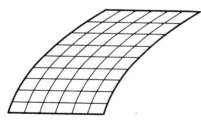

12. Paul cuts out the parts for a bird house from a piece of plywood. Each square on the pattern is 5 cm by 5 cm.
    (a) How many centimetres of cutting are required?
    (b) Paul's saw cuts at 1 cm/s. How many seconds are required to cut out the parts?

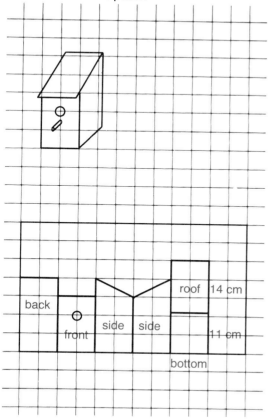

13. Terry is framing a picture. The picture is 20 cm by 25 cm.
    A 10 cm border called a mat surrounds the picture.
    The frame is assembled as shown below.

frame
15¢/cm

glass
2¢/cm²

mat
1¢/cm²

picture
20 cm × 25 cm

(a) Find the area of the mat.
(b) Find the area of the glass.
(c) Find the perimeter of the frame.
(d) Complete this bill.

Item	Cost
mat	
glass	
frame	
Total	

MICRO MATH

NEW

```
10 PRINT"AREA OF A PARALLELOGRAM"
20 INPUT"BASE IS ";B
30 INPUT"HEIGHT IS ";H
40 LET A=B*H
50 PRINT"THE AREA IS ";A
60 END
```

RUN

POLYOMINOES

A polyomino is a simply connected set of squares. The squares are joined along their edges. The polyominoes get their name from the number of squares in each pattern. Here is a list of polyominoes.

Name	Number of Squares	Arrangements
Monomino	1	
Domino	2	
Tromino	3	
Tetromino	4	
Pentomino	5	

There are 8 other pentomino patterns.
Find them.

EXERCISE

1. A checkerboard is divided into 8 rows and 8 columns.

   (a) How many monominoes will it take to completely cover the checkerboard?

   (b) How many dominoes will it take to completely cover the checkerboard?

   (c) Can you completely cover the checkerboard using only trominoes?

2. Start with one monomino in the position shown. Completely cover the checkerboard using 21 straight trominoes.

 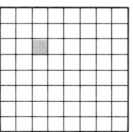

3. Start with a monomino in any corner and completely cover the checkerboard using 21 right trominoes.

 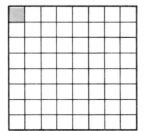

4. Each pentomino contains 5 squares. The 12 different pentominoes contain a total of 60 squares.
   Cut out the twelve pentominoes from cardboard.

   (a) Start with the shaded tetromino and completely cover the checkerboard using only the 12 pentominoes.

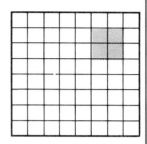

   (b) Start with a monomino in each corner, and completely cover the checkerboard using only the twelve pentominoes.

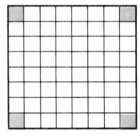

   (c) The twelve pentominoes will cover 60 squares.
   Completely cover a 5 by 12 checkerboard using the 12 pentominoes.

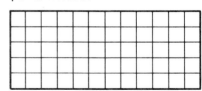

   (d) Completely cover a 4 by 15 checkerboard using the 12 pentominoes.

12.10 CHAPTER 12 REVIEW EXERCISE

1. Find the perimeter of the following.

(a)

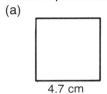

4.7 cm

(b)

6.3 cm

(c)

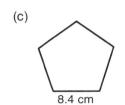

8.4 cm

(d)

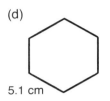

5.1 cm

2. Find the area of the following to the nearest tenth.

(a)

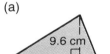

9.6 cm

17.8 cm

(b)

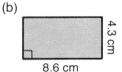

4.3 cm

8.6 cm

(c)

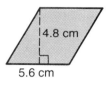

4.8 cm

5.6 cm

(d)

6.4 cm

(e)

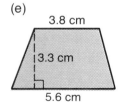

3.8 cm

3.3 cm

5.6 cm

(f)

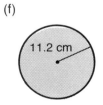

11.2 cm

3. Find the perimeter.

(a)

4 cm

2 cm   5 cm

3 cm

(b)

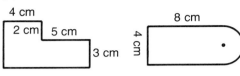

8 cm

4 cm

(c)

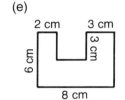

10 cm

8 cm

(d)

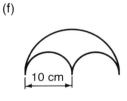

6 cm

12 cm

(e)

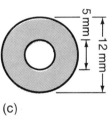

2 cm   3 cm

3 cm

6 cm

8 cm

(f)

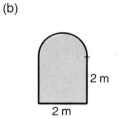

10 cm

4. Find the area.

(a)

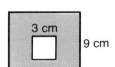

5 mm

12 mm

(b)

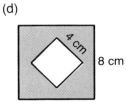

2 m

2 m

(c)

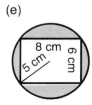

3 cm

9 cm

(d)

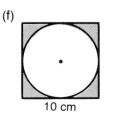

4 cm

8 cm

(e)

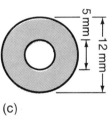

8 cm

5 cm

6 cm

(f)

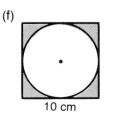

10 cm

5. The following is a diagram of a new track at a recreation centre.

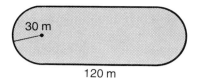

30 m

120 m

(a) Find the distance around the track.
(b) Find the area of the interior of the track.

6. Circular lids 8.8 cm in diameter are cut from a strip of aluminum 9.5 cm wide.

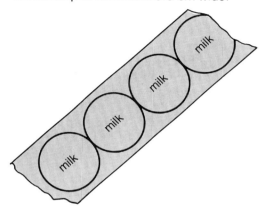

(a) How many lids can be cut from a strip of aluminum 965 cm long?
(b) What is the area of one lid?

8.8 cm

(c) What is the area of the strip of aluminum before punching out the lids?

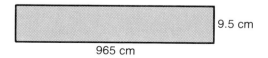

9.5 cm

965 cm

(d) What is the area of the waste material?

7. In soccer, the playing field is called a pitch. Following is a diagram of a pitch.

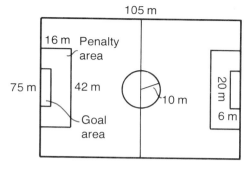

105 m

16 m Penalty area

75 m   42 m

10 m

20 m

6 m

Goal area

(a) Find the area of the pitch.
(b) Find the area of the penalty area.
(c) Find the area of the goal area.
(d) Find the area of the face-off circle.

8. Find the area of the church window shown in the diagram.

3.2 m

1.7 m

9. The following pattern is to be cut from plywood.

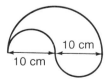

10 cm

10 cm

(a) Find the total length of the cut.
(b) How long will it take to cut the pattern if the saw cuts at the rate of 1.5 cm/s?

CHAPTER 12 TEST

1. Find the perimeter of each figure.
   (a) 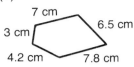 (b) (c)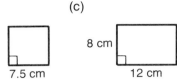

2. Find the area of each figure.
   (a) (b)  (c)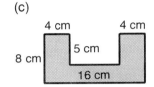

3. Find the area of each figure.
   (a) (b) (c)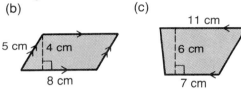

4. (a) Find the circumference of the circle with diameter 20 cm.
   (b) Find the area of a circle with radius 1.5 m.

5. A field, 140 m by 120 m, is to be fenced. What is the length of fence needed?

6. A park is to be sodded as shown.
   (a) Find the area to be sodded.
   (b) What is the cost of the job at $7.20/m²?

   20 m
   30 m
   30 m
   55 m

7. A school track has the dimensions shown in the diagram.
   (a) Find the perimeter of the track.
   (b) Find the area of the interior of the track.

   150 m
   80 m

13

SURFACE AREA AND VOLUME

REVIEW AND PREVIEW TO CHAPTER 13

DRAWING THREE-DIMENSIONAL FIGURES

In the following chapter, we shall be working with three-dimensional figures such as cubes, cylinders, and pyramids. Following are some hints on drawing figures in three dimensions.

1. Parallel edges in space are represented by parallel lines on the page.

2. Edges that are invisible to us are drawn with broken lines.

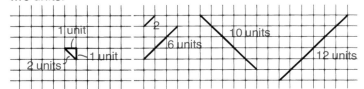

3. When drawing scale figures on squared paper, edges which are perpendicular to the page are drawn diagonally through the squares. Each square's diagonal represents two units.

EXERCISE

A

1. Read the length of each line segment using the definitions above.

    (a) $\overline{AB}$ (b) $\overline{CD}$ (c) $\overline{EF}$

    (d) $\overline{GH}$ (e) $\overline{IJ}$ (f) $\overline{KL}$

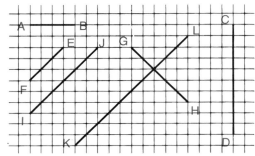

B

2. Draw each of the following on squared paper.

    (a)

    (b)

    (c)

    (d)

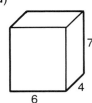

3. Draw each of the following on squared paper.

(a)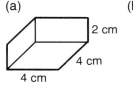
2 cm
4 cm
4 cm

(b)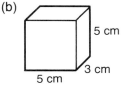
5 cm
5 cm
3 cm

(c)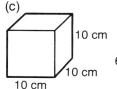
10 cm
10 cm
10 cm

(d)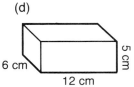
5 cm
6 cm
12 cm

(e)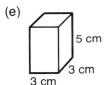
5 cm
3 cm
3 cm

(f)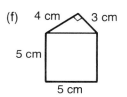
4 cm   3 cm
5 cm
5 cm

4. Draw each of the following on squared paper.
   (a) rectangular solid 3 cm by 4 cm by 5 cm
   (b) rectangular solid 3 cm by 6 cm by 8 cm
   (c) cube 5 cm by 5 cm by 5 cm
   (d) cube 8 cm by 8 cm by 8 cm

Prisms are straight-edged solids whose bases are parallel and congruent. The other faces are parallelograms.

5. Draw these prisms on squared paper.

(a)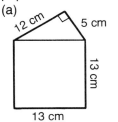
12 cm   5 cm
13 cm
13 cm

(b)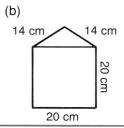
14 cm   14 cm
20 cm
20 cm

C

Circular faces in space can be represented by circles or ellipses, depending on the view.

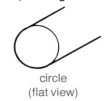
circle
(flat view)

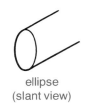
ellipse
(slant view)

6. Draw each of the following on squared paper.

(a)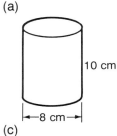
10 cm
8 cm

(b)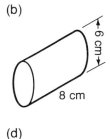
6 cm
8 cm

(c)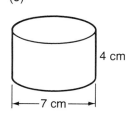
4 cm
7 cm

(d)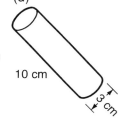
10 cm
3 cm

(e)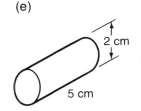
2 cm
5 cm

(f)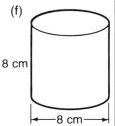
8 cm
8 cm

(g)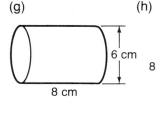
6 cm
8 cm

(h)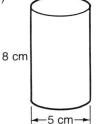
8 cm
5 cm

13.1 SURFACE AREA OF A RECTANGULAR SOLID

In a rectangular solid, all surfaces are rectangles. The following are examples of rectangular solids.

 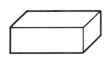

To find the surface area of the solid at the left, we imagine that we open the solid and lay it flat to form 6 rectangles.

AREA OF A
RECTANGLE

$A = \ell \times w$

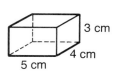

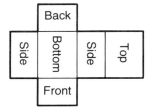

We find the surface area by adding the areas of the six rectangles.

Surface Area $= 15 \text{ cm}^2 + 12 \text{ cm}^2 + 20 \text{ cm}^2 + 12 \text{ cm}^2 + 20 \text{ cm}^2 + 15 \text{ cm}^2$
$\qquad\qquad = 94 \text{ cm}^2$

The surface area can also be found without opening out the solid if we organize our work carefully.

Example 1. Find the surface area of this rectangular solid.

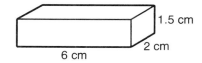

Solution:

Area of top and bottom $= 6 \text{ cm} \times 2 \text{ cm} + 6 \text{ cm} \times 2 \text{ cm} = 24 \text{ cm}^2$
Area of front and back $= 6 \text{ cm} \times 1.5 \text{ cm} + 6 \text{ cm} \times 1.5 \text{ cm} = 18 \text{ cm}^2$
Area of sides $= 2 \text{ cm} \times 1.5 \text{ cm} + 2 \text{ cm} \times 1.5 \text{ cm} = 6 \text{ cm}^2$

To find the surface area, we find the sum of these.

Surface Area $=$ (top and bottom) $+$ (front and back) $+$ (two sides)
$\qquad\qquad\quad = \quad$ (24 cm²) $\quad + \quad$ (18 cm²) $\quad + \quad$ (6 cm²)
$\qquad\qquad\quad = 48 \text{ cm}^2$

Example 2. Find the surface area of the rectangular solid with
dimensions 2.4 cm by 6.2 cm by 8.5 cm to the nearest tenth.

Solution:
Draw a diagram first.

Surface Area = top and + front and + two
            bottom   back   sides
= 2 × 20.4 cm² + 2 × 52.7 cm² + 2 × 14.88 cm²
= 175.96 cm²

∴ The surface area is 176.0 cm²
  to the nearest tenth.

6.2 cm

8.5 cm   2.4 cm

EXERCISE

A

1. The figure formed by opening out a solid
   is called a net.
   Find the area of the solids represented by
   each of these nets.

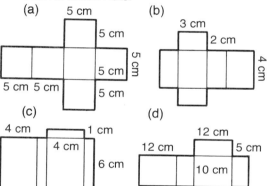

(a) 5 cm

(b) 3 cm   2 cm

(c) 4 cm   1 cm

(d) 12 cm

B

2. Find the surface area of each of these
   rectangular solids to the nearest tenth.

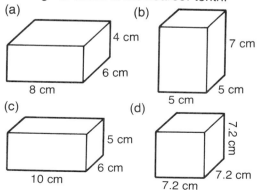

(a) 4 cm   6 cm   8 cm

(b) 7 cm   5 cm   5 cm

(c) 5 cm   6 cm   10 cm

(d) 7.2 cm 7.2 cm 7.2 cm

APPLICATIONS

3. A small carton is
   10 cm by 10 cm by 20 cm.
   Find the surface area of the box.

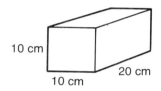

10 cm   10 cm   20 cm

C

4. A house foundation 15 m by 10 m is
   waterproofed with black asphaltum to a
   height of 1.5 m.
   (a) Make a diagram.
   (b) What area is waterproofed?
   (c) What is the cost at $3.00/m²?

5. Draw a net that will fold into a toothpaste
   box 18 cm by 2.8 cm by 3 cm.

13.2 VOLUME OF A RECTANGULAR SOLID

The volume of a solid is the amount of space that it occupies. The basic unit of volume is the cubic metre (m³). A cubic metre is the amount of space occupied by a cube 1 m by 1 m by 1 m.

One cubic centimetre (1 cm³) is the amount of space occupied by a cube 1 cm by 1 cm by 1 cm. We shall use this cube to show how to find the volume of rectangular solids. How many cubes will fit into an empty box 6 cm by 4 cm by 3 cm?

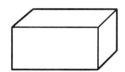

How many cubes can you put in one row along the bottom?

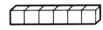

How many cubes can you put in one layer on the bottom?

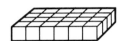

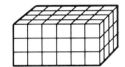

How many layers can you stack in the box?

The volume of the box is 72 cm³ because you can stack 72 cubes to fill the box.
We can also find the volume of the box by multiplying
6 × 4 × 3 = 72.

> The formula for the volume of a rectangular solid is
> $$V = \ell \times w \times h \quad \text{or} \quad V = \ell wh$$

Example 1. Find the volume of the rectangular solid with dimensions 5.6 cm by 4.3 cm by 2.9 cm to the nearest tenth.

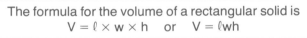

Solution: ℓ = 5.6 cm, w = 4.3 cm, h = 2.9 cm
$V = \ell \times w \times h$
$V = 5.6 \times 4.3 \times 2.9$
$\quad = 69.832$
The volume is 69.8 cm³, to the nearest tenth.

Example 2. Find the volume of a box 1.0 m by 0.6 m by 15 cm to the nearest hundredth.

Solution: First, express all dimensions in the same unit.
ℓ = 1.0 m, w = 0.6 m, h = 15 cm = 0.15 m
$V = \ell \times w \times h$
$V = 1.0 \times 0.6 \times 0.15$
$\quad = 0.090$
The volume is 0.09 m³, to the nearest hundredth.

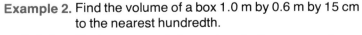

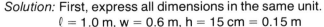

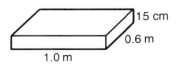

EXERCISE

Round off all answers to the nearest tenth.

A

1. Find the number of cubes in each of the following.

(a)

(b)

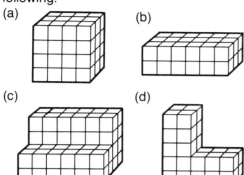

(c)

(d)

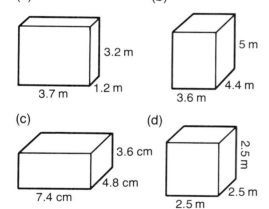

B

2. Find the volume of each of the following.

(a)

3.2 m
3.7 m
1.2 m

(b)

5 m
4.4 m
3.6 m

(c)

3.6 cm
4.8 cm
7.4 cm

(d)

2.5 m
2.5 m
2.5 m

APPLICATIONS

3. A rectangular room is 6.2 m by 4.5 m by 2.4 m.
   (a) Make a diagram.
   (b) What is the volume of air in the room?
   (c) A ventilating fan removes 8 m³/min of air in the room.
       How long will it take the fan to remove an amount of air equal in area to the volume of the room?

4. The box on a dump truck is 3.0 m by 1.8 m by 0.8 m.
   (a) What is the volume of a level load in the box?
   (b) What is the mass of a load of sand if 1 m³ of sand has a mass of 1.5 t? (One cubic metre of sand has a mass of one tonne.)

C

5. A rectangular swimming pool is 12 m by 6 m by 1.4 m.
   (a) What is the volume of the pool?
   (b) 1 m³ = 1000 L
       How many litres (L) of water are required to fill the pool?
   (c) A garden hose delivers water at the rate of 20 L/min.
       How long will it take to fill the pool using two hoses?

ⅢⅠⅭℜⅅ Ⅲⅆⅅℜ

```
NEW
10 PRINT"VOLUME OF A"
20 PRINT"RECTANGULAR SOLID"
30 INPUT"LENGTH IS ";L
40 INPUT" WIDTH IS ";W
50 INPUT"HEIGHT IS ";H
60 LET A = L*W*H
70 PRINT"THE AREA IS ";A
80 END
RUN
```

13.3 SURFACE AREA AND VOLUME OF RIGHT PRISMS

We have found surface areas and volumes of rectangular solids in previous sections. These solids fall into the general category of right prisms. Right prisms are three-dimensional figures whose sides are rectangles and whose bases are congruent polygons. Four examples of right prisms are shown.

In this section we find the surface area and volume of right prisms in general.

The surface area, SA, is found by adding the area of the sides and the bases.

SA = (area of sides) + (area of bases)

The volume of a right prism is found by multiplying the area of the base by the height of the prism.

V = (area of base) × (height)

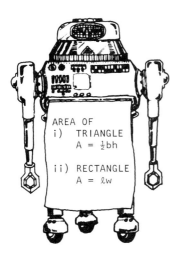

AREA OF
i)   TRIANGLE
     $A = \frac{1}{2}bh$

ii) RECTANGLE
     $A = \ell w$

Example. Calculate the surface area and volume of the right prism.

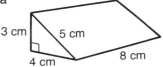

3 cm   5 cm   4 cm   8 cm

Solution:

Surface area:
SA = (area of sides) + (area of bases)
area of base $= \frac{1}{2} \times 3 \times 4$
$= 6$
area of sides: $\begin{cases} 5 \times 8 = 40 \\ 4 \times 8 = 32 \\ 3 \times 8 = 24 \end{cases}$
SA = (40 + 32 + 24) + (6 + 6)
$= 96 + 12$
$= 108$
The surface area is 108 cm².

Volume:
V = (area of base) × (height)
area of base $= \frac{1}{2} \times 3 \times 4$
$= 6$
V = 6 × 8
$= 48$
The volume is 48 cm³.

EXERCISE

B

1. Find the surface area of these right prisms.

(a)
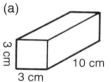
3 cm
3 cm
10 cm

(b)
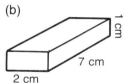
1 cm
7 cm
2 cm

(c)
22 cm
16 cm
10 cm

(d)

15 cm
8 cm
17 cm
16 cm

(e)
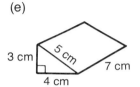
3 cm
5 cm
7 cm
4 cm

(f)
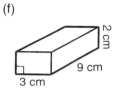
2 cm
9 cm
3 cm

2. Find the volume of these right prisms.

(a)

4 cm
A = 3 cm²

(b)
6 cm
A = 12 cm²

(c)
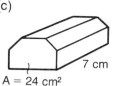
7 cm
A = 24 cm²

(d)
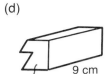
9 cm
A = 8 cm²

(e)
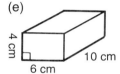
4 cm
10 cm
6 cm

(f)
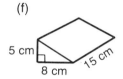
5 cm
8 cm
15 cm

3. Find the surface area and volume of each of the following right prisms.

(a)
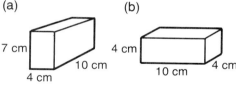
7 cm
10 cm
4 cm

(b)
4 cm
10 cm
4 cm

(c)
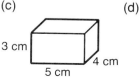
3 cm
5 cm
4 cm

(d)

6 cm
3 cm
4 cm

(e)

7 cm
7 cm
7 cm

(f)
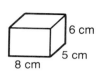
6 cm
8 cm
5 cm

4. Find the surface area and volume of each of these right prisms.

(a)

4 cm
3 cm
4 cm
5 cm

(b)
6 cm
8 cm
5 cm
10 cm

(c)
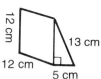
12 cm
13 cm
12 cm
5 cm

(d)

24 cm
25 cm
30 cm
7 cm

13.4 SURFACE AREA OF A CYLINDER

The following objects are examples of cylinders.

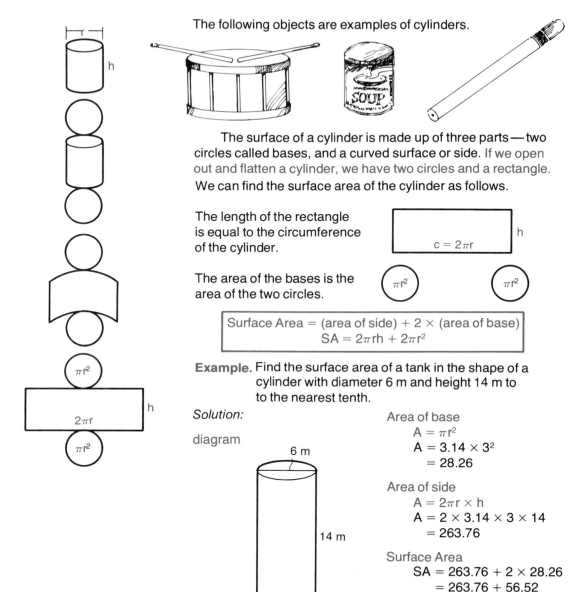

The surface of a cylinder is made up of three parts — two circles called bases, and a curved surface or side. If we open out and flatten a cylinder, we have two circles and a rectangle. We can find the surface area of the cylinder as follows.

The length of the rectangle is equal to the circumference of the cylinder.

$$c = 2\pi r \qquad h$$

The area of the bases is the area of the two circles.

$$\pi r^2 \qquad \pi r^2$$

Surface Area = (area of side) + 2 × (area of base)
$$SA = 2\pi rh + 2\pi r^2$$

Example. Find the surface area of a tank in the shape of a cylinder with diameter 6 m and height 14 m to to the nearest tenth.

Solution:

diagram

6 m

14 m

Area of base
$$A = \pi r^2$$
$$A = 3.14 \times 3^2$$
$$= 28.26$$

Area of side
$$A = 2\pi r \times h$$
$$A = 2 \times 3.14 \times 3 \times 14$$
$$= 263.76$$

Surface Area
$$SA = 263.76 + 2 \times 28.26$$
$$= 263.76 + 56.52$$
$$= 320.28$$

The surface area is 320.3 m^2 to the neareast tenth.

We can also find the surface area using the formula:
$$SA = 2\pi rh + 2\pi r^2$$
$$SA = 2 \times 3.14 \times 3 \times 14 + 2 \times 3.14 \times 3^2$$
$$= 263.76 + 56.52$$
$$= 320.28$$

EXERCISE

Round off all answers to the nearest tenth.

B

1. Find the surface area of the following cylinders.

(a)   (b)

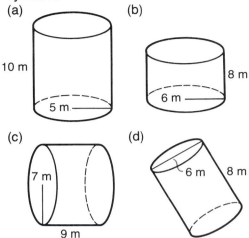

10 m

5 m

8 m

6 m

(c)   (d)

7 m

9 m

6 m   8 m

APPLICATIONS

2. A soup tin has a diameter 8 cm, and has a height of 12 cm.

(a) What is the area of the label around the tin?

(b) What is the area of each of the bases?

(c) What is the total area?

3. A gasoline storage tank is in the shape of a cylinder with diameter 6.4 m, and height 10.7 m.

6.4 m

10.7 m

(a) What is the total surface area of the tank?

(b) How much rust preventor is required to coat the entire tank if a 24 L can covers 200 m² of surface?

C

4. A hothouse for growing tomatoes is in the shape of a half-cylinder.

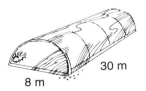

30 m

8 m

The house is 30 m long and 8 m wide, as shown.

(a) Find the area to be covered in plastic, including the ends.

(b) What is the cost of the plastic at $3.25/m²?

5. A solar collector used for heating water contains 20 m of black plastic pipe, 2.4 cm in diameter.
What is the surface area of the pipe?

MICRO MATH

NEW

```
10 PRINT"TOTAL AREA"
20 PRINT"OF A CYLINDER"
30 INPUT"RADIUS IS ";R
40 INPUT"HEIGHT IS ";H
50 LET A=2*3.14*R↑2+2*3.14*R*H
60 PRINT"THE SURFACE AREA IS ";A
70 END
```

RUN

Line 50 can also be written:

```
50 LET A=2*3.14*R*R+H
```

Why?

13.5 VOLUME OF A CYLINDER

| The volume of 1 cm of material piled on an area of 1 cm² is 1 cm³. | The volume of 2 cm of material piled on an area of 1 cm² is 2 cm³. | What is the volume of material piled 2 cm deep on an area of 4 cm²? |

Using this idea, we can find the volume of a cylinder using the principle:

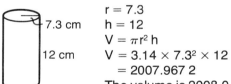

The base is a circle, and the area is

$B = \pi r^2$

To calculate the volume of a cylinder,
$V = B \times h$
$V = \pi r^2 \times h$ or $V = \pi r^2 h$

Example 1. Find the volume of a cylinder with diameter 14.6 cm and height 12 cm to the nearest tenth.

> Given data are considered to be exact. Data from measurement are only as accurate as the instruments we use in measuring.

Solution:

7.3 cm

12 cm

$r = 7.3$
$h = 12$
$V = \pi r^2 h$
$V = 3.14 \times 7.3^2 \times 12$
$\quad = 2007.967\,2$
The volume is 2008.0 cm³ to the nearest tenth.

Example 2. A water tank has a radius 0.40 m.
(a) How much water is in the tank when the depth is 0.8 m?
(b) How much water is in the tank when the depth is 1.5 m?
Give your answer to the nearest tenth.

Solution:
The water in the tank forms a cylinder. We find the amount of water by finding the volume of a cylinder.

(a)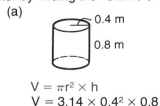
0.4 m
0.8 m

$V = \pi r^2 \times h$
$V = 3.14 \times 0.4^2 \times 0.8$
$\quad = 0.401\,92$
The volume of water is 0.4 m³ to the nearest tenth.

(b)
0.4 m
1.5 m

$V = \pi r^2 \times h$
$V = 3.14 \times 0.4^2 \times 1.5$
$\quad = 0.753\,6$
The volume of water is 0.8 m³ to the nearest tenth.

EXERCISE

Round off all answers to the nearest tenth.

A

1. State the radius and height to find the volume.

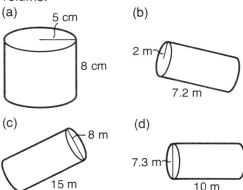

(a) 5 cm, 8 cm

(b) 2 m, 7.2 m

(c) 8 m, 15 m

(d) 7.3 m, 10 m

B

2. Find the volume of each of the following.

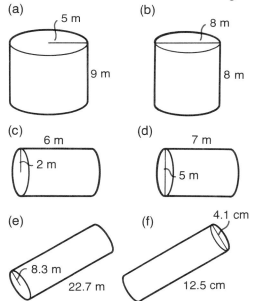

(a) 5 m, 9 m

(b) 8 m, 8 m

(c) 6 m, 2 m

(d) 7 m, 5 m

(e) 8.3 m, 22.7 m

(f) 4.1 cm, 12.5 cm

3. Find the volume of each of these cylinders.
   Give your answer to the nearest tenth.
   (a) radius 7.2 m,   height 4.8 cm
   (b) radius 3.6 cm,   height 1.2 cm
   (c) diameter 49 cm,   height 25 cm
   (d) diameter 7 m,   height 3 m
   (e) radius 4.2 cm,   2.8 cm

APPLICATIONS

4. The tank on a truck is a cylinder 6 m long, with a diameter of 1.60 m.
   What is the volume of the tank?

5. The body of a model rocket is a cylinder 24 cm long with a diameter of 2.5 cm.
   What is the volume of the body of the rocket?

C

6. (a) A water tank has a diameter 5 m, and height 20 m.
       How many cubic metres of water will it hold?
   (b) A water pipe to the tank is 10 cm in diameter and 22.5 km long.
       How much water is required to fill the pipe?

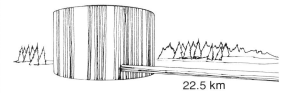

22.5 km

7. Complete this table to see what happens to the volume of a cylinder when you double the radius and height.

	Radius	Height	Volume
(a)	5 cm	5 cm	
(b)	10 cm	5 cm	
(c)	5 cm	10 cm	
(d)	10 cm	10 cm	

MICRO MATH

NEW

```
10 PRINT"VOLUME OF A CYLINDER"
20 INPUT"RADIUS IS ";R
30 INPUT"HEIGHT IS ";H
40 LET V=3.14*R↑2*H
50 PRINT"VOLUME IS ";V
60 END
```

RUN

13.6 SURFACE AREA OF A PYRAMID

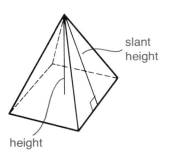

slant height

height

A pyramid has a polygon as base, and the sides are triangles with a common vertex. A regular pyramid has a regular polygon as its base and the sides are congruent isosceles triangles. The vertical height and the slant height of a pyramid are not the same.

We find the surface area of a pyramid as follows.
$$SA = (\text{area of base}) + (\text{area of faces})$$

Example. A pyramid has a square base 6 cm by 6 cm and a slant height of 5 cm.
Find the surface area.

Solution: Area of base $= 6 \times 6$
$= 36$

Area of sides $= 4 \times (\frac{1}{2} \times 6 \times 5)$
$= 60$
$SA = 36 + 60$
$= 96$

The surface area is 96 cm².

EXERCISE

A

1. State the slant height in each of the following pyramids.
   (a) 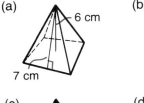 6 cm 7 cm

   (b) 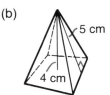 5 cm 4 cm

   (c) 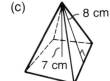 8 cm 7 cm

   (d) 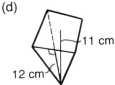 11 cm 12 cm

B

2. Find the surface area of each pyramid.
   (a) 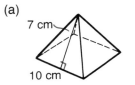 7 cm 10 cm

   (b) 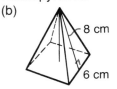 8 cm 6 cm

APPLICATIONS

3. The roof of a park shelter is in the shape of a pyramid. The base is a square with sides 30 m and slant height 24 m. Find the surface area.

C

4. The great pyramid of Khufu (shown below at the right), built at Gizeh in Egypt about 4700 B.C., has a square base with sides 230.34 m. The vertical height of the pyramid is 146.71 m and the slant height is 186.52 m. The pyramid was constructed of rough blocks and then covered with a layer of finely finished stone.
What area of the Great Pyramid was covered in finely finished stone?

13.7 VOLUME OF A PYRAMID

The hopper on a truck used for sanding roads is in the shape of a pyramid. The base of the pyramid is a square with sides 2.4 m long. The height of the pyramid is the depth of the hopper, which is 1.8 m. To calculate how much sand this truck can carry, we calculate the volume of the square-based pyramid.

The formula for the volume of a squared-based pyramid is:

$$V = \frac{1}{3} \times \ell \times w \times h$$

Find the volume of the truck hopper to the nearest tenth.

$\ell = 2.4,$ $w = 2.4,$ $h = 1.8$

$$V = \frac{1}{3} \times \ell \times w \times h$$

$$V = \frac{1}{3} \times 2.4 \times 2.4 \times 1.8$$

$$= 3.456$$

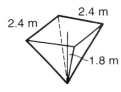

The volume of the hopper is 3.5 m³ to the nearest tenth.

EXERCISE

B

1. Find the volume of each square-based pyramid to the nearest centimetre.

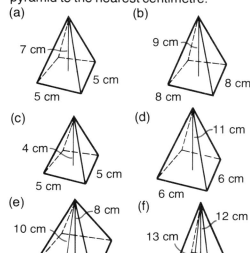

(a)   7 cm   5 cm   5 cm

(b)   9 cm   8 cm   8 cm

(c)   4 cm   5 cm   5 cm

(d)   11 cm   6 cm   6 cm

(e)   8 cm   10 cm   6 cm   6 cm

(f)   12 cm   13 cm   10 cm

2. Find the volume of a square-based pyramid with sides 10 m and height 7 m.

3. Find the volume of the square-based pyramid with sides 10 m, height 12 m, and slant height 13 m.

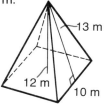

13 m   12 m   10 m

MICRO MATH

NEW
```
10 PRINT"VOLUME OF A"
20 PRINT"SQUARE-BASED PYRAMID"
30 INPUT"LENGTH OF BASE IS ";L
40 INPUT" WIDTH OF BASE IS ";W
50 INPUT"          HEIGHT IS ";H
60 LET V=L*W*H/3
70 PRINT"VOLUME IS ";V
80 END
```
RUN

13.8 SURFACE AREA OF A CONE

To find the amount of sheet metal required to make this shape you need to find the surface area of a cone. The surface area of a cone consists of the area of the curved surface plus the area of the circular base.

To find the surface area of a cone:
    Area of the base:
        $A = \pi r^2$
    Area of the curved surface:
        $A = \pi rs$
where r is the radius of the cone,
        s is the slant height.

The surface area of a cone is:
    $SA = \pi r^2 + \pi rs$ or $SA = \pi r(r + s)$

For the given shape,
        radius, r = 5 cm
    slant height, s = 8 cm
        $SA = \pi r^2 + \pi rs$
        $SA = 3.14 \times 5^2 + 3.14 \times 5 \times 8$
            $= 204.1$
The surface area is 204.1 cm².

EXERCISE

A

1. Name the radius and the slant height you would use to find the surface area.
    (a)   (b)

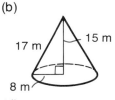

    (c)   (d)

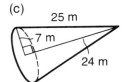
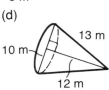

B

2. Find the surface area to the nearest tenth.
    (a)   (b)

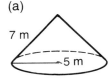
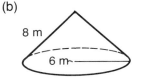

APPLICATIONS

3. A tent is in the shape of a cone. The radius of the base is 3 m and the slant height is 4.5 m.
    (a) Find the surface area of the tent.
    (b) How much canvas is required if you have to add 15% for stitching and waste?

MICRO MATH

NEW

```
10 PRINT"SURFACE AREA OF A CONE"
20 INPUT"      RADIUS IS ";R
30 INPUT"SLANT HEIGHT IS ";S
40 LET A=3.14*R*(R+S)
50 PRINT"THE SURFACE AREA IS ";A
60 END
```

RUN

13.9 VOLUME OF A CONE

A paper cup is in the shape of a cone. The diameter of the base of the cone is 6 cm, and the height (depth of the cup) is 11.5 cm. We can find the amount of water that the cup will hold by finding the volume of the cone.

> The formula for the volume of a cone is:
> $$V = \frac{1}{3} \times \pi \times r^2 \times h \quad \text{or} \quad V = \frac{1}{3}\pi r^2 h$$

Find the volume of the cone to the nearest tenth.

$r = 3, h = 11.5.$

$V = \frac{1}{3} \times \pi \times r^2 \times h$

$V = \frac{1}{3} \times 3.14 \times 3^2 \times 11.5$

$\quad = 108.33$

The volume of the cone is 108.3 cm³ to the nearest tenth. The amount of water is 108.3 mL (1 cm³ = 1 mL).

EXERCISE

B

1. Find the volume of each cone to the nearest tenth.

(a)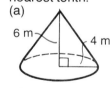

(b)

(c)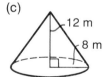

(d)

(e)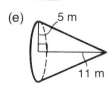

(f)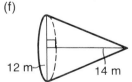

2. A pile of crushed stone is in the shape of a cone. The diameter of the base of the cone is 10 m and the height is 6 m. Find the amount of crushed stone in the pile.

APPLICATIONS

3. The following is a picture of a shelter for sand to be used on roads in the winter. The diameter of the base is 18 m and the height is 15 m.
Find the volume of the largest cone of sand that can be stored under this shelter.

MICRO MATH

NEW

```
10 PRINT"VOLUME OF A CONE"
20 INPUT"RADIUS OF BASE IS ";R
30 INPUT"        HEIGHT IS ";H
60 LET V=3.14*R^2*H/3
70 PRINT"VOLUME IS ";V
80 END
```

RUN

13.10 SURFACE AREA OF A SPHERE

The following objects are examples of spheres.

To find the area of a sphere we use this formula.

Area of a sphere
$SA = 4\pi r^2$

Example. Find the surface area of the sphere with diameter 10 cm.

Solution: r = 5 cm
$$SA = 4\pi r^2$$
$$SA = 4 \times 3.14 \times 5^2$$
$$= 314$$
The surface area is 314 cm².

EXERCISE

1. Find the surface area of each sphere to the nearest square centimetre.

(a)

6 cm

(b)

15 cm

(c)

12 cm

(d)

5 cm

(e)

9 cm

(f)

12 cm

APPLICATIONS

2. Find the surface area of a spherical tank whose radius is 3 m.

3. Find the surface area of a spherical tank with diameter 7 m.

ᴍɪᴄʀᴏ ᴍᴀᴛʜ

NEW

```
10 PRINT"SURFACE AREA OF A SPHERE"
20 INPUT"RADIUS IS ";R
30 LET A=4*3.14*R↑2
40 PRINT"SURFACE AREA IS";A
50 END
```

RUN

13.11 VOLUME OF A SPHERE

A tank is in the shape of a sphere. The diameter of the sphere is 6 m. We can find the capacity of the tank by finding the volume.

> The formula for the volume of a sphere is:
> $$V = \frac{4}{3} \times \pi \times r^3 \quad \text{or} \quad V = \frac{4}{3}\pi r^3$$

Find the volume of the spherical tank to the nearest tenth.

r = 3.

$$V = \frac{4}{3} \times \pi \times r^3$$

$$V = \frac{4}{3} \times 3.14 \times 3^3$$

$$= 113.04$$

The volume of the tank is 113.0 m³ to the nearest tenth.

EXERCISE

Round off all answers to the nearest tenth.

B

1. Find the volume of each sphere.

   (a)
   5 cm

   (b)
   7 cm

   (c)
   12 cm

   (d)
   6 cm

   (e)
   18 cm

   (f)
   24 cm

   (g)
   15 cm

   (h)
   12 cm

2. Find the volume of a sphere with radius 12 cm.

APPLICATIONS

3. A marble has a diameter of 13 mm.
   (a) Find the volume of one marble.
   (b) What is the volume of 24 marbles?

4. The following is a diagram of a ball bearing. A bearing for a go-cart has 16 ball bearings, each having a diameter of 3 mm.
   (a) What is the volume of one ball bearing?
   (b) What is the volume of the spheres in the bearing?

ⲘⲓⲤⲢⲞ ⲘⲀⲦⲎ

NEW

```
10 PRINT"VOLUME OF A SPHERE"
20 INPUT"RADIUS OF SPHERE IS ";R
30 LET V=4*3.14*R↑3/3
40 PRINT"VOLUME IS ";V
50 END
```

RUN

EXTRA EXTRA EXTRA EXTRA EXTRA

VANISHING POINTS

Railway tracks seem to meet at a point.
The point is called a vanishing point (V.P.).

The cube is located at
three different positions in
relation to the observer's eye
level but, in each case, it is
slightly to the left of where
the viewer is located.

Different parts of the cube can
be seen from each position.

The vanishing point is the
point where the edges of the
cube seem to meet at eye level.

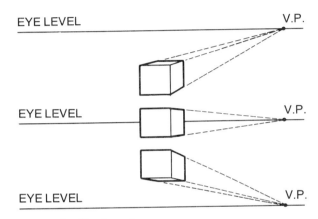

A knowledge of vanshing points helps create the illusion of
reality when sketching three-dimensional objects.

The following examples show how to sketch an object using
1 vanishing point and 2 vanishing points.

ONE VANISHING POINT

Step 1. Draw a horizontal line to
represent eye level. Mark
a vanishing point on the
line. Draw a front face of
the cube.

Step 2. Join the vertices of the
face to the vanishing point.

Step 3. Complete the sketch by using
these lines as edges of the
cube.

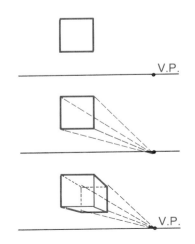

By changing the position of the front face of the cube you can change the view of the cube.

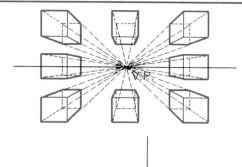

TWO VANISHING POINTS

Step 1.   Draw a horizontal line to represent eye level. Mark 2 vanishing points on the line. Draw the front edge of the cube.

V.P.   V.P.

Step 2.   Join the end points of the front edge to the vanishing points.

V.P.   V.P.

Step 3.   Draw the two front faces of the cube. Join the new vertices to the vanishing points.

V.P.   V.P.

Step 4.   Use these lines to complete the cube.

V.P.   V.P.

By changing the position of the front edge of the cube you can change the view of the cube.

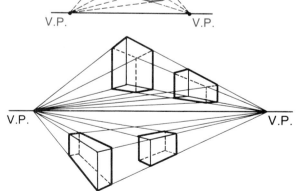

V.P.   V.P.

EXERCISE

1. Use 1 vanishing point to sketch the figure in two different views.

2. Use 2 vanishing points to sketch the figure in two different views.

13.12 CHAPTER 13 REVIEW EXERCISE

Give answers to the nearest whole number.

1. Find the surface area of each of the following.

(a)

(b)
6 cm
5 cm
8 cm

5 cm
5 cm
5 cm

(c)
6 cm
8 cm

(d)
4 cm
5 cm
7 cm

(e)
8 cm
6 cm
6 cm

(f)
7 cm

(g)
25 cm
12 cm

(h)
3.6 cm
12.5 cm

(i)
3.6 cm
2.4 cm
4.2 cm

(j)
12 cm
8 cm

2. Find the volume of each of the following.

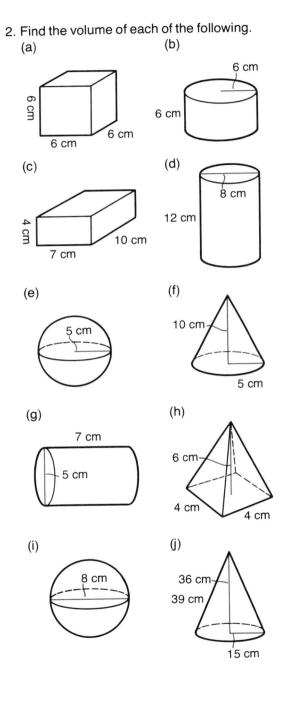

(a)
6 cm
6 cm
6 cm
6 cm

(b)
6 cm
6 cm

(c)
4 cm
7 cm
10 cm

(d)
8 cm
12 cm

(e)
5 cm

(f)
10 cm
5 cm

(g)
7 cm
5 cm

(h)
6 cm
4 cm
4 cm

(i)
8 cm

(j)
36 cm
39 cm
15 cm

APPLICATIONS

3. A conveyor belt at a gravel pit drops screened gravel onto a pile which takes the shape of a cone.
How many cubic metres of material are there when the pile is 15 m high and the base has a diameter of 20 m?

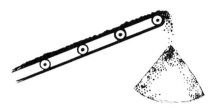

4. The sheet metal class made dippers in the shape of a cone as shown.

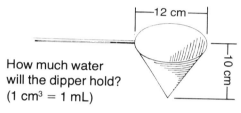

How much water will the dipper hold?
(1 cm³ = 1 mL)

5. A grain storage silo is in the shape of a cylinder with a conical top. The diameter is 6 m; the height of the base is 4 m; the height of the cone is 2 m.
How many cubic metres of grain will it hold?

2.0 m

4.0 m

6.0 m

6. The Egyptian pyramid built for Pharaoh Menkaura in about 4550 B.C., has a base 105 m by 105 m and a height of 64 m.
What is the volume of this monument?

7. A beef cattleman has a silo on the farm for feed storage. The silo has a diameter of 4 m and a height of 10 m.
How many cubic metres of feed can be stored in the silo?

8. Mrs. Hanes is having a new roof put on her cottage. The cottage is 8 m by 8 m and has a pyramid roof. The slant height of the roof is 4.8 m.

(a) What is the area of the roof to be shingled?
(b) Roofing is sold in whole bundles that cover 3 m².
What is the cost of materials at $6.50 per bundle?

9. A foundation is being poured with ready-mix concrete. There are 40 m of footing 0.5 m wide and 0.15 m deep. There are 40 m of basement wall 0.25 m wide and 2 m high.
What is the total amount of concrete to be ordered?

10. The inside diameter of a hollow ball is 20 cm. The outside diameter is 20.2 cm. What is the volume of rubber in the ball to the nearest cubic centimetre?

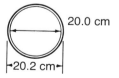

20.0 cm

20.2 cm

11. A Corvette has an eight-cylinder engine. Each cylinder has a diameter of 10.16 cm and a height of 8.84 cm.
(a) What is the volume of one cylinder?
(b) What is the volume of the 8 cylinders?
(c) Express the volume in litres if 1000 cm³ = 1 L.

CHAPTER 13 TEST

Round off all answers to the nearest tenth.

1. Find the surface area of each figure.

(a)　　　　　　　　　　　　(b)

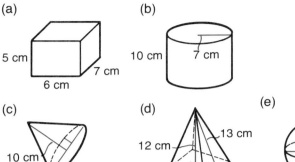

5 cm　　　7 cm　　　　10 cm　7 cm

6 cm

(c)　　　　　　　　(d)　　　　　　　　(e)

10 cm　　12 cm　　　12 cm　　13 cm

　　　　　　　　　　　10 cm　　10 cm

　　　　　　　　　　　　　　　　7 cm

2. Find the volume of each figure.

(a)　　　　　　　　　　　　(b)

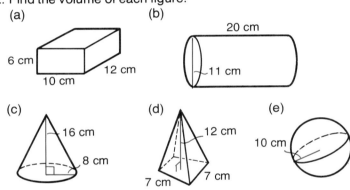

6 cm　　　　12 cm　　　　20 cm

10 cm　　　　　　　　　11 cm

(c)　　　　　　　　(d)　　　　　　　　(e)

16 cm　　　　12 cm　　　10 cm

8 cm

7 cm　　7 cm

3. The dimensions of a soap box are 12 cm by 32 cm by 21 cm.
   What is the volume of the soap box?

4. A hopper is in the shape of a cylinder mounted on a cone. The diameter of the cylinder is 2.4 m, and the depth of the cone is 1.4 m. The height of the cylinder is 3 m. Find the volume of the hopper.

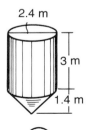

2.4 m

3 m

1.4 m

5. A silo is a cylinder with a half sphere on top. The radius of the diameter of the silo is 5 m, and the height is 12 m. Find the volume of the cylinder.

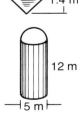

12 m

5 m

GEOMETRY

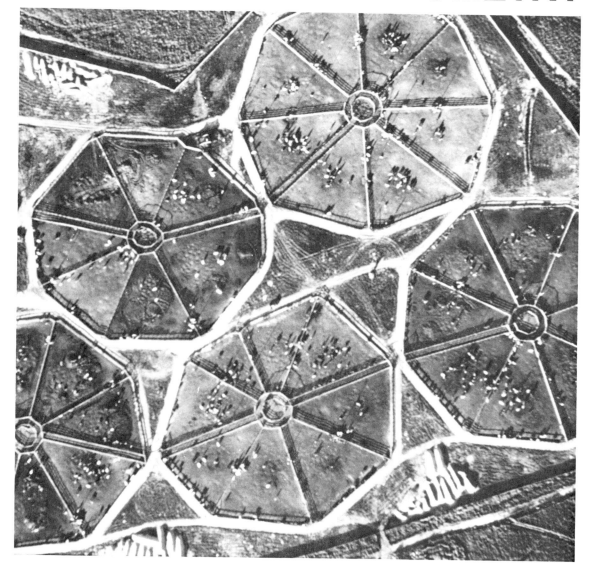

REVIEW AND PREVIEW TO CHAPTER 14

SEEING SHAPES

We receive information from pictures. Because of the way we see things, certain figures create illusions. The following are examples of different types of illusions.

Length

Which is longer, the horizontal line segment, or the vertical line segment?

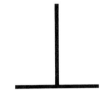

Perspective

Are the sides of the triangle straight or bent?
What effect do the circles have?

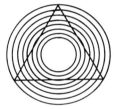

Reversing

Some figures can be drawn as reversible figures. The box with a lid is an example. The box seems to change position as your eyes focus on different parts.
In how many ways do you see the figure?

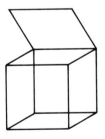

Impossible Figures

Look carefully at the figure. What is wrong with it?

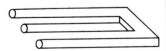

EXERCISE

1. Is the height of the hat greater than its width?

2. Which line segment is longer?

3. Are the three men in the picture all the same size?

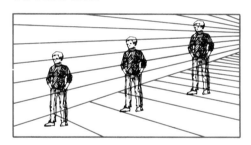

4. Is the length of $\overline{AB}$ the same as the length of $\overline{BC}$?

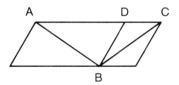

5. Are the horizontal lines bent?

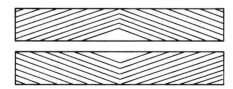

6. The following reversible figures can be seen in at least two ways.
In how many ways do you see each figure?
Describe what you see.

(a)   (b)

 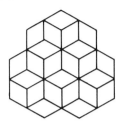

(c)

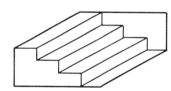

(d)

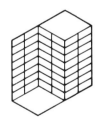

7. Look carefully at the following figures.
Explain what is wrong.

(a)   (b)

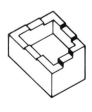 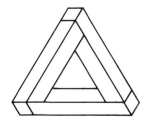

14.1 BASIC FACTS FOR GEOMETRY

The two basic objects used in geometry are the point and the line.

A television picture is made up of thousands of points or dots. You do not notice the spaces between the dots because the dots are so close to each other.

The idea of tightly packed points is sometimes used in mathematics. The picture below suggests that a line contains many points.

Actually, a line contains an unlimited number of points. Lines are shown as follows.

The arrowheads mean that a line extends an indefinite distance in both directions.

· ·	two points
· · · ·	four points
· · · · · · · ·	eight points
··············	more points
····················	more points
••••••••••••••••••••••	many more points
————————————	Line

The following chart shows how we name the basic facts needed for geometry.

Name	Diagram	Labelled Diagram	Words	Symbol
Point	•	A •	Point A	A
Line		B A ℓ	Line AB or Line BA Line ℓ	$\overleftrightarrow{AB}$ $\overleftrightarrow{BA}$ ℓ
Ray		B A	Ray AB	$\overrightarrow{AB}$
Line Segment		B A	Line segment AB or Line segment BA	$\overline{AB}$ $\overline{BA}$
Angle		A B C A B C	Angle ABC or Angle CBA or Angle B $\overrightarrow{BA}$ and $\overrightarrow{BC}$ are the arms of the angle. B is the vertex. $\overline{BA}$ and $\overline{BC}$ are the arms of the angle. B is the vertex.	∠ABC or ∠CBA or ∠B

EXERCISE

A

1. Tell what each symbol means in words.
   (a) $\overleftrightarrow{PQ}$
   (b) $\overrightarrow{ST}$
   (c) $\overline{DE}$
   (d) $\angle RST$
   (e) $\angle FED$
   (f) $\angle R$

2. Name 5 line segments in the following diagram.

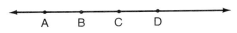

3. Name 6 angles in the diagram.

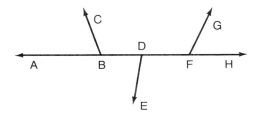

B

4. In the following diagram name
   (a) 3 points.
   (b) 3 lines.
   (c) 3 rays.
   (d) 3 angles.
   (e) 3 line segments.

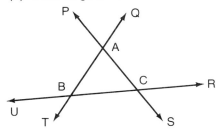

5. In the following diagram name
   (a) 4 points.
   (b) 4 lines.
   (c) 4 rays.
   (d) 4 angles.
   (e) 4 line segments.

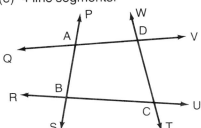

6. Draw a labelled diagram for each of the following.
   (a) $\angle DEF$
   (b) line BC
   (c) ray GF
   (d) line m
   (e) line segment GH

7. Measure each line segment to the nearest tenth of a centimetre.
   (a) ─────────
   (b) ──────────────
   (c) ───────────
   (d) ───────

8. Measure each line segment to the nearest millimetre.
   (a) ──────────────
   (b) ──────────
   (c) ───────────────
   (d) ─────────

CHALLENGE

Name all the line segments you can make by joining the points in the diagram.

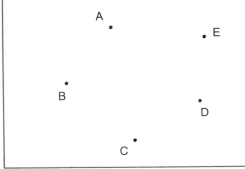

14.2 MEASURING ANGLES

There are angles everywhere.

A skier jumps at an angle.

All passenger jets land
at the same angle.

Angles are measured in degrees using a protractor.
To measure the size of an angle we measure how much one ray
has been rotated from the other ray.

There are 360° in a complete turn.

There are 180° in a half-turn.

There are 90° in a quarter-turn.

Example. Measure ∠ABC

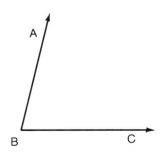

Solution:

1. Estimate: Is the angle greater
   than or less than 90°?

2. Place the centre of
   the protractor on the
   vertex B and the baseline
   along one of the rays.

3. Choose the scale that
   has 0° on a ray.
   Read the measure of
   the angle.

   ∠ABC = 76°

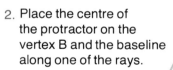

4. Does the measure agree with
   your estimate?

We can also use a protractor to construct angles.

EXERCISE

A

1. Determine the size of the angles on the protractor below.

  (a) ∠ABC   (b) ∠EBC   (c) ∠FBC
  (d) ∠GBC   (e) ∠HBD   (f) ∠IBD
  (g) ∠JBD   (h) ∠EBD   (i) ∠HBC
  (j) ∠FBD   (k) ∠JBC   (l) ∠DBC

2. Determine the size of the angles on the protractor below.

  (a) ∠DCA   (b) ∠FCA   (c) ∠ECA
  (d) ∠HCB   (e) ∠ICB   (f) ∠JCB
  (g) ∠ECB   (h) ∠ICA   (i) ∠FCB
  (j) ∠ACB   (k) ∠BCF   (l) ∠ACH

B

3. Use a protractor to construct each of the following angles in your notebook.

  (a) ∠ABC = 40°   (b) ∠DEF = 65°
  (c) ∠PQR = 23°   (d) ∠RST = 79°
  (e) ∠WXY = 90°   (f) ∠CDE = 145°
  (g) ∠BCD = 168°   (h) ∠TUV = 180°

4. Estimate the size of each angle.

  (a)   (b)

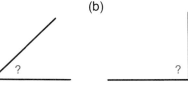

  (c)   (d)

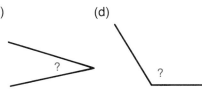

5. Without measuring, sketch each angle. (Use a ruler.) Then use a protractor to check the accuracy of your work.

  (a) 45° angle   (b) 15° angle
  (c) 85° angle   (d) 160° angle

6. Construct the following angles.

  (a) ∠ABC = 245°
  (b) ∠DEF = 340°

CHALLENGE

Find the missing number.

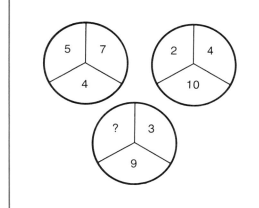

14.3 CLASSIFYING ANGLES

We give angles special names according to their size.

Acute angle	Right Angle	Obtuse Angle	Straight Angle	Reflex Angle
Less than 90°	90°	Greater than 90° but less than 180°	180°	Between 180° and 360°

Some pairs of angles have special names.

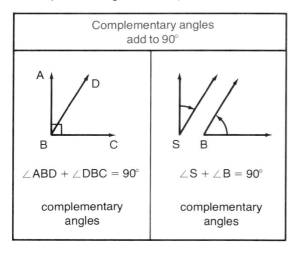

Complementary angles add to 90°

∠ABD + ∠DBC = 90°

complementary angles

∠S + ∠B = 90°

complementary angles

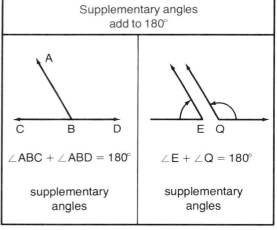

Supplementary angles add to 180°

∠ABC + ∠ABD = 180°

supplementary angles

∠E + ∠Q = 180°

supplementary angles

When two lines intersect, they form four angles. Two angles that are opposite each other, such as ∠1 and ∠3 in the diagram, are called vertically opposite angles.

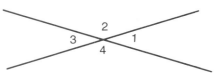

Suppose ∠1 = 30°.
Since ∠1 + ∠2 = 180° (straight line),
then ∠2 = 150°.

Since ∠2 + ∠3 = 180° (straight line),
then ∠3 = 30°,

and ∠1 = ∠3.

Vertically opposite angles are always equal.

EXERCISE

A

1. Classify the following angles as acute, right, obtuse, straight, or reflex.

(a)
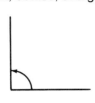

(b)

(c)
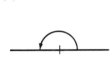

(d)

(e)

(f)
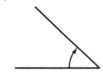

2. Use the diagram. Classify the angles as acute, right, obtuse or straight.

(a) ∠ABC   (b) ∠ACD
(c) ∠BCD   (d) ∠BAD
(e) ∠CAD   (f) ∠ADC

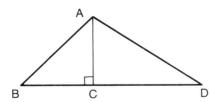

B

3. What angle is complementary to each of the following angles?

(a) 70°   (b) 15°   (c) 23°
(d) 8°   (e) 83°   (f) 67°

4. What angle is supplementary to each of the following angles?

(a) 60°   (b) 150°   (c) 90°
(d) 47°   (e) 113°   (f) 139°

5. Determine the missing measures.

(a)
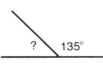

(b)
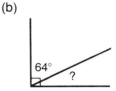

(c)
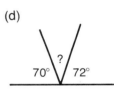

(d)

6. (a) Draw any two intersecting lines.
   (b) Measure each of the four angles.
   (c) What fact have you verified?

7. Complete the table for the two intersecting lines.

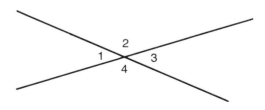

	∠1	∠2	∠3	∠4
(a)	35°			
(b)		120°		
(c)			67°	
(d)				138°

14.4 CLASSIFYING TRIANGLES

Triangles are found in many places.

We give triangles special names according to the lengths of their sides.

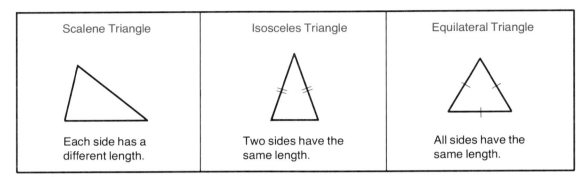

Scalene Triangle	Isosceles Triangle	Equilateral Triangle
Each side has a different length.	Two sides have the same length.	All sides have the same length.

We also give triangles special names according to the size of their angles.

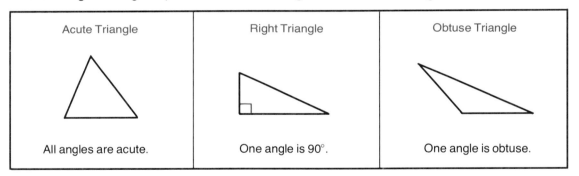

Acute Triangle	Right Triangle	Obtuse Triangle
All angles are acute.	One angle is 90°.	One angle is obtuse.

The following experiment illustrates one of the most important ideas in geometry.

Draw a triangle on a piece of paper.
Cut the triangle out.

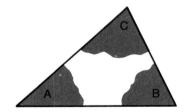

Tear off the three corners of the triangle.
Arrange them as shown.

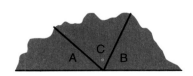

The angles appear to make a straight line, or 180°.

The sum of the angles of any triangle is always 180°.

EXERCISE

A

1. Classify the triangles by sides.

   (a)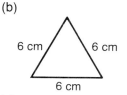

   (b)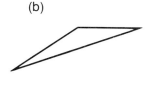

3 cm, 5 cm, 5 cm

6 cm, 6 cm, 6 cm

   (c)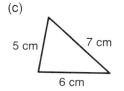

   (d)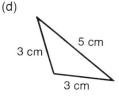

5 cm, 7 cm, 6 cm

3 cm, 5 cm, 3 cm

2. Classify the triangles by angles.

   (a)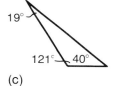

   (b)

19°, 121°, 40°

58°, 60°, 62°

   (c)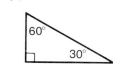

   (d)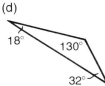

60°, 30°

18°, 130°, 32°

B

3. Measure the sides and then classify the triangles by sides.

   (a)

   (b)

   (c)

   (d)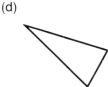

4. Classify the triangles by angles.

   (a)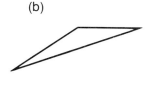

   (b)

   (c)

   (d)

5. (a) Draw any acute triangle.
   (b) Measure each angle.
   (c) Find the sum of the angles.

6. (a) Draw any obtuse triangle.
   (b) Measure each angle.
   (c) Find the sum of the angles.

7. Determine the missing measures.

   (a)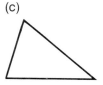

   (b)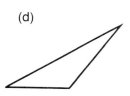

60°, 50°, ?

?, 43°

   (c)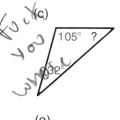

   (d)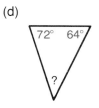

105°, ?, 32°

72°, 64°, ?

   (e)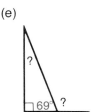

   (f)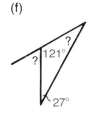

?, 69°, ?

?, ?, 121°, 27°

14.5 POLYGONS

Polygons are figures that have line segments as sides.
We name a polygon by the number of sides it has.

Name	Number of Sides	Diagram
Triangle	3	
Quadrilateral	4	
Pentagon	5	
Hexagon	6	
Septagon	7	
Octagon	8	
Nonagon	9	
Decagon	10	
Hendecagon	11	
Dodecagon	12	

Regular polygons have equal sides and equal angles.

To find the sum of the interior angles
of a pentagon, we proceed as follows.

Step 1. Draw all the diagonals from
any one vertex.

Step 2. Count the number of triangles.

Step 3. The sum of the interior angles
of a triangle is 180°.
There are 3 triangles.
$$3 \times 180° = 540°$$
The sum of the interior angles of a pentagon is 540°.

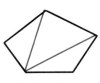

3 triangles

EXERCISE

A

1. Name each of the following polygons.

   (a)

   (b)

   (c)

   (d)

   (e)

   (f)

2. How many diagonals can be drawn from one vertex in each of the following polygons?
   (a) quadrilateral   (b) hexagon
   (c) octagon   (d) decagon
   (e) nonagon   (f) dodecagon

B

3. Complete the chart to determine the sum of the interior angles of the polygons.

Sides	Number of Diagonals from One Vertex	Number of Triangles	Sum of Interior Angles
4	1	2	360°
5			
6			
7			
8			
9			
10			
11			
12			

4. The sum of the interior angles of a pentagon is 540°. A pentagon has 5 angles. In a regular pentagon, all the angles are equal. Each of the angles is
   $540° ÷ 5 = 108°$.

   Calculate the size of each angle in each regular polygon.

   (a)

   (b)

   (c)

5. A pentagon has 5 exterior angles.

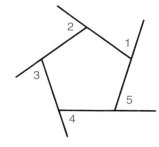

   The sum of the 5 straight angles is
   $5 × 180° = 900°$.
   The sum of the interior angles is 540°.
   Therefore, the sum of the exterior angles is
   $900° - 540° = 360°$.

   Calculate the sum of the exterior angles of
   (a) a quadrilateral;
   (b) a hexagon;
   (c) an octagon;
   (d) a decagon.

14.6 CONSTRUCTING SEGMENTS AND ANGLES

CONSTRUCTING A LINE SEGMENT EQUAL TO A GIVEN LINE SEGMENT

Construct a line segment equal to $\overline{AB}$ on ℓ.

CONSTRUCTION
1. Place the compass points on A and B.

2. Mark the same distance on ℓ.

$$\overline{CD} = \overline{AB}$$

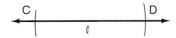

CONSTRUCTING AN ANGLE EQUAL TO A GIVEN ANGLE

Construct an angle equal to $\angle ABC$.

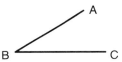

CONSTRUCTION
1. Draw ray ST.

2. With centre B, draw an arc to cut $\overline{AB}$ and $\overline{BC}$ at X and Y. With centre S and the same radius, draw an arc to cut $\overrightarrow{ST}$ at M.

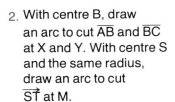
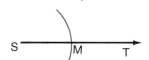

3. With centre M and radius $\overline{XY}$ draw an arc to locate N.

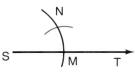

4. Join $\overline{SN}$.

$$\angle ABC = \angle NSM$$

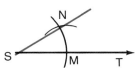

EXERCISE

B

1. Use your ruler to draw a line segment similar to the one shown.
   Construct a line segment equal to it.

   (a)

   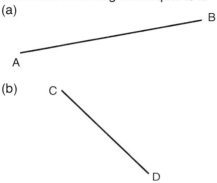

   (b)

   (c)

2. Use your ruler to draw an angle similar to the one shown.
   Construct an angle equal to it.

   (a)

   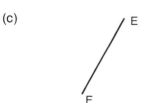

   (b)

   (c)

   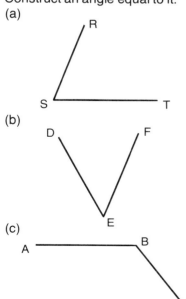

THE GAME OF NIM

This is a game for two players.

To start, arrange 9 toothpicks as follows.

Players take turns removing one, two, or three toothpicks as they wish.
(At least one toothpick must be removed.) The player that must take the last toothpick is the person who loses.

You can play NIM on a microcomputer using the following Micro Math program.

MICRO MATH

NEW

```
10 PRINT"NIM"
20 N=9
30 PRINT"THERE ARE";N;"STONES LEFT."
40 INPUT"TAKE ONE, TWO, OR THREE STONES";D
50 PRINT"I TAKE";4-D;"STONES."
60 N=N-4
70 IF N>1  THEN 30
80 PRINT"THERE IS ONLY ONE STONE LEFT. I WIN AGAIN."
90 END
```

RUN

14.7 BISECTING ANGLES

When you bisect something, you divide it into two equal parts.

The median of a highway divides the road into two equal parts.

The bisector of an angle is a line, ray, or line segment that divides the angle into two equal parts.

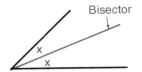

We use the following steps to bisect an angle using a compass and straight-edge (ruler).

CONSTRUCTING A BISECTOR OF AN ANGLE

Bisect ∠ABC.

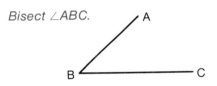

CONSTRUCTION

1. With centre B, draw an arc to cut the arms of the angle at M and N.

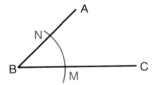

2. With centre M, draw an arc.

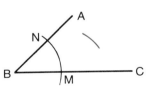

3. With centre N and the same radius as in Step 2, draw an arc to locate point D.

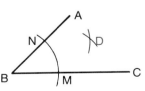

4. Join $\overline{BD}$.
   $\overline{BD}$ is the bisector of ∠ABC.

   $$\angle ABD = \angle CBD$$

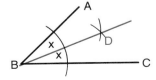

EXERCISE

B

1. Draw an angle similar to, but larger than, the one shown.
   Bisect the angle.
   (a)

   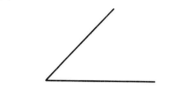

   (b)

   (c)

   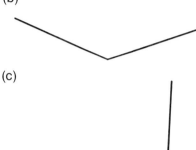

2. (a) Use a protractor to draw an angle of 80°.
   (b) Bisect the angle.
   (c) Check the size of each new angle by measuring.

3. (a) Draw an angle of 150°.
   (b) Bisect the angle.
   (c) Check the size of each new angle by measuring.

4. Draw a triangle similar to, but larger than, the one shown.
   Bisect each angle of the triangle.

   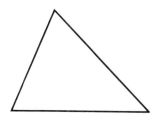

5. Draw a triangle similar to, but larger than the one shown.
   Bisect each angle of the triangle.

6. (a) Draw an angle of 160°.
   (b) Use a compass and straight-edge to divide this angle into 4 equal parts.

7. (a) Draw an angle of 180°.
   (b) Bisect the angle.
   (c) What is the measure of each new angle?

8. (a) Draw an angle of 180°.
   (b) Bisect the angle.
   (c) Bisect one of the new angles.
   (d) What is the size of each of the smaller angles?

C

9. Use a compass and straight-edge to draw a compass rose.

   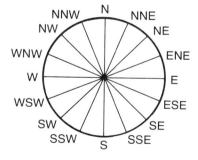

14.8 CONSTRUCTING PERPENDICULARS

Lines that are perpendicular meet at 90°. The picture contains many examples of perpendicular lines.

There are two types of constructions for perpendiculars.

CONSTRUCTING A PERPENDICULAR TO A LINE FROM A POINT NOT ON THE LINE

Construct a perpendicular to $\overline{AB}$ from P.

CONSTRUCTION

1. With centre P, draw an arc to cut $\overline{AB}$ at M and N.

2. With centres M and N and the same radius, draw arcs to intersect at C.

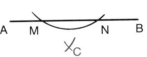

3. Join $\overline{CP}$ to intersect $\overline{AB}$ at D. $\overline{DP} \perp \overline{AB}$

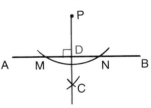

CONSTRUCTING A PERPENDICULAR TO A LINE FROM A POINT ON THE LINE

Construct a perpendicular to $\overline{AB}$ at P.

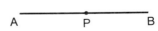

CONSTRUCTION

1. ∠APB is a straight angle.

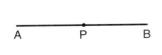

2. Bisect ∠APB

3. $\overline{CP} \perp \overline{AB}$

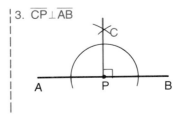

EXERCISE

B

1. Copy each of the following diagrams. Construct the perpendicular from P to $\overline{AB}$.

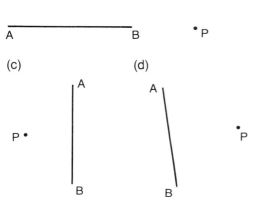

(a)
• P

(b)

A   B

A   B   • P

(c)

(d)

P •

A

B

A

• P

B

2. Copy each of the following diagrams. Construct the perpendicular to $\overline{DE}$ at x.

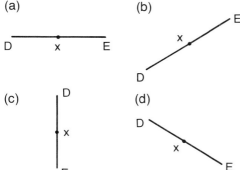

(a)

D   x   E

(b)

E

x

D

(c)

D

x

E

(d)

D

x

E

3. (a) Draw a triangle similar to, but larger than, the one shown.

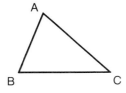

A

B   C

(b) Construct the perpendicular from A to $\overline{BC}$ to intersect $\overline{BC}$ at D.
($\overline{AD}$ is called an altitude of △ABC.)

4. (a) Draw a triangle similar to, but larger than, the one shown.

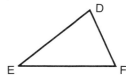

D

E   F

(b) Construct the perpendicular from D to $\overline{EF}$.

(c) Measure the perpendicular and $\overline{EF}$ in millimetres.

(d) Calculate the area of the triangle.

5. (a) Draw a triangle similar to, but larger than, the one shown.

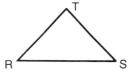

T

R   S

(b) Construct the perpendicular from R to $\overline{ST}$.

(c) Calculate the area of the triangle.

6. (a) Draw a triangle similar to, but larger than, the one shown.

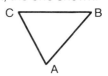

C   B

A

(b) Construct the perpendicular from:
   i) A to $\overline{BC}$
   ii) B to $\overline{AC}$
   iii) C to $\overline{AB}$

7. (a) Draw a triangle similar to, but larger than, the one shown.

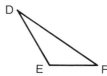

D

E   F

(b) Extend $\overline{FE}$ and construct the perpendicular from D to $\overline{FE}$.

14.9 RIGHT BISECTORS

The bisector of an angle cuts the angle into two equal parts.

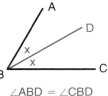

$$\angle ABD = \angle CBD$$

The bisector of a line segment cuts the line segment into two equal parts.

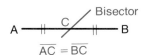

$$\overline{AC} = \overline{BC}$$

The right bisector of a line segment cuts the line segment into two equal parts at right angles.

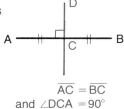

$$\overline{AC} = \overline{BC}$$
$$\text{and } \angle DCA = 90°$$

CONSTRUCTING THE RIGHT BISECTOR OF A LINE SEGMENT

Construct the right bisector of $\overline{AB}$.

A ———————————————— B

CONSTRUCTION

1. Use centre A.
   Draw an arc with a radius greater than $\frac{1}{2}$ the length of $\overline{AB}$.

2. Use centre B and the same radius as step 1. Draw an arc intersecting the first arc at C and D.

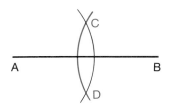

3. Join $\overline{CD}$ to intersect $\overline{AB}$ at E. $\overline{CD}$ is the right bisector of $\overline{AB}$.
   $$\overline{AE} = \overline{EB}$$
   $$\text{and } \angle CEA = \angle CEB = 90°$$

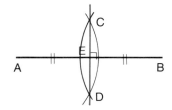

EXERCISE

B

1. (a) Draw a line segment 8 cm in length.
   (b) Construct the right bisector of the line segment.

2. (a) Draw a line segment 10 cm in length.
   (b) Construct the right bisector of the line segment.

3. Draw line segments in each of the following positions.
   Construct the right bisector of each.
   (a)   (b)

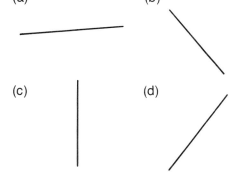

   (c)   (d)

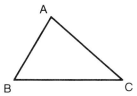

4. Draw a line segment 12 cm in length. Use a straight-edge and compass to divide the line into four equal parts.

5. (a) Draw a triangle similar to, but larger than, the one shown.

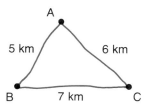

   (b) Construct the right bisector of $\overline{BC}$.

6. (a) Draw a line segment 10 cm in length on a piece of paper.
   (b) Find the right bisector by folding the paper.

7. (a) Draw a triangle similar to, but larger than, the one shown.

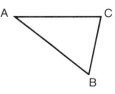

   (b) Construct the right bisectors of $\overline{AB}$, $\overline{BC}$, and $\overline{AC}$.

8. (a) Draw a triangle similar to, but larger than, the one shown.

   (b) Construct the right bisectors of $\overline{DE}$ and $\overline{EF}$.
      Name the point of intersection G.
   (c) With centre G and radius $\overline{GF}$, draw a circle.

9. The map shows the location of three towns and the distances between them.

   The owner of a new radio station wants to locate the broadcast tower so that it is the same distance from each town. To determine the position of the tower, you proceed as follows.

   (a) Join A to B and B to C.
   (b) Draw the right bisector of $\overline{AB}$.
   (c) Draw the right bisector of $\overline{BC}$.
   (d) Label the intersection point D.
      The tower should be located at D.
   (e) How far is the tower from A, B, and C?

14.10 CONSTRUCTIONS USING REFLECTIONS

Many of the constructions you have done using a ruler and a compass can also be done by reflections using a Semi Transparent Mirror (STM). The following are some examples.

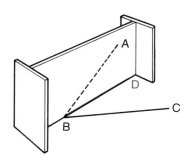

Semi Transparent Mirror (STM)

BISECTING AN ANGLE

Bisect ∠ABC.

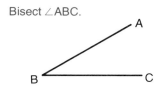

CONSTRUCTION
1. Stand the STM on your page so that the edge is on B.

2. Rotate the STM about B so that the image of $\overline{BC}$ matches with $\overline{BA}$.

3. Draw a ray $\overrightarrow{BD}$ along the STM.
   $$\angle ABD = \angle CBD$$
   and $\overline{BD}$ bisects ∠ABC

RIGHT BISECTING A LINE SEGMENT

Construct the right bisector of line segment $\overline{AB}$.

CONSTRUCTION
1. Stand the STM on your page so that the image of A is on B.

2. Draw the line $\overline{DE}$ on the edge of the STM to intersect $\overline{AB}$ at F.
   $$\overline{AF} = \overline{FB}$$
   and $\angle DFA = \angle DFB = 90°$

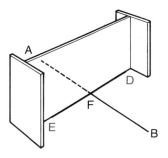

CONSTRUCTING A PERPENDICULAR ON A LINE

Construct a perpendicular to $\overline{AB}$ at P.

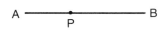

CONSTRUCTION
1. Stand the STM at P.

2. Rotate the STM so that the image of $\overrightarrow{PB}$ matches with $\overrightarrow{PA}$.

3. Draw $\overleftrightarrow{CP}$ along the STM. $\overline{CP}$ is perpendicular to $\overline{AB}$.
   $$\overline{CP} \perp \overline{AB}$$

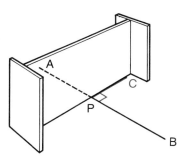

CONSTRUCTING A PERPENDICULAR TO A LINE

Construct a perpendicular from P to $\overline{AB}$.

CONSTRUCTION
1. Stand the STM at P.

2. Rotate the STM so that the image of the line falls on itself.

3. Draw $\overline{PE}$ along the STM to intersect $\overline{AB}$ at F.
$\overline{PF} \perp \overline{AB}$

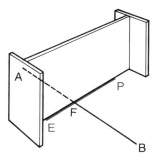

EXERCISE

1. Draw an angle similar to, but larger than, the one shown.
Bisect the angle using an STM.

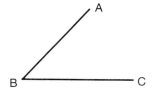

2. Draw a line segment 6 cm long.
Construct the right bisector of the line segment using an STM.

3. Construct a diagram similar to the one shown.
Construct the perpendicular to $\overline{AB}$ at P using an STM.

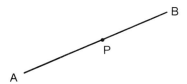

4. Draw a diagram similar to, but larger than, the one shown.
Construct the perpendicular to $\overline{AB}$ from P using an STM.

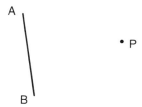

5. Draw a triangle similar to, but larger than, the one shown.
Bisect each of the angles of the triangle using an STM.

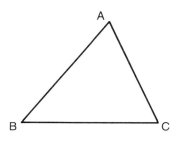

14.11 PARALLEL LINES

Parallel lines are lines that never meet.
In a drawing we indicate parallel lines or
parallel line segments by arrowheads.

Line AB is parallel to line CD
or $\overleftrightarrow{AB} \| \overleftrightarrow{CD}$

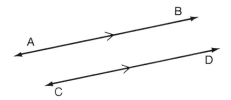

Parallel lines are found in many places.

The diagram at the right shows two parallel
lines cut by a third line. The cutting line is
called a transversal. There are 8 angles formed
when a transversal cuts 2 parallel lines. These
angles have special properties and are given
special names.

Alternate Angles

Alternate angles form
a ⌐ pattern and are
equal. There are 2 pairs
of alternate angles.

$\angle d = \angle f$
$\angle c = \angle e$

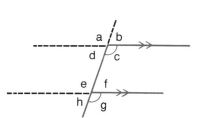

Corresponding Angles

Corresponding angles form
an ⌐ pattern and are equal.
There are 4 pairs of
corresponding angles.

$\angle c = \angle g$
$\angle b = \angle f$
$\angle d = \angle h$
$\angle a = \angle e$

Co-interior Angles

Co-interior angles form
a ⌐ pattern and add to 180°.
There are 2 pairs of co-interior
angles.

$\angle c + \angle f = 180°$
$\angle d + \angle e = 180°$

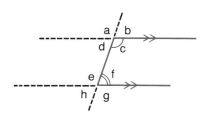

EXERCISE

A

1. (a) Name two pairs of alternate angles.
   (b) Name four pairs of corresponding angles.
   (c) Name two pairs of co-interior angles.

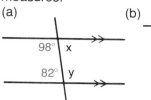

2. Classify each pair of angles as alternate angles, corresponding angles, co-interior angles, or none of these.

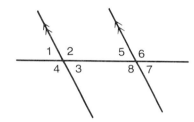

   (a) ∠1 and ∠5   (b) ∠2 and ∠8
   (c) ∠4 and ∠8   (d) ∠1 and ∠7
   (e) ∠3 and ∠8   (f) ∠5 and ∠3
   (g) ∠7 and ∠3   (h) ∠2 and ∠5

B

3. Construct a diagram similar to, but larger than, the one shown.

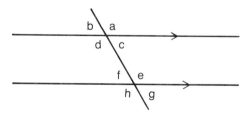

   Measure the angles and complete the following.
   Alternate Angles ∠c = ∠f = ▨
   　　　　　　　　　∠d = ∠e = ▨
   Corresponding Angles ∠a = ∠e = ▨
   　　　　　　　　　∠c = ∠g = ▨
   　　　　　　　　　∠b = ∠f = ▨
   　　　　　　　　　∠d = ∠h = ▨

   Co-interior Angles ∠c + ∠e = ▨
   　　　　　　　　　∠d + ∠f = ▨

4. Use the Z pattern to find the missing measures.
   (a)　　　　　　　　　　(b)

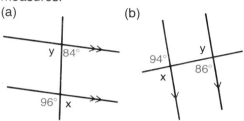

5. Use the F pattern to find the missing measures.
   (a)　　　　　　　　　　(b)

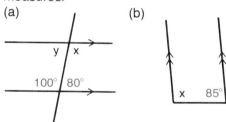

6. Use the L pattern to find the missing measures.
   (a)　　　　　　　　　　(b)

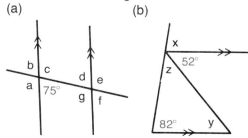

7. Calculate the missing measures.
   (a)　　　　　　　　　　(b)

14.12 LINES AND ANGLES

The following is a summary of some relationships between lines and angles.

Complementary angles add to 90°.

Supplementary angles add to 180°.

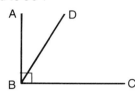

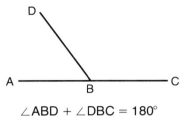

∠ABD + ∠DBC = 90°

∠ABD + ∠DBC = 180°

When two lines intersect, the vertically opposite angles are equal.

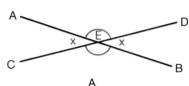

∠AEC = ∠DEB
∠AED = ∠CEB

The sum of the interior angles of any triangle is 180°.

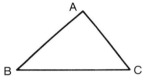

∠A + ∠B + ∠C = 180°

When a transversal cuts two parallel lines,

    i) the alternate angles are equal;

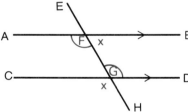

∠BFG = ∠CGF
∠AFG = ∠FGD

    ii) the corresponding angles are equal;

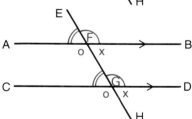

∠EFB = ∠FGD
∠BFG = ∠GDH
∠EFA = ∠FGC
∠AFG = ∠CGH

    iii) the co-interior angles add to 180°.

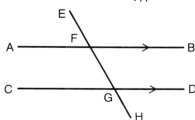

∠BFG + ∠FGD = 180°
∠AFG + ∠FGC = 180°

EXERCISE

B

1. Calculate the missing values.

(a)

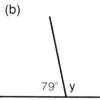

57°
x

(b)

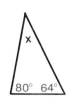

79° y

(c)

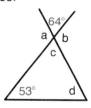

x
y
47°
z

(d)

x
80° 64°

2. Calculate the missing values.

(a)

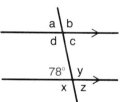

a
72° 57°
b c d

(b)

64°
a b
c
53° d

(c)

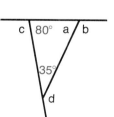

a b
d c
78° y
x z

(d)

c 80° a b
35°
d

(e)

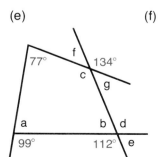

77° f 134°
c
g
a
b d
99° 112° e

(f)

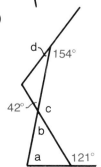

d 154°
42° c
b
a 121°

3. Calculate the missing values.

(a)

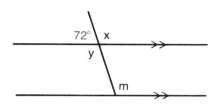

72° x
y
m

(b)

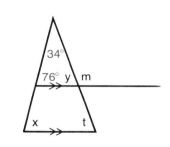

34°
76° y m
x t

(c)

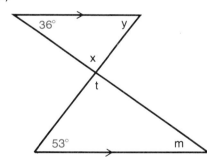

36° y
x
t
53° m

(d)

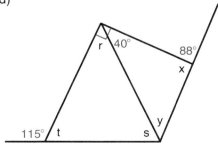

r 40° 88°
x
115° t s y

EXTRA EXTRA EXTRA EXTRA EXTRA

FUN WITH YOUR CALCULATOR

1. Press

   C + 8 + 5 + 2 =

   Find three other patterns on the keyboard that also add to 15.

2. (a) Enter three numbers in a straight line through the centre.

   7 8 9
   4 5 6
   1 2 3

   (b) Press the addition key, then press the same three numbers in reverse.
   Write your answer.

   (c) Find the sum of all groups of numbers through the centre.

3. (a) $654 - 456 = 198$
   is a subtraction pattern using a group of numbers through the centre.
   Find the three other patterns.

   (b) Find the pattern in the differences.

4. (a) Divide.
   $1 \div 3$
   $10 \div 33$
   $100 \div 333$
   $1000 \div 3333$

   (b) Predict the next two patterns and check your predictions.

5. (a) Divide.
   $1 \div 9$ $1 \div 99$
   $2 \div 9$ $2 \div 99$
   $3 \div 9$ $3 \div 99$

   (b) Predict your result when you divide 1, 2, and 3 by 999, and check your predictions.

6. Multiply.
   37×3 $37\,037 \times 3$
   37×6 $37\,037 \times 6$
   37×9 $37\,037 \times 9$
   Explain the patterns.

7. (a) Multiply.
   1919×2
   1919×3
   1919×4

   (b) Predict what the next numbers will be. Were you correct? Why?

8. (a) Enter 1234.
   (b) Add, subtract, multiply, or divide by any two-digit number until you change 1234 to 4321. The best solution is the shortest.
   (c) Repeat part (b) for 12345.
   (d) Repeat part (b) for 123456.

9. Perform these calculations and find the patterns.
   (a) 1112^2 and 2111^2
   (b) 1113^2 and 3111^2
   (c) 1121^2 and 1211^2
   (d) 1122^2 and 2211^2
   (e) 1212^2 and 2121^2

10. The digits displayed on a calculator are made up of 7 lines.

    Suppose we needed more than the ten digits, 0 to 9, as displayed on a calculator.
    How many more numbers can we design for use on a calculator?
    (All lines are continuous, or connected. All new digits must be the same height as the 8.)

14.13 CONGRUENT FIGURES

Congruent figures have exactly the same size and shape.

EXERCISE

Identify the pairs of congruent figures.

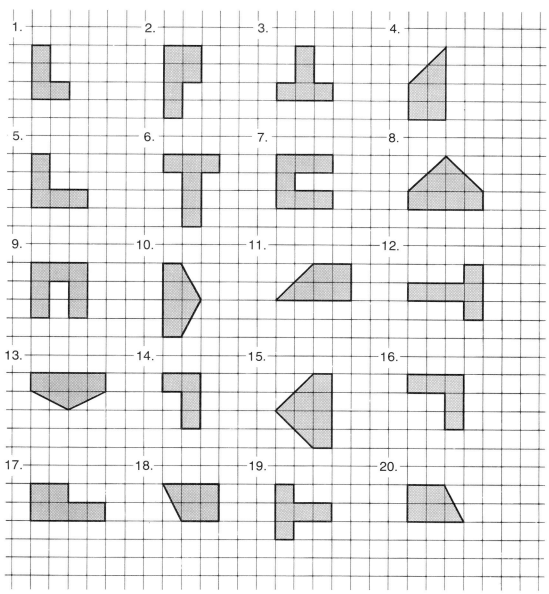

14.14 CONGRUENT TRIANGLES

Congruent figures have the same size and shape.

△ABC and △DEF are congruent.
They have the same size and shape.

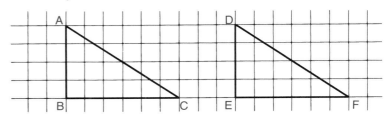

Imagine sliding △ABC over to fit on △DEF. You fit point B on point E; point A on point D; point C on point F.

When the vertices are matched in this way:
    ∠B and ∠E are called corresponding angles;
    $\overline{AB}$ and $\overline{DE}$ are called corresponding sides.

> When triangles are congruent, corresponding angles and corresponding sides are always equal.

When △ABC is congruent to △DEF, we write
    △ABC ≅ △DEF

△ABC ≅ △DEF means that all of the following are true:

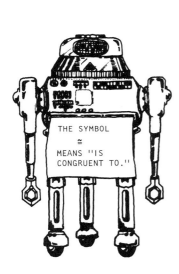

THE SYMBOL ≅ MEANS "IS CONGRUENT TO."

∠A = ∠D		$\overline{AB} = \overline{DE}$
∠B = ∠E	and	$\overline{BC} = \overline{EF}$
∠C = ∠F		$\overline{AC} = \overline{DF}$

Example.
The two triangles shown are congruent.
(a) Name the corresponding angles that are equal.
(b) Name the corresponding sides that are equal.

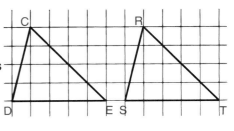

Solution:
(a) ∠C = ∠R
    ∠D = ∠S
    ∠E = ∠T
(b) $\overline{CD} = \overline{RS}$
    $\overline{DE} = \overline{ST}$
    $\overline{CE} = \overline{RT}$

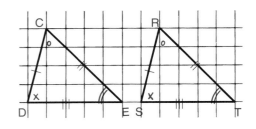

EXERCISE

A

1. The two triangles are congruent.

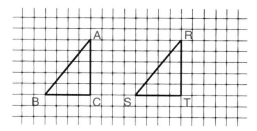

   (a) Name the corresponding angles that are equal.

   (b) Name the corresponding sides that are equal.

B

2. The pairs of triangles are congruent. Name the corresponding angles and sides that are equal.

(a)

(b)

(c)

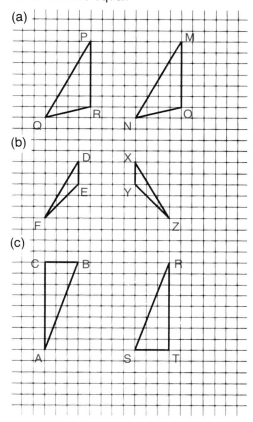

3. The pairs of triangles are congruent. Name the corresponding angles and sides that are equal.

(a)

(b)

(c)

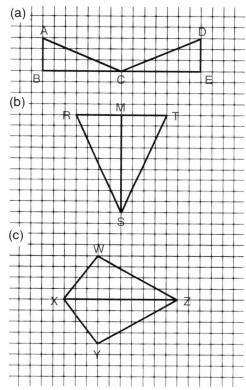

CHALLENGE

Copy this figure. Show how to divide it into 3 equal parts. Each part must have the same size and shape.

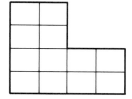

14.15 PARTS OF A CIRCLE

The pictures show some of the ways a circle is used.

The following diagrams illustrate the important parts of a circle.

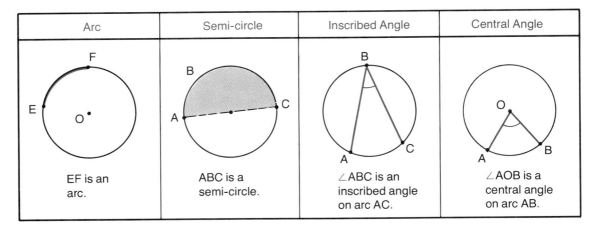

Radius	Diameter	Chord	Circumference
$\overline{OA}$ is a radius.	$\overline{AB}$ is a diameter.	$\overline{CD}$ is a chord.	The circumference is the perimeter of the circle.

Arc	Semi-circle	Inscribed Angle	Central Angle
EF is an arc.	ABC is a semi-circle.	$\angle ABC$ is an inscribed angle on arc AC.	$\angle AOB$ is a central angle on arc AB.

EXERCISE

B

1. Construct a circle with radius 6 cm.

2. Construct a circle with diameter 10 cm.

3. Identify the following parts in the diagram.
   (a) 3 radii
   (b) 2 diameters
   (c) 2 chords

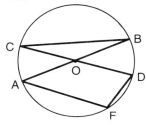

4. Identify the following parts in the diagram.
   (a) 3 arcs
   (b) 2 diameters
   (c) 2 semi-circles

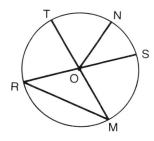

5. (a) Name the inscribed angle on arc CD.
   (b) Name the central angle on arc CD.

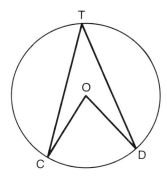

6. (a) Name the inscribed angle on chord $\overline{AB}$.
   (b) Name the central angle on chord $\overline{AB}$.

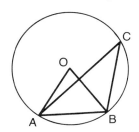

7. Identify the following.
   (a) 2 inscribed angles on arcs
   (b) 2 inscribed angles on chords

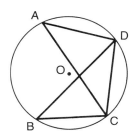

8. Identify 4 inscribed angles.

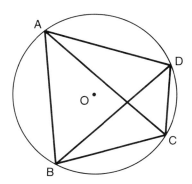

14.16 PROPERTIES OF CIRCLES

In this section you will discover some important properties of a circle.

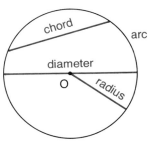

Lines in a Circle

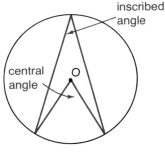

Angles in a Circle

EXERCISE

B

1. (a) Construct a circle with radius 4 cm.
   (b) Mark an arc AB on the circle.
   (c) Draw an inscribed angle on the arc.
   (d) Measure the inscribed angle.

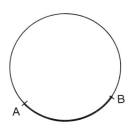

2. (a) Construct a circle with radius 4.5 cm.
   (b) Mark arc CD on the circle.
   (c) Draw a central angle on the arc.
   (d) Measure the central angle.

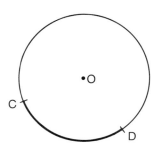

Chords

3. (a) Construct a circle with radius 5 cm. Label the centre 0.
   (b) Draw a chord $\overline{AB}$.

   (c) Construct the right bisector of $\overline{AB}$.
   (d) What point does the right bisector pass through?

4. (a) Construct a circle by tracing a circular object.
   (b) Draw two chords $\overline{AB}$ and $\overline{CD}$.

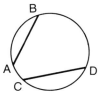

   (c) Draw the right bisectors of $\overline{AB}$ and $\overline{CD}$.
   (d) At what point do the chords intersect?

Central and Inscribed Angles

5. (a) Construct a circle with radius 5 cm.
   (b) Mark the centre 0.
       Mark arc AB.
       Construct a central angle ∠AOB and an inscribed angle ∠ACB.

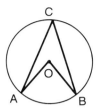

   (c) Measure ∠AOB and ∠ACB.
   (d) How is the size of ∠AOB related to the size of ∠ACB?

6. (a) Construct a circle with radius 4.5 cm.
       Mark Chord $\overline{CD}$.
   (b) Construct a central angle ∠COD and an inscribed angle ∠CTD.

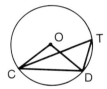

   (c) Measure ∠COD and ∠CTD.
   (d) How are the angles related?

7. (a) Repeat the steps in Question 6 using circles with different radii and different arcs.
   (b) Write a statement about the relationship between the size of a central angle and the size of an inscribed angle on the same arc.

Inscribed Angles

8. (a) Construct a circle with radius 5 cm.
   (b) Mark arc AB.
       Construct two inscribed angles on arc AB.
   (c) Measure the angles.
   (d) How are they related?

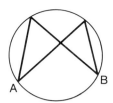

9. (a) Repeat the steps in Question 8 using circles with different radii and different arcs.
   (b) Write a statement about the relationship between two inscribed angles on the same arc.

Angles in a Semi-circle

10. (a) Construct a circle with radius 5 cm.
        Mark the centre 0.
    (b) Draw a diameter $\overline{AB}$.
    (c) Construct an inscribed angle ∠ACB on the diameter.

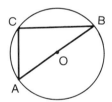

    (d) Measure ∠ACB.

CHALLENGE

The famous Yang-Yin symbol is made using 3 circles.

Use your compass to construct a Yang-Yin symbol.

14.17 USING THE CIRCLE PROPERTIES

The results of the investigations in the previous section can be summarized as follows.

The right bisector of any chord in a circle passes through the centre of the circle.

A central angle is twice the size of an inscribed angle on the same arc.

Inscribed angles on the same arc are equal.

An inscribed angle drawn on a diameter is 90°.

Example. Find the missing values.

(a)

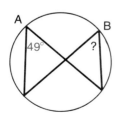

(b)

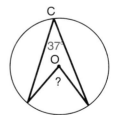

(b) ∠O is a central angle.
    ∠C is an inscribed angle on
    the same arc.
    ∠O = 2 × ∠C
    Since ∠C = 37°
    ∠O = 2 × 37°
        = 74°

Solution:
(a) ∠A and ∠B are inscribed angles
    on the same arc.
    ∠A = ∠B
    Since ∠A = 49°, ∠B = 49°.

EXERCISE

A

1. Find the missing value.

2. Find the missing value.

3. Find the missing value.

B

4. Find the missing values.

(a)

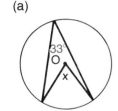

(b)

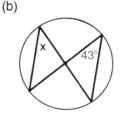

(c)

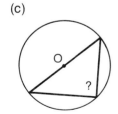

(d)

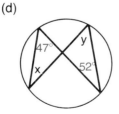

(e)

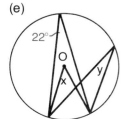

(f)

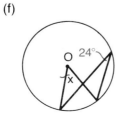

5. (a) Draw three points in your notebook as shown.

R •   • T

S •

(b) Construct the right bisectors of $\overline{RS}$ and $\overline{ST}$ to intersect at 0.
(c) With centre 0, draw a circle to pass through R, S, and T.

6. (a) Three towns are located as shown on the map.

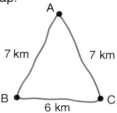

(b) Construct the triangle in your notebook using 1 km = 1 cm.
(c) Determine where a water tower should be located so that it is the same distance from each town.

7. (a) Construct a circle by tracing a circular object.
(b) Locate the centre of the circle by drawing the right bisectors of the two chords.

CHALLENGE

Copy this figure. Show how to divide it into 4 equal parts. Each part must have the same size and shape.

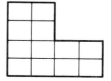

14.18 SOLIDS, SHELLS, AND SKELETONS

Three-dimensional objects can be classified as either solids, shells, or skeletons.

solid   shell   skeleton

BRICK   SHOE BOX   SCAFFOLDING

The terms used to describe parts of these figures are: face, edge, and vertex.

Usually the top and bottom faces are called bases.

The CUBE has 6 faces, 12 edges, and 8 vertices.

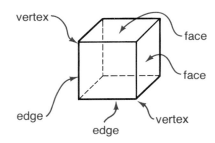

A PRISM is a figure with congruent polygons for ends and parallelograms for sides.

A RECTANGULAR PRISM is a figure with congruent polygons for ends and rectangles for sides. Each face is indicated with an F.

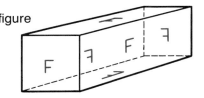

A RIGHT PYRAMID is a common figure. Following are two examples of right pyramids. The sides of a pyramid are triangles. The vertices are marked in red.

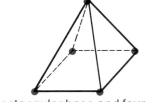

Rectangular base and four sides

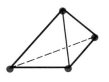

Triangular base and three sides

An example of a RIGHT PRISM is a pup tent.
The floor and 2 sides are rectangular
and the 2 ends are triangular, for a
total of 5 faces.

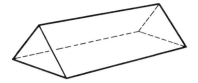

EXERCISE

1. (a) The chart below contains pictures of various three-dimensional figures. Copy the chart in
your notebook. Count the number of faces, edges, and vertices for each figure and
record the answers in your chart. Then in the final column, calculate F + V − E. The first
one is done for you.

	Name	Figure	Vertices V	Faces F	Edges E	F + V − E
i)	Cube		6	8	12	6 + 8 − 12 = 2
ii)	Right Prism					
iii)	Right Pyramid— triangular base					
iv)	Right Pyramid— rectangular base					
v)	Right Prism					

(b) What is the answer to F + V − E in each case?
This result is known as Euler's Theorem, after Leonhard Euler, who first discovered it.

14.19 CONSTRUCTING POLYHEDRONS

The following are the nets for a regular tetrahedron, a regular hexahedron, a regular octahedron, a right pyramid, and a right prism.

(a) Regular Tetrahedron

(b) Regular Hexahedron (Cube)

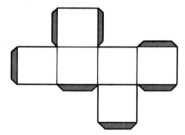

(c) Regular Octahedron

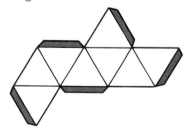

(d) Right Pyramid

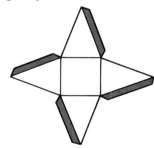

(e) Right Prism

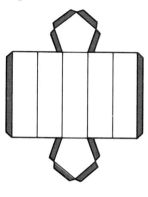 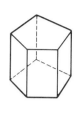

(f) Right Prism

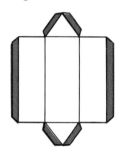 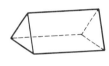

There are two other regular polyhedrons, the dodecahedron
and the icosahedron.

(g) The Dodecahedron

(h) The Icosahedron

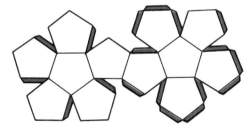  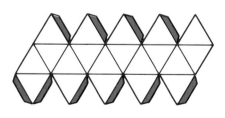

EXERCISE

Use the nets to construct the polyhedrons.

DEGREES IN THE SKY

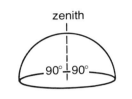

One way to locate stars and constellations in the sky is to use degrees.

This is an easy way to locate stars, since we think of the sky above us as half a sphere—180° from horizon to horizon or 90° from horizon to zenith.

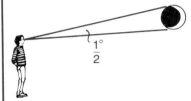

The moon is about one-half a degree across.

Your little finger held at arm's length measures approximately one degree.

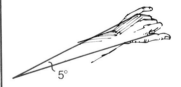

Held at arm's length, the three middle fingers held close together cover about five degrees.

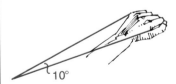

The distance across the knuckles of a fist covers about ten degrees.

The index finger and the little finger extended as far from each other as possible span about fifteen degrees.

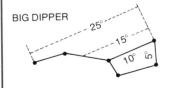

The Big Dipper gives us an easy way to check our measures of 5, 10, 15 and 25 degrees. Check these measures against the Big Dipper to see how they work, with your arm length and fist size.

For longer distances, use multiples of the 10° fist. Starting with the last knuckle, at the first star fix your eyes at the leading knuckle. Now advance the fist to that point and repeat the steps until you reach the second star.

The following map gives the degree distances for some stars for a late spring evening. Use your hands to locate these stars in the sky.

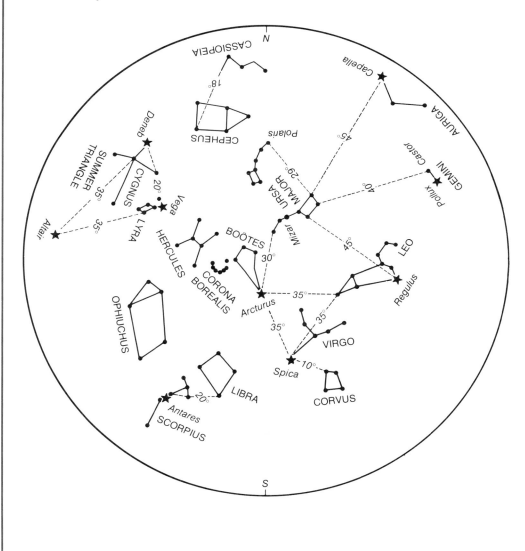

14.20 CHAPTER 14 REVIEW EXERCISE

1. In the following diagram name
   - (a) 3 points.
   - (b) 3 lines.
   - (c) 3 rays.
   - (d) 3 angles.
   - (e) 3 line segments.

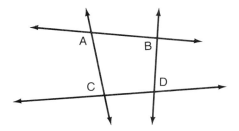

2. Use a protractor to construct each of the following angles.
   - (a) 34°
   - (b) 123°
   - (c) 90°
   - (d) 103°

3. Classify the following angles as acute, right, straight, obtuse, or reflex.
   - (a)
   - (b)

   - (c)
   - (d)

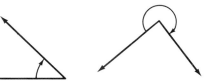

   - (e)
   - (f)

4. Classify the triangles by sides.
   - (a)
   - (b)

   - (c)

5. Classify the triangles by angles.
   - (a)
   - (b)

   - (c)

6. Draw an angle similar to, but larger than, the one shown.
   Bisect the angle.

7. Copy the following diagram.
   Construct the perpendicular from P to $\overline{AB}$.

   • P

   A   B

8. (a) Draw a line segment 7 cm in length.
   (b) Construct the right bisector.

9. Calculate the missing values.

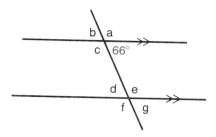

10. Calculate the missing values.
    (a)   (b)

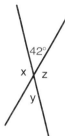
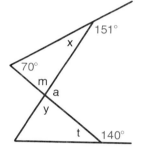

11. The two triangles are congruent.
    (a) Name the corresponding angles that are equal.
    (b) Name the corresponding sides that are equal.

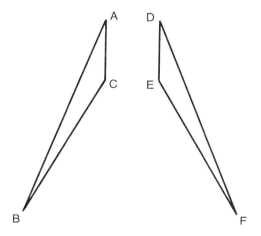

12. Identify the following parts in the diagram.
    (a) 2 radii
    (b) 2 diameters
    (c) 2 chords
    (d) 2 arcs

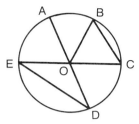

13. Identify the following in the diagram.
    (a) an inscribed angle
    (b) a central angle

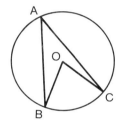

14. Find the missing values.
    (a)   (b)

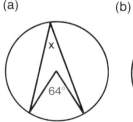
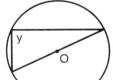

    (c)

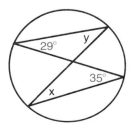

CHAPTER 14 TEST

1. Classify the following angles.

   (a)   (b)   (c)

2. Classify the triangles by sides.

   (a)   (b)   (c)

3. Draw an angle similar to the one shown. Bisect the angle.

4. Construct the perpendicular from P to $\overline{AB}$.

   A ————————————— B

   • P

5. Calculate the missing values.

   (a)   (b)

   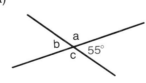   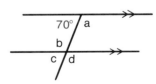

   (c)   (d)

   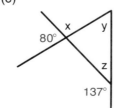   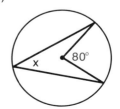

15

TRANSFORMATIONAL GEOMETRY

REVIEW AND PREVIEW TO CHAPTER 15

TILE PATTERNS

Paving tiles are placed so that the ground is completely covered. There are no gaps and the tiles do not overlap.

In mathematics we call this tiling the plane.

Only three regular polygons will tile the plane. These are:
- i)   an equilateral triangle;
- ii) a square;
- iii) a regular hexagon.

Some examples of these patterns are shown below.

Equilateral Triangles

Squares

Regular Hexagons

Any triangle or quadrilateral will tile the plane. The following are some examples.

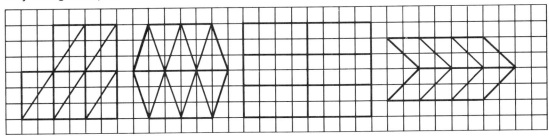

The plane can be tiled by many shapes.

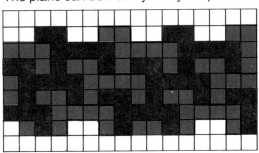

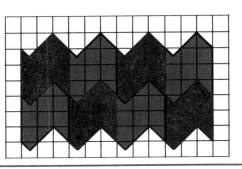

EXERCISE

1. Tile the plane with the following shapes.

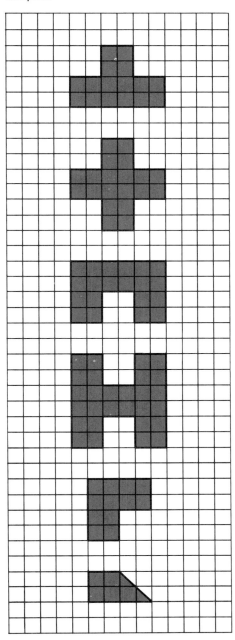

2. This shape has been used to tile the plane as shown below.

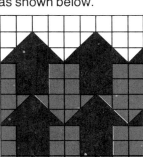

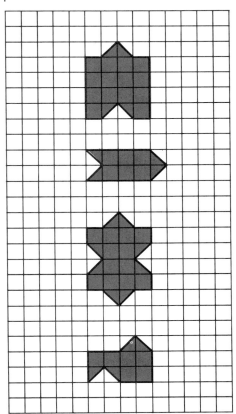

Use the following shapes to tile the plane.

15.1 SLIDES, FLIPS, AND TURNS

In the previous section we used patterns to tile the plane. In this section we shall look at some of the ways patterns are formed.

Slides

A slide moves a figure in a certain direction. A slide arrow ⟶ is used to show the direction and length of the slide.

Flips

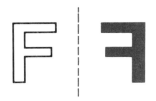

A flip reflects a figure about a line called the flip line. The dotted line – – – is the flip line.

Turns

A turn rotates a figure about a point. The turn arrow ⟳ gives the direction of the turn and the amount of turn. The turn centre ⊙ shows the point the figure is turned about.

Slides, flips, and turns are also used to make strip patterns.

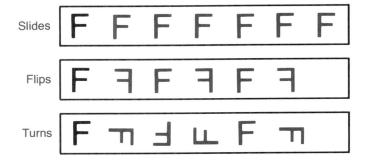

EXERCISE

A

1. Identify the strip patterns as slides, flips, or turns.

(a)

(b)

(c) R R R R R

(d)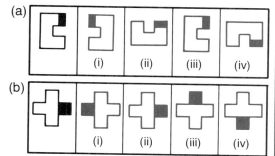

(e) B B B B B B

(f)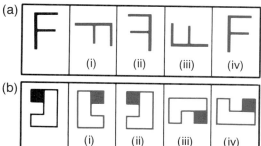

B

2. Which figure on the right is a slide image of the black figure?

(a)

(i)	(ii)	(iii)	(iv)

(b)

(i)	(ii)	(iii)	(iv)

3. Which figure on the right is a flip image of the black figure?

(a) F

(i)	(ii)	(iii)	(iv)

(b)

(i)	(ii)	(iii)	(iv)

4. Which figure on the right is a turn image of the black figure?

(a)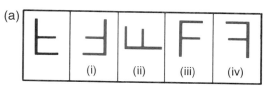

(i)	(ii)	(iii)	(iv)

(b)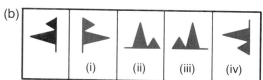

(i)	(ii)	(iii)	(iv)

5. Identify each figure on the right as a slide, flip, or turn image of the black figure.

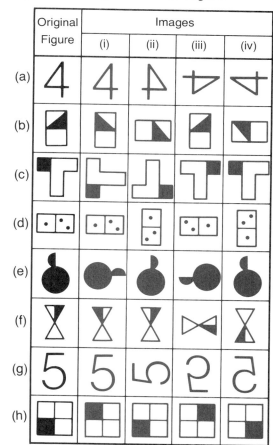

Original Figure	Images			
	(i)	(ii)	(iii)	(iv)
(a)				
(b)				
(c)				
(d)				
(e)				
(f)				
(g)				
(h)				

15.2 TRANSLATIONS

Each letter in the message on the blimp moves the same distance in the same direction at regular intervals. Each move is a translation or a slide.

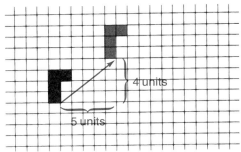

The black figure at the left has been moved
   5 units to the Right,
   4 units Up.

We can write this translation using the ordered pair (5R,4U), where 5R means "5 right" and 4U means "4 up."

The translation arrow shows
i)   the distance the figure is translated;
ii) the direction of the translation.

△ABC has sides with lengths
   $\overline{AB}$ = 4 units
   $\overline{BC}$ = 3 units
   $\overline{AC}$ = 5 units

The translation (6R,4D) gives the image △A′B′C′ with

   $\overline{A'B'}$ = 4 units
   $\overline{B'C'}$ = 3 units
   $\overline{A'C'}$ = 5 units

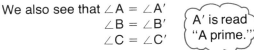

We also see that $\angle A = \angle A'$
   $\angle B = \angle B'$
   $\angle C = \angle C'$

A′ is read "A prime."

| The lengths of line segments and the sizes of angles do not change in a translation. |

Example. △ABC has vertices A(1,5), B(1,1), and C(3,4). Use the translation (6L,5D) and find the image of △ABC.

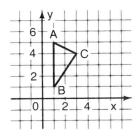

Solution: Step 1.　Plot △ABC.

Step 2.　Translate each vertex
6 units to the left and
5 units down to locate
A′, B′, and C′.

Step 3.　Join A′, B′, and C′.

△A′B′C′ is the translation image of △ABC.

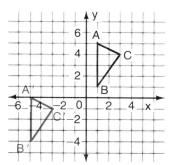

EXERCISE

A

1. Name the following translation arrows using the ordered pair notation (R or L, U or D).

(a)　　　(b)　　　(c)

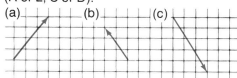

B

2. Draw arrows on grid paper to show the following translations.
   (a) (4R,3U)　　　(b) (2L,3D)
   (c) (5R,2D)　　　(d) (5L,4U)
   (e) (6R, 0)　　　(f) (0,5D)

3. Each black figure has been translated. Name the translation.

(a)　　　(b)

(c)　　　(d)

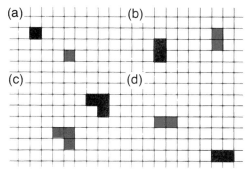

4. Plot each point and translate it as indicated.

	POINT	TRANSLATION
(a)	(4,5)	(3R,4U)
(b)	(0,7)	(4L,5D)
(c)	(6,−4)	(5R,4D)
(d)	(−3,−2)	(6L,2U)

5. Plot each point on grid paper. Find the image of each point for each translation arrow.

(i)　　(ii)　　(iii)　　(iv)

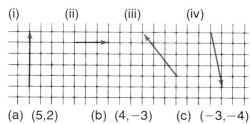

(a) (5,2)　　(b) (4,−3)　　(c) (−3,−4)

6. Copy each figure on grid paper. Find the image using the given translation.
   (a) (4R,5U)　　　(b) (6L,3D)

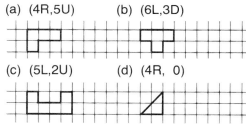

   (c) (5L,2U)　　　(d) (4R, 0)

7. Plot each triangle on grid paper. Use the translation to find the image of each.
   (a) A(3,1), B(5,4),　C(1,6)　(4R,5U)
   (b) D(1,1), E(1,5),　F(−3,3)　(5L,4D)
   (c) X(5,0), Y(3,−3), Z(0,−4)　(6L, 0)

8. Express each translation as an ordered pair.
   (a) A(3,4)　to　A′(5,7)
   (b) B(6,0)　to　B′(2,4)
   (c) C(4,−2)　to　C′(5,3)
   (d) D(−1,−1)　to　D′(−3,7)

15.3 REFLECTIONS

The picture shows an example of a reflection.

A reflection is a flip about a mirror line.

Point P is reflected in the reflection line MN. P' is the image of P. The perpendicular distance from P to MN equals the perpendicular distance from P' to MN.

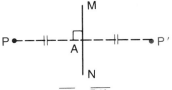

$\overline{PA} = \overline{P'A}$

△ABC has sides with lengths

$\overline{AB}$ = 4 units $\overline{BC}$ = 3 units $\overline{AC}$ = 5 units

A reflection in the mirror line MN gives the image △A'B'C' with

$\overline{A'B'}$ = 4 units
$\overline{B'C'}$ = 3 units
$\overline{A'C'}$ = 5 units

We also see that   ∠A = ∠A'
∠B = ∠B'
∠C = ∠C'

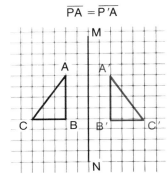

The lengths of line segments and the sizes of angles do not change in a reflection.

In △ABC, the letters A, B, C are read in a clockwise direction. In the image figure, △A'B'C', the letters A', B', C' are read in a counter-clockwise direction. We say that the sense of a figure is reversed following a reflection.

Example. △ABC has vertices A(−4,6), B(−4,0), and C(−1,1). Reflect △ ABC in the y-axis.

Solution: Step 1.   Plot △ABC.

Step 2.   Find the image points of A, B, and C.
A(−4,6)   →   A'(4,6)
B(−4,0)   →   B'(4,0)
C(−1,1)   →   C'(1,1)

Step 3.   Join A', B', and C'.

△A'B'C' is the reflection image of △ABC.

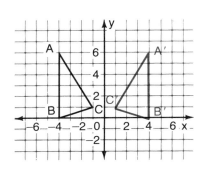

EXERCISE

A

1. Which points are reflections of each other?

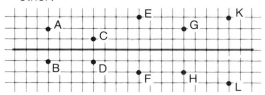

B

2. Plot each point.
   Find the image of each point for the reflection line.
   - (a) (5,2)   x-axis
   - (b) (1,4)   y-axis
   - (c) (−4,3)   y-axis
   - (d) (−2,−6)   x-axis
   - (e) (6,−3)   x-axis
   - (f) (5,0)   y-axis

3. Copy each of the following onto grid paper.
   Draw the reflection image.

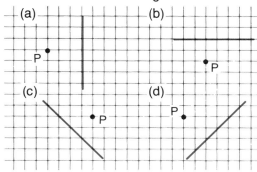

4. Plot each figure on a set of axes.
   Draw the reflection image in the reflection line.

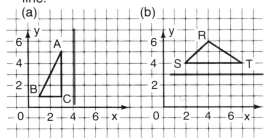

5. Plot each figure on a set of axes.
   Draw the reflection image in the reflection line.

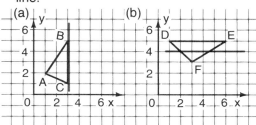

6. △ABC has vertices A(1,3), B(5,4), and C(5,1).
   Reflect △ABC in the x-axis.

7. △RST has vertices R(−6,−5), S(−5,−1), and T(−2,−3).
   Reflect △RST in the y-axis.

8. Rectangle ABCD has vertices A(4,−3), B(−4,−3), C(−4,−6), and D(4,−6).
   Reflect rectangle ABCD in the x-axis.

9. Each of the following shows a figure and its reflection image.
   Copy the figures onto grid paper.
   Find the reflection line.

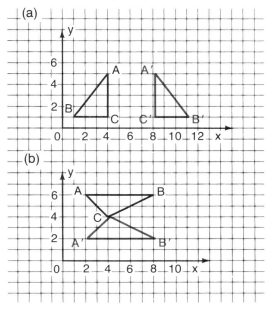

15.4 ROTATIONS

A ferris wheel and a record are applications of a rotation about a point.

The black flag has been rotated $\frac{1}{4}$-turn (90°) in a clockwise direction about ⊚ , the centre of rotation (or turn centre). The turn arrow shows the direction of the turn and the amount of turn.

To draw an image following a rotation you must know the following information.

1. The centre of rotation or turn centre. ⊚

2. The amount of rotation or turn.

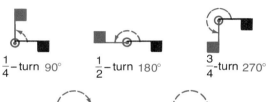

$\frac{1}{4}$-turn 90° $\frac{1}{2}$-turn 180° $\frac{3}{4}$-turn 270°

3. The direction of the rotation or turn.

clockwise (cw)   counter-clockwise (ccw)

△ABC has sides with lengths
   $\overline{AB} = 4$, $\overline{BC} = 3$, and $\overline{AC} = 5$

A counter-clockwise rotation of 180° about B gives the image △A′B′C′ with
   $\overline{A'B'} = 4$, $\overline{B'C'} = 3$, and $\overline{A'C'} = 5$

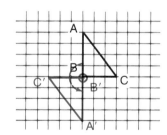

We also see that ∠A = ∠A′
   ∠B = ∠B′
   ∠C = ∠C′

> The lengths of line segments and the sizes of angles do not change in a rotation.

Example. △ABC has vertices A(1,1), B(1,4), and C(5,1). Find the image of △ABC after a 90° clockwise rotation about C.

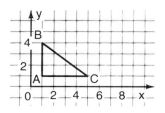

Solution: Step 1.   Plot △ABC.

Step 2.   Find the image of each vertex.

A(1,1)   →   A'(5,5)
B(1,4)   →   B'(8,5)
C(5,1)   →   C'(5,1)

Step 3.   Join A', B', and C'.

△A'B'C' is the rotation image of △ABC.

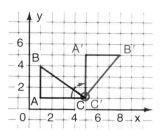

EXERCISE

A

1. The black flag has been rotated to give the red flag as an image.
Name the rotation.

(a)   (b)   (c)

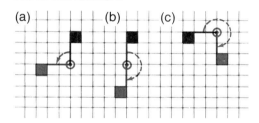

2. The black flag has been rotated to give the red flag as an image.
Name the rotation. There are two answers for each — one clockwise and one counter-clockwise.

(a)   (b)   (c)

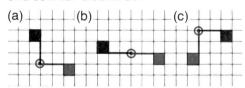

B

3. Copy each figure onto grid paper.
Draw the rotation image for each.

(a)

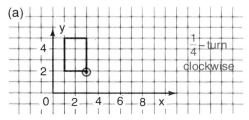

$\frac{1}{4}$-turn clockwise

(b)

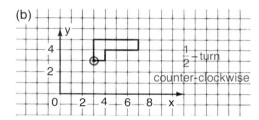

$\frac{1}{2}$-turn counter-clockwise

4. △DEF has vertices D(0,0), E(0,4), and F(5,0).
Find the image of △DEF after a 180° counter-clockwise rotation about D.

5. Copy each figure onto grid paper.
Draw the rotation image for each.

(a)

$\frac{1}{4}$-turn clockwise

(b)

$\frac{1}{4}$-turn counter-clockwise

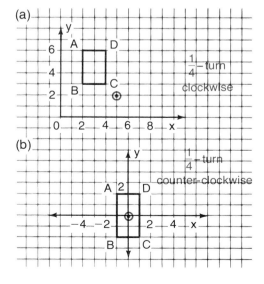

THE GOLDEN RECTANGLE

The golden rectangle is found in the works of many great artists. The ratio of the length to the width of a golden rectangle is about 1.618 to 1.

We can draw a golden rectangle using only ruler and compass.

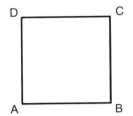

1. Construct a square and label it ABCD.

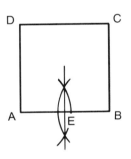

2. Bisect $\overline{AB}$ and label the midpoint E.

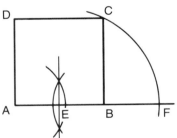

3. With centre E and radius equal to $\overline{EC}$, draw an arc to cut the extension of AB at F.

4. With centre F and radius $\overline{AD}$, and centre D and radius $\overline{AF}$, draw arcs to intersect at G.

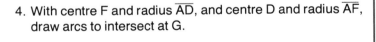

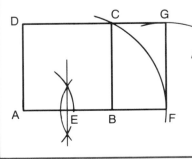

AFGD is a golden rectangle.

5. (a) Measure $\overline{AD}$ and $\overline{AF}$.
   (b) Find the ratio $\overline{AF}$ to $\overline{AD}$.

EXERCISE

1. Which of the following are golden rectangles?

    (a)

    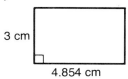

    3 cm

    4.854 cm

    (b)

    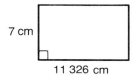

    7 cm

    11 326 cm

    (c)

    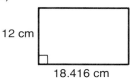

    12 cm

    18.416 cm

    (d)

    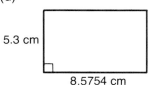

    5.3 cm

    8.5754 cm

2. Find the length of each of these golden rectangles.

    (a)

    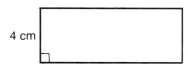

    4 cm

    (b)

    6.8 cm

APPLICATIONS

3. The following pictures show the use of the golden rectangle in art and architecture.

    The Parthenon in Athens, Greece.

    The Vatican in Rome.

    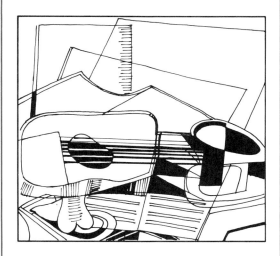

    Find other examples of the golden rectangle in art and architecture.

15.5 LINE SYMMETRY

The object in the picture has two lines of symmetry.

A line of symmetry is an imaginary line such that if the figure is folded on the line the two halves will match.

In the following figures, the red line is a line of symmetry.

Some figures have more than one line of symmetry.

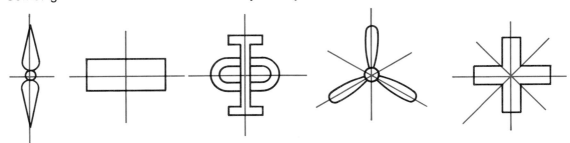

A triangle can be classified according to the number of lines of symmetry it has.

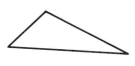

The scalene triangle has no lines of symmetry.

The isosceles triangle has one line of symmetry.

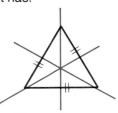

The equilateral triangle has three lines of symmetry.

If you are given half of a figure and the line of symmetry, you can complete the figure.

EXERCISE

B

1. Print all the capital letters of the alphabet.
   Find all the lines of symmetry for each.
   The first one is done for you.

2. How many lines of symmetry does each of the following figures have?

   (a)

   (b)

   (c)

   (d)

3. The following are the symbols for the planets.
   How many lines of symmetry does each have?

   (a) Mercury   (b) Venus   (c) Earth

   (d) Mars   (e) Jupiter   (f) Saturn

   (g) Uranus   (h) Neptune   (i) Pluto

4. Copy each of the following.
   Use the line of symmetry to draw the other half of the figure.
   (a)   (b)

   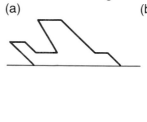

5. The following word has a horizontal line of symmetry.

   BED

   What are some other words that have a horizontal line of symmetry?

6. The following are words that show two different kinds of vertical line symmetry.

   MOM

   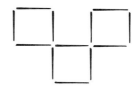

   What are some other words that have a vertical line of symmetry?

CHALLENGE

Move 3 toothpicks to form 4 squares, each having the same size.

15.6 TURN SYMMETRY

The figure at the right does not have any lines of symmetry.

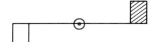

If the figure is turned about point P, the figure will fit onto itself after a turn of 180°.

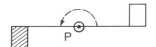

If we continue to turn the figure, it will fit onto itself again after a turn of 360°.

We say that the figure has turn symmetry, or rotational symmetry, of order 2, since it fits onto itself twice during a turn of 360°.

> The order of turn symmetry for a figure is the number of times a figure fits onto itself during a complete turn (360°).

The propeller fits onto itself 3 times during a complete turn. We say the propeller has turn symmetry of order 3.

1   2   3

The sand dollar has turn symmetry of order 5.
It fits onto itself 5 times during a complete turn.

    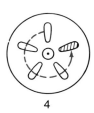 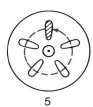

1   2   3   4   5

EXERCISE

B

1. What is the order of turn symmetry for each figure?

   (a)

   (b)

   (c)

   (d)

   (e)

   (f)

2. What is the order of turn symmetry for each figure?

   (a)

   rectangle

   (b)

   square

   (c)

   equilateral triangle

   (d)

   regular pentagon

3. When water drops are sprinkled onto a dry skillet, the drops will dance and skim across the skillet. The drops form many different shapes. A few of these shapes are shown below.
   What is the order of turn symmetry for each shape?

   (a)

   (b)

   (c)

   (d)

   (e)

   (f)

CHALLENGE

POINT SYMMETRY
When a figure has turn symmetry of order 2, it is said to have point symmetry. Which of the following figures have point symmetry?

(a)

(b)

(c)

(d)

15.7 ENLARGEMENTS AND REDUCTIONS

The black square has been enlarged
by doubling the length of each side.
We say that the square has been enlarged
by a scale factor, k = 2.

The black rectangle has been reduced
in size by making the sides of the image
one-third the size of the black
rectangle. We say that the rectangle has

been reduced by a scale factor, $k = \frac{1}{3}$.

We can use the origin on the Cartesian
plane to make enlargements and reductions.

Step 1.   △ABC is plotted on the grid.

Step 2.   Join $\overline{OA}$, $\overline{OB}$, $\overline{OC}$.

Step 3.   Double the lengths of $\overline{OA}$, $\overline{OB}$,
          and $\overline{OC}$ to locate A′, B′, and C′.

Step 4.   Join A′, B′, and C′.
          △A′B′C′ is an enlargement of △ABC.
          We see that
          $$\frac{\overline{OA'}}{\overline{OA}} = \frac{\overline{OB'}}{\overline{OB}} = \frac{\overline{OC'}}{\overline{OC}} = 2$$

The scale factor, k, for the enlargement is 2.

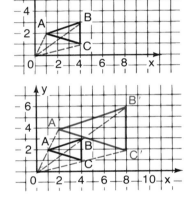

An enlargement or reduction is often called a dilatation.

Example. Find the image of the square
for a reduction where $k = \frac{1}{2}$.

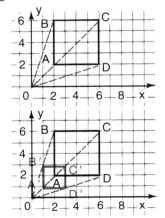

Solution: Step 1.   Join $\overline{OA}$, $\overline{OB}$, $\overline{OC}$, and $\overline{OD}$.

Step 2.   Find $\frac{1}{2}$ of $\overline{OA}$, $\overline{OB}$, $\overline{OC}$, and $\overline{OD}$
          to locate A′, B′, C′, and D′.

Step 3.   Join A′, B′, C′, and D′.
          The square A′B′C′D′ is the
          reduction of square ABCD.

EXERCISE

B

1. A figure and its image are shown. What is the scale factor?

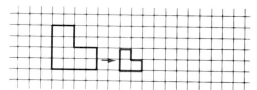

2. A triangle and its enlargement image are shown.

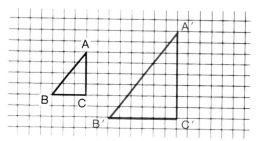

   (a) What is the scale factor?
   (b) Calculate the ratios
   $$\frac{AB}{A'B'}, \quad \frac{BC}{B'C'}, \quad \frac{AC}{A'C'}$$
   (c) How are the corresponding angles related?

3. Copy the figure onto grid paper. Enlarge it by a scale factor of 3.

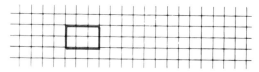

4. Copy the figure onto grid paper. Reduce it by a scale factor of $\frac{1}{2}$.

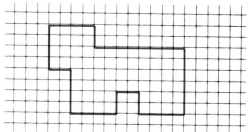

5. △ABC is plotted on a grid. Use the origin to enlarge the triangle by a scale factor of 2.

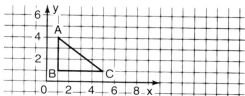

6. The square ABCD is plotted on a grid. Use the origin to reduce the square by a scale factor of $\frac{1}{2}$.

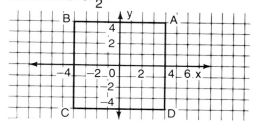

7. △ABC has vertices A(1,1), B(4,1), and C(1,5).
   (a) Plot △ABC on a grid.
   (b) Multiply each of the coordinates by 2 and plot the new coordinates on the grid.
   (c) How are the two triangles related?

8. The square ABCD and its image A′B′C′D′ are plotted on a grid.

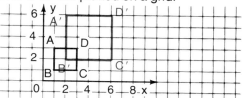

   (a) What is the scale factor?
   (b) What is the area of ABCD?
   (c) What is the area of A′B′C′D′?
   (d) What is the ratio of the sides of the squares?
   (e) What is the ratio of the areas of the squares?
   (f) How are the ratio of the sides and the ratio of the areas related?

15.8 DISTORTIONS ON A REGULAR GRID

Figures can be distorted by multiplying the x coordinates and the y coordinates by different numbers.

The black sailboat has been distorted by multiplying the x coordinates by 2.

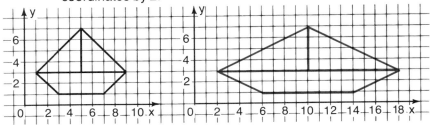

In the following example the sailboat has been distorted by multiplying the y coordinates by $\frac{1}{2}$.

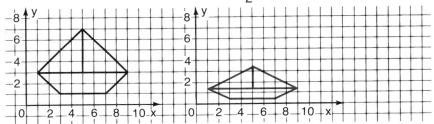

EXERCISE

B

1. How is each distorted figure obtained?

(a)

(b)

(c)

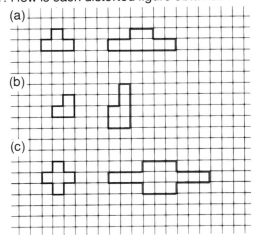

(d)

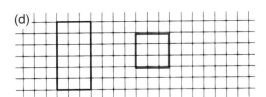

2. (a) Copy the figure onto grid paper.

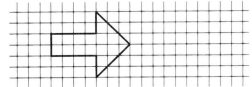

(b) Distort the figure by multiplying the x coordinates by 3.

(c) Distort the figure by multiplying the y coordinates by 2.

15.9 GRAPHING ON A DISTORTED GRID

In this section we shall take a figure on a square grid and draw its image on a distorted grid. To do this you must match the points on the square grid with the corresponding points on the distorted grid.

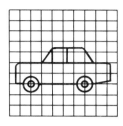 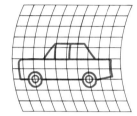

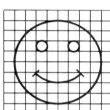 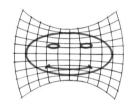

EXERCISE

B

1. Each of the following is drawn on a square grid.

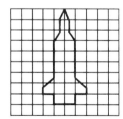 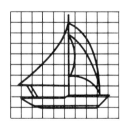 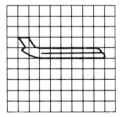

Transfer the above figures onto distorted grids.

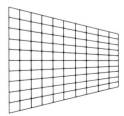 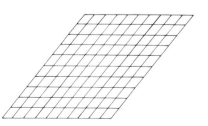 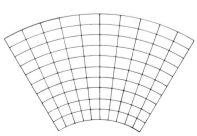

AIRCRAFT NAVIGATION

Every aircraft is equipped with a compass for navigating. A pointer attached to the centre of the compass shows the direction in which the plane is being steered. This direction is called the heading. The speed at which the pilot flies the plane is called the air speed.

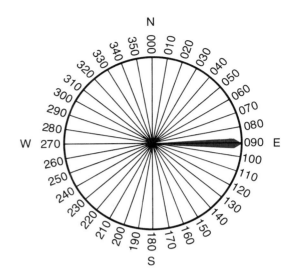

To solve navigation problems we use arrows, called vectors. The direction of the vector represents the heading. The length of the vector represents the air speed.

If 1 cm represents a speed of 100 km/h, the vector $\overrightarrow{AB}$ at the right represents a heading of 090° at an air speed of 400 km/h.

The heading and the air speed of a plane are affected by the wind speed and wind direction. Wind speed and wind direction are also represented by vectors.

If 1 cm represents 100 km/h, the vector $\overrightarrow{CD}$ at the right represents a north wind blowing at 150 km/h. (The direction from which the wind blows is always given.)

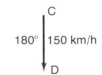

When we know the heading and air speed of a plane and the wind direction and wind speed, we can determine the actual direction and speed of the plane. The actual direction of the plane is called the track. The actual speed is called the ground speed.

Example. A plane is flying with a heading of 090° at an air speed of 500 km/h. A north wind is blowing at a speed of 150 km/h. Determine the track and ground speed of the plane.

Solution

1. Let 1 cm represent 100 km/h. Draw vector $\overrightarrow{AB}$ to represent the heading and air speed of the plane.

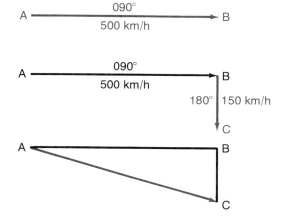

2. Draw vector $\overrightarrow{BC}$ to represent the wind direction and wind speed.

3. Join $\overline{AC}$. The vector $\overrightarrow{AC}$ represents the track and ground speed of the plane.
   By measuring, ∠BAC is 16°, so the track of the plane is 106°.
   By measuring, $\overline{AC} \doteq 5.2$ cm, so the ground speed is 520 km/h.

EXERCISE

B

1. Use 1 cm to represent 100 km/h and draw the following vectors.
   (a) A heading of 180° at an air speed of 400 km/h.
   (b) A heading of 180° at an air speed of 600 km/h.
   (c) A heading of 270° at an air speed of 500 km/h.

2. A plane is flying with a heading of 180° at an air speed of 600 km/h. An east wind is blowing at a speed of 100 km/h.
   Find the track and ground speed of the plane.

3. A jet is flying with a heading of 000° at an air speed of 1200 km/h. A west wind is blowing at a speed of 200 km/h.
   Find the track and ground speed of the jet.

4. A south wind is blowing at a speed of 150 km/h. A plane is flying at a speed of 700 km/h on a heading of 090°.
   Find the track and ground speed of the plane.

5. A north wind is blowing at a speed of 100 km/h. A plane is flying with a heading of 045° at a speed of 800 km/h.
   Find the track and ground speed of the plane.

15.10 CHAPTER 15 REVIEW EXERCISE

1. Identify each figure on the right as a slide, flip, or turn image of the black figure.

Original Figure	Images			
	(i)	(ii)	(iii)	(iv)
(a)				
(b)				
(c)				

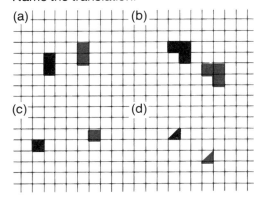

2. Each black figure has been translated. Name the translation.

(a)

(b)

(c)

(d)

3. △ABC has vertices A(2,2), B(4,2) and C(5,6)
   (a) Plot △ABC on grid paper.
   (b) Use the translation (2R,4D) to find the image of the triangle.

4. Express each translation as an ordered pair.
   (a) A(1,2) to B(4,−3)
   (b) D(3,0) to E(−5,6)

5. Plot each figure on a set of axes. Draw the reflection image in the reflection line.

(a)

(b)

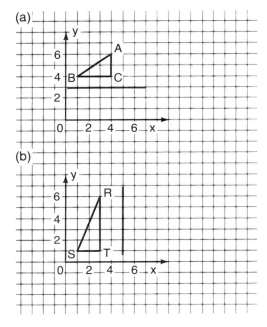

6. △DEF has vertices D(1,1), E(5,2), and F(4,6).
   (a) Reflect △DEF in the x-axis.
   (b) Reflect △DEF in the y-axis.

7. The following shows a figure and its reflection image.
   Copy the figures onto grid paper and find the reflection line.

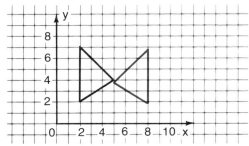

8. The black flag has been rotated to give the red flag as an image.
   Name the rotation.
   (There are 2 answers for each.)

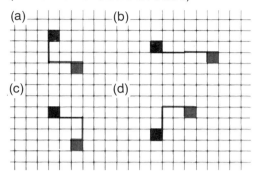

(a)   (b)

(c)   (d)

9. △ABC has vertices A(1,1), B(4,1), and C(1,3).
   Find the image of △ABC after a 90° counter-clockwise rotation about A.

10. How many lines of symmetry does each of the following figures have?

   (a)   (b)

11. Copy the following and use the line of symmetry to draw the other half.

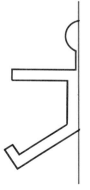

12. What is the order of turn symmetry for each figure?

   (a)   (b)

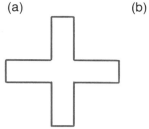

13. Copy the figure onto grid paper. Enlarge it by a scale factor of 3.

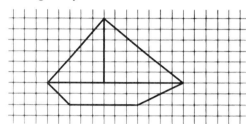

14. Copy the figure onto grid paper. Reduce it by a scale factor of $\frac{1}{2}$.

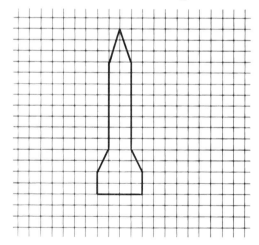

CHAPTER 15 TEST

1. Identify each figure on the right as a slide, flip, or turn of the original figure.

Original	Images			
Figure	(i)	(ii)	(iii)	(iv)
4	⊿	⊳	4	ᗄ

2. △DEF has vertices D(5,3), E(4,7), and F(0,0).

   (a) Plot △DEF on grid paper.
   (b) Use the translation (4L,5D) to find the image of the triangle.

3. △ABC has vertices A(−4,1), B(−3,5), and C(−1,1).

   (a) Plot △ABC on grid paper.
   (b) Reflect △ABC in the y-axis.
   (c) Reflect △ABC in the x-axis.

4. △RST has vertices R(−5,−5), S(−5,−1), and T(−1,−1). Find the image of △RST after a 180° clockwise rotation about T.

5. How many lines of symmetry does the following figure have?

6. What is the order of turn symmetry of the following figure?

CUMULATIVE REVIEW

1. Perform the indicated operation.

(a)
```
  5623
   836
+ 4483
```

(b)
```
  8167
- 2438
```

(c)
```
 8045
× 624
```

(d) $65\overline{)20\,865}$

(e) $365 + 18 \times 63$

(f) $2546 - 1992 \div 24$

2. Calculate.

(a) $56.7 + 34.5 + 19.2$

(b) $501.3 + 9.46 + 0.8 + 0.29$

(c) $69.73 - 14.25$

(d) $9.1 - 0.633$

(e) 5.6×0.45

(f) $9.45 \div 0.7$

(g) $10.14 \div 13$

3. Round off as indicated.

(a) 625 to the nearest ten

(b) 1.625 to the nearest tenth

(c) 25.508 to the nearest hundredth

(d) 0.516 428 to the nearest thousandth

(e) 6 255 405 to the nearest million

4. Find the equivalent fractions.

(a) $\dfrac{3}{4} = \dfrac{\blacksquare}{12}$

(b) $\dfrac{4}{5} = \dfrac{\blacksquare}{25}$

(c) $\dfrac{4}{\blacksquare} = \dfrac{12}{15}$

(d) $\dfrac{3}{8} = \dfrac{21}{\blacksquare}$

5. Simplify.

(a) $\dfrac{3}{5} + \dfrac{2}{3}$

(b) $\dfrac{5}{8} - \dfrac{1}{3}$

(c) $3\dfrac{5}{8} - 1\dfrac{1}{2}$

(d) $6\dfrac{1}{4} - 2\dfrac{3}{8}$

(e) $\dfrac{3}{4} \times \dfrac{2}{3}$

(f) $4\dfrac{1}{2} \times 1\dfrac{1}{3}$

(g) $\dfrac{5}{8} \div 1\dfrac{1}{4}$

(h) $3\dfrac{2}{3} \div 1\dfrac{5}{6}$

6. Change to decimals.

(a) $\dfrac{3}{4}$

(b) $\dfrac{4}{5}$

(c) $\dfrac{5}{8}$

(d) $\dfrac{1}{4}$

(e) $\dfrac{3}{8}$

(f) $\dfrac{3}{10}$

(g) $\dfrac{1}{3}$

(h) $\dfrac{2}{3}$

(i) $\dfrac{2}{9}$

(j) $\dfrac{1}{11}$

(k) $\dfrac{3}{11}$

(l) $\dfrac{1}{7}$

7. Change these decimals to fractions.

(a) 0.25

(b) 0.35

(c) 1.5

(d) 3.75

(e) 0.255

(f) 0.675

(g) $0.\overline{6}$

(h) $0.\overline{2}$

(i) $0.\overline{7}$

(j) $0.\overline{235}$

(k) $0.6\overline{05}$

(l) $0.2\overline{65}$

8. Simplify.

(a) $-1 + 5 - 7$

(b) $4 - 7 - 11$

(c) $6 + 11 - 24$

(d) $-4 - 5 - 6$

(e) $7 - (-3)$

(f) $-8 - (-6) - 5$

(g) $-3(5)$

(h) $4(-7)$

(i) $-6(-3)$

(j) $(-4)(-5)$

9. Simplify.

(a) $234 - 456$

(b) $-628 + 875$

(c) $525 - (-500)$

(d) $-3566 - (-4123)$

(e) $603 + (-527)$

(f) $-265 - (-318)$

(g) $(-35)(63)$

(h) $(64)(-82)$

(i) $(-63)(-18)$

(j) $-(-23)(-45)$

10. Find the value of n in each of the following.

(a) $325 = 3.25 \times 10^n$

(b) $427\,000 = 4.27 \times 10^n$

(c) $0.0255 = 2.55 \times 10^n$

(d) $0.00325 = 3.25 \times 10^n$

11. Write in scientific notation.

(a) 675

(b) 25 400

(c) 875 000

(d) 2 345 000

(e) 0.275

(f) 0.0075

(g) 0.065

(h) 0.000 275

12. Find the square root of each of the following.

(a) $\sqrt{81}$

(b) $\sqrt{121}$

(c) $\sqrt{144}$

(d) $\sqrt{169}$

(e) $\sqrt{576}$

(f) $\sqrt{1024}$

(g) $\sqrt{2304}$

(h) $\sqrt{4\,000\,000}$

13. Find the square root to the nearest tenth.
    (a) $\sqrt{18}$ (b) $\sqrt{37}$

    (c) $\sqrt{45}$ (d) $\sqrt{60}$

    (e) $\sqrt{325}$ (f) $\sqrt{500}$

14. Write as a percent.
    (a) 0.25 (b) 0.07
    (c) 0.65 (d) 0.5
    (e) 2.75 (f) 3.05
    (g) $\dfrac{3}{100}$ (h) $\dfrac{23}{100}$
    (i) $\dfrac{4}{25}$ (j) $\dfrac{75}{100}$

15. Write as decimals.
    (a) 25% (b) 68%
    (c) 27% (d) 55%
    (e) 100% (f) 325%
    (g) 115% (h) 2%

16. Find.
    (a) 24% of 835
    (b) 65% of 518
    (c) 7% of 5005
    (d) 85% of 85 000
    (e) 35% of 415 000

17. Find these ratios.

    △ ○ △ ○ △ ○ □ ○ ○
    □ ○ □ △ ○ □ ○ △ ○

    (a) △ to □
    (b) ○ to △
    (c) □ to ○

18. At a music camp, there were 12 sax players, 18 trumpet players, 8 trombone players, and 15 clarinet players.
    Find the following ratios.
    (a) trombone players to trumpet players
    (b) sax players to trumpet players
    (c) trumpet players to sax players
    (d) sax players to clarinet players
    (e) clarinet players to trumpet players

19. There were 48 students, 64 parents, and 6 teachers at the volleyball team dinner. Express the ratio of students to teachers to parents in lowest terms.

20. Solve for x in the following proportions.
    (a) $\dfrac{x}{5} = \dfrac{4}{10}$ (b) $\dfrac{3}{x} = \dfrac{9}{12}$
    (c) $\dfrac{6}{12} = \dfrac{x}{36}$ (d) $\dfrac{5}{6} = \dfrac{20}{x}$

21. Calculate.
    (a) 25% of 36
    (b) 75% of 30
    (c) 10% of 63
    (d) 82% of 125
    (e) 10% of 10

22. Find these percents.
    (a) What percent of 100 is 33?
    (b) What percent of 65 is 13?
    (c) What percent of 32 is 16?
    (d) What percent of 32 is 8?
    (e) What percent of 3 is 1?

23. Real estate commission is 6%. What is the commission on a sale of $165 000?

24. In a shipment of 256 spark plugs, 32 were for lawnmowers.
    (a) What percent of the spark plugs were for lawnmowers?
    (b) What percent of the spark plugs were not for lawnmowers?

25. In the election for student council president, 1025 students voted. Terry got 425 votes and Bev got 40% of the votes. The rest of the votes went to Jason.
    (a) Who won the election?
    (b) How many votes did Bev and Jason get?

26. The table gives the approximate length of several reptiles.
    Display this information on a bar graph.

Reptile	Length (m)
Anaconda	10
King Cobra	6
Python	9
Rattlesnake	2.5
Grass Snake	1
Boa Constrictor	5

27. The table gives the position of the song Red Moon Rising on the Top Ten Chart for a twelve-week period.
Display this information on a broken line graph.

Week	Position
Week 1	10
Week 2	9
Week 3	5
Week 4	2
Week 5	1
Week 6	1
Week 7	3
Week 8	1
Week 9	4
Week 10	4
Week 11	7
Week 12	8

28. The table gives the approximate attendance at the zoo for one week. Display this information on a pictograph.

Day	Visitors
Monday	800
Tuesday	700
Wednesday	900
Thursday	600
Friday	1200
Saturday	1500
Sunday	1000

29. Find the mean of each set of numbers.
(a) 15, 17, 21, 14, 23
(b) 61, 65, 66, 61, 67, 64

30. Find the median of each set of numbers.
(a) 45, 47, 35, 52, 64, 55, 30
(b) 80, 87, 82, 84, 86, 88

31. Find the mode of each set of numbers.
(a) 33, 34, 33, 35, 37, 34, 35, 34
(b) 12, 14, 15, 11, 12, 14, 16, 17

32. A box contains 4 blue cubes, 5 yellow cubes, and 6 green cubes.

If you select one cube from the box, what is the probability that
(a) the cube is blue?
(b) the cube is green?
(c) the cube is yellow?

33. If $x = -3$, evaluate each of the following.
(a) $x + 6$ (b) $3x - 7$
(c) $x^2 + 9$ (d) $2x^2 - 1$

34. If $x = -2$ and $y = 4$, evaluate each of the following.
(a) $x - y$ (b) $y - x$
(c) $x^2 + y$ (d) $x^2 - y^2$
(e) $2xy - 7$ (f) $1 - x - y$

35. Simplify.
(a) $3x + 5x + x$
(b) $4m - 2m + 6m$
(c) $5x + 4y - 7x + y$
(d) $6 - x - y + x - y + 7$

36. Expand.
(a) $4(x + 7)$
(b) $-2(3t - 7)$
(c) $-(4x + 1)$
(d) $3(x + 2) + 5(x - 1)$
(e) $9 - 3(s + 2) + 2(s - 1)$

37. Simplify.
(a) $2x \times 3x$
(b) $6a \times 5a$
(c) $(-3m^2)(4m^3)$
(d) $(-5y^3)(-2y^4)$
(e) $(12x^3) \div (3x)$
(f) $(-10y^4) \div (5y^2)$
(g) $(-20m^5) \div (-2m^3)$
(h) $(-18x^3y^2) \div (-2xy)$

38. Expand.
(a) $3x(x + 1)$
(b) $2m(m - 5) - 3m(2m + 1)$
(c) $(x + 2)(x + 3)$
(d) $(m - 6)(m + 7)$
(e) $(t - 6)(t - 9)$

39. Factor.
(a) $4x + 8y$
(b) $3x - 12$
(c) $5x^2 + 2x$
(d) $4x^3 - 6x^2 + 2x$

40. Solve.
   (a) $x + 4 = 7$ (b) $m - 3 = 5$
   (c) $2n = 8$ (d) $\frac{x}{3} = 4$
   (e) $2x + 1 = 7$ (f) $3m - 5 = 10$
   (g) $7n = 5n + 8$ (h) $3x - 2 = x + 8$
   (i) $-6x = 12$ (j) $-7m = -21$
   (k) $2(x + 1) = 10$ (l) $5(t - 2) - 3 = 2$
   (m) $\frac{x}{4} = \frac{1}{2}$ (n) $\frac{x}{3} = \frac{x}{4}$

41. Solve.
   (a) $x + 7 > 10$ (b) $t - 3 \leqslant 4$
   (c) $3m - 1 < 11$ (d) $2x + 3 > 7$
   (e) $\frac{m}{3} \geqslant 5$ (f) $\frac{x}{2} + 1 \leqslant 3$

42. Solve. Graph the solution.
   (a) $x - 3 \leqslant 2$, $x \in w$
   (b) $x + 2 > 6$, $x \in w$
   (c) $3x - 5 \geqslant 1$, $x \in w$
   (d) $2x + 3 < 1$, $x \in I$

43. When seventeen is subtracted from a certain number the result is twenty-one. Find the number.

44. The ground speed of an aircraft is 1350 km/h. There is a head wind of 200 km/h. What is the air speed?

45. Find the mass x so that the seesaw balances.

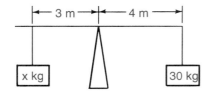

46. Expand.
   (a) $(x + 2)(x + 1)$ (b) $(m - 1)(m + 3)$
   (c) $(t - 4)(t + 4)$ (d) $(y - 7)(y - 6)$
   (e) $(n + 2)^2$ (f) $(y - 3)^2$

47. An electric passenger train can travel at a speed of 160 km/h. How long will it take the train to travel 800 km?

48. The perimeter of the rectangle is 48 cm. Find the length and width.

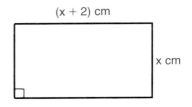

49. The area of the rectangle is 45 cm². Find the value of x.

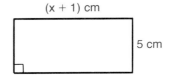

50. Complete the table of values. Draw the graph of the equation.

$x + y = 7$

x	y
7	
4	
0	
−1	
−3	

51. The tide comes in and goes out every 12 h. Low tide occured at 08:00. Sketch a general graph of the height of tide versus the time of day for one day.

HEIGHT OF THE TIDE

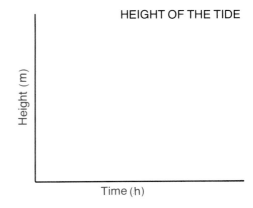

52. The table gives the distance travelled versus time for a car travelling at 50 km/h.

Time (h)	Distance (km)
0	0
1	50
2	100
3	150
4	200

(a) Graph this relation.

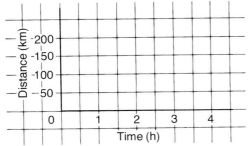

(b) Use the graph to determine the approximate distance travelled in
   i) 1.5 h   ii) 3.5 h

(c) Use the graph to determine the approximate time to travel
   i) 75 km   ii) 130 km

53. Determine the slope of the line passing through each pair of points.
(a) $C(1,1)$, $D(6,6)$
(b) $M(-4,7)$, $N(0,-1)$
(c) $A(2,-3)$, $B(-4,-3)$

54. Calculate the length of each line segment.
(a) $A(7,5)$, $B(3,2)$
(b) $M(-6,7)$, $N(-1,-5)$
(c) $S(-2,5)$, $T(-2,-2)$
(d) $C(4,3)$, $D(-2,-5)$

55. Find the perimeter of the following.

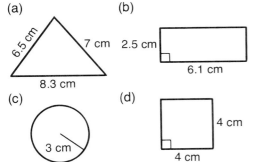

56. Find the area of the following.

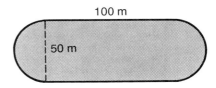

(a)   (b)   (c)   (d)

57. Following is the diagram of a playing field surrounded by a track.

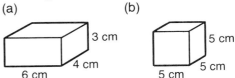

(a) Find the distance around the track.
(b) What is the area of the interior of the track?

58. Find the surface area of each of the following.

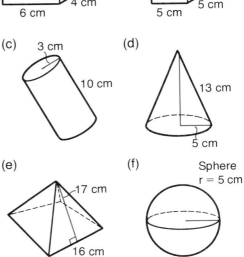

(a)   (b)   (c)   (d)   (e)   (f) Sphere r = 5 cm

59. Find the volume of each of the following.

(a)

4 cm
4 cm
5 cm

(b)

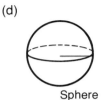
10 cm
16 cm

(c)

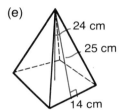
10 cm
5 cm

(d)

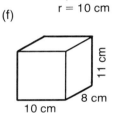
Sphere
r = 10 cm

(e)

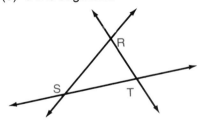
24 cm
25 cm
14 cm

(f)

11 cm
8 cm
10 cm

60. In the following diagram name:
(a) 3 points   (b) 3 lines
(c) 3 rays   (d) 3 angles
(e) 3 line segments

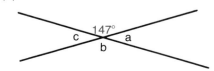
R
S
T

61. Use your protractor to construct each of the following angles.
(a) $\angle ABC = 50°$ (b) $\angle DEF = 35°$
(c) $\angle RST = 66°$ (d) $\angle BCD = 8°$
(e) $\angle FGH = 135°$ (f) $\angle XYZ = 154°$

62. Determine the missing measures.
(a)

147°
c   a
b

(b)

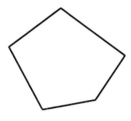
79°
42°
?

63. Calculate the sum of the interior angles of each of the polygons.
(a)

(b)

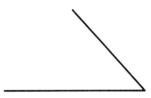

64. Draw an angle similar to the one shown. Bisect the angle.

65. Copy the diagram.
Construct the perpendicular from P to $\overline{AB}$.

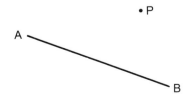
• P
A
B

66. Copy the diagram.
Construct the perpendicular to $\overline{AB}$ at P.

67. Draw a line segment 7 cm in length.
Construct the right bisector of the line segment.

68. Calculate the missing measures.
(a)

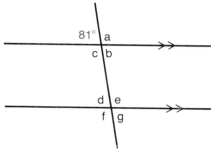

(b)

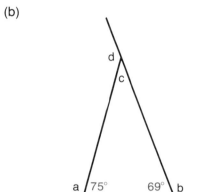

69. The triangles are congruent.
Name the pairs of angles and sides that are equal.

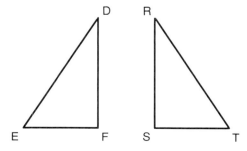

70. Find the missing values.
(a)   (b)

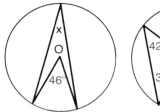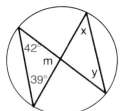

71. Identify each figure on the right as a slide, flip, or turn image of the black figure.

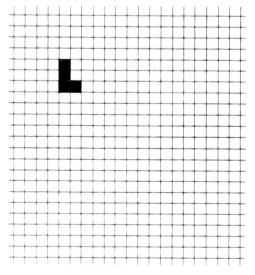

72. Copy the figure on grid paper.
Find the image of the figure using the translation (6R,5D).

73. △ABC has vertices A(1,2), B(7,2), and C(5,5).
Reflect △ABC in the x-axis.

74. Rectangle ABCD has vertices A(3,4), B(3,0), C(6,0), and D(6,4).
Find the image of the rectangle after a 180° clockwise rotation about B.

75. How many lines of symmetry does each figure have?
(a)   (b)

 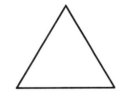

76. What is the order of turn symmetry for each figure?
(a)   (b)

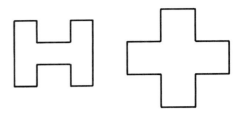

77. △ABC has vertices A(2,2), B(4,2), and C(2,5).
   (a) Draw the triangle on a grid.
   (b) Use the origin to enlarge the triangle by a scale factor of 3.

ANSWERS

EXERCISE 1.1

2. (a) millions (b) hundred thousands (c) thousands (d) hundred million (e) billion
3. (a) ten millions (b) ten thousand (c) thousand (d) millions (e) billions
4. (a) 12 000 (b) 8 000 000 (c) 4018 (d) 150 000 (e) 75 000 000 (f) 5 900 000 000
5. Pluto, Mercury, Mars, Venus, Earth, Neptune, Uranus, Saturn, Jupiter

EXERCISE 1.2

1. (a) 7359   (b) 81 775   (c) 18 957   (d) 161 010
2. (a) 5713   (b) 41 156   (c) 915   (d) 35 100   (e) 205
   (f) 39 695
3. (a) 8190   (b) 33 761   (c) 43 788   (d) 44 496
4. (a) 118   (b) 27   (c) 66   (d) 244
5. (a) 25 102   (b) 1761   (c) 68   (d) 25 704   (e) 683
   (f) 550 264   (g) 19 404   (h) 234
6. (a) 16 361   (b) 28 755   (c) 98 118   (d) 62   (e) 1 012 530
   (f) 3 508 812   (g) 39 076
7. (a) 506   (b) 21   (c) 1708   (d) 511   (e) 62
   (f) 125 003   (g) 1357   (h) 63
8. 539 101 km^2 9. 1680
10. (a) 384 000   (b) 109 200 000   11. 81   12. 510 000 000

EXERCISE 1.3

2. (a) ones   (b) tens   (c) hundredths   (d) hundredths   (e) hundredths
   (f) thousandths
3. (a) 3   (b) 500   (c) 0.009   (d) 0.06   (e) 500 000
   (f) 20
4. (a) 2111   (b) 11 220   (c) 207 000   (d) 4.3   (e) 10.7
   (f) 7.12   (g) 0.125   (h) 450 000
6. (a) 325.68   (b) 25.35   (c) 7.456   (d) 5036   (e) 30 207
   (f) 4.068   (g) 0.507   (h) 30.406

EXERCISE 1.4

1. (a) 66.901   (b) 35.485   (c) 10.243   (d) 43.728   (e) 34.89
   (f) 63.335   (g) 73.625   (h) 406.375
2. (a) 61.025   (b) 0.16   (c) 121.85   (d) 643.07
3. (a) 21.842   (b) 448.78   (c) 3.005   (d) 17.203   (e) 235.4
   (f) 14.625   (g) 2.799
4. (a) 50.86   (b) 11.387   (c) 65.105   (d) 10.68   (e) 116.657
   (f) 9.122   5. (a) Foyt   (b) 28.117   6. $4191.31

EXERCISE 1.5

1. (a) 23.750   (b) 549.36   (c) 0.012
2. (a) 3132   (b) 400.05   (c) 28.269   (d) 125.96   (e) 19.5
   (f) 0.1971   (g) 16.7   (h) 25.776   (i) 529.25
3. (a) 1.7   (b) 5.61   (c) 5.8   (d) 1.14   (e) 46.8
   (f) 68.4   (g) 2.54   (h) 5.45   (i) 63.8   (j) 81.9
4. (a) 32.4   (b) 2.8   (c) 8.24   (d) 13.855   (e) 45.8
   (f) 0.713   (g) 0.1495   (h) 6.95   (i) 3881.25   (j) 143 948.75
   (k) 19 018.321 (l) 462.798
5. $8.04   6. $12.94   7. $8.75   8. 18 m

EXERCISE 1.6

	Base	Exponent			Base	Exponent
1. (a)	3	5		(d)	7	5
(b)	2	4		(e)	11	6
(c)	6	3		(f)	8	7

2. (a) 2^4 (b) 3^3 (c) 61^3 (d) 475^2 (e) 525^5
3. (a) $5 \times 5 \times 5$ (b) $3 \times 3 \times 3 \times 3 \times 3$ (c) $47 \times 47 \times 47 \times 47$ (d) 65×65 (e) $375 \times 375 \times 375$
   (f) $425 \times 425 \times 425$
4. (a) 2^3 (b) 2^4 (c) 2^5 (d) 2^6
5. (a) 9   (b) 8   (c) 125   (d) 36   (e) 216
   (f) 343   (g) 16   (h) 32   (i) 64
6. (a) 3^2 (b) 3^5 (c) 47^3

EXERCISE 1.7

1. (a) 9   (b) 5   (c) 5   (d) 5   (e) 6   (f) 10
2. (a) 3^7 (b) 2^6 (c) 6^5 (d) 5^5 (e) 4^5
    (f) 7^7 (g) 31^5 (h) 5^7 (i) 35^7 (j) 25^7
    (k) 75^{11} (l) 27^9 (m) 395^8 (n) 5^7
3. (a) 2^7 (b) 2^7 (c) 3^5 (d) 5^5 (e) 10^4
    (f) 2^{10} (g) 5^6 (h) 10^5
4. (a) 2^5 (b) 6^4 (c) 250   (d) 3^4

EXERCISE 1.8

1. (a) 3   (b) 5   (c) 4   (d) 5   (e) 2   (f) 3
2. (a) 3^2 (b) 5^3 (c) 5^5 (d) 6^2 (e) 31^2
    (f) 48   (g) 15^5 (h) 75^4 (i) 12^2 (j) 63^2
3. (a) 1246^2 (b) 6305^2
4. (a) $3^7 \div 1^4$ (b) $2^8 \div 2^4$ (c) $65^4 \div 65^2$ (d) $39^6 \div 39^4$ (e) $25^5 \div 25^3$

EXERCISE 1.9

1. (a) 3^6 (b) 3^6 (c) 5^6 (d) 5^4 (e) 2^{10}
    (f) 2^8 (g) 2^8 (h) 4^4 (i) 6^6 (j) 5^0
2. (a) 2^4 (b) 3^9 (c) 1^6 (d) 2^3 (e) 10^6 (f) 10^9
3. (a) 0.3^4 (b) 0.2^6 (c) 1.1^2 (d) 1.2   (e) 3.5^6 (f) 0.7^6

EXERCISE 1.10

1. (a) 5   (b) 10   (c) 7   (d) 5   (e) 12
    (f) 6   (g) 11   (h) 6
2. (a) 26   (b) 10   (c) 14   (d) 12   (e) 0
    (f) 35   (g) 2   (h) 14
3. (a) 8   (b) 13   (c) 1   (d) 9   (e) 1
    (f) 15   (g) 8   (h) 5
4. (a) 18   (b) 30   (c) 20   (d) 10   (e) 3
    (f) 3   (g) 28   (h) 8   (i) 9
5. (a) 35   (b) 24   (c) 24   (d) 2   (e) 30
    (f) 47   (g) 68   (h) 5
6. (a) 165   (b) 4   (c) 5   (d) 43   (e) 58
    (f) 2   (g) 2   (h) 2   (i) 70   (j) 5
7. $(1 + 2 + 3)^2$

EXERCISE 1.11

1. (a) 380   (b) 280   (c) 64 310   (d) 25 620
2. (a) 27 000   (b) 34 000   (c) 7000   (d) 65 000
3. (a) 64 300   (b) 5700   (c) 7200   (d) 8000
4. (a) 70 000   (b) 440 000   (c) 6 360 000   (d) 250 000
5. (a) 75.3   (b) 6.4   (c) 6.2   (d) 35.9
6. (a) 3.28   (b) 56.80   (c) 0.49   (d) 0.06
7. (a) 3.123   (b) 6.077   (c) 0.036   (d) 0.216

EXERCISE 1.12

1. (a) 1.867 59   (b) 343.348   (c) 4.434 98   (d) 0.006 589 59   (e) 1.748 54
    (f) 142.1697   (g) 3.981 444

EXERCISE 1.13

1. (a) 15   (b) 25   (c) 35   (d) 20   (e) 5   (f) 40
2. (a) 7   (b) 11   (c) 1   (d) 13   (e) 5   (f) 19
3. (a) 1   (b) 7   (c) 28   (d) 16   (e) 13   (f) 25
4. (a) 5   (b) 7   (c) 8   (d) 25   (e) 13
    (f) 25   (g) 1   (h) 6   (i) 24   (j) 13
5. (a) 22   (b) 0   (c) 17   (d) 6   (e) 4
    (f) 6   (g) 6.5   (h) 10.7
6. (a) $x + 3$ (b) $(x + 5)^2$ (c) $x^2 - 20$ (d) $3x + 7$

EXERCISE 1.14

1. (a) 34   (b) 22   (c) 60   (d) 18
2. (a) 24   (b) 30   (c) 96   (d) 23.2
3. (a) 43   (b) 17   (c) 22   (d) 22
4. (a) 204   (b) 17.6   (c) 82   (d) 32
5. (a) 204.1   (b) 43.96   (c) 188.4   (d) 138.16
    (e) 83.21   (f) 109.9

6. (a) 20.52   (b) 36.55   (c) 874   (d) 40.3
7. (a) 5625   (b) 39.69   (c) 2025   (d) 10.24
8. (a) 14   (b) 5.78   (c) 420   (d) 11.2
9. (a) 42   (b) 45.05   (c) 2795   (d) 47.31
10. (a) 706.5   (b) 132.665   (c) 17 662.5   (d) 94.985
11. (a) 910   (b) 13.365   (c) 1800   (d) 49.5
12. (a) 120   (b) 96   (c) 672   (d) 38.22
13. (a) 216   (b) 3375   (c) 1728   (d) 125 000
14. (a) 3140   (b) 169.56
15. 28.8   16. 46.08   17. 69.12
18. 40   19. 1256   20. 9420

1.15 CHAPTER 1 REVIEW EXERCISE

1. (a) 11 892   (b) 1288   (c) 23   (d) 1 366 024   (e) 47
   (f) 99   (g) 14 923   (h) 97 005   (i) 65
2. (a) 3639   (b) 104 861   (c) 4 158 891   (d) 158 841   (e) 235
   (f) 2 945 160   (g) 443   (h) 3339   (i) 6092   (j) 2601
   (k) 525 625
3. (a) 14.249   (b) 20.8   (c) 515.445   (d) 4.8
   (e) 25.8   (f) 699.077   (g) 16.84   (h) 319.9
4. (a) 370   (b) 0.4   (c) 76 000 000   (d) 55
6. (a) hundredths   (b) tenths   (c) thousandths   (d) hundred thousands
   (e) hundredths   (f) tens
7. (a) 10   (b) 2 hundredths   (c) 3   (d) 4   (e) 5
   (f) 8 thousandths
8. (a) 24   (b) 11   (c) 512   (d) 11   (e) 17   (f) 0
9. (a) 7   (b) 9   (c) 12   (d) 14   (e) 14   (f) 29
10. (a) 44.1   (b) 240.1   (c) 30.625   (d) 132.496   11. 51.4

EXERCISE 2.1

1. 156.8   2. 40
3. (a) 3540   (b) 708   (c) 42 480
4. (a) Polaski   (b) 125 791   5. (a) 17   (b) $15.13
6. (a) 255   (b) 225   (c) 480
7. 676 s   8. 13   9. 7
10. 3071   11. $731   12. 7
13. $5   14. $189.95   15. (a) 1.1×10^9 (b) 9.5×10^{12}
16. 1 h 53 min   17. 1.6   18. 1.26 s
19. (a) 27°C   (b) 3°C   20. (a) 47 277   (b) $378 216
21. 15 300 000   22. 27 946 a   23. 5508
24. (a) 37   (b) 202.4   (c) 190.75 g   (d) 900 mm
   (e) $26.25   (f) 312.4 g   (g) 601.66 g

EXERCISE 2.2

1. (a) 306   (b) 604   (c) 403   (d) 204   (e) 902
   (f) 506   (g) 709   (h) 705
3. 0,1
4. (a) 20   (b) 10   (c) 13   (d) 21   (e) 19
   (f) 25

EXERCISE 2.3

1. Newfoundland, Atlantic, Eastern, Central, Mountain, Pacific, Yukon
2. (a) 11:00   (b) 10:00   (c) 8:00   (d) 8:00   (e) 7:00
   (f) 6:00
3. (a) Atlantic   (b) Central   (c) Atlantic   (d) Mountain   (e) Pacific
   (f) Eastern

EXERCISE 2.4

1. 18
2. Alta—T, B.C.—V, Man.—R, N.B.—E, Nfld—A, N.S.—B
   Ont.—K, L, M, N, P, P.E.I.—C, Que—G, H, J, Sask.—S N.W.T.—X, YUKON—Y
4. (a) V   (b) M   (c) A   (d) T

EXERCISE 2.5

1. 500 500   2. (a) 3200   (b) 2.81
3. Yes   4. 55.3   5. Plan 1

EXERCISE 2.6

1. (a) 1868   (b) 2171
3. (a) Everest, Aconcagua, McKinley, Kilimanjaro, Massif   (b) 2885   (c) 231
4. 1271.4
5. (a) i) 5:47   ii) 6:51   iii) 4:05   iv) 5:11   v) 4:59
   (b) 52 min   (c) 51 min   (d) 17:12 on Sunday

EXERCISE 2.9

1. $133
4. 4927.5
7. $8379
2. 297.5 km
5. 3.25 h
8. 455
3. 124
6. $6000
9. 280 mm

EXERCISE 2.11

1. (e)   2. (e) Ed   3. (c)   4. (b)

EXERCISE 2.12

1. $1.25, $2.50, $3.75, $5.00, $6.25, $7.50, $8.75, $10.00, $11.25, $12.50
3. 16, 30, 48, 70, 96, 126, 160, 198, 240

EXERCISE 2.13

1. (a) 1331   (b) 6003   (c) 1209   (d) $22 511.25
2. $762
3. Kings, Aces, Reds, Blues
4. (b) $52.5   (c) $75   (d) $90   (e) $138.75

EXERCISE 2.14

1. (a) $2904   (b) $2130   (c) 84   (d) 107   (e) 328
   (f) $1868
2. (1 300, 24 700) (1 400, 25 200) (1 500, 25 500) (1 600, 25 600) (1 700, 25 500) (1 800, 25 200) (1 900, 24 700)
5. blouse, slacks   6. York
7. (a) juice, fish, cake, milk   (b) soup, steak, pie, shake   (c) $34.65
8. All the same

2.15 CHAPTER 2 REVIEW EXERCISE

1. (a) Dead Sea   (b) 311
2. (a) $1.20   (b) $1.60   (c) $4.10
3. 49 535
4. $5496
5. (a) 180 000 000   (b) 1.3 s
6. (a) 5600   (b) 4480
7. (a) 14   (b) 215 h 42 min
9. (a) Manitoba Saskatchewan Alberta   (b) 1 963 172
10. (a) 40 000 000   (b) 1 428 600 000
11. (a) 482.5   (b) 227   (c) 47 342.9 g

REVIEW AND PREVIEW TO CHAPTER 3

EXERCISE 1 FACTORS

1. (a) 1, 2, 3, 4, 6, 12   (b) 1, 2, 4, 5, 10, 20
   (c) 1, 2, 3, 4, 6, 8, 12, 24   (d) 1, 2, 3, 5, 6, 10, 15, 30
   (e) 1, 2, 3, 4, 6, 9, 12, 18, 36   (f) 1, 2, 3, 6, 7, 14, 21, 42
   (g) 1, 2, 5, 10, 25, 50   (h) 1, 2, 4, 31, 62, 124
   (i) 1, 2, 3, 4, 6, 8, 10, 12, 15, 16, 24, 30, 60, 120, 240
2. (a) 30   (b) 50   (c) 5   (d) 49   (e) 13   (f) 9
5. (a) 30   (b) 140   (c) 105   (d) 84   (e) 72
   (f) 120   (g) 300   (h) 3528
6. (a) $2^2 \times 7$ (b) $3^2 \times 5$ (c) $3^2 \times 7$ (d) $3^2 \times 2^3$ (e) 2^6
   (f) $2^4 \times 3$ (g) 2^8 (h) 5^3 (i) $2^3 \times 3 \times 5 \times 7$
7. (a) $2^2 \times 29$ (b) $2^2 \times 3 \times 17$ (c) $3^2 \times 2 \times 7$ (d) $2^4 \times 3 \times 7$ (e) $2^4 \times 7$
   (f) $2^2 \times 7^2$ (g) $3^2 \times 2 \times 17$ (h) $2^4 \times 3^3$ (i) $2^4 \times 3^2 \times 7$

EXERCISE 2 GCF

1. (a) 1, 5   (b) 1, 2, 3, 6   (c) 1, 3, 9   (d) 1, 5   (e) 1, 2, 4, 8   (f) 1, 2, 5, 10
2. (a) 5   (b) 8   (c) 9   (d) 24   (e) 32   (f) 24
3. (a) 11   (b) 3   (c) 12   (d) 8   (e) 6   (f) 5
4. (a) 4   (b) 15   (c) 9   (d) 24   (e) 24   (f) 18

EXERCISE 3 LCM

1. (a) 12   (b) 80   (c) 75   (d) 72   (e) 90
    (f) 42   (g) 30   (h) 60   (i) 42
2. (a) 180   (b) 300   (c) 120   (d) 360   (e) 60   (f) 210
3. (a) 105   (b) 120   (c) 192   (d) 336   (e) 150   (f) 84
4. 240 turns—large wheel

EXERCISE 3.1

1. (a) $\dfrac{1}{3}$ (b) $\dfrac{3}{8}$ (c) $\left(\dfrac{1}{2}\right)$ (d) $\dfrac{3}{11}$ (e) $\dfrac{5}{8}$ (f) $\left(\dfrac{2}{5}\right)$

2. (a) $\dfrac{3}{4}$ (b) $\dfrac{4}{6}$ (c) $\dfrac{2}{3}$ (d) $\dfrac{4}{9}$ (e) $\dfrac{8}{12}$ (f) $\dfrac{8}{14}$

3. (a) $\dfrac{29}{54}$ (b) $\dfrac{15}{54}$ (c) $\dfrac{10}{54}$

4. (a) $\dfrac{7}{25}$ (b) $\dfrac{12}{25}$ (c) $\dfrac{6}{25}$

5. (a) $\dfrac{8}{54}$ (b) $\dfrac{16}{54}$ (c) $\dfrac{14}{54}$ (d) $\dfrac{8}{54}$

7. (a) $\dfrac{3}{4}$ (b) $\dfrac{3}{8}$ (c) $\dfrac{4}{8}$

EXERCISE 3.2

3. (a) 30   (b) 28   (c) 15   (d) 2   (e) 60
    (f) 40   4. d, e

5. (a) $\dfrac{3}{4}$ (b) $\dfrac{2}{3}$ (c) $\dfrac{4}{5}$ (d) $\dfrac{9}{10}$ (e) $\dfrac{1}{2}$

    (f) $\dfrac{5}{6}$ (g) $\dfrac{6}{7}$ (h) $\dfrac{13}{20}$ (i) $\dfrac{1}{4}$

6. (a) $\dfrac{2}{5}, \dfrac{1}{2}, \dfrac{2}{3}, \dfrac{3}{4}, \dfrac{7}{8}$ (b) $\dfrac{9}{8}, \dfrac{6}{5}, \dfrac{3}{2}, \dfrac{5}{3}, \dfrac{10}{3}$ (c) $\dfrac{4}{5}, \dfrac{7}{8}, \dfrac{5}{4}, \dfrac{3}{1}, \dfrac{9}{2}$

7. Same

8. (a) $\dfrac{3}{4}, \dfrac{3}{4}$

EXERCISE 3.3

1. (a) $\dfrac{1}{4}$ (b) $\dfrac{1}{9}$ (c) $\dfrac{3}{8}$ (d) $\dfrac{3}{16}$ (e) $\dfrac{1}{3}$ (f) $\dfrac{1}{4}$
2. (a) 4   (b) 2   (c) 4   (d) 6   (e) 5   (f) 2.5
3. (a) $\dfrac{1}{10}$ (b) $\dfrac{1}{2}$ (c) $\dfrac{1}{8}$ (d) $\dfrac{1}{2}$ (e) $\dfrac{1}{8}$ (f) $\dfrac{1}{2}$
4. (a) $\dfrac{7}{3}$ (b) $\dfrac{21}{8}$ (c) $\dfrac{7}{4}$ (d) $\dfrac{13}{3}$
5. (a) 6   (b) 52   (c) $\dfrac{15}{2}$ (d) $\dfrac{7}{2}$
6. (a) 4 L   (b) 2 L
7. (a) $84   (b) $340   (c) $186
8. (a) $\dfrac{3}{8}$ (b) $\dfrac{1}{6}$ (c) $4\dfrac{1}{6}$

EXERCISE 3.4

1. (a) $\dfrac{3}{2}$ (b) $\dfrac{5}{4}$ (c) $\dfrac{7}{8}$ (d) 2   (e) $\dfrac{1}{8}$
   (f) $\dfrac{3}{4}$ (g) $\dfrac{4}{9}$ (h) $\dfrac{1}{9}$ (i) 1

2. (a) $\dfrac{3}{2}$ (b) $\dfrac{8}{3}$ (c) $\dfrac{29}{8}$ (d) $\dfrac{17}{4}$ (e) $\dfrac{11}{3}$
   (f) $\dfrac{7}{4}$ (g) $\dfrac{19}{8}$ (h) $\dfrac{10}{3}$

3. (a) $1\dfrac{1}{3}$ (b) $2\dfrac{1}{2}$ (c) $2\dfrac{1}{3}$ (d) $1\dfrac{3}{4}$ (e) $4\dfrac{1}{3}$
   (f) $3\dfrac{1}{3}$ (g) $2\dfrac{2}{3}$ (h) $7\dfrac{1}{2}$

4. (a) $\dfrac{2}{3}$ (b) $\dfrac{9}{8}$ (c) $\dfrac{15}{16}$ (d) $\dfrac{1}{3}$ (e) $\dfrac{1}{4}$
   (f) 8   (g) $\dfrac{4}{27}$ (h) $\dfrac{5}{2}$ (i) $\dfrac{1}{4}$ (j) $\dfrac{25}{8}$

5. (a) $\dfrac{9}{8}$ (b) $\dfrac{75}{52}$ (c) $\dfrac{20}{33}$ (d) $\dfrac{27}{38}$ (e) $\dfrac{25}{8}$
   (f) $\dfrac{10}{3}$ (g) $\dfrac{7}{10}$ (h) $\dfrac{51}{8}$ (i) 1   (j) $\dfrac{11}{8}$

6. 1120　　　　　　7. 14　　　　　　8. 8　　　　　　9. 6
10. (a) 265　　　　　 (b) 173　　　　　 (c) 96　　　　　 (d) 183

EXERCISE 3.5

1. (a) 6　　　　　　b. 1　　　　　　c. 12　　　　　d. 2
2. (a) 8　　　　　　b. 12　　　　　c. 5　　　　　d. 4
3. (a) $\frac{3}{5}$　　　　　b. 1　　　　　c. 1　　　　　d. 1

4. a. $1\frac{5}{12}$　　(b) $\frac{7}{8}$　　(c) $1\frac{1}{8}$　　(d) $1\frac{1}{2}$　　(e) $3\frac{5}{6}$　　(f) $7\frac{3}{4}$

5. (a) $1\frac{1}{8}$　　(b) $\frac{5}{6}$　　(c) $\frac{11}{12}$　　(d) $1\frac{5}{12}$　　(e) $7\frac{3}{4}$　　(f) $5\frac{1}{12}$

6. (a) $1\frac{3}{8}$　　(b) $1\frac{1}{6}$　　(c) $\frac{13}{14}$　　(d) $1\frac{1}{8}$　　(e) $\frac{19}{24}$　　(f) $1\frac{1}{12}$

　(g) $1\frac{1}{12}$　　(h) $1\frac{5}{9}$

7. (a) 14　　(b) $10\frac{3}{4}$　　(c) $4\frac{1}{6}$　　(d) $6\frac{13}{20}$　　(e) $1\frac{19}{20}$　　(f) $16\frac{1}{6}$

8. (a) $1\frac{5}{12}$　　(b) $1\frac{7}{12}$　　(c) $1\frac{3}{8}$　　(d) 1　　(e) $7\frac{1}{2}$　　(f) $11\frac{1}{2}$

9. 288

EXERCISE 3.6

1. (a) $\frac{3}{8}$　　(b) $\frac{2}{5}$　　(c) $\frac{1}{6}$　　(d) $\frac{1}{6}$

3. (a) $\frac{1}{2}$　　(b) $\frac{1}{4}$　　(c) $\frac{1}{2}$　　(d) $\frac{2}{5}$　　(e) $\frac{2}{3}$　　(f) $\frac{1}{3}$

4. (a) $\frac{1}{4}$　　(b) $\frac{1}{2}$　　(c) $\frac{3}{8}$　　(d) $\frac{1}{8}$　　(e) $\frac{1}{2}$　　(f) $\frac{1}{2}$

5. (a) $3\frac{3}{8}$　　(b) $3\frac{1}{6}$　　(c) $4\frac{1}{3}$　　(d) $4\frac{3}{10}$　　(e) $2\frac{1}{4}$　　(f) $5\frac{3}{8}$

6. (a) $\frac{1}{20}$　　(b) $\frac{7}{24}$　　(c) $\frac{1}{12}$　　(d) $\frac{2}{15}$

7. (a) $3\frac{1}{6}$　　(b) $5\frac{1}{6}$　　(c) $4\frac{1}{15}$　　(d) $2\frac{3}{8}$

8. (a) $1\frac{2}{3}$　　(b) $3\frac{7}{10}$　　(c) $2\frac{7}{12}$　　(d) $1\frac{5}{8}$

EXERCISE 3.7

1. $6\frac{1}{2}$　　　　　　2. $4\frac{3}{4}$　　　　　　3. $\$6\frac{1}{2}$　　　　　　4. $9

5. (a) $153　　　　　(b) $306　　　　　6. 8

7. (a) $\frac{1}{3}$　　　　　(b) 45　　　　　8. (a) $\frac{16}{25}$　　　　　(b) $\frac{9}{25}$

EXERCISE 3.8

1. (a) 3　　　　(b) 36　　　　(c) 05　　　　(d) 425　　　　(e) 7　　　　(f) 105
2. (a) 0.1　　　(b) 0.2　　　(c) 0.3　　　(d) 0.7　　　(e) 0.4　　　(f) 0.8
　(g) 0.25　　(h) 0.5　　(i) 0.75　　(j) 0.05　　(k) 0.18　　(l) 0.65
3. (a) $3.\overline{2}$　　　(b) 4.625　　　(c) $0.4\overline{5}$　　　(d) 0.035
　(e) $5.2\overline{1}$　　(f) 0.071　　(g) 0.142 857
4. (a) 0.25　　(b) 0.75　　(c) 0.125　　(d) 0.625　　(e) $0.\overline{6}$
　(f) 1.5　　(g) 0.1　　(h) 0.3　　(i) 0.18　　(j) $0.2\overline{7}$
　(k) $0.07\overline{4}$　　(l) $0.7\overline{3}$
5. (a) $0.41\overline{6}$　　(b) $0.29\overline{16}$　　(c) $0.5\overline{3}$　　(d) $0.\overline{3}$　　(e) 0.375
　(f) 0.523 809　　(g) 0.106　　(h) 0.380 952 4　　(i) 0.483 871
6. Henry 0.708, Richard 0.724
7. Edna 0.708, Jane 0.6

EXERCISE 3.9

1. (a) 25　　　(b) 375　　　(c) 2　　　(d) 23　　　(e) 305
　(f) 4　　(g) 235　　(h) 07　　(i) 253　　(j) 005
2. (a) $\frac{71}{100}$　　(b) $\frac{3}{10}$　　(c) $\frac{3}{5}$　　(d) $\frac{123}{1000}$　　(e) $\frac{627}{1000}$
　(f) $\frac{373}{1000}$　　(g) $\frac{19}{100}$　　(h) $\frac{11}{100}$　　(i) $\frac{7}{100}$　　(j) $\frac{231}{1000}$

3. (a) $\dfrac{18}{25}$ (b) $\dfrac{13}{20}$ (c) $\dfrac{19}{100}$ (d) $\dfrac{7}{20}$ (e) $\dfrac{1}{40}$

    (f) $\dfrac{1}{4}$ (g) $\dfrac{1}{200}$ (h) $\dfrac{3}{8}$ (i) $\dfrac{101}{200}$ (j) $\dfrac{5}{8}$

4. (a) $1\dfrac{1}{2}$ (b) $2\dfrac{1}{4}$ (c) $3\dfrac{3}{4}$ (d) $4\dfrac{2}{5}$ (e) $55\dfrac{3}{5}$

    (f) $23\dfrac{23}{100}$ (g) $7\dfrac{3}{8}$ (h) $43\dfrac{17}{20}$ (i) $6\dfrac{11}{20}$ (j) $3\dfrac{5}{8}$

5. (a) $\dfrac{2}{3}$ (b) $\dfrac{4}{9}$ (c) $\dfrac{13}{99}$ (d) $\dfrac{6}{11}$ (e) $\dfrac{5}{9}$

    (f) $\dfrac{7}{45}$ (g) $2\dfrac{3}{11}$ (h) $\dfrac{7}{110}$

6. (a) $\dfrac{2}{9}$ (b) $\dfrac{51}{99}$ (c) $\dfrac{8}{9}$ (d) $\dfrac{913}{990}$ (e) $\dfrac{23}{99}$

    (f) $\dfrac{251}{495}$

7. (a) $\dfrac{5}{9}$ (b) 1

EXERCISE 3.10

3. (a) 6   (b) 2   (c) −3   (d) 2   (e) 5
    (f) 7   (g) 0   (h) 3
4. (a) 6   (b) 6   (c) −2   (d) −3   (e) −4
    (f) −11   (g) −3   (h) 0
5. (a) $\{\ldots, -4, -2, 0, 2, 4, \ldots\}$ (b) $\{\ldots, -5, -3, -1, 1, 3, 5, \ldots\}$ (c) $\{2, 1, 0, \ldots\}$
    (d) $\{-2, -3, -4, \ldots\}$ (e) $\{1, 2, 3, \ldots\}$ (f) $\{-2, -1, 0, \ldots\}$
    (g) $\{-3, -2, -1, 0, 1, 2\}$
8. (a) >   (b) <   (c) >   (d) =   (e) >
    (f) >   (g) <   (h) <

EXERCISE 3.11

2. (a) 8   (b) −2   (c) 3   (d) −7   (e) 0
    (f) 2   (g) −5   (h) −5
3. (a) 7   (b) 9   (c) −8   (d) −3   (e) 0
    (f) 2   (g) −12   (h) 6   (i) −12
4. (a) −1   (b) 2   (c) −12   (d) −12   (e) −5
    (f) −5   (g) 1   (h) −11
5. (a) 14   (b) 0   (c) −1   (d) −2   (e) −4
    (f) 5   (g) 0   (h) −4
6. (a) 11°C   (b) −4°C
7. (a) −1°C   (b) 3°C   (c) −8°C   (d) −13°C
8. −3°C, −6°C, −8°C, −9°C, −8°C, −6°C
9. (a) 120   (b) −104   (c) −285   (d) −623   (e) −521
    (f) 819   (g) −502   (h) −201

EXERCISE 3.12

2. (a) 3°, 5°, −9°, −2°, −4°, 1°, 3°, 15°, 4°
3. (a) 3   (b) 9   (c) 6   (d) 3   (e) −10
    (f) −5   (g) 5   (h) −7
4. (a) 7   (b) 0   (c) −5   (d) −11   (e) 22
    (f) 12   (g) 1   (h) 17   (i) 3
5. (a) −15   (b) −2   (c) 27   (d) −47   (e) −29
    (f) −18   (g) −25   (h) −60
6. (a) 0   (b) −26   (c) 35   (d) −17   (e) −22
    (f) −1   (g) 0   (h) 10
7. (a) 74   (b) 8794   (c) 22   (d) 348   (e) 37

EXERCISE 3.13

1. (a) +   (b) −   (c) +   (d) −   (e) −
    (f) −
2. (a) 6   (b) −15   (c) −24   (d) 0   (e) 0
    (f) 18   (g) −35   (h) −16
3. (a) −12   (b) −35   (c) −30   (d) −12   (e) −70
    (f) 72   (g) 18   (h) 0
4. (a) −30   (b) −8   (c) −7   (d) −8   (e) 49
    (f) −33   (g) 48   (h) 60
5. (a) 9   (b) −9   (c) 25   (d) 25   (e) 64
    (f) 81   (g) 121   (h) −49   (i) −121
6. (a) 195   (b) −221   (c) −550   (d) 287   (e) −1848
    (f) −1071   (g) −2250   (h) 1920   (i) −8400   (j) 39 375

7. (a) $-6 \times (-4)$ (b) $(-6)^2$ (c) $(-4) \times (-5)$ (d) $(-7)^2$ (e) -12×4
    (f) $-6 \times (-7)$ (g) $(-8)^2$
8. (a) 21   (b) -12 (c) -36 (d) -9 (e) -25
    (f) 18   (g) 0   (h) 15
9. (a) -4 (b) -7 (c) 72   (d) 0   (e) -7
    (f) 23   (g) 40   (h) -47 (i) 21
10. (a) 81   (b) $-66°C$

EXERCISE 3.14

1. (a) -2 (b) -4 (c) 4   (d) 5   (e) -4
    (f) 8   (g) 0   (h) -1 (i) -1
2. (a) -4 (b) -1 (c) 9   (d) 5   (e) -1
    (f) 0   (g) 9   (h) -9
3. (a) -2 (b) -7 (c) 5   (d) -6 (e) 11
    (f) 9   (g) 3   (h) -7
4. (a) -5 (b) 1   (c) 0   (d) -7 (e) -4
    (f) 4   (g) 6   (h) -5
5. (a) -4 (b) 3   (c) 12   (d) 81   (e) 45
    (f) 15   (g) 2   (h) 63
6. (a) -8 (b) -5 (c) -14 (d) 6   (e) 14
    (f) 27   (g) -8 (h) 13
7. (a) -44 (b) 11   (c) 19   (d) 37   (e) -7
    (f) 0

EXERCISE 3.15

1. (a) -4 (b) -6 (c) 8   (d) 14   (e) 2
    (f) 7   (g) -11 (h) 3
2. (a) 4   (b) -2 (c) -1 (d) 0   (e) -1
    (f) 27   (g) -4 (h) -6
3. (a) -1 (b) -7 (c) 7   (d) 1   (e) 1
    (f) 25   (g) 21   (h) 25   (i) 29   (j) 54
4. (a) 8   (b) -2 (c) 16   (d) 6   (e) 10
    (f) 68   (g) 60   (h) -22
5. (a) 17   (b) 4   (c) -17 (d) 64   (e) -32
    (f) -6 (g) 81   (h) -27

EXERCISE 3.16

1. (a) 3   (b) 2   (c) 4   (d) 5   (e) 1
    (f) 2   (g) 6   (h) 4   (i) 6
2. (a) 4   (b) 5   (c) 4   (d) 6   (e) 3
    (f) 5   (g) 7   (h) 5   (i) 2
3. (a) 5.4×10^3 (b) 5.2×10^5 (c) 7.28×10^6 (d) 6.0×10^3 (e) 3.02×10^6
    (f) 3.02×10^7
4. (a) 9.3×10^7 (b) 6.505×10^{12} (c) 2.353×10^{12} (d) 6.0×10^{12} (e) 2.57×10^{12}
    (f) 3.52×10^{14}
5. (a) 9.97×10^6 (b) 9.6×10^4 (c) 3.56×10^5 (d) 4.06×10^5 (e) 2.65×10^4
6. 2.2×10^{16}
7. 4.0×10^{23} 8. (a) 3600   (b) 275 000   (c) 635   (d) 500 000

EXERCISE 3.17

1. (a) -2 (b) -3 (c) -1 (d) -4 (e) -6
    (f) -5 (g) -6 (h) -3 (i) -3
2. (a) -2 (b) -4 (c) -3 (d) -6 (e) -5
    (f) -1 (g) -2 (h) -3 (i) -4
3. (a) 6.5×10^{-3} (b) 6.75×10^{-6} (c) 7.5×10^{-1} (d) 9.3×10^{-3} (e) 3.75×10^{-3}
    (f) 3.05×10^{-3}
4. (a) 1.25×10^{-4} (b) 6.75×10^{-6} (c) 4.5×10^{-8} (d) 3.05×10^{-7} (e) 1.205×10^{-6}
    (f) 4.44×10^{-9}
5. (a) 1.98×10^{-3} (b) 6.0×10^{-9} (c) 1.67×10^{-21} (d) 1.0×10^{-6} (e) 2.8×10^{-8}
    (f) $5.0 \times 10^{-4}, 2.4 \times 10^3$
6. (a) 0.002 5   (b) 0.000 000 37   (c) 0.000 001 25   (d) 0.000 000 061 5

3.18 CHAPTER 3 REVIEW EXERCISE

1. (a) $\frac{1}{4}$ (b) $\frac{1}{4}$ (c) $\frac{3}{4}$ (d) $\frac{2}{3}$

2. $\frac{5}{9}, \frac{2}{3}, \frac{8}{11}, \frac{11}{15}, \frac{3}{4}, \frac{4}{5}$ 3. (a) 4
    (b) 6

4. (a) $\frac{13}{4}$ (b) $\frac{17}{3}$

5. (a) $\frac{5}{8}$ (b) $\frac{12}{25}$ (c) $8\frac{5}{9}$ (d) $14\frac{2}{3}$

6. (a) $\frac{8}{9}$ (b) $\frac{3}{4}$ (c) $1\frac{23}{52}$ (d) 2

7. (a) $2\frac{2}{5}$ (b) $\frac{3}{20}$ (c) $3\frac{3}{4}$ (d) 6

8. (a) $\frac{5}{6}$ (b) $1\frac{11}{20}$ (c) $\frac{5}{12}$ (d) $\frac{1}{6}$ (e) $5\frac{1}{6}$
   (f) $1\frac{5}{6}$ (g) $2\frac{1}{4}$ (h) $5\frac{7}{8}$

9. (a) 0.25 (b) 0.75 (c) 0.2 (d) 0.375 (e) 0.625
   (f) 0.875 (g) 0.4 (h) 0.6 (i) 0.8

10. (a) $\frac{17}{50}$ (b) $\frac{11}{20}$ (c) $\frac{3}{4}$ (d) $\frac{57}{100}$ (e) $\frac{1}{4}$
    (f) $\frac{9}{25}$ (g) $\frac{4}{5}$ (h) $\frac{1}{5}$ (i) $\frac{27}{100}$ (j) $\frac{1}{8}$
    (k) $\frac{7}{8}$ (l) $\frac{5}{8}$

11. (a) $0.\overline{6}$ (b) $0.\overline{27}$ (c) $0.\overline{4}$ (d) $0.\overline{5}$ (e) $0.\overline{63}$
    (f) $0.8\overline{1}$ (g) $0.\overline{285\,714}$ (h) $0.\overline{571\,428}$ (i) $0.\overline{857\,142}$

12. (a) $\frac{2}{9}$ (b) $\frac{2}{3}$ (c) $\frac{4}{9}$ (d) $\frac{7}{9}$ (e) $\frac{35}{99}$
    (f) $\frac{305}{999}$ (g) $\frac{4}{11}$ (h) $\frac{5}{11}$ (i) $\frac{325}{999}$ (j) $\frac{25}{99}$

13. (a) -3 (b) $6 (c) 1254 (d) $ 0.25

14. (a) 5 (b) -5 (c) -3 (d) -8

15. (a) 4 (b) -6 (c) 11 (d) -8 (e) 9
    (f) -6

16. (a) $\{1, 2, 3, \ldots\}$ (b) $\{\ldots, -4, -2, 0, 2, 4, \ldots\}$ (c) $\{\ldots, -3, -2, -1\}$
    (d) $\{-2, -1, 0, 1, \ldots\}$ (e) $\{\ldots, 4, 5, 6\}$ (f) $\{-3, -2, -1, \ldots, 3, 4\}$
    (g) $\{\ldots, 1, 2, 3\}$ (h) $\{-4, -3, -2, \ldots\}$

18. (a) $\{-2, 0, 2, 4, \ldots\}$ (b) $\{-3, -2, -1, 0, 1, 2, \ldots\}$ (c) $\{2, 1, 0, -1, \ldots\}$
    (d) $\{3, 1, -1, -3, \ldots\}$ (e) $\{\ldots -4, -2, 0, 2, 4, \ldots\}$

19. (a) -9 (b) -4 (c) 8 (d) -4 (e) -15
    (f) 6

20. (a) -12 (b) -20 (c) -6 (d) 21 (e) -36
    (f) -2 (g) 27 (h) 10

21. (a) 2.5×10^7 (b) 3.6×10^5 (c) 2.35×10^6 (d) 2.35×10^3 (e) 2.5×10
    (f) 3.51×10^4 (g) 1.25 (h) 2.5×10^{-1} (i) 2.5×10^{-3} (j) 3.75×10^{-2}
    (k) 2.15×10 (l) 2.75×10^{-3}

22. (a) 32 500 (b) 545 000 (c) 12 500 000 (d) 0.002 05 (e) 0.000 015 5
    (f) 6250 (g) 0.000 077 5

23. (a) -6 (b) 8 (c) 3 (d) -9 (e) 2
    (f) 6 (g) 7 (h) -10

24. (a) 1 (b) 11 (c) 14 (d) -18 (e) 14
    (f) -12 (g) -36 (h) -16 (i) 9 (j) 52

25. $\frac{1}{3}$

26. 2

27. $2\frac{5}{12}$ h

REVIEW AND PREVIEW TO CHAPTER 4

1. (a) 9 (b) 8 (c) 4 (d) 16 (e) 32
   (f) 64 (g) 27 (h) 81 (i) 25 (j) 64
3. (a) 3^2 (b) 2^5 (c) 2^5 (d) $4^3 - 4^1$ (e) both
4. (a) 15 625 (b) 176 400 (c) 625 (d) 1296 (e) 10 000
   (f) 1 000 000 (g) 4096 (h) 2500 (i) 5625 (j) 625
5. (a) NO (b) YES (c) NO (d) NO
6. (a) -9 (b) 28 (c) 80 (d) 60 (e) 43
   (f) 105 (g) 5

7. (a) 1.2 (b) 10.1 (c) 7.01 (d) 16.29 (e) 22.51
   (f) 69.07 (g) 41.37
8. (a) 9 (b) 6 (c) 5 (d) 8 (e) 25
   (f) 11 (g) 4 (h) 1
9. (a) 8 (b) 21 (c) 34 (d) 64 (e) -1
   (f) -9 (g) 2 (h) -8

EXERCISE 4.1

1. (a) 6 (b) 3 (c) 7 (d) 4 (e) 5
   (f) 8 (g) 9 (h) 2 (i) 1
2. (a) 10 (b) 12 (c) 11 (d) 13 (e) 16
   (f) 15

3. (a, iii) (b, iv) (c, i) (d, ii)
4. (a) 8   (b) 3   (c) 25   (d) 5

EXERCISE 4.2

1. (a) 5.4   (b) 6.5   (c) 7.1   (d) 8.2   (e) 9.4
   (f) 9.6
2. (a) 7.48   (b) 9.22   (c) 4.36   (d) 6.71   (e) 8.49
   (f) 4.24

EXERCISE 4.3

1. (a) 3.5   (b) 7.7   (c) 6.7   (d) 4.1   (e) 8.5
   (f) 7.9   (g) 9.2   (h) 9.6
2. (a) 9.2   (b) 7.7   (c) 4.9   (d) 6.1   (e) 6.4
   (f) 5.5

EXERCISE 4.4

1. (a) 5.4   (b) 5.7   (c) 6.5   (d) 7.1   (e) 7.7
   (f) 8.1   (g) 8.7   (h) 9.4   (i) 9.5
2. (a) 8.06   (b) 6.25   (c) 4.90   (d) 8.19   (e) 9.11
   (f) 7.42
3. (a) 289   (b) 729   (c) 1369   (d) 1764   (e) 2809
   (f) 4624   (g) 5184   (h) 7056   (i) 8281
4. (a) 6.1   (b) 9.9   (c) 9.4   (d) 0.7   (e) 369
   (f) 17.03   (g) 72.8   (h) 180
5. (a) 336.5   (b) 338.2   (c) 347   (d) 343   (e) 324.3
   (f) 316.2

EXERCISE 4.5

1. (a) 10.0   (b) 13.0   (c) 17.0   (d) 15.0
2. (a) 8.6   (b) 14.4   (c) 15.0   (d) 2.8
3. (a) 18.0   (b) 12.5   (c) 6.7   (d) 7.1
4. (a) 7.6   (b) 8.5   (c) 1.4   (d) 10.6
5. (a) 6.0   (b) 5.0   (c) 25.0   (d) 19.2
6. (a) 11.6   (b) 10.6   (c) 12.1   (d) 43.7
7. 5.7   8. 12.5
9. (a) 100   (b) 72.1   (c) 27.9
10. 3.6   11. (a) 31.6   (b) 36.9   12. 77.8

EXERCISE 4.6

1. (a) 4.5   (b) 5.5   (c) 6.3
2. (a) 1.42   (b) 2.46   (c) 3.18   (d) 5.03   (e) 5.51
   (f) 6.36
3. (a) 10.2   (b) 16.5   (c) 19.7   (d) 21.3   (e) 25.5
   (f) 38.1   (g) 276.4
4. 2.41 s

4.7 CHAPTER 4 REVIEW EXERCISE

1. (a) 4   (b) 6   (c) 9   (d) 8   (e) 5
   (f) 7   (g) 10   (h) 12
2. (a) 225   (b) 289   (c) 324   (d) 361   (e) 484
   (f) 625
3. (a) 15   (b) 18   (c) 16   (d) 20   (e) 24
   (f) 30   (g) 27   (h) 21
4. (a) 5.2   (b) 5.9   (c) 7.1   (d) 8.7   (e) 10.5
   (f) 11.2   (g) 17.3   (h) 13.2
5. (a) 2.65   (b) 4.24   (c) 4.47   (d) 4.36
6. (a) >   (b) =   (c) >   (d) <   (e) >   (f) <
7. (a) >   (b) >   (c) <   (d) <   (e) >   (f) >
8. (a) 13   (b) 17   (c) 14.1   (d) 14   (e) 18.4   (f) 8.7
9. 5.8   10. 16   11. 8.2
12. 90   13. 7.8   14. 62.4
15. (a) 8   (b) 4.2   (c) 11.0   (d) 17.3

REVIEW AND PREVIEW TO CHAPTER 5

1. (b) 29 + 85 = 114   (c) 71 − 29 = 42
   (d) 24 × 9 = 216   (e) 72 ÷ 9 = 8
2. (a) 112   (b) 31

3.

								x	x	x	x	x	x	x	x
				x	x	x	x					x	x	x	x
		x	x			x	x			x	x			x	x
	x		x		x		x		x		x		x		x
0	1	2	3	4	5	6	7	8	9	10	11	12	13	14	15

x	x	x	x	x	x	x	x	x	x	x	x	x	x	x	x
								x	x	x	x	x	x	x	x
				x	x	x	x					x	x	x	x
		x	x			x	x			x	x			x	x
	x		x		x		x		x		x		x		x
16	17	18	19	20	21	22	23	24	25	26	27	28	29	30	31

4. (a) $2^6 = 64$ (0 to 63)   5. (a) $2^7 = 128$ (0 to 127)

EXERCISE 5.1

1. (a) 116   (b) 10   (c) 262   (d) 69 336

2. (a) same number as you start with.
3. (age, pop)   4. 5   5. a, c, d
6. (a) 160.00   (b) 158.54   (c) 162.78   (d) 160.51

EXERCISE 5.2

1. (a) Turn off switch; Take out old bulb; Put in light bulb; Turn on switch
   (b) Decide the amount of your deposit; Count your deposit money; Fill in the deposit slip; Hand the slip and money to the teller; Teller counts your deposit money; Receive a record slip of the transaction.
   (c) Insert enough change; Select the drink you want; Push selection button; Wait while cup is filled; Take your change; Lift cup from machine; Walk away; Drink your drink.

EXERCISE 5.3

1. (a) 20   (b) 21   (c) −4   (d) −4   (e) 125
   (f) −125
2. (a) 6•7   (b) −6/3   (c) 5↑3   (d) 3+9   (e) 12−7
   (f) 3.5•2
3. (a) 3•(5+7)   (b) (6+4)•(8−2)   (c) (5−3)↑2   (d) (−3)↑2+7   (e) (−4)↑2/(2•4)
   (f) (3•5)•(−2)
4. (a) −1   (b) 4   (c) 5   (d) 3   (e) 243
   (f) 1
5. (a) (5−3)↑2   (b) 6↑2−1   (c) (12−2)↑2   (d) (2•3)↑2   (e) 3↑2
   (f) 2•3↑2
6. (a) X+Y   (b) X•Y   (c) 3•x   (d) x↑2   (e) x↑2+y↑2
   (f) (x+y)↑2   (g) 2•(L+W)   (h) 2•3.14•R   (i) 3.14•R↑2   (j) L•W
   (k) X•Y/Z   (l) x•(y−z)   (m) (A+B)•H/2

EXERCISE 5.4

1. (a) clears all memory   (b) writes anything in quotes or value of a variable
   (c) stops a program   (d) begins execution of a program
2. (a) 30   (b) −125   (c) 25   (d) 2   (e) 42
   (f) 625   (g) 37.68   (h) 50
22. (a) i) 10 PRINT (−6.5)↑2+(15.3)↑2
             20 END
         ii) 10 PRINT (−6.5+15.3)↑2
             20 END
    (b) i) is greater

EXERCISE 5.5

1. A 'LET' Assigns a value to a variable for the computer to use later in a program.
2. (a) 10   (b) 3   (c) 343   (d) 12   (e) 4   (f) 314

EXERCISE 5.6

1. A program command that instructs the computer to accept data input by a user.

2. (a) 15	(b) 9	(c) 20	(d) 23.6
3. (a) 9	(b) 36	(c) 16	(d) 33.64
4. (a) 62.8	(b) 94.2	(c) 125.6	(d) 28.26
5. (a) 2	(b) 12.5		

6. NEW
10 INPUT X
20 PRINT X+5
30 END
RUN

7. NEW
10 INPUT X
20 PRINT X↑3
30 END
RUN

(a) 1   (b) 64   (c) 343   (d) −8

8. NEW
10 INPUT X
20 INPUT Y
30 PRINT (X+Y)↑2
40 END
RUN

(a) 49   (b) 0   (c) 36   (d) 25

9. NEW
10 INPUT R
20 PRINT 3.14*R↑2
30 END
RUN

(a) 314   (b) 137.665   (c) 1040.0936

10. NEW
10 INPUT L
20 INPUT W
30 PRINT 2*(L+W)
40 END
RUN

(a) 22   (b) 34   (c) 22.2

11. NEW
10 INPUT X
20 INPUT Y
30 INPUT Z
40 PRINT X+Y−Z
50 END

(a) 6   (b) 0   (c) 32

5.7 CHAPTER 5 REVIEW EXERCISE

3. i) 36, 51, 90   ii) 648, 828, 1296

5. (a) 35	(b) 64	(c) 4	(d) 22	(e) 3
(f) 6	(g) 70	(h) 30	(i) 5	
7. (a) 5*12	(b) 7*2	(c) 21/3	(d) 6↑2/4	

8. 36   9. 625   10. 3140

11. 19   12. 8   13. 1130.4

14. (a) 20	(b) 5	(c) 30	(d) 34
15. (a) 52	(b) 4.21	(c) 12	(d) 67
16. (a) 16	(b) 128	(c) 67	
17. (a) 40	(b) 78	(c) 50	

REVIEW AND PREVIEW TO CHAPTER 6

1. $66.60	2. 9	3. 20
4. $57.29	5. (a) 442.5	(b) 48
6. (a) 24.8	(b) 150.9	
7. (a) 259	(b) 40	8. 22.5
9. (a) 5 178 461.5	(b) 521.4 s	10. $118.75

EXERCISE 6.1

1. (a) 6 : 5	(b) 5 : 6	(c) 1 : 1		
2. (a) 5 : 6	(b) 7 : 5	(c) 7 : 6	(d) 6 : 5	(e) 7 : 18
(f) 5 : 18				
3. (a) 15 : 11	(b) 2 : 7	(c) 35 : 83	(d) 5 : 9	(e) 12 : 1
4. (a) 12 : 11	(b) 11 : 16	(c) 4 : 3		
5. (a) 1 : 3	(b) 92 : 45	(c) 2 : 5		
6. (a) 5 : 10	(b) 1 : 5	(c) 5 : 25	(d) 25 : 10	
7. (a) 2 : 3	(b) 4 : 1	(c) 4 : 3	(d) 5 : 3	(e) 2 : 5
(f) 1 : 2				

EXERCISE 6.2

1. (a) $\frac{1}{4}$ (b) $\frac{4}{1}$ (c) $\frac{2}{5}$ (d) 1 : 2 (e) $\frac{1}{2}$

(f) 7 : 1 (g) $\frac{3}{5}$ (h) $\frac{3}{1}$ (i) 2 : 1 (j) 1 : 3

(k) 2 : 3 (l) 2 : 5 (m) 1 : 6 (n) $\frac{2}{1}$ (o) $\frac{2}{9}$

3. (a) Yes (b) No (c) No (d) Yes (e) No
(f) Yes

4. (a) $\frac{3}{1}$ (b) $\frac{1}{5}$ (c) $\frac{4}{1}$ (d) $\frac{5}{1}$ (e) $\frac{2}{1}$

(f) $\frac{3}{1}$ (g) $\frac{20}{1}$ (h) $\frac{25}{1}$

5. (a) No (b) 3w
6. AD

EXERCISE 6.3

1. (a) 3 (b) 5 (c) 1 (d) 4 (e) 36
(f) 20
2. (a) 5 (b) 12 (c) 4 (d) 8 (e) 10
(f) 5
3. (a) 2.9 (b) 3.4 (c) 1.0 (d) 6.9 (e) 1.2
(f) 8.8 (g) 23.3 (h) 16.7
4. 30 5. 224
6. (a) 55 (b) 140 7. (a) 27 600 (b) 6

EXERCISE 6.4

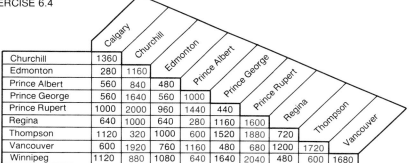

EXERCISE 6.5

1. (a) 12 : 4 : 3 (b) 8 : 5 : 2 (c) 2 : 8 : 15 (d) 8 : 13 : 2 (e) 3 : 1 : 1
2. (a) 8 : 4 : 6 (b) 4 : 8 : 6 (c) 6 : 4 : 8
3. (a) 34, 51 (b) 12, 36 (c) 4, 5 (d) 4, 14 (e) x = 150, y = 75
4. (a) 27 : 17 (b) 17 : 16 (c) 27 : 16 (d) 16 : 17
5. (a) 60 (b) 200
6. (a) $2083.33 (b) $1666.67
7. (a) 27 (b) 18
8. (a) 1 : 5 : 10 (b) 5 : 10 : 25 (c) 10 : 10 : 50 (d) 25 : 50 : 50

EXERCISE 6.6

1. $4000, $6000
2. 60, 90
3. 124, 93, 31
4. $35 000, $21 000, $7000
5. 115, 161, 46
6. 615, 246
7. (a) 5 : 2 (b) $80, $32
8. (a) 4 : 6 : 5 (b) $20 000, $30 000, $25 000

EXERCISE 6.7

1. 3 2. 4 3. $1\frac{1}{5}$ 4. $2\frac{2}{5}$ 5. $1\frac{5}{7}$

6. $1\frac{1}{3}$ 7. $3\frac{3}{7}$ 8. 3 min 20 s 9. 2 h 24 min 10. $1\frac{3}{7}$

EXERCISE 6.8

1. (a) 25%   (b) 68%
2. (a) 25%   (b) 18%
3. (a) 25%   (b) 30%   (c) 50%   (d) 25%   (e) 20%
   (f) 50%
4. (a) 25   (b) 6   (c) 60   (d) 36
5. (a) 19%   (b) 7%   (c) 21%   (d) 35%   (e) 18%
   (f) 70%   (g) 75%   (h) 80%   (i) 12%
6. (a) 21%   (b) 35%   (c) 75%   (d) 62%   (e) 50%
   (f) 30%   (g) 23%   (h) 17%   (i) 7%
7. (a) $\frac{3}{25}$ (b) $\frac{7}{20}$ (c) $\frac{47}{100}$ (d) $\frac{13}{20}$ (e) $\frac{1}{4}$
   (f) $\frac{9}{50}$ (g) $\frac{17}{25}$ (h) $\frac{37}{100}$ (i) $\frac{3}{4}$ 8. 48%

EXERCISE 6.9

1. (a) 0.17   (b) 0.38   (c) 0.25   (d) 0.63   (e) 0.76
   (f) 0.125   (g) 0.375   (h) 0.187   (i) 1.25   (j) 2.58
   (k) 3.12   (l) 12.25
2. (a) 37%   (b) 68%   (c) 5%   (d) 53%   (e) 1%
   (f) 80%   (g) 150%   (h) 375%   (i) 608%   (j) 75%
   (k) 250%   (l) 305%
3. (a) 125   (b) 182   (c) 409   (d) 243   (e) 572
   (f) 1962   (g) 5125   (h) 15 800
4. (a) 130   (b) 51.5   (c) 430.9   (d) 507.6   (e) 5372.9
   (f) 5071.9   (g) 1806.9   (h) 9760.5   (i) 320.3   (j) 6290
5. $964.68   6. (a) $5520   (b) $1380   7. 24 179

EXERCISE 6.10

1. (a) 50%   (b) 75%   (c) 10%   (d) 40%   (e) 80%
   (f) 70%   (g) 30%   (h) 15%
2. (a) $\frac{21}{100}$ (b) $\frac{7}{20}$ (c) $\frac{3}{5}$ (d) $\frac{3}{20}$ (e) $\frac{9}{20}$
   (f) $\frac{3}{10}$ (g) $\frac{3}{4}$ (h) $\frac{7}{10}$
3. (a) 57.1%   (b) 42.9%   (c) 70.3%   (d) 11.4%   (e) 33.3%
   (f) 56%   (g) 72.7%   (h) 61.5%
4. (a) $\frac{12}{25}$ (b) $1\frac{1}{4}$ (c) $\frac{1}{5}$ (d) $1\frac{1}{2}$ (e) $\frac{3}{40}$ (f) $\frac{1}{200}$
5. 20%   6. 91.7%   7. 3%   8. 45%
9. (a) 5   (b) 2.4   (c) 48   (d) 24.5   (e) 22.5   (f) 14

EXERCISE 6.11

1. (a) 24   (b) 18   (c) 12.35   (d) 5.95   (e) 15.9
   (f) 54.6
2. (a) 20%   (b) 20%   (c) 10%   (d) 80%   (e) 40%
3. 45%   4. 45   5. 30   6. 75%   7. 25%
8. (a) 125   (b) 1375   9. 20   10. (a) $8   (b) 20%

EXERCISE 6.12

1. (a) 23¢   (b) $1.28   (c) $1.64   (d) 95¢   (e) 39¢
   (f) 8¢   (g) $3.85   (h) $3.29   (i) 73¢
2. (a) $3.15   (b) $4.41   (c) $8.75   (d) 61¢   (e) 35¢
   (f) $1.25   (g) 4¢   (h) $4.59   (i) 12¢
3. (a) 29¢   (b) 54¢   (c) 90¢   (d) $1.77   (e) $3.90
   (f) $5.40   (g) $7.17   (h) $19.80   (i) $46.50
4. (a) $980   (b) $1645   (c) $940   (d) $5576   (e) $5622
   (f) $3750   (g) $6680   (h) $3225   (i) $1029   (j) $2012.50
5. $13.86   6. $1855.00   7. (a) $20.00   (b) $269.95   8. $10 500.00

EXERCISE 6.13

1. $2.99
2. $31.08
3. (a) 70¢   (b) $130.74   (c) $573.00   (d) $264.14   (e) $812.06
   (f) $42.34
4. (a) $1500.00   (b) $11 000.00
5. (a) $19.43, $110.07   (b) $1.79, $10.16   (c) $487.50, $2762.50   (d) $48.68, $275.82

EXERCISE 6.14

1. (a) 0.07   (b) 0.12   (c) 0.05   (d) 0.18   (e) 0.085
   (f) 0.1125   (g) 0.1575   (h) 0.205

2. (a) $\frac{6}{73}$ (b) $\frac{12}{73}$ (c) $\frac{18}{73}$ (d) $\frac{5}{52}$ (e) $\frac{27}{52}$
   (f) $\frac{69}{365}$ (g) $\frac{157}{365}$ (h) $\frac{244}{365}$

3. (a) \$72   (b) \$350   (c) \$1800   (d) \$780
4. (a) \$22.19   (b) \$61.64   (c) \$142.05   (d) \$42.74   (e) \$11.56
5. (a) \$160   (b) \$660
6. (a) \$2.33   (b) \$131.33
7. (a) \$960   (b) \$6960
8. (a) \$59.18   (b) \$147.95   (c) \$207.13

6.15 CHAPTER 6 REVIEW EXERCISE

1. (a) 4 : 3   (b) 3 : 2   (c) 1 : 2
2. 3 : 16 : 9   3. b, c, d, f
4. (a) 8   (b) 1   (c) 18   (d) 7   (e) 9   (f) 9
5. (a) 2   (b) 4   (c) 1   (d) 24   (e) 6   (f) 2
6. 15, 25
7. (a) 25%   (b) 25%   (c) 30%   (d) 40%
8. (a) 3%   (b) 30%   (c) 6%   (d) 25%   (e) 45%
   (f) 63%   (g) 7%   (h) 36%   (i) 5%   (j) 32%
   (k) 35%   (l) 22%
9. (a) 0.2   (b) 0.5   (c) 0.08   (d) 0.45   (e) 0.15
   (f) 0.48   (g) 0.75   (h) 0.60   (i) 0.80
10. (a) $\frac{1}{4}$ (b) $\frac{2}{5}$ (c) $\frac{3}{5}$ (d) $\frac{51}{100}$ (e) $\frac{7}{100}$
    (f) $\frac{3}{4}$ (g) $\frac{27}{100}$ (h) $\frac{18}{25}$ (i) $\frac{1}{5}$
11. (a) 15   (b) 6   (c) 40   (d) 120   (e) 400
    (f) 8.26   (g) 7.8   (h) 125.4
12. (a) 50%   (b) 25%   (c) 25%   (d) 20%   (e) 25%
    (f) 50%   (g) 25%   (h) 14%   (i) 7%
13. 2 : 5   14. 25%   15. 240
16. (a) 3 : 2   (b) \$30, \$20   17. $2\frac{2}{5}$ 18. 24
19. (a) \$5700   (b) \$4110   (c) \$6480   (d) \$8850
20. $\doteq$5%   21. 80%   22. \$127.08   23. \$133.15

REVIEW AND PREVIEW TO CHAPTER 7

EXERCISE 1
1. 0.25   2. 0.37   3. 0.54   4. 0.15   5. 0.06   6. 0.09
7. 1.   8. 1.35   9. 0.125   10. 0.236   11. 0.869   12. 0.063

EXERCISE 2
1. 45   2. 37   3. 50   4. 67   5. 80   6. 4
7. 9   8. 23.5   9. 48.6   10. 4.6   11. 30.7   12. 125

EXERCISE 3
1. 50   2. 25   3. 75   4. 30   5. 40   6. 60
7. 70   8. 35   9. 34

EXERCISE 4
1. $\frac{1}{4}$ 2. $\frac{1}{2}$ 3. $\frac{3}{4}$ 4. $\frac{7}{20}$ 5. $\frac{21}{50}$ 6. $\frac{1}{5}$
7. $\frac{4}{5}$ 8. $\frac{3}{50}$ 9. $\frac{3}{100}$

EXERCISE 5
1. 20   2. 12   3. 40   4. 30   5. 129.6   6. 672
7. 30   8. 11   9. 456   10. 46.8

EXERCISE 6
1. 12.5   2. 62.5   3. 33.3   4. 28.6   5. 16.7   6. 11.1

EXERCISE 7
1. 50   2. 75   3. 25   4. 14   5. 21

EXERCISE 8
1. \$16.10   (b) \$246.10   2. 782   3. (a) 72   (b) 28

EXERCISE 7.1

1. 27, 29, 14, 6, 3, 1

2. Movie Type	Frequency	Ratio	%
Adventure	7	7/25	28%
Comedy	6	6/25	24%
Crime	2	2/25	8%
Drama	3	3/25	12%
Romance	4	4/25	16%
Other	3	3/25	12%
Totals	25		100%

3. Seafood	Frequency	Ratio	%
Fish	20	1/4	25%
Clams	12	3/20	15%
Lobster	28	7/20	35%
Oysters	8	1/10	10%
Scallops	4	1/20	5%
Shrimp	8	1/10	10%
Totals	80		100%

EXERCISE 7.2

1. (a) Food	Frequency	Ratio	%	(b) No. of Servings
Hamburgers	7	7/50	14%	56
Hot dogs	9	9/50	18%	72
Pizza	21	21/50	42%	168
Sandwiches	13	13/50	26%	104
Totals	50		100%	400

2. (a) Type	Frequency	Ratio	%	(b) No. of People
Billboards	24	2/25	8%	12 000
Catalogues	66	11/50	22%	33 000
Magazines	15	1/20	5%	7 500
Newspapers	96	8/25	32%	48 000
Radio	39	13/100	13%	19 500
Television	60	1/5	20%	30 000
Totals	300		100%	150 000

EXERCISE 7.3

1. (a) PRAVDA   (b) NEW YORK TIMES

   (c) 5 500 000   LONDON SUN
      5 000 000   LONDON MIRROR
      8 500 000   IZVESTIA
      2 000 000   LONDON EXPRESS
      1 500 000   NEW YORK TIMES
     11 000 000   PRAVDA

2. (a) August   (b) 7   (c) February   (d) 60
3. (a) Erie   (b) Superior   (c) Huron, Ontario   (d) 70, 225, 280, 225, 400
4. (a) N   (b) $30   (c) $325

EXERCISE 7.6

1. (D, 1200) (CH, 450) (C, 600) (G, 750)
2. (M, 27) (DJ, 6) (C, 12) (S, 6) (N, 9)
4. 40% Uniforms   5. 60% Payments
   20% Equipment   20% Gasoline
   10% Travel   15% Insurance
   30% Other   5% Maintenance

EXERCISE 7.7

1. (a) 30   (b) Wednesday   (c) Thursday   (d) 165

EXERCISE 7 8

1. (a) 30   (b) 17   (c) 83   (d) 43   (e) 142
2. (a) 24.3   (b) 26.3   (c) 67.8   (d) 206.4
3. (a) 8.6   (b) 30.6   (c) 101.0
4. $4.17   5. 85   6. 11.7   7. 22.25
8. Week 1   211   Week 2   219   Week 3   194   9. (b) 6

EXERCISE 7.9

1. (a) 12   (b) 86   (c) 29   (d) 7.5   (e) 8.7
   (f) 158.5
2. 72

EXERCISE 7.10

1. (a) 3   (b) 9   (c) 22   (d) none   (e) 84
   (f) $8\frac{1}{2}$, 9
2. 2

EXERCISE 7.11

1.	MEAN	MEDIAN	MODE
(a)	6	6	—
(b)	10	10	10
(c)	5	4	3
(d)	2	1	1
2.	MEAN	MEDIAN	MODE
(a)	12	13	9
(b)	8	9	10
(c)	16.5	16.5	—
(d)	10	9.5	9
(e)	2.8	3	2 & 3
(f)	7	8	9
(g)	11	10	10
3.	MEAN	MEDIAN	MODE
(a)	72	70	70
(b)	8.4	8.2	—
(c)	119	95	90
4.	MEAN	MEDIAN	MODE
(a)	29	30	20
(b)	41	30	20
(c)	changes by 12		
(d)	NO		
(e)	NO		
5.	MEAN	MEDIAN	MODE
(a)	70 000	50 000	30 000
(b)	Median		
6.	MEAN	MEDIAN	MODE
(a)	11.5	8	5
(b)	Mean		
7.	MEAN	MEDIAN	MODE
(a)	10	9.5	9
(b)	9(Mode)		
8.	MEAN	MEDIAN	MODE
(a)	2.3	1	1
(b)	Mean		

EXERCISE 7.12

1. (H, H), (H, T), (T, H), (T, T)
2. (R, B), (B, W), (R, W)
3. (a) R, B, G, O   (b) (R, B), (B, G), (G, O), (O, R), (R, G), (B, O)
   (c) (R, B, G), (R, G, O), (B, G, O), (R, B, O)   (d) (R, B, G, O)
4. (point up, H), (point down, T) (point up, T), (point down, H)
5. (1, up)   (1, down)
   (2, up)   (2, down)
   (3, up)   (3, down)
   (4, up)   (4, down)
   (5, up)   (5, down)
   (6, up)   (6, down)
6. (Heads, Top up), (Heads, Bottom up), (Heads, Side)
   (Tails, Top up), (Tails, Bottom up), (Tails, Side)
7. [P, D, N]   (H, H, H), (H, H, T), (H, T, H), (H, T, T) (T, H, H), (T, H, T), (T, T, H), (T, T, T)
8. [P, N, D, Q]   (H, H, H, H), (H, H, H, T), (H, H, T, H), (H, H, T, T), (H, T, H, H), (H, T, H, T), (H, T, T, H), (H, T, T, T),
                   (T, H, H, H), (T, H, H, T), (T, H, T, H), (T, H, T, T), (T, T, H, H), (T, T, H, T), (T, T, T, H), (T, T, T, T)

EXERCISE 7.13

1. (a) 4/7   (b) 3/7
2. (a) 1/6   (b) 1/2   (c) 1/3   (d) 1/3

3. (a) 2/5   (b) 4/15   (c) 1/3
4. (a) 1/4   (b) 1/2
5. (a)   (b) 1/4   (c) 1/2

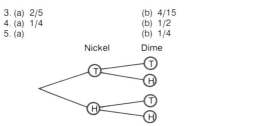

6. (a)

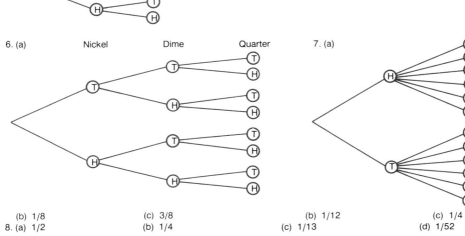

     (b) 1/8   (c) 3/8   (b) 1/12   (c) 1/4
8. (a) 1/2   (b) 1/4   (c) 1/13   (d) 1/52

7.14 CHAPTER 7 REVIEW EXERCISE

1.

Type of Show	Frequency	Ratio	%
Comedy	8	8/25	32%
Mystery	6	6/25	24%
Drama	3	3/25	12%
Police	5	1/5	20%
Western	2	2/25	8%
Other	1	1/25	4%
Total	25		

2. (a) Bombay   (b) Berlin   (c) 4°   (d) 16°

5. Muscle—25 kg
    Fat—10 kg
    Bone—9 kg
    Other—6 kg

7. (a) 30   (b) 32   (c) 129
8. (a) 22   (b) 12   (c) 74.5
9. (a) 6   (b) 13 & 14   (c) 20 & 21

10.

	MEAN	MEDIAN	MODE
(a)	10	11	6
(b)	19	18	—
(c)	51.5	52.5	54

11.

	Nickel	Dime	Quarter

12. (a) 5/11   (b) 6/11
13. (a) 14   (b) 14

REVIEW AND PREVIEW TO CHAPTER 8

EXERCISE 1
| 1. 6 | 2. 20 | 3. 13 | 4. 34 | 5. 10 | 6. 2 |
| 7. 8 | 8. 5 | 9. 8 | 10. 16 | 11. 15 | 12. 9 |

EXERCISE 2
| 1. 13 | 2. 5 | 3. 17 | 4. 9 | 5. 10 | 6. 7 |
| 7. 12 | 8. 1 | 9. 12 | 10. 44 | 11. 16 | 12. 1 |

EXERCISE 3
| 1. 16 | 2. 4 | 3. 2 | 4. 6 | 5. 11 | 6. 7 |
| 7. 14 | 8. 5 | 9. 3 | 10. 2 | | |

EXERCISE 4
| 1. 2.5 | 2. 65 | 3. 12 | 4. 6.8 | 5. 12.2 | 6. 192 |
| 7. 7.1 | 8. 7.5 | 9. −1.6 | 10. 45 | | |

EXERCISE 5
| 1. 24 | 2. 32 | 3. 29.16 | 4. 111.35 |

EXERCISE 6
| 1. 32 | 2. 24 | 3. 100 | 4. 48 |

EXERCISE 8.1

1. (a) 17   (b) 5   (c) 7   (d) 24   (e) 4   (f) 31
2. (a) 8, 14, 20, 26   (b) 4, 9, 13, 28   (c) 12, 28, 32, 0   (d) 3, 7, 9, 15
3. (a) 3   (b) 9   (c) 30   (d) 3   (e) 23   (f) 46
4. (a) 42   (b) 5   (c) 20   (d) 29   (e) 14   (f) 12
5. (a) 13   (b) 2   (c) 35   (d) 74   (e) 33   (f) 200
6. (a) 12   (b) 2   (c) 31   (d) 10   (e) 16   (f) 9
7. 4, 8, 12, 16   8. 10, 19, 25, 31   9. 2, 27, 42, 52   10. 20, 17, 12, 0   11. 59, 83, 149
12. (a) 30, 9, 14, 25   (b) 6, 9, 14, 17   (c) 15, 6, 8, 12   (d) 2, 12, 3, 9

EXERCISE 8.2

1. (a) 9   (b) 25   (c) 36   (d) 7   (e) 8
  (f) 125   (g) 100   (h) 16   (i) 125   (j) 1000
  (k) 81   (l) 243
2. (a) 3^3 (b) 4^5 (c) y^4 (d) m^2 (e) $2x^3$
  (f) r^2s^3 (g) $6y^4z^2$
3. (a) 9   (b) 18   (c) 24   (d) 38   (e) 31
  (f) 39
4. (a) $2 \times 2 \times 2$ (b) $x \times x$ (c) $y \times y \times y \times y$ (d) $x \times x \times x \times x \times y \times y$
  (e) $2 \times n \times n \times n \times n$ (f) $3 \times x \times x \times y \times y \times y \times y$ (g) $5 \times m \times m \times m \times n \times n \times n$
  (h) $8 \times a \times a \times a \times b \times b \times c$
5. (a) 16   (b) 64   (c) 16   (d) 40   (e) 7
  (f) 7   (g) 12   (h) 8   (i) 6   (j) 6
6. 2, 5, 10, 17   7. 1, 15, 53
8. (a) 12   (b) 13   (c) 5   (d) 25   (e) 30
  (f) 23   (g) 30   (h) 32
9. (a) 5, 10, 26, 65   (b) 7, 14, 34, 47
12. (a) $3x \times 3x$ b. $4y \times 4y$ c. $2xy \times 2xy$ d. $5x^2y \times 5x^2y$

EXERCISE 8.3

1. (a) 1, 2	(b) 2, 11	(c) 3, 11	(d) 4, 2	2. (a) 1, 1	(b) 2, 10
2, 4	3, 14	5, 19	6, 3	2, 4	3, 15
3, 6	4, 17		8, 4	3, 9	4, 22
4, 8	5, 20			4, 16	

EXERCISE 8.4

1. (a) −3   (b) −4   (c) 2   (d) 6   (e) 1   (f) −10
2. (a) −8   (b) −7   (c) −9   (d) −25   (e) −11   (f) −8
  (g) 13   (h) 11
3. (a) 4   (b) 8   (c) −8   (d) 12   (e) −4   (f) 16
4. (a) 10   (b) 5   (c) 21   (d) −48   (e) −14   (f) 32
5. (a) 6   (b) 8   (c) −8   (d) −3   (e) 1   (f) −1
  (g) 10   (h) 1
6. (a) 0   (b) −4   (c) 4   (d) −7   (e) 8   (f) −16
  (g) 12   (h) 14

EXERCISE 8.5

1. (a) binomial   (b) monomial   (c) trinomial   (d) monomial   (e) binomial
  (f) trinomial

2. (a) like   (b) unlike   (c) unlike   (d) like   (e) like
   (f) unlike   (g) unlike   (h) like   (i) unlike   (j) like
3. (a) $11x$ (b) $9ab$ (c) $1a$ (d) $-4x^2$ (e) $-12y$
   (f) $-12xy$
4. (a) $8x$ (b) $16a$ (c) $15m$ (d) $9y$ (e) $21x$
   (f) $11y$ (g) $15a$ (h) $10x^2$ (i) $7y^2$ (j) $13t$
5. (a) $2x$ (b) $3a$ (c) $4y$ (d) $5t$ (e) $7x^2$
   (f) $14y^2$
6. (a) $7x$ (b) $6y$ (c) $6t$ (d) $8a$ (e) $8x^2$
   (f) $10y^2$
7. (a) $1x$ (b) $-4t$ (c) $5a$ (d) $-2y$ (e) $-3x$
   (f) $-7x$ (g) $-8x$ (h) $-16b$ (i) $-11x^2$ (j) $-2x$
   (k) $-6y$ (l) $-3a$
8. (a) $5x + 6y$ (b) $7a + 9b$ (c) $11s + 5t$ (d) $6x + 3y$
9. (a) $-2x - 1y$ (b) $-1a + 2b$ (c) $3s - 5t$ (d) $-6x - 3y$ (e) $-1x^2 + 7$
10. (a) $7x^2 + 9x + 3$ (b) $-5y^2 + 1y + 5$ (c) $-2a - 11b - 3$ (d) $-2x - 2y - 4$
   (e) $-1t - 2s - 4$ (f) $-9x - 4$ (g) $-2a - 12b - 3$
11. (a) $7x + 7y$ (b) $7a - 3b + 13$ (c) $-1x^2 - 7x - 2$
   (d) $-9s - 12t - 11$ (e) $2y^2 - 9y + 1$ (f) $2a - 3b - 4$

EXERCISE 8.6

1. (a) -6 (b) -11 (c) 5 (d) 14 (e) -9
   (f) 16 (g) $-2x$ (h) $3b$ (i) $-4x^2$ (j) $7y^2$
   (k) $3xy$ (l) $-2t$ (m) $-2x - 2y$ (n) $-x - 7$ (o) $-x + 9$
   (p) $-2x^2 + 1$ (q) $3x + 4$ (r) $2x^2 + 3x + 1$ (s) $-5x + 2y + 7$ (t) $-2m - 3n + 5$
2. (a) $2x + 4y$ (b) $3a + 2b$ (c) $1s + 4t$ (d) $2x^2$ (e) $4x^2 + 1$
   (f) $2a + 1b + 4$
3. (a) $1x + 7y$ (b) $6x^2 + 10$ (c) $2a + 7b$ (d) $1x^2 + 15$ (e) $7t$
   (f) $1x^2 + 10x + 10$ (g) $5a + 7b$ (h) $5x + 13y$
4. (a) $3x - 5y$ (b) $2a - 5b$ (c) $3x^2 - 7$ (d) $16s$ (e) $-1x + 6y$
   (f) $1x^2 + 3x - 12$ (g) $-10a - 2b$ (h) $-3y^2 + 3y + 6$ (i) $2x^2 - 9x + 11$ (j) $-3a + 1b - 13$
   (k) $4x + 2y - 2$ (l) $2x^2 + 3xy + 3y^2$ (m) $-5a - 9b - 13$ (n) $2s - 2$ (o) O (p) $-3a - 2c$
5. (a) $-1a + 2b$ (b) $-1x + 2y$ (c) $7x^2 + x - 3$ (d) $-3x^2 + 3x - 6$ (e) $-5a + 3b$ (f) $x^2 + 3x - 7$

EXERCISE 8.7

1. (a) $2x + 8$ (b) $3y + 15$ (c) $5t + 15$ (d) $4m + 24$ (e) $3x - 12$ (f) $2t - 10$
2. (a) $6x + 9$ (b) $12y + 20$ (c) $10a + 20b$ (d) $6x - 4y$ (e) $24a - 4b$
   (f) $2a + 3b - 4$ (g) $10x - 15y - 5$ (h) $7x^2 - 14x - 7$
3. (a) $-2x - 6$ (b) $-3a - 12$ (c) $-4y + 8$ (d) $-2x + 14$ (e) $-t + 4$ (f) $-7x + 21$
4. (a) $-4a - 6$ (b) $-9x + 12$ (c) $-2x + 3y$ (d) $-20a + 8b$ (e) $-2x^2 - 6x + 2$
   (f) $-y^2 + 2y - 4$ (g) $-4 + 8a - 4a^2$ (h) $-x + y + 5$ (i) $-10 + 20x + 10x^2$
5. (a) $5x + 12$ (b) $9a + 13$ (c) $7t - 11$ (d) $5x + 1y$ (e) $2b - 14$ (f) $-3x - 8$
6. (a) $13x - 8$ (b) $10t + 6$ (c) $8y - 16$ (d) $4y - 4$
7. (a) $x^2 - 4x$ (b) $3t^2 + 17$ (c) $4y^2 - y - 6$ (d) $-5a + 3b + 4$ (e) $-10x - 3y$ (f) $-2x - 4$
8. (a) $-5a - 8b + 13$ (b) $x^2 - 2x - 16$ (c) $-5x^2 + 4y^2$ (d) $-4t^2 + 5t + 3$ (e) $2x - 13$ (f) $-6x + 6y + 4$
9. (a) $2\ell + 2w$ (b) $\pi R^2 - \pi r^2$

EXERCISE 8.8

1. (a) $8xy$ (b) $12ab$ (c) $12rs$ (d) $21m$ (e) $48rt$
   (f) $10a^2b^2$ (g) $4m^2n$ (h) $12r^2$ (i) $20a^2bc$ (j) $72b$
   (k) $21ab$
2. (a) $12xy$ (b) $12ab$ (c) $6x^2y^2$ (d) $40abc$ (e) $-6xy$
   (f) $-20ab$ (g) $14x^2y^2$ (h) $-16ab$ (i) $-18xyz$ (j) $14mn$
3. (a) $8x^2y^2$ (b) $15t^2s$ (c) $-18abc^2$ (d) $-30x^2y^2$ (e) $16xyz$
   (f) $-30a^2b^2$ (g) $-14rsty$
4. (a) $4a^2b$ (b) $-12xyz$ (c) $15xy$ (d) $10t^2s$ (e) $-27s^2t$
   (f) $-20abc^2$
5. (a) $24abc$ (b) $-40xyz$ (c) $12mnt$ (d) $-6a^2b^2c^2$ (e) $-24xyzt$
   (f) $20abc$ (g) $24rst$

EXERCISE 8.9

1. (a) x^7 (b) a^6 (c) b^3 (d) y^5 (e) m^{13}
   (f) r^5 (g) t^7 (h) c^4
2. (a) x^7 (b) a^8 (c) t^7 (d) m^3 (e) y^4
   (f) w^9 (g) b^5 (h) s^7
3. (a) x^5y^2 (b) m^5n^3 (c) w^7x^4 (d) a^7b^3 (e) r^4s^2
   (f) x^4y^2 (g) s^6t^6 (h) x^3y^6
4. (a) $14x^5$ (b) $15t^7$ (c) $30a^3$ (d) $12m^4$ (e) $48y^5$
   (f) $8t^5$ (g) $6x^7$ (h) $60m^6$

5. (a) $36x^3y^2$ (b) $6a^2b^6$ (c) $24r^5s$ (d) $20s^5t$ (e) $18x^5$
6. (a) $-6x^3$ (b) $10t^4$ (c) $-12y^6$ (d) $12m^6$ (e) $15a^4$
   (f) $-14y^7$
7. (a) $6a^5b^5$ (b) $8x^3y^3$ (c) $-15r^3s^7$ (d) $-16a^5b^5$ (e) $-6a^2b^2c^3$
   (f) $-6r^3s^2t^2$ (g) $-14a^5b^2c^2$ (h) $100x^3y^2$
8. (a) $18x^4$ (b) $-12a^4b^3$ (c) $-24s^3t^3$ (d) $30x^3y^3$ (e) $-24t^3s^2$
   (f) $6x^4y^3$ (g) $3x^3y^3$

EXERCISE 8.10

1. (a) $2x$ (b) $3b$ (c) $4t$ (d) $8r$ (e) $4m$
   (f) $4abc$ (g) t (h) $6xy$
2. (a) 4 (b) 5 (c) $3c$ (d) $2s$ (e) $5a$
   (f) $6x$ (g) 7 (h) 9
3. (a) 4 (b) $4x$ (c) $2t$ (d) 5 (e) 2
   (f) $2bc$ (g) 4 (h) z (i) $5a$ (j) 1
4. (a) $-5a$ (b) $-2x$ (c) $6w$ (d) t (e) $-6x$
   (f) $5ab$ (g) $-7t$ (h) $-s$
5. (a) -6 (b) 5 (c) -9 (d) -11 (e) $-4y$
   (f) $6s$
6. (a) $-6b$ (b) $-3yz$ (c) 3 (d) $-5y$ (e) $-4b$
   (f) $-4st$ (g) 8 (h) $-10c$ (i) -1 (j) bc
   (k) -6 (l) 2 (m) $2a$ (n) $-3r$

EXERCISE 8.11

1. (a) x^1 (b) a^3 (c) m^4 (d) $t^0 = 1$ (e) w^3
   (f) x^2
2. (a) m^5 (b) y^5 (c) 1 (d) t (e) c^4
3. (a) $4x^2$ (b) $4m$ (c) $2t$ (d) $4a^2$ (e) $3x$
   (f) t^1 (g) $6m^2$ (h) $4x$ (i) $10y^2$ (j) $2a^2$
   (k) m^1
4. (a) $4ab$ (b) $4x^2y^3$ (c) $2m^2$ (d) $5s^2$ (e) $2a^2$
   (f) $2y^4$ (g) $3m^3n^2$ (h) $3t^2$ (i) $3a^2$
5. (a) $-4a^2$ (b) $3x$ (c) $-5m^2$ (d) $-5m^2n$ (e) $-2a^2$
   (f) $-4x$ (g) $-7m^5$ (h) $-3a^2b$ (i) $-4mn$ (j) $-9x^3y^3$
   (k) $6t$ (l) $-a$ (m) $-xy^2$
6. (a) x^7 (b) t^6 (c) $m^0 = 1$ (d) c (e) x^2
   (f) m^4

EXERCISE 8.12

1. (a) x^6 (b) a^{12} (c) w^6 (d) a^9 (e) t^8
   (f) m^{10}
2. (a) 3^4 (b) 2^{12} (c) 5^6 (d) 4^{12}
3. (a) a^4b^6 (b) m^6n^6 (c) $s^{12}t^6$ (d) $x^{20}y^4$ (e) a^3b^{12}
   (f) $m^{10}n^{20}$
4. (a) $8x^6$ (b) $9m^6$ (c) $16a^8$ (d) $27y^{15}$ (e) $4m^2$
   (f) $10\,000x^{16}$ (g) $81t^{12}$ (h) $32s^{30}$
5. (a) $8a^6b^6$ (b) $9x^6y^4$ (c) $16m^{16}n^4$ (d) $16x^4y^8$ (e) $125a^9b^3$
   (f) $27x^{12}y^6$
6. (a) $-8x^6$ (b) $9a^8$ (c) $16t^{10}$ (d) $-8m^9$ (e) $-1y^{20}$
   (f) $-1b^{42}$
7. (a) $4x^4y^6$ (b) $-27a^9b^3$ (c) $m^{20}n^{12}$ (d) $16r^6t^4$ (e) $-x^{20}y^5$
   (f) $16a^{12}b^8$ (g) $125r^6t^3$ (h) $-1000s^3t^3$ (i) $-32r^{10}s^5t^{15}$ (j) $x^{18}y^6$
8. (a) 32 (b) 4 (c) 16 (d) 64
9. (a) -1 (b) -1 (c) 1 (d) 1

EXERCISE 8.13

1. x^2, $3x$, $x^2 + 3x$, $x^2 + 3x$ 2. (a) m^2, $5m$, $m^2 + 5m$, $m^2 + 5m$ (b) 84
3. (a) $4t^2$, $6t$, $4t^2 + 6t$, $4t^2 + 6t$ (b) 88
4. x^2, $2x$, x, 2, $x^2 + 3x + 2$, $x^2 + 3x + 2$
5. (a) m^2, $3m$, $4m$, 12, $m^2 + 7m + 12$, $m^2 + 7m + 12$ (b) 90
6. (a) t^2, $5t$, $2t$, 10, $t^2 + 7t + 10$, $t^2 + 7t + 10$,   (b) 88

EXERCISE 8.14

1. (a) $3x^2 + 3x$ (b) $2a^2 + 8a$ (c) $4t^2 - 12t$ (d) $5m^2 - 10m$ (e) $y^2 - 4y$
2. (a) $-2x^2 - 6x$ (b) $-3m^2 - 12m$ (c) $-2t^2 + 6t$ (d) $-5m^2 + 5m$ (e) $-x^2 - 2x$
   (f) $-x^2 + 3x$
3. (a) $4x^2 - 6x$ (b) $6a^2 - 3a$ (c) $-6t^2 - 6t$ (d) $-12m^2 + 20m$ (e) $5y + 15y^2$
   (f) $3x + 12x^2$ (g) $-2m + 6m^2$ (h) $-t + 2t^2$

4. (a) $2x^2 + 5x + 6$ (b) $3t^2 + 10t + 12$ (c) $2m^2 + 9m$ (d) $6x^2 + 14x$ (e) $2w^2 + w - 12$
   (f) $3y^2 - 17y - 12$ (g) $-2x^2 + 3x$ (h) $-3m^2 + 9m + 15$ (i) $-5a^2 + a$ (j) $8x^2 + 5x$
   (k) $2m^2 - 2m$
5. (a) $4x^2 + 11x + 6$ (b) $5y^2 - 14y$ (c) $4t^2 + 17t$ (d) $-12w^2 + 26w - 42$ (e) $-5a^2 + a$
   (f) $8m^2 + m$ (g) $-18x^2 + 17x$
6. (a) $3x^2 + 6x + 2$ (b) $-4m + 14$ (c) $t^2 + 8t + 4$ (d) $-4w^2 + 14w + 3$ (e) $11r^2 - 9r - 11$
   (f) 2

EXERCISE 8.15

1. (1) x^2 (2) $3x$ (3) x (4) 3 (5) $x^2 + 4x + 3$ (6) $x^2 + 4x + 3$
2. (a) $x^2 + 3x + 2$ (b) $t^2 + 7t + 12$ (c) $m^2 + 10m + 25$ (d) $y^2 + 9y + 14$ (e) $x^2 + 10x + 16$
3. (a) $x^2 - 7x + 12$ (b) $m^2 - 3x + 2$ (c) $t^2 - 2t + 1$ (d) $y^2 - 13y + 42$ (e) $r^2 - 6r + 9$
4. (a) $x^2 + x - 6$ (b) $m^2 - m - 20$ (c) $y^2 - 3y - 4$ (d) $a^2 - 25$ (e) $x^2 - 1$
5. (a) $x^2 + x - 30$ (b) $y^2 - 5y + 6$ (c) $m^2 + 3m - 28$ (d) $t^2 + 15t + 56$ (e) $x^2 + 16x + 60$
   (f) $w^2 - 9$ (g) $r^2 - 3r - 54$ (h) $t^2 - 5t + 6$
6. (a) $2x^2 + 7x + 3$ (b) $3t^2 - 4t - 4$ (c) $3m^2 + 7m + 2$ (d) $4x^2 - 7x + 3$ (e) $6a^2 + a - 2$
   (f) $6y^2 - 11y + 4$ (g) $-4x^2 + 1$
7. (a) $x^2 + 6x + 9$ (b) $y^2 - 4y + 4$ (c) $m^2 + 8m + 16$ (d) $t^2 - 6t + 9$
8. (a) $x^2 - 1$ (b) $m^2 - 9$ (c) $y^2 - 16$ (d) $a^2 - 25$ (e) $t^2 - 4$ (f) $a^2 - b^2$
9. (a) $x^3 + 4x^2 + 5x + 2$ (b) $x^3 - 4x^2 + 6x - 3$ (c) $t^3 + 6t^2 + 7t - 6$

EXERCISE 8.16

1. (a) $x + y$ (b) $2a + b$ (c) $s + 2t$ (d) $4m + 2$ (e) $x + 1$
   (f) $a - 2b$ (g) $m - 2n$ (h) $3x - 2$ (i) $a - 1$
2. (a) $x^2 + 2x + 3$ (b) $t^2 + 2t + 3$ (c) $m^2 - 2m + 3$ (d) $2a^2 - 3a - 1$ (e) $2r^2 - r + 1$
   (f) $2x^2 - 2x + 3$ (g) $a^2 - a + 3$ (h) $r^2 - r - 1$
3. (a) $x + 2$ (b) $2a + 3$ (c) $a - 2$ (d) $6t - 7$ (e) $3w + 1$
   (f) $2x - 1$
4. (a) $x^2 + 2x + 3$ (b) $2m^2 - 3m - 4$ (c) $2t^2 - t + 4$ (d) $a^2 + 3a - 1$

EXERCISE 8.17

1. (a) 2 (b) 2 (c) $3x$ (d) $4x$ (e) 2
2. (a) 1 (b) $5x^2$ (c) $3x^2$ (d) $5r$ (e) $8x$ (f) $2c$ (g) $3a^2$
3. (a) $3y$ (b) 16 (c) 2 (d) $-4b$ (e) $-4y$ (f) $-2x$
4. (a) $7y$ (b) $-5c$ (c) $3y^2$ (d) $-2bc$ (e) $7q^2r$ (f) -1

EXERCISE 8.18

1. (a) $x + 3$ (b) $x - 5$
2. (a) $x + 3$ (b) $x + 7$ (c) $x - 2$ (d) $x - 6$
3. (a) $x + 5$ (b) x (c) $x - 3$ (d) x (e) $x - 2$
   (f) $x + 3$ (g) $a + b$ (h) $2a + b$

EXERCISE 8.19

1. (a) 2 (b) 7 (c) 6 (d) x (e) a
   (f) $5x$ (g) $4ab$ (h) xy
2. (a) 2 (b) 3 (c) 4 (d) 6 (e) $2b$
   (f) 4
3. (a) $a + b$ (b) $x - y$ (c) $x + 2$ (d) $a - 3$ (e) $a + 2b + 3c$
   (f) $x - 2$ (g) $3x^2 + 2x + 1$
4. (a) 3 (b) 2 (c) x (d) a (e) x
   (f) x^2 (g) a
5. (a) $4(a + b)$ (b) $2(x - y)$ (c) $3(x + 2)$ (d) $5(b - 2)$ (e) $4(2y - 1)$
   (f) $2(a + 3b - 4c)$ (g) $2(2x^2 + y)$ (h) $7(x^2 - 2x + 3)$ (i) $5(4a + b - 3)$ (j) $6(t^2 - t + 2)$
6. (a) $x(x + 3)$ (b) $a(a - 2)$ (c) $a(5x + 6y)$ (d) $x(4y - 7a)$ (e) $2a(x + y)$
   (f) $3m(x - 2y)$ (g) $5t(2x - y)$ (h) $3x(x + 4)$ (i) $5a(a - 3)$ (j) $4x^2(2x - 1)$
7. (a) $3xy(2x - y)$ (b) $2ab(2a + 3 - 4b)$ (c) $7xy(2xy - y + 1)$
   (d) $2ab(3c - x + 5y)$ (e) $7a(a^2 + 2a - 1)$ (f) $2x(4m - 2n + 3)$
   (g) $2x^2(3x - 5y - 4y^2)$

EXERCISE 8.20

1. (a) 4 (b) 2 (c) 3 (d) x (e) a
2. (a) $x + 3$ (b) $a - 10$ (c) $m + 5$ (d) $r - 6$ (e) $3x + 2$ (f) $5m - 1$
3. (a) $(x - 4)(x + 4)$ (b) $(n - 3)(n + 3)$ (c) $(t - 1)(t + 1)$ (d) $(r - 11)(r + 11)$
   (e) $(y - 7)(y + 7)$ (f) $(s - 9)(s + 9)$ (g) $(x - 8)(x + 8)$ (h) $(b - 12)(b + 12)$
4. (a) $(2x - 5)(2x + 5)$ (b) $(3m - 1)(3m + 1)$ (c) $(4t - 7)(4t + 7)$ (d) $(5n - 11)(5n + 11)$
   (e) $(8x - 3)(8x + 3)$ (f) $(10a - 1)(10a + 1)$ (g) $(2s - 9)(2s + 9)$
5. (a) $(4 - x)(4 + x)$ (b) $(6 - y)(6 + y)$ (c) $(9 - m)(9 + m)$ (d) $(10 - t)(10 + t)$
   (e) $(3 - 2x)(3 + 2x)$ (f) $(11 - 4m)(11 + 4m)$ (g) $(9 - 5t)(9 + 5t)$ (h) $(8 - 3x)(8 + 3x)$

EXERCISE 8.21

1. (a) 3, 2   (b) 4, 2   (c) 2, 1   (d) −3, −1   (e) −1, −1   (f) −4, −3
    (g) −5, −2   (h) −4, 3   (i) 4, −2   (j) 4, −3   (k) 5, −2
2. (a) $x + 2$ (b) $m + 1$ (c) $t + 3$ (d) $y − 3$ (e) $a − 3$ (f) $z − 8$
    (g) $x + 5$ (h) $t − 6$ (i) $r − 2$ (j) $n − 5$
3. (a) $(x + 5)(x + 1)$ (b) $(t + 7)(t + 2)$ (c) $(m + 5)(m + 4)$ (d) $(n + 2)(n + 2)$
    (e) $(y − 2)(y − 1)$ (f) $(k − 3)(k − 2)$ (g) $(a − 4)(a − 3)$ (h) $(b − 6)(b − 2)$
    (i) $(x − 6)(x + 4)$ (j) $(m + 4)(m − 3)$ (k) $(x − 7)(x + 5)$ (l) $(n + 8)(n − 3)$
    (m) $(y − 7)(y + 3)$ (n) $(a − 3)(a − 3)$ (o) $(x − 1)(x − 1)$

8.22 CHAPTER 8 REVIEW EXERCISE

1. (a) 4   (b) 9   (c) 125   (d) 36   (e) 64   (f) 10 000
2. (a) 12   (b) 5   (c) 11   (d) 10
3. (a) 5   (b) 11   (c) 4   (d) 5   (e) 4   (f) −5
4. (a) $8x$ (b) $2m$ (c) $10t$ (d) $4x^2$ (e) 0   (f) $−2y$
    (g) $−6x$ (h) $−m$ (i) $−3y$ (j) $−4t$ (k) $9y$
    (l) $−2t$
5. (a) $3x + 12$ (b) $7y − 14$ (c) $15x + 10y$ (d) $12x − 8y + 16$
6. (a) $6xy$ (b) $8x^2y^2$ (c) x^7 (d) t^8 (e) $10m^5$ (f) $6n^5$
    (g) x^5 (h) $5t^4$ (i) m^{12} (j) m^7
7. (a) $2x^2 + 6x$ (b) $5t^2 − 5t$ (c) $−3x^2 + 12x$ (d) $−4m^2 − 12m$ (e) $y^2 + 5y$ (f) $−x^2 − 3x$
8. (a) 1, 5   (b) −4, −10
    2, 7   −3, −7
    3, 9   −2, −4
    4, 11   −1, −1
    5, 13   0, 2
                1, 5
9. (a) 5   (b) 8   (c) −1   (d) 13   (e) 0   (f) 12
10. (a) 1   (b) −1   (c) −1   (d) 5   (e) 8   (f) 6
11. (a) $8x + 7y$ (b) $3x + 2y$ (c) $11m − 9t$ (d) $−7x + 3y$ (e) $9m − 5n + 7$
    (f) $t − 2x − 6y + 9$ (g) $−2x − 2y − 9$
12. (a) $−2x + 10$ (b) $8a − 12b − 28$ (c) $−4x^2 − 2x + 6$ (d) $−x + y + 6$ (e) $7x + 12$
    (f) $−4x − 2$ (g) $−5t − 17$ (h) $x + y + 9$ (i) $−5x − 20$
13. (a) $15x^5$ (b) $14a^4$ (c) $5n^6$ (d) $8y^6$ (e) $−12x^3$
    (f) $6m^5$ (g) $−16a^3b^4$ (h) $−6r^3s^3t$ (i) $20a^3b^3c^2$ (j) $21x^4y^3$
14. (a) $3x^2$ (b) $5t^2$ (c) $−4b^3$ (d) $7s^3$ (e) $5x^2y$
    (f) $−4a^2b$ (g) $5a^3$ (h) $9x^2y$ (i) $4mn^2$ (j) $−6r^2s$
15. (a) a^4b^6 (b) $8x^9y^6$ (c) $−27r^6s^3$ (d) $m^{16}n^8$ (e) $16x^6y^6$
    (f) $81a^4b^8c^{12}$
16. (a) $2x^2 + 8x$ (b) $12y^2 − 4y$ (c) $6x^2 + 6x − 18$ (d) $−w^2 − 23w$ (e) $8x^2 − 5x − 5$
    (f) $6m^2 − 4n^2 − 5mn$
17. (a) $x^2 + 5x + 6$ (b) $t^2 − 2t − 8$ (c) $t^2 + 15t + 54$ (d) $x^2 − 9x + 20$ (e) $m^2 − 16$
    (f) $y^2 − 8y + 15$ (g) $2x^2 + 9x − 5$ (h) $−9x^2 + 1$
18. (a) $x^2 + 2x$ (b) $2a^2 − 3a − 3$ (c) $4x − 7$ (d) $2r − 3$ (e) $x^2 + 2x − 3$
    (f) $5t^2 − 2t + 8$
19. (a) $3(a + b)$ (b) $2(x − 5)$ (c) $a(3x + 2y)$ (d) $7r(2t − 3s)$
20. (a) $(x − 3)(x + 3)$ (b) $(t − 5)(t + 5)$ (c) $(x + 3)(x + 1)$ (d) $(m − 4)(m + 2)$ (e) $(y + 5)(y − 2)$
    (f) $(a + 2)(a + 2)$

REVIEW AND PREVIEW TO CHAPTER 9

EXERCISE 1
1. $8x$ 2. $14y$ 3. $12a$ 4. x 5. $8b$
6. $2t$ 7. $13x + 2y$ 8. $9x^2$ 9. $6xy$ 10. $2a + 11b$

EXERCISE 2
1. $2x$ 2. $−2a$ 3. $−x$ 4. $−11t$ 5. $−2m − 6n$
6. $−s − 7t$ 7. $−4x^2$ 8. $−7m − 7n + 5$ 9. $−5xy$ 10. $−4y + 3x$

EXERCISE 3
1. $2x + 8$ 2. $12y − 20$ 3. $10a + 15b$ 4. $24x − 42$ 5. $−2x + 6$
6. $−6t − 18$ 7. $−5x − 7$ 8. $24m + 40n$ 9. $−9s + 6t$ 10. $−14m − 63$

EXERCISE 4
1. (a) 6   (b) 18   (c) 9   (d) 5   (e) 19   (f) 4
2. (a) 7   (b) 1   (c) 72   (d) 31   (e) 4   (f) 10
    (g) −2   (h) −4
3. (a) 3   (b) 7   (c) −11   (d) −20   (e) −1   (f) −17
    (g) 18   (h) 15

EXERCISE 5
1. 2   2. 3   3. 9   4. 10   5. 6   6. 11
7. 3   8. 11   9. 2   10. 4

EXERCISE 9.1

1. (a) 4   (b) 3   (c) 8   (d) 4
(e) 6   (f) 2   (g) 3   (h) 34
2. Yes   3. No   4. Yes   5. Yes
6. Yes   7. No   8. Yes   9. No
12. (a) 3   (b) 7   (c) 2   (d) 4   (e) 6
(f) 5   (g) 2   (h) 5   (i) 3
13. (a) 8   (b) 15   (c) 8   (d) 16   (e) 19
(f) 21   (g) 3   (h) 5   (i) 3   (j) -3

EXERCISE 9.2

1. (a) 8   (b) 7   (c) 11   (d) 10   (e) 5   (f) 10
2. (a) 42   (b) 27   (c) 14   (d) 35   (e) 11   (f) 4
3. (a) 53   (b) 74   (c) 65   (d) 74   (e) 80   (f) 70
4. (a) 9   (b) 9   (c) 5   (d) 16   (e) 15   (f) 7
5. (a) 7.3   (b) 6.6   (c) 9.1   (d) 9.4   (e) 1.8   (f) 6.2
6. (a) 12   (b) 17   (c) 1   (d) 19   (e) 41   (f) 19

EXERCISE 9.3

1. (a) 1   (b) 3   (c) 5   (d) 6   (e) 2   (f) 1
2. (a) 5   (b) 11   (c) 9   (d) 7   (e) 33   (f) 24
3. (a) 10   (b) 8   (c) 34   (d) 26   (e) 9   (f) 28
4. (a) 14   (b) 1   (c) 13   (d) 7   (e) 28   (f) 19
5. (a) 4.7   (b) 3.5   (c) 0.5   (d) 7.4   (e) 3.2   (f) 4.5
6. (a) 89   (b) 262   (c) 108   (d) 311   (e) 348   (f) 261
(g) 21   (h) 26   (i) 77   (j) 118

EXERCISE 9.4

1. (a) 3   (b) 2   (c) 2   (d) 4   (e) 3   (f) 4
(g) 4   (h) 3   (i) 4   (j) 6   (k) 2   (l) 4
2. (a) 5   (b) 9   (c) 7   (d) 6   (e) 9   (f) 11
(g) 4   (h) 11   (i) 12   (j) 1
3. (a) 5   (b) 2   (c) 6   (d) 3   (e) 6   (f) 2
(g) 8   (h) 6   (i) 4   (j) 0
4. (a) 4.2   (b) 12.3   (c) 40   (d) 0.2   (e) 31   (f) 7
(g) 5   (h) 40
5. (a) 36   (b) 49   (c) 15   (d) 8   (e) 14   (f) 31
6. (a) 10   (b) 6   (c) 4   (d) 2   (e) 6   (f) 5

EXERCISE 9.5

1. (a) 6   (b) 15   (c) 6   (d) 45   (e) 24
(f) 14   (g) 40   (h) 72   (i) 56
2. (a) 117   (b) 70   (c) 42   (d) 60   (e) 63
(f) 66   (g) 320   (h) 186   (i) 108
3. (a) -6 (b) -2 (c) -16 (d) 0   (e) -30
(f) -18 (g) -45 (h) -56 (i) -60
4. (a) 3.9   (b) 1   (c) 26   (d) 62

EXERCISE 9.6

1. (a) 5   (b) 2   (c) 18   (d) 36
2. (a) $2x + 3$ (b) $3t - 1$ (c) $4m + 5$ (d) $\frac{x}{2} - 3$ (e) x
3. (a) $-1 \to \div 2$ (b) $+5 \to \div 3$ (c) $+1 \to \div 2$ (d) $-3 \to \div 4$
4. (a) 1   (b) 4   (c) 4   (d) 2   (e) 4
(f) 6
5. (a) 6   (b) 15   (c) 12   (d) 8

EXERCISE 9.7

1. (a) 11   (b) 19   (c) 15   (d) 10   (e) 10
(f) 9   (g) 13   (h) 7
2. (a) 5   (b) 6   (c) 4   (d) 2   (e) 3
(f) 5   (g) 3   (h) 2
3. (a) 4   (b) 4   (c) 5   (d) 8   (e) 5
(f) 4   (g) 2   (h) 7
4. (a) 3   (b) 3   (c) 5   (d) 2   (e) 3
(f) 3   (g) 5   (h) 2
5. (a) 4   (b) 3   (c) 2   (d) 8   (e) 2
(f) 13   (g) 2   (h) 3

6. (a) 8   (b) 9   (c) 28   (d) 10   (e) 8
   (f) 15   (g) 12   (h) 25

EXERCISE 9.8

1. (a) 3   (b) 9   (c) −1   (d) −4   (e) 4
    (f) −6   (g) 2   (h) −5   (i) 5   (j) −5
    (k) −8   (l) −1   (m) −4   (n) −2   (o) −7
    (p) 3
2. (a) −4   (b) −3   (c) 2   (d) −3   (e) −1
    (f) 9   (g) −1   (h) −1   (i) −2   (j) 1
3. (a) −1   (b) −2   (c) −2   (d) 3   (e) 3
    (f) −1
4. (a) −4   (b) 3   (c) 3   (d) −2   (e) −1
    (f) −2   (g) 6   (h) −8   (i) 1   (j) −3

EXERCISE 9.9

1. (a) 4   (b) 3   (c) 4   (d) 1   (e) 9
    (f) 6   (g) 2   (h) 3   (i) 4   (j) 3
2. (a) 4   (b) 5   (c) 4   (d) 3   (e) 7
    (f) 5   (g) 3   (h) 5
3. (a) −4   (b) −1   (c) −4   (d) −5   (e) 3
    (f) 2   (g) −2   (h) −3   (i) −2   (j) −4
    (k) 5   (l) 1
4. (a) 4   (b) 3   (c) 2   (d) −3   (e) 4
    (f) −7   (g) −3   (h) −9   (i) 6   (j) 3
5. CANADIAN

EXERCISE 9.10

1. (a) 1   (b) 3   (c) 4   (d) −5   (e) 3
    (f) −2
2. (a) 4   (b) 1   (c) 0   (d) −8   (e) 3
3. (a) 2   (b) 5   (c) 2   (d) −2   (e) 12
4. (a) −4   (b) 4   (c) −1   (d) −1   (e) −2
5. (a) 7   (b) −6   (c) −4   (d) 13
6. (a) 3   (b) −7   (c) 8   (d) −1   (e) 5
7. (a) $1\frac{1}{4}$ (b) 2   (c) −2   (d) 1   (e) 4
8. (a) 2   (b) −2   (c) −10   (d) 1   (e) −1
9. 3   10. 4

EXERCISE 9.11

1. (a) 0.2   (b) 0.8   (c) −1.4   (d) 5.0   (e) −3.8
2. (a) 10   (b) 50   (c) 3   (d) 4   (e) −3
3. (a) 0.6   (b) 0.4   (c) 0.6   (d) 1   (e) 0.7
4. (a) 3.5   (b) −2.3   (c) −0.5   (d) −0.7   (e) −1.6
5. (a) 2   (b) 3   (c) −6   (d) −5   (e) −2
6. (a) 2   (b) 0.5   (c) 5.2   (d) 6.6   (e) −1.2

EXERCISE 9.12

1. (a) 18   (b) 8   (c) −3   (d) 8   (e) −15
    (f) −12   (g) −8   (h) −9
2. (a) $\frac{1}{2}$ (b) $\frac{4}{3}$ (c) $\frac{5}{4}$ (d) 2   (e) 4
    (f) $\frac{10}{3}$ (g) $\frac{16}{5}$ (h) $\frac{5}{2}$ (i) $\frac{7}{2}$
3. (a) 6   (b) −12   (c) −8   (d) −15   (e) −24
    (f) 24
4. (a) 3   (b) 2   (c) −2   (d) 3   (e) $\frac{4}{5}$

EXERCISE 9.13

1. (a) <   (b) >   (c) <   (d) <   (e) >
    (f) <
2. (a) true   (b) false   (c) true   (d) true   (e) false
3. (a) >   (b) <   (c) <   (d) >   (e) <
    (f) >
4. (a) x<4, xϵW   (b) x>2, xϵW   (c) x>8, xϵW
5. (a) {6,7,8,...}   (b) {0,1,2}   (c) {8,9,10,...}   (d) {0,1,2,3,4,5}
6. (a) {0,1,2}   (b) {6,7,8,...}   (c) {3,4,5,...}   (d) {0,1,2,...,6,7,8}
7. (a) {0,1,2,3}   (b) {6,7,8,...}   (c) {5,6,7,...}   (d) {0,1,2,...,8,9,10}

EXERCISE 9.14

1. (a) true   (b) false   (c) false   (d) true   (e) true
  (f) false   (g) false
2. (a) (ii),(vi)   (b) (i),(iv)   (c) (iii),(v)
3. (a) {4,5,6,...}   (b) {5,6,7,...}   (c) {0,1,2,3}   (d) {0,1,2,3,4,5,6}
  (e) {0,1,2,3,4,6,7,8,...}   (f) {0,1,3,4,5,...}
4. (a) {0,1,2,3,4}   (b) {9,10,11,...}   (c) {0,1,2,4,5,6,...}   (d) {0,1,...,6,7,8}
  (e) {4,5,6,...}
5. (a) {0,1,2,3}   (b) {6,7,8,...}   (c) {0,1,2,4,5,6,...}
  (d) {0,1,2,3,4,5,6}   (e) {5,6,7,...}   (f) {0,1,2,3,4,5,6,8,9,10,...}
  (g) {0,1,2,3}   (h) {13,14,15,...}

EXERCISE 9.15

1. (a) x>7   (b) x>8   (c) x<8   (d) x≥3   (e) x≤4   (f) x>3   (g) x≥−2
  (h) x<1   (i) x≤−2   (j) x>2
2. (a) x>5, XϵW   (b) x<11, XϵW   (c) x≥5, XϵW   (d) x≤5, XϵW   (e) x<3, Xϵl   (f) x≥−4, Xϵl
  (g) x<−2, Xϵl   (h) x≤−1, Xϵl   (i) x≥−2, Xϵl   (j) x<2, Xϵl

EXERCISE 9.16

1. (a) x>3, XϵW   (b) x>5, XϵW   (c) x<4, XϵW   (d) x≥1, XϵW   (e) x≤2, Xϵl
  (f) x<−3, Xϵl   (g) x>−3, Xϵl   (h) x<−7, Xϵl   (i) x≥−8, Xϵl   (j) x≤−2, Xϵl
2. (a) x>4   (b) x<3   (c) x≥2   (d) x≤3   (e) x>−4
  (f) x<−2   (g) x>−5   (h) x≤−9   (i) x≥−8   (j) x>−1

EXERCISE 9.17

1. (a) >   (b) <   (c) <   (d) >   (e) >
2. (a) x>3   (b) x<4   (c) x≥−2   (d) x≤−2   (e) x<−2
  (f) x>−1   (g) x≤3
3. (a) x>2, Xϵl   (b) t<−3, tϵl   (c) x>−3, Xϵl   (d) x≤3, Xϵl

EXERCISE 9.18

1. (a) x>8   (b) x<6   (c) x≥−8   (d) x≤−6   (e) x<−2
  (f) x>−12   (g) x≤8   (h) x≥2   (i) x≤0   (j) x<0
2. (a) x<6   (b) t≥8   (c) x>−4   (d) x≤4   (e) x≤0

EXERCISE 9.19

1. (a) x<3   (b) x>3   (c) x≤3   (d) x≥2   (e) x>−3
  (f) x<−6   (g) x≥−4   (h) x≤−4
2. (a) x>2   (b) x<4   (c) x≥2   (d) x≤4   (e) x<−3
  (f) x>−1   (g) x≤−1   (h) x≥−2
3. (a) x>4   (b) x<9   (c) x≥2   (d) x≤28   (e) x>−9
  (f) x<−4   (g) x≤15   (h) x<−2   (i) x≥−3
4. (a) x>8   (b) x<3   (c) x≥4   (d) x≤−15   (e) x<−2
  (f) x>6   (g) x≤4   (h) x≥−5
5. (a) x<2   (b) x>4   (c) x≤3   (d) x≤−2   (e) x>1
  (f) x<2
6. (a) x>3   (b) x<1   (c) x≥3   (d) x≤−4

9.20 CHAPTER 9 REVIEW EXERCISE

1. (a) x = 5   (b) m = 6   (c) t = 6   (d) y = 5   (e) x = 4
  (f) t = 6   (g) m = 7   (h) y = 7   (i) x = 3   (j) m = 5
  (k) t = 4   (l) t = 6   (m) x = 8   (n) m = 5   (o) t = 21
  (p) w = 8
2. (a) x = −2   (b) y = −1   (c) t = −2   (d) m = −9   (e) n = −4
  (f) x = 10   (g) x = −3   (h) t = −7   (i) n = 4   (j) n = −3
  (k) x = −6   (l) m = −20   (m) t = 0   (n) r = −6
3. (a) x>5   (b) y<4   (c) t≤6   (d) m≥6   (e) x≥−1
  (f) n≤3   (g) m≤5   (h) x≥1   (i) x<−2   (j) t>4
  (k) t<−5   (l) m>−4   (m) x≥−4   (n) t≤3   (o) x>12
  (p) m<−6   (q) t≥−5   (r) n≤−8
4. (a) 91   (b) 65   (c) 63   (d) 13   (e) 5
  (f) 21   (g) 70   (h) 499   (i) 5   (j) 18
  (k) 8   (l) 19   (m) 18   (n) 16   (o) 92
  (p) 98   (q) 90   (r) 171
5. (a) 1.3   (b) 8.0   (c) 43.9   (d) 14.2   (e) 2.4
  (f) 4.1   (g) 8.2   (h) 32.0   (i) 2.4   (j) 21.2
6. (a) 3   (b) 3   (c) 5   (d) 4   (e) 6
  (f) 2   (g) 5   (h) 9   (i) 12   (j) 3
  (k) 16   (l) 3

7. (a) −4   (b) −3   (c) −3   (d) −6   (e) −3
   (f) 2

8. (a) 7   (b) 4   (c) −9   (d) −3   (e) 6
   (f) 2   (g) 2   (h) 0

9. (a) $\frac{9}{2}$ (b) 4   (c) 3   (d) 2   (e) −11
   (f) $\frac{4}{3}$ (g) 4   (h) 2

10. (a) 3   (b) 1   (c) 3   (d) −9   (e) 0
   (f) 3   (g) −1   (h) 4

11. (a) 0.5   (b) 7.9   (c) 0.6   (d) 3   (e) 15
   (f) 2

12. (a) 2   (b) 4   (c) 6   (d) 7   (e) 20
   (f) 3

13. (a) $x<2$ (b) $x>5$ (c) $x\geq7$ (d) $x\leq11$

14. (a) $x>4$ (b) $x>-5$ (c) $x\leq-1$ (d) $x\leq2$ (e) $x>8$
   (f) $x<-3$ (g) $t\geq-8$ (h) $w\geq6$

15. (a) $x>4$ (b) $t<5$ (c) $m\geq-1$ (d) $x\leq-2$ (e) $x<4$
   (f) $m\geq15$

REVIEW AND PREVIEW TO CHAPTER 10

EXERCISE 1
1. 13   2. 4   3. 16   4. 8   5. 15   6. 8
7. 0   8. 6   9. 8   10. 7

EXERCISE 2
1. −1   2. 3   3. −7   4. 1   5. 13   6. −3
7. −1   8. −1   9. −6   10. −4

EXERCISE 3
1. 2   2. 3   3. −3   4. −5   5. −3   6. 4
7. −3   8. −4   9. 2   10. 1

EXERCISE 4
1. 4   2. −4   3. −3   4. 3   5. −2   6. 8
7. −3   8. −11   9. 0   10. 1

EXERCISE 5
1. $77.22   2. $12.23   3. 5h   4. 190

EXERCISE 10.1

1. (a) $n+4$ (b) $n-6$ (c) $5n$ (d) $2+n$ (e) $n \div 7$
   (f) $3n$ (g) $n-2$ (h) $12-n$

2. (a) $5+x$ (b) $y-4$ (c) $6x$ (d) $y \div 3$ (e) $x+8$
   (f) $y-4$ (g) $7x$ (h) $9y$ (i) $x+y$ (j) xy
   (k) $x+8$ (l) $y-1$ (m) $s+t$ (n) st (o) $6 \div x$

3. (a) $8n$ (b) $n \div 2$ (c) $3+n$ (d) $n-4$ (e) $n+7$
   (f) $n-2$ (g) $3n$ (h) $8+n$ (i) $9+n$ (j) $7n$
   (k) $n \div 8$ (l) $11 \div n$ (m) $n+6$ (n) $n+12$ (o) $n-16$

4. (a) $\ell+2$ (b) $5w$ (c) $c \div 2$ (d) $7x$ (e) $a+2$
   (f) $a-3$ (g) $10x$ (h) $5y$ (i) $12x$ (j) $c+3$
   (k) $c-7$

5. (a) 15, 21, 48, 3x, 21y, 33z   (b) 9, 11, 22, $x+3$, $4y+3$ (c) 18, 47, 64, $x \div 2$, $3x$ 6. (a) 20   (b) 22

EXERCISE 10.2

1. (a) $6n=18$ (b) $n+9=14$ (c) $n-5=11$ (d) $n \div 2=7$ (e) $8+n=15$

2. (a) $4n=20$ (b) $n \div 2=5$ (c) $n-4=9$ (d) $n+6=14$

3. (a) $n+5=12$ (b) $n-4=11$ (c) $2a=28$ (d) $a \div 3=6$ (e) $a+7=22$
   (f) $\ell+10=31$ (g) $w-4=8$

EXERCISE 10.3

1. 29   2. 38   3. 17   4. 102   5. 28
6. 124   7. 44   8. 23

EXERCISE 10.4

1. 1050   2. 950   3. 1125   4. 960   5. (a) head wind   (b) 75
6. (a) tail wind   (b) 50   7. 1190   8. 1120, 1285, 1370, 1055, 120 tail, 90 head

EXERCISE 10.5

1. (a) Yes   (b) No   (c) Yes   (d) Yes
2. (a) 50   (b) 150   (c) 60   (d) 72
3. (a) 2   (b) 5   (c) 3   (d) 2.8

EXERCISE 10.6

1. (a) 80   (b) 160   (c) 320   (d) 480   (e) 280
2. (a) 150   (b) 375   (c) 50   (d) 3   (e) 70
3. (a) 72   (b) 10 days   4. (a) 32.5   (b) 3 h   5. 36
6. (a) 299   (b) 247.5   (c) 612   (d) 1.5   (e) 4.5   (f) 1.2

EXERCISE 10.7

1. (a) 112 mm   (b) 132 mm   (c) 124 mm   (d) 123 mm
2. (a) 14   (b) 18
3. (a) 7, 5   (b) 14, 6   (c) 17, 8   (d) 8, 5
4. (a) 8, 10, 11   (b) 5, 6, 7   (c) 13, 15, 13, 15   (d) 15, 20, 21, 17   (e) 8, 13, 15, 5   (f) 6, 7, 8, 5, 10

EXERCISE 10.8

1. (a) 8   (b) 9   (c) 10   (d) 7   (e) 5   (f) 7
2. (a) 8   (b) 4   (c) 24   (d) 25
3. (a) 27   (b) 17   (c) 18   (d) 38
4. 7   5. −9   6. −6

EXERCISE 10.9

1. 27   2. 62   3. 289   4. 80   5. 4
6. 108   7. 6   8. 37.68   9. 50.24   10. 72
11. 6   12. 282.6   13. 113.04

EXERCISE 10.10

1. (a) 14   (b) 10   2. (a) 44.1   (b) 490   3. (a) 31   (b) 57
4. 60   5. 56   6. (a) 190   (b) 4950

EXERCISE 10.11

1. (a) T.C. = 6.50n   (b) \$123.50
2. (a) S = 12h   (b) i) \$204 ii) \$312 iii) \$510
3. (a) S.P. = 1.8C.P.   (b) i) \$1260 ii) \$2340 iii) \$5400
4. (a) N = 14d   (b) i)98   (c) ii) 182   (d) iii) 434
5. (a) P = 2w + 1t   (b) i) 55   ii) 93
6. (a) C = 10d + 0.13k   (b) \$410   (c) \$265

10.12 CHAPTER 10 REVIEW EXERCISE

1. (a) $x + 8$ (b) $6x$ (c) $x - 3$ (d) $\dfrac{x}{4}$ (e) $5x$ (f) $x + 4$

   (g) $9 + x$ (h) $x + 3$ (i) $5w$ (j) $10y$
2. 28   3. 22   4. 975   5. 955   6. 10   7. 3
8. 1.5   9. 6,9   10. 9, 10, 14   11. 7   12. 12   13. 14
14. (a) 924 600   (b) 703 500   (c) 3.5   15. (a) d = 330t   (b) 990 m

REVIEW AND PREVIEW TO CHAPTER 11

3. (a) (D,6)   (b) (B,3)   (c) (B,4)   (d) (D,4)   (e) (A,5)   (f) (E,6)
   (g) (F,2)   (h) (B,2)

EXERCISE 11.1

1. (a) 12, 20, 5, 2   (b) 1, −2, −7, −9
2. (a) 11, 5, −3, −5   (b) −2, −11, −17, −29   (c) −3, −7, −15, −27
3. −1, −5, −11, −17   4. 2, −8, −13, −23   5. \$1.35, \$2.70, \$4.05, \$5.40   6. 10, 5.55, 1.85, 0.7

EXERCISE 11.2

1. (a) 4, 0, 9, 12, 7   (b) 1, −1, −2, −6   (c) 9, 4, 2, 1   (d) −2, −5, −14, −26

EXERCISE 11.4

1. (a) A   (b) E   (c) L   (d) B   (e) I   (f) J
   (g) G   (h) D   (i) C   (j) K   (k) H   (l) F
2. A(2,9)   B(5,2)   C(9,7)   D(1,5)   E(8,0)   F(0,2)
   G(4,6)   H(10,10)   I(0,7)   J(3,0)   K(7,5)   L(6,8)

EXERCISE 11.5

1. (a) M   (b) D   (c) G   (d) A   (e) F   (f) B
   (g) C   (h) E   (i) J   (j) H   (k) I   (l) K

2. A(4,4)   B(−6,2)   C(−3,−4)   D(3,−6)   E(7,2)   F(−3,6)
   G(−7,−2)   H(7,−4)   I(3,0)   J(0,3)   K(−4,0)   L(0,−6)

EXERCISE 11.6

1. (a) 0, 2, 4, 6   (b) 2, 1, 0, −1   (c) 1, 3, 5, 7

EXERCISE 11.9

2.

	rise	run	slope
AB	3	4	$\frac{3}{4}$
CD	2	−5	$\frac{2}{5}$
EF	4	2	2
GH	3	−4	$\frac{3}{4}$
NM	2	6	$\frac{1}{3}$

1.

	rise	run	slope
AB	2	6	$\frac{1}{3}$
CD	4	2	2
EF	2	3	$\frac{2}{3}$
GH	3	6	$\frac{1}{2}$
MN	3	4	$\frac{3}{4}$

3. (a) $\frac{4}{5}$ (b) $\frac{2}{3}$ (c) $\frac{1}{9}$ (d) $-\frac{1}{4}$ (e) 3   (f) $-\frac{8}{7}$

4. (a) $\frac{1}{2}$ (b) $\frac{1}{2}$ (c) $\frac{1}{2}$ Equal because it is the same.

EXERCISE 11.10

1. (a) 5   (b) 4   (c) 6   (d) 8
2. (a) 3   (b) 4   (c) 6   (d) 7
3. $\overline{AB} = \sqrt{194}$ $\overline{AC} = 5$ $BC = 13$
4. $DF = 8, FE = 10, DE = \sqrt{164}$
5. $|AB| = 5$ $|\overline{CD}| = \sqrt{53}$ $|EF| = \sqrt{26}$ $|GH| = \sqrt{53}$
6. (a) $\sqrt{52}$ (b) 13   (c) $\sqrt{58}$ (d) $\sqrt{74}$
7. $\sqrt{17}, \sqrt{45}, \sqrt{50}$
8. (a) $|AB| = 4$ $|\overline{BC}| = 5$ $|\overline{AC}| = 3$ (b) 12

EXERCISE 11.12

1. (a) 4.5   (b) 2.4   (c) 3.9   2. (a) 2.3   (b) 12.3   (c) 20.3
3. (b) i) 6.2 ii) 6.9   4. 22.m²   5. 6.7 cm × 6.7 cm   6.

n	n²
1.7	3
3.3	11
0	0
4.1	17
2.5	6.3
4.4	19.4

11.13 CHAPTER 11 REVIEW EXERCISE

1. (a) A   (b) C   (c) G   (d) H   (e) B   (f) E   (g) D
   (h) F   (i) I
2. A = (−3,5)   B = (−6,−4)   C = (3,−2)   D = (1,2)   E = (6,0)   F = (0,−5)
   G = (−2,0)   H = (0,4)   I = (−5,3)   J = (5,6)
3. 7, −1, −9, −17   4. 2, 4, 5, 7, 10   7.

x	y
4	4
2	6
0	8
−1	9
−3	11

9. (a) $\frac{4}{3}$ (b) $\frac{7}{8}$ (c) 2   (d) $\frac{-7}{5}$ (e) −3   (f) 0   (g) no slope
10. (a) 6   (b) 6   (c) $\sqrt{41}$ (d) $\sqrt{26}$ (e) $\sqrt{61}$ (f) $\sqrt{18}$
11. (b) $350   (c) 1.5 h

REVIEW AND PREVIEW TO CHAPTER 12

LINEAR UNITS OF MEASUREMENT

1. (a) 2600   (b) 265   (c) 5.23   (d) 45.98   (e) 458.6
   (f) 25.6   (g) 0.025   (h) 0.564
2. (a) 260   (b) 56   (c) 3.6   (d) 45.8   (e) 450
   (f) 25   (g) 2.5   (h) 7500

AREA UNITS OF MEASUREMENT

1. (a) 3 600 000   (b) 165 000   (c) 25 000   (d) 50 000   (e) 28 000
   (f) 5000   (g) 7.5   (h) 0.36
2. (a) 3.6   (b) 0.5   (c) 2500   (d) 15   (e) 2.5
   (f) 25
3. (a) 30 000   (b) 25 000   (c) 5000   (d) 500   (e) 50
   (f) 5   (g) 250   (h) 7000

VOLUME AND CAPACITY UNITS OF MEASUREMENT

1. (a) 1 000 000   (b) 250 000   (c) 1 500 000   (d) 50 000
   (e) 1 800 000   (f) 500   (g) 25 000 000   (h) 70 000
2. (a) 25   (b) 0.015   (c) 0.000 025   (d) 0.0015   (e) 0.000 001
   (f) 3.5   3. 753 cm^3, 0.004 m^3, 8000 cm^3, 0.7 m^3, 3.5 m^3
4. (a) 3000   (b) 5400   (c) 250   (d) 3 500 000   (e) 25
   (f) 100   (g) 0.275   (h) 5
5. (a) 2500   (b) 250   (c) 5   (d) 375   (e) 45
   (f) 5800   (g) 800   (h) 10 500
6. 1.5 L of pop for 79¢ is best value (0.053¢/mL)

MASS UNITS OF MEASUREMENT

1. (a) 5000   (b) 2500   (c) 1500   (d) 2 500 000   (e) 0.5
   (f) 5   (g) 0.025   (h) 25
2. (a) 2000   (b) 15 000   (c) 500   (d) 150 000   (e) 125
   (f) 3500   (g) 0.5   (h) 125
3. (a) 5000   (b) 2500   (c) 500   (d) 35   (e) 25
   (f) 150   (g) 4   (h) 1125
4. (a) ii)   (b) ii)   (c) i)
5. (a) 2 kg of hamburger for $4.00
   (b) 1.5 kg of flour for 79¢

EXERCISE 12.1

1. (a) 10   (b) 14   (c) 12   (d) 13   (e) 4   (f) 12
2. (a) 16   (b) 22   (c) 16   (d) 18   (e) 18   (f) 20
3. (a) 16 cm   (b) 16 cm   (c) 26 cm   (d) 13 cm
4. (a) 13.8   (b) 18.8   (c) 23.6   (d) 13.6   5. 274 m

EXERCISE 12.2

1. (a) 15   (b) 18   (c) 6.8   (d) 12.5
2. (a) 14   (b) 10   (c) 14   (d) 10
3. (a) 13   (b) 30   (c) 54.4   (d) 20.4
4. (a) 18.6   (b) 18.9   (c) 37.8   (d) 26.8
5. (a) 400 m   (b) $5100

EXERCISE 12.3

1. (a) 4   (b) 8   (c) 9   (d) 12   (e) 15   (f) 25
2. (a) 2   (b) 5.5   (c) 6   (d) 5   (e) 6   (f) 9
3. (a) 49   (b) 64   (c) 6.25   (d) 13.69
4. (a) 17.28   (b) 7.75   (c) 32   (d) 70.68
5. (a) 8.28   (b) 17.64   6. quadrupled

EXERCISE 12.4

1. (a) 27   (b) 16   (c) 320   (d) 57   (e) 80
   (f) 20
2. (a) 72   (b) 95   (c) 60   (d) 28
3. (a) $708.75   (b) $463.50   (c) $752.63   (d) $1091.25

EXERCISE 12.5

1. (a) 20   (b) 144   (c) 44   (d) 66
2. (a) 40   (b) 15   (c) 24.5   (d) 45
3. (a) 35   (b) 70   (c) 39   (d) 30
4. (a) 8.225   (b) 7.8   (c) 54.06   (d) 47.74

EXERCISE 12.6

1. (a) 31.36   (b) 305.76   2. 3828 cm^2 3. (a) $A = \dfrac{nbh}{2}$ (b) 4   4. 23 400

EXERCISE 12.7

1. (a) 9.42   (b) 13.188   (c) 15.7   (d) 38.308   (e) 18.212
   (f) 18.84

2. (a) 11.0   (b) 45.8   (c) 80.1   (d) 22.0   (e) 103.6
    (f) 38.9
3. (a) 199.39   (b) 199.39   (c) $\doteq$2393   (d) 7   4. (a) 282.6
5. 15.95   6. (a) 28.60   (b) 120   7. doubled

EXERCISE 12.8

1. (a) 19.63   (b) 50.24   (c) 314   (d) 28.26
2. (a) 6.3   (b) 7.54   (c) 37.68   (d) 235.5
3. 1.33   4. (a) 1384.74   (b) at least 8   5. 201   6. quadrupled

EXERCISE 12.9

1. (a) 6.43   (b) 83.44   (c) 6.28   (d) 9
2. (a) 7326   (b) $23 809.50
3. (a) 3098.8   (b) 1.35   (c) 2861.8   (d) 2790.8
4. (a) 40 066   (b) 41 636   5. 83.55   6. (a) 41.1   (b) 43.9
7. 80 384   8. (a) 207.24   (b) 207.24   (c) 621.72   9. 1017.36
10. (a) 344   (b) 368   (c) 1068
11. 2550   12. (a) 135   b. 135
13. (a) 1300   b. 500   c. 170   d. $1300, $10, $25.50

12.10 CHAPTER 12 REVIEW EXERCISE

1. (a) 18.8   (b) 18.9   (c) 42   (d) 30.6
2. (a) 85.4   (b) 37.0   (c) 26.9   (d) 41.0   (e) 15.5
    (f) 393.9
3. (a) 28   (b) 26.28   (c) 48.56   (d) 42.84   (e) 34
    (f) 62.8
4. (a) 93.42   (b) 5.57   (c) 72   (d) 48   (e) 30.5
    (f) 21.5
5. (a) 428.4   (b) 10 026
6. (a) 109   (b) 60.8   (c) 9167.5   (d) 2541
7. (a) 7875   (b) 672   (c) 120   (d) 314
8. 6.6
9. (a) 62.8   (b) 41.9

REVIEW AND PREVIEW TO CHAPTER 13

1. (a) 4   (b) 10   (c) 6   (d) 10   (e) 12   (f) 20

EXERCISE 13.1

1. (a) 150   (b) 52   (c) 68   (d) 460
2. (a) 208   (b) 190   (c) 280   (d) 311.0
3. 1000   4. (b) 75   (c) $225

EXERCISE 13.2

1. (a) 48   (b) 36   (c) 72   (d) 32
2. (a) 14.2   (b) 79.2   (c) 127.9   (d) 15.6
3. (b) 67   (c) 8.4   4. (a) 4.3   (b) 6.5 t
5. (a) 101   (b) 101 000   (c) 2525

EXERCISE 13.3

1. (a) 138   (b) 46   (c) 1464   (d) 760   (e) 96   (f) 102
2. (a) 12   (b) 72   (c) 168   (d) 72   (e) 240   (f) 300

3.

	Surface Area	Volume
(a)	276	280
(b)	192	160
(c)	94	60
(d)	108	72
(e)	294	343
(f)	236	240

4. (a) 60 cm², 24 cm³   (b) 168 cm², 120 cm³   (c) 425 cm², 360 cm³   (d) 1855 cm², 2520 cm³

EXERCISE 13.4

1. (a) 471   (b) 527.5   (c) 703.4   (d) 207.2
2. (a) 301.4   (b) 100.5   (c) 402
3. (a) 279.3   (b) 34 L   4. (a) 427.0   (b) $1387.88   5. 1.5 m²

EXERCISE 13.5

1. (a) $r = 5, h = 8$ (b) $r = 2, h = 7.2$ (c) $r = 4, h = 15$ (d) $r = 3.65, h = 10$

2. (a) 706.5　　　　(b) 401.9　　　　(c) 75.4　　　　(d) 137.4　　　　(e) 4901.3
　　(f) 1485.3
3. (a) 781.3　　　　(b) 48.8　　　　(c) 3846.5　　　(d) 115.4　　　　(e) 155.1
4. 12　　　　　　5. 117.8　　　　6. (a) 392.5　　　(b) 1767.1
7. (a) 391.5　　　　(b) 783　　　　(c) 783　　　　(d) 1566

EXERCISE 13.6

1. (a) 7　　　　　(b) 5　　　　　(c) 8　　　　　(d) 12
2. (a) 240　　　　(b) 132　　　　3. 2340　　　　4. 85 926.03

EXERCISE 13.7

1. (a) 58　　　　(b) 192　　　　(c) 33　　　　(d) 132　　　　(e) 96
　　(f) 400　　　　2. 233　　　　3. 400

EXERCISE 13.8

1. (a) 3, 5　　　　(b) 8, 17　　　　(c) 7, 25　　　　(d) 5, 13
2. (a) 188　　　　(b) 264　　　　3. (a) 71　　　　(b) 81.2

EXERCISE 13.9

1. (a) 100　　　　(b) 236　　　　(c) 804　　　　(d) 236　　　　(e) 288
　　(f) 528　　　　2. 157　　　　3. 1272

EXERCISE 13.10

1. (a) 452　　　　(b) 2826　　　　(c) 1809　　　　(d) 314　　　　(e) 113
　　(f) 452　　　　2. 113.0 m²　　　3. 153.9 m²

EXERCISE 13.11

1. (a) 523　　　　(b) 1436　　　　(c) 7235　　　　(d) 904　　　　(e) 3052
　　(f) 7235　　　　(g) 1766　　　　(h) 904
2. 904　　　　　3. (a) 1150　　　　(b) 27 600　　　4. (a) 14　　　　(b) 224

13.12 CHAPTER 13 REVIEW EXERCISE

1. (a) 150　　　　(b) 527　　　　(c) 207　　　　(d) 166　　　　(e) 132
　　(f) 615　　　　(g) 1394　　　　(h) 161　　　　(i) 68　　　　(j) 201
2. (a) 216　　　　(b) 678　　　　(c) 280　　　　(d) 603　　　　(e) 523
　　(f) 262　　　　(g) 137　　　　(h) 32　　　　(i) 268　　　　(j) 8478
3. 1 570　　　　4. 377　　　　5. 132　　　　6. 235 200　　　7. 126
8. (a) 141　　　　(b) $305.50　　　9. 23　　　　10. 127
11. (a) 716　　　　(b) 5728　　　　(c) 6

REVIEW AND PREVIEW TO CHAPTER 14

1. No　　　　2. Same　　　　3. Yes　　　　4. Yes　　　　5. No　　　　6. Answers vary
7. (a) Impossible; as a stairway, it only goes around again.
　　(b) Impossible; to build it you would have to twist the material.

EXERCISE 14.1

1. (a) line PQ　　　　　(b) ray ST　　　　　(c) line segment DE
　　(d) angle RST　　　　(e) angle FED　　　　(f) angle R
2. AB, AC, AD, BC, BD, CD　　3. Answers vary
4. Answers vary　　　　5. Answers vary
7. (a) 3.1 cm　　　　(b) 5.2 cm　　　　(c) 4.1 cm　　　　(d) 2.6 cm
8. (a) 48 mm　　　　(b) 43 mm　　　　(c) 55 mm　　　　(d) 36 mm

EXERCISE 14.2

1. (a) 60°　　　　(b) 90°　　　　(c) 76°　　　　(d) 45°　　　　(e) 54°
　　(f) 9°　　　　(g) 30°　　　　(h) 90°　　　　(i) 126°　　　　(j) 104°
　　(k) 150°　　　　(l) 180°
2. (a) 45°　　　　(b) 80°　　　　(c) 90°　　　　(d) 52°　　　　(e) 3°
　　(f) 32°　　　　(g) 90°　　　　(h) 177°　　　　(i) 100°　　　　(j) 180°
　　(k) 100°　　　　(l) 128°
4. (a) 45°　　　　(b) 90°　　　　(c) 30°　　　　(d) 120°

EXERCISE 14.3

1. (a) right　　　　(b) acute　　　　(c) straight　　　　(d) obtuse　　　　(e) reflex　　　　(f) acute
2. (a) acute　　　　(b) right　　　　(c) straight　　　　(d) obtuse　　　　(e) acute　　　　(f) acute

3. (a) 20°   (b) 75°   (c) 67°   (d) 82°   (e) 7°   (f) 23°
4. (a) 120°   (b) 30°   (c) 90°   (d) 133°   (e) 67°   (f) 41°
5. (a) 45°   (b) 26°   (c) 95°   (d) 38°
7. (a) 35°, 145°, 35°, 145°   (b) 60°, 120°, 60°, 120°   (c) 67°, 113°, 67°, 113°   (d) 42°, 138°, 42°, 138°

EXERCISE 14.4

1. (a) isosceles   (b) equilateral   (c) scalene   (d) isosceles
2. (a) obtuse   (b) acute   (c) right   (d) obtuse
3. (a) equilateral   (b) isosceles   (c) scalene   (d) scalene
4. (a) right   (b) obtuse   (c) acute   (d) obtuse
7. (a) 70°   (b) 47°   (c) 43°   (d) 44°   (e) 21°, 111°   (f) 32°, 59°

EXERCISE 14.5

1. (a) quadrilateral   (b) hexagon   (c) octagon   (d) pentagon   (e) septagon   (f) decagon
2. (a) 1   (b) 3   (c) 5   (d) 7   (e) 6   (f) 9
4. (a) 90°   (b) 120°   (c) 135°   5. all 360°

EXERCISE 14.11

4. (a) $x = 82°, y = 98°$ (b) $x = 70°, y = 60°$
5. (a) $x = 84°, y = 96°$ (b) $x = 86°, y = 94°$
6. (a) $x = 100°, y = 80°$ (b) 95°
7. (a) $a = 105°$ $b = 75°$ $c = 105°$ $d = 75°$ $e = 105°$ $f = 75°$ $g = 105°$
   (b) $x = 82°$, $y = 52°$, $z = 46°$

EXERCISE 14.12

1. (a) 33°   (b) 101°   (c) $x = 133°$ $y = 47°$ $y = 133°$ (d) 36°
2. (a) $a = 51°$ $b = 57°$ $c = 51°$ $d = 72°$ (b) $a = 116°$ $b = 116°$ $c = 64°$ $d = 63°$
   (c) $a = 78°$ $b = 102°$ $c = 78°$ $d = 102°$ $x = 102°$ $y = 102°$ $z = 78°$
   (d) $a = 65°$ $b = 115°$ $c = 100°$ $d = 145°$
   (e) $a = 81°$ $b = 68°$ $c = 134°$ $d = 112°$ $e = 68°$ $f = 46°$ $g = 46°$
   (f) $a = 79°$ $b = 42°$ $c = 138°$ $d = 26°$
3. (a) $x = 108°$ $y = 108°$ $m = 108°$ (b) $x = 76°$ $y = 70°$ $m = 110°$ $t = 70°$
   (c) $x = 91°$ $y = 53°$ $t = 91°$ $m = 36°$ (d) $x = 92°$ $y = 48°$ $r = 50°$ $s = 65°$ $t = 65°$

EXERCISE 14.13

(1,14) (2,17) (3,19) (4,11) (5,16) (6,12) (7,9) (8,15) (10,13) (18,20)

EXERCISE 14.14

1. (a) $\triangle A = \triangle R, \triangle B = \triangle S, \triangle C = \triangle T$ (b) $\overline{AB} = \overline{RS}, \overline{BC} = \overline{ST}, \overline{AC} = \overline{RT}$
2. (a) $\triangle P = \triangle M, \triangle Q = \triangle N, \triangle R = \triangle O, \overline{PQ} = \overline{MN}, \overline{QR} = \overline{NO}, \overline{PR} = \overline{MO}$
   (b) $\triangle F = \triangle Z, \triangle D = \triangle X, \triangle E = \triangle Y, \overline{DF} = \overline{XZ}, \overline{DE} = \overline{XY}, \overline{FE} = \overline{ZY}$
   (c) $\triangle C = \triangle T, \triangle B = \triangle S, \triangle A = \triangle R, \overline{CB} = \overline{TS}, \overline{AC} = \overline{RT}, \overline{BA} = \overline{SR}$
3. (a) $\triangle A = \triangle D, \triangle B = \triangle E, \triangle ACB = \triangle DCE, \overline{AB} = \overline{DE}, \overline{AC} = \overline{DC}, \overline{BC} = \overline{EC}$
   (b) $\triangle R = \triangle T, \triangle RSM = \triangle TSM, \triangle RMS = \triangle SMT, \overline{RM} = \overline{TM}, \overline{RS} = \overline{TS}, \overline{MS} = \overline{MS}$
   (c) $\triangle W = \triangle Y, \triangle WXZ = \triangle YXZ, \triangle WZX = \triangle YZX, \overline{WX} = \overline{YX}, \overline{WZ} = \overline{YZ}, \overline{XZ} = \overline{XZ}$

EXERCISE 14.17

1. 28°   2. 36°   3. 90°
4. (a) 66°   (b) 43°   (c) 90°   (d) $x = 52°, y = 47°$ (e) $x = 44°, y = 22°$ (f) 48°

EXERCISE 14.18

1. $F + V - E = 2$

14.20 CHAPTER 14 REVIEW EXERCISE

3. (a) obtuse   (b) right   (c) acute   (d) reflex   (e) straight   (f) obtuse
4. (a) isosceles   (b) scalene   (c) equilateral   5. (a) right   (b) obtuse   (c) acute
9. $a = 114°$ $b = 66°$ $c = 114°$ $d = 66°$ $e = 114°$ $f = 114°$ $g = 66°$
10. (a) $x = 138°$ $y = 42°$ $z = 138°$ (b) $x = 29°$ $y = 81°$ $m = 81°$ $a = 99°$ $t = 40°$
11. (a) $\triangle A = \triangle D, \triangle C = \triangle E, \triangle B = \triangle F$ (b) $\overline{AC} = \overline{DE}, \overline{AB} = \overline{DF}, \overline{BC} = \overline{FE}$
13. (a) $\triangle BAC$ (b) $\triangle BOC$ 14. (a) 32°   (b) 90°   (c) $x = 29°, y = 35°$

EXERCISE 15.1

1. (a) slides   (b) turns   (c) flips   (d) turns   (e) slides   (f) flips
2. (a) iii   (b) ii   3. (a) ii   (b) i   4. (a) iv   (b) ii

	(i)	(ii)	(iii)	(iv)
5. (a)	slide	flip	turn	turn
(b)	flip	turn	slide	turn
(c)	turn	turn	flip	slide
(d)	slide	turn	flip	turn
(e)	turn	flip	turn	slide
(f)	flip	slide	turn	turn
(g)	slide	turn	turn	flip
(h)	turn	slide	turn	flip or turn

EXERCISE 15.2

1. (a) (R3,U4)   (b) (2L,3U)   (c) (R3,D5)
3. (a) (3R,2D)   (b) (5R,1U)   (c) (3L,3D)   (d) (5L,3U)
8. (a) (2R,3U)   (b) (4L,4U)   (c) (1R,5U)   (d) (2L,8U)

EXERCISE 15.3

1. C & D
   G & H
   K & L

EXERCISE 15.4

1. (a) 90° ccw   (b) 180° cw   (c) 270° cw
2. (a) 90° cw, 270° ccw   (b) 180° cw, 180° ccw   (c) 90° cw, 270° ccw

EXERCISE 15.5

2. (a) 1   (b) 2   (c) 3   (d) 5
3. (a) 1   (b) 1   (c) 4   (d) 0   (e) 0
   (f) 0   (g) 1   (h) I   (i) 0

EXERCISE 15.6

1. (a) 2   (b) 3   (c) 4   (d) 5   (e) 3   (f) 5
2. (a) 2   (b) 4   (c) 3   (d) 5
3. (a) 2   (b) 3   (c) 4   (d) 4   (e) 6   (f) 8

EXERCISE 15.7

1. $\frac{1}{2}$ 2. (a) 2   (b) 2, 2, 2   (c) $\angle A = \angle A'$, $\angle B = \angle B'$, $\angle C = \angle C'$

8. (a) 2   (b) 4   (c) 16   (d) $\frac{1}{2}$ or 1 : 2   (e) $\frac{1}{4}$ or 1 : 4
   (f) Area Ratio is square of the ratio of the sides

EXERCISE 15.8

1. (a) (x–coords) × 2   (b) (y–coords) × 2   (c) (x–coords) × 3
   (d) (y–coords × $\frac{1}{2}$)

15.10 CHAPTER 15 REVIEW EXERCISE

1.	(i)	(ii)	(iii)	(iv)
(a)	F	S	T	F
(b)	T	S	T	S
(c)	S	F	T	T

2. (a) (3R,1U)   (b) (3R,2D)   (c) (5R,1U)   (d) (3R,2D)
4. (a) (3,–5)   (b) (–8,6)
8. (a) 9° cw, 270° ccw   (b) 180° cw, 180° ccw   (c) 270° cw, 90° ccw
   (d) 270° cw, 90° ccw
10. (a) 2   (b) 3   12. (a) 4   (b) 2

CUMULATIVE REVIEW

1. (a) 10 942   (b) 5729   (c) 5 020 080   (d) 321   (e) 1499   (f) 2463
2. (a) 110.4   (b) 511.85   (c) 55.48   (d) 8.467   (e) 2.52   (f) 13.5
   (g) 0.78
3. (a) 630   (b) 1.6   (c) 25.51   (d) 0.516   (e) 6 000 000
4. (a) 9   (b) 20   (c) 5   (d) 56

5. (a) $1\frac{4}{15}$　　(b) $\frac{7}{24}$　　(c) $2\frac{1}{8}$　　(d) $3\frac{7}{8}$　　(e) $\frac{1}{2}$　　(f) 6

(g) $\frac{1}{2}$　　(h) 2

6. (a) 0.75　　(b) 0.8　　(c) 0.625　　(d) 0.25　　(e) 0.375　　(f) $0.\overline{3}$

(g) 0.3　　(h) 0.6　　(i) 0.2　　(j) 0.09　　(k) 0.27　　(l) $0.\overline{142857}$

7. (a) $\frac{1}{4}$　　(b) $\frac{7}{20}$　　(c) $1\frac{1}{2}$　　(d) $3\frac{3}{4}$　　(e) $\frac{51}{200}$　　(f) $\frac{27}{40}$

(g) $\frac{2}{3}$　　(h) $\frac{2}{9}$　　(i) $\frac{7}{9}$　　(j) $\frac{235}{999}$　　(k) $\frac{599}{990}$　　(l) $\frac{263}{990}$

8. (a) -3　　(b) -14　　(c) -7　　(d) -15　　(e) 10　　(f) -7

(g) -15　　(h) -28　　(i) 18　　(j) 20

9. (a) -222　　(b) 247　　(c) 1025　　(d) 557　　(e) 76　　(f) 53

(g) -2205　　(h) -5248　　(i) 1134　　(j) -1035

10. (a) 2　　(b) 5　　(c) -2　　(d) -3

11. (a) 6.75×10^2　　(b) 2.54×10^4　　(c) 8.75×10^5　　(d) 2.345×10^6　　(e) 2.75×10^{-1}

(f) 7.5×10^{-3}　　(g) 6.5×10^{-2}　　(h) 2.75×10^{-4}

12. (a) 9　　(b) 11　　(c) 12　　(d) 13　　(e) 24　　(f) 32

(g) 48　　(h) 2000

13. (a) 4.2　　(b) 6.1　　(c) 6.7　　(d) 7.7　　(e) 18.0　　(f) 22.4

14. (a) 25%　　(b) 7%　　(c) 65%　　(d) 50%　　(e) 275%　　(f) 305%

(g) 3%　　(h) 23%　　(i) 16%　　(j) 75%

15. (a) 0.25　　(b) 0.68　　(c) 0.27　　(d) 0.55　　(e) 1.0　　(f) 3.25

(g) 1.15　　(h) 0.02

16. (a) 200.4　　(b) 336.7　　(c) 350.35　　(d) 72 250　　(e) 145 250

17. (a) 5 : 4　　(b) 7 : 5　　(c) 4 : 7

18. (a) 8 : 18　　(b) 12 : 18　　(c) 18 : 12　　(d) 12 : 15　　(e) 15 : 18

19. 24 : 3 : 32

20. (a) 2　　(b) 4　　(c) 18　　(d) 24

21. (a) 9　　(b) 22.5　　(c) 6.3　　(d) 102.5　　(e) 1

22. (a) 33　　(b) 20　　(c) 50　　(d) 25　　(e) $33\frac{1}{3}$

23. $9900　　24. (a) 12.5%　　(b) 87.5%　　25. (a) Terry　　(b) (410, 190)

29. (a) 18　　(b) 64　　30. (a) 47　　31. (a) 34　　(b) 12, 14

32. (a) $\frac{4}{15}$　　(b) $\frac{2}{5}$　　(b) 85　　(c) $\frac{1}{3}$

33. (a) 3　　(b) -16　　(c) 18　　(d) 17

34. (a) -6　　(b) 6　　(c) 8　　(d) -12　　(e) -23　　(f) -1

35. (a) $9x$　　(b) $8m$　　(c) $-2x + 5y$　　(d) $-2y + 13$

36. (a) $4x + 28$　　(b) $-6t + 14$　　(c) $-4x - 1$　　(d) $8x + 1$　　(e) $-1s + 1$

37. (a) $6x^2$　　(b) $30a^2$　　(c) $-12m^5$　　(d) $10y^7$　　(e) $4x^2$　　(f) $-2y^2$

(g) $10m^2$　　(h) $9x^2y$

38. (a) $3x^2 + 3$　　(b) $-4m^2 - 13m$　　(c) $x^2 + 5x + 6$　　(d) $m^2 + m - 42$　　(e) $t^2 - 15t + 54$

39. (a) $4(x + 2y)$　　(b) $3(x - 4)$　　(c) $x(5x + 2)$　　(d) $2x(2x^2 - 3x + 1)$

40. (a) 3　　(b) 8　　(c) 4　　(d) 12　　(e) 4　　(f) 5

(g) 4　　(h) 5　　(i) -2　　(j) 3　　(k) 4　　(l) 3

(m) 2　　(n) 0

41. (a) $x > 3$　　(b) $t \leq 7$　　(c) $m \leq 4$　　(d) $x > 2$　　(e) $m \geq 15$　　(f) $x \leq 4$

42. (a) $x \leq 5$　　(b) $x > 4$　　(c) $x \geq 2$　　(d) $x < -1$

43. 38　　44. 1150　　45. 40

46. (a) $x^2 + 3x + 2$　　(b) $m^2 + 2m - 3$　　(c) $t^2 - 16$　　(d) $y^2 - 13y + 42$　　(e) $n^2 + 4n + 4$　　(f) $y^2 - 6y + 9$

47. 5　　48. 11 by 13　　49. 8

50. 0, 3, 7, 8, 10　　52. (b) (i) 75 (ii) 175　　(c) (i) 1.5 (ii) 2.6

53. (a) 1　　(b) -2　　(c) 0

54. (a) 5　　(b) 13　　(c) 7　　(d) 10

55. (a) 21.8　　(b) 17.2　　(c) 18.84　　(d) 16

56. (a) 24　　(b) 35　　(c) 32.5　　(d) 314

57. (a) 357　　(b) 6962.5

58. (a) 108　　(b) 150　　(c) 301　　(d) 282.6　　(e) 800　　(f) 314

59. (a) 80　　(b) 1256　　(c) 262　　(d) 4187　　(e) 2800　　(f) 880

62. (a) $a = 33°$, $b = 147°$, $c = 33°$　　(b) 59°　　63. (a) 540°　　(b) 720°

68. (a) $a = 99°$　　$b = 81°$　　$c = 99°$　　$d = 81°$　　$e = 99°$　　$f = 99°$　　$g = 81°$

(b) $a = 105°$　　$b = 111°$　　$c = 36°$　　$d = 144°$

69. Angles (D,R) (F,S) (E,T)　　Sides (DF,RS) (DE,RT) (FE,ST)

70. (a) 23°　　(b) $x = 42°$　　$y = 39°$　　$m = 99°$

71. (a) turn, flip, turn, slide　　(b) turn, slide, flip, turn　　(c) slide, flip, turn, flip

75. (a) 2　　(b) 3　　76. (a) 2　　(b) 4

GLOSSARY

Acute Angle: An angle whose measure is less than 90°.

Acute Triangle: A triangle with three acute angles.

Alternate Angles: ∠A and ∠B are alternate angles.

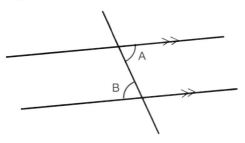

Altitude of a Triangle: The perpendicular distance from a vertex to the opposite side. (See *Height*).

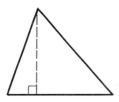

Angle: The figure formed by two rays, or two line segments, with a common end point.

Angle Bisector: A line that divides an angle into two equal parts.

Arc: A part of the circumference of a circle.

Area: The number of square units required to cover a surface.

Associative Property: When three or more numbers are added or multiplied, the operations may be performed in any order:

$$(3 + 5) + 7 = 3 + (5 + 7)$$
$$(2 \times 3) \times 4 = 2 \times (3 \times 4)$$

Average: The average, or mean, of a set of numbers is found by adding all the numbers and then dividing by the number of numbers in the set.

Axes: The intersecting scales on a graph.

Bar Graph: A graph using bars to represent information.

Base (of a power): The base of a power is the number that is used as the factor.

Base (of a polygon): Any side of a polygon may be referred to as the base.

Base (of a solid): See the shaded faces in the diagrams.

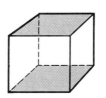

Bisect: To separate a figure into two congruent parts.

Bisector (of an angle): A ray or line which divides an angle into two equal angles.

Bit: The smallest unit of information in a computer.

Broken Line Graph: A graph drawn using line segments. A line graph shows how something changes.

Byte: A group of 8 bits.

Cartesian Coordinates: An ordered pair of numbers that locates a point on a grid.

Chord: A line segment that joins two points on the circumference of a circle.

Circle: A closed figure with all of its points the same distance from a point called the centre.

Circle Graph: A graph in which a circle is divided into sectors. A circle graph shows how something is divided.

Circumference: The perimeter of a circle.

$$C = 2 \times \pi \times r$$
$$C = \pi \times d$$

Co-Interior Angles: S and T are co-interior angles.

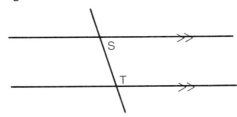

Common Factor: A number which is a factor of two or more numbers.

Common Multiple: A number which is a multiple of two or more numbers.

Commutative Property: When two numbers are added or multiplied, the operation may be performed in any order.
$$3 + 5 = 5 + 3$$
$$4 \times 6 = 6 \times 4$$

Complementary Angles: Two angles whose sum is 90°.

Composite Number: A number that has more than two factors.

Contained Angle: With respect to sides AC and AB, $\angle$A is the contained angle.

Congruent Figures: Figures having the same size and shape.

Coordinates: See *Cartesian Coordinates.*

Corresponding Angles: Angles that have the same relative position in geometric figures. $\angle$D and $\angle$E are corresponding angles.

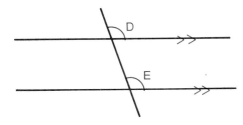

Corresponding Sides: Sides that have the same relative position in geometric figures.

Cube: A polyhedron with six congruent square faces.

Cylinder: A cylinder has a curved surface and two faces that are circles.

Data: Facts or information.

Decagon: A polygon with 10 sides.

Decahedron: A polyhedron with 10 faces.

Degree: The unit for measuring angles.
$$1° = \frac{1}{360} \text{ of a complete turn.}$$

Denominator: In the fraction $\frac{3}{4}$, 4 is the denominator. It tells the number of equal parts in the whole or the group.

Diagonal: A line segment joining two non-adjacent vertices in a polygon.

Diameter: A chord that passes through the centre of a circle.

Discount: An amount deducted from the price of an article.

Distributive Property:
$$a(b + c) = ab + ac$$

Divisible: A number is divisible by another number when the remainder is zero.

Dodecagon: A polygon with 12 sides.

Dodecahedron: A polyhedron with 12 faces.

Edge: An edge in a polyhedron is formed when two faces meet.

END Statement: The last statement in a computer program.

Equation: A number sentence which contains the symbol =.

Equilateral Triangle: A triangle with all sides the same length.

Equivalent Fractions: Fractions that represent the same number or amount. Examples of equivalent fractions are
$$\frac{3}{4}, \frac{6}{8}, \frac{9}{12}.$$

Equivalent Ratios: Ratios that represent the same fractional number or amount.

Expanded Form: 356 in expanded form is
$$300 + 50 + 6$$
or $\quad 3 \times 100 + 5 \times 10 + 6$

Exponent: A number that shows how many times a base is to be used as a factor.

Exponent

$$\mathbf{2}^4$$

Base

Exterior Angle: An angle formed by extending one side of a polygon.

Face: A plane surface of a polyhedron.

Factors: The numbers multiplied to name a product.

Flow chart: An organized diagram that displays the steps in solving a problem.

Fraction: A number that describes part of a whole or part of a group.

Frequency: The number of times an item or event occurs in a list of figures.

Graph: A representation of information in pictorial form.

Greatest Common Factor: The largest number that divides two or more numbers.

Grid: A pattern of dots or lines.

Height: The perpendicular distance from a vertex to the opposite side.

 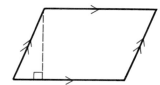

Hendecagon: A polygon with 11 sides.

Heptagon: A polygon with 7 sides.

Hexagon: A polygon with 6 sides.

Hexahedron: A polyhedron with 6 faces.

Hypotenuse: The side lying opposite to the right angle in a right-angled triangle.

Identity: The sum of any number and zero is that number.

$$7 + 0 = 7$$

The product of any number and one is that number.

$$7 \times 1 = 7$$

0 is the identity element for addition.

1 is the identity element for multiplication.

Image: The figure produced by a transformation.

Inequality: A number sentence that contains either $<$, $>$, or $\neq$.

Inequation: See *Inequality:*

INPUT Statement: A statement that tells the computer that a value will be inserted.

Integers: The set of numbers consisting of the whole numbers and their opposites.

$$1 = \{\ldots, {}^-3, {}^-2, {}^-1, 0, {}^+1, {}^+2, {}^+3, \ldots\}$$

Interest: the money received or payed for investing or borrowing money.

Intersecting Lines: Two lines that intersect at one point.

Isosceles Triangle: A triangle with two equal sides.

LET Statement: A statement in a computer program that assigns a value to a variable.

Like Terms: Terms that have exactly the same variable.

Line: A set of points shown as $\longleftrightarrow$

Line of Symmetry: A line that divides a figure into two congruent parts.

Line Segment: A part of a line with two end points shown as $\bullet\!\!-\!\!\!-\!\!\bullet$

Lowest Common Denominator (LCD): The lowest multiple shared by two or more denominators.

Lowest Common Multiple (LCM): The lowest multiple shared by two or more numbers.

Lowest Terms: A fraction (or ratio) is expressed in its lowest terms if the numerator and the denominator have no common factor other than 1.

Mass: The amount of matter in an object.

Magnitude: Size.

Mapping: A correspondence of points between an object and an image.

Mean: See *Average.*

Median: When a set of numbers is arranged in order from smallest to largest, or largest to smallest, the median is the middle number.

Mid-point: The mid-point of a line segment divides the line segment into two equal parts.

Mixed Number: A number of which part is a whole number and part is a fraction, such as $3\frac{4}{5}$.

Mode: The mode of a set of numbers is the number that occurs most often.

Multiple: The multiples of 5 are

$$5 \times 1 = 5$$
$$5 \times 2 = 10$$
$$5 \times 3 = 15$$

and so on

Net: A pattern for constructing a polyhedron.

Nonagon: A polygon with 9 sides.

Number Line: A pictorial representation of a set of numbers.

Numeral: A symbol which represents a number. 7, VII, ⊮ Il are numerals which represent the same number.

Numerator: In the fraction $\frac{3}{4}$, 3 is the numerator. It tells the number of equal parts being considered in the whole or group.

Obtuse Angle: An angle whose measure is greater than 90° but less than 180°.

Obtuse Triangle: A triangle with one obtuse angle.

Octagon: A polygon with 8 sides.

Octahedron: A polyhedron with 8 faces.

Ordered Pair: A pair of numbers which indicates a point on a graph or translation.

Order of Operations: The rules to be followed when simplifying expressions. These rules are sometimes referred to as BODMAS or BEDMAS.

Origin: The intersection of the horizontal axis and the vertical axis on a graph.

Parallel Lines: Two lines in the same plane that never meet.

Parallelogram: A quadrilateral with opposite sides parallel.

Pentagon: A polygon with 5 sides.

Percent: A fraction (or ratio) in which the denominator is 100.

Perimeter: The distance around a polygon.

Perpendicular Lines: Lines that intersect at right angles.

Pi(π): The quotient that results when the circumference of a circle is divided by its diameter.

Pictograph: A graph using picture symbols to represent data.

Polygon: A closed figure formed by line segments.

Polyhedron: A three-dimensional object having polygons as faces.

Population: The set of all things being considered.

Power: A product obtained by using a base as a factor one or more times.

$$3^4$$

Prime Factoring: A composite number expressed as a product of prime numbers.

Prime Number: A number with exactly two different factors — itself and 1.

PRINT Statement: A line in a program that tells the computer what to write on the screen or printer.

Prism: A polyhedron with two parallel and congruent bases in the shape of polygons. The remaining faces are parallelograms.

Probability: The probability of an event is a ratio of the number of ways an outcome can occur to the number of possible outcomes.

Program: A set of instructions that a computer carries out in order.

Proportion: An equation that states that two ratios are equal.

$$\frac{3}{4} = \frac{6}{8}$$

Pyramid: A polyhedron with three or more triangular faces and the base in the shape of a polygon.

Pythagorean Theorem: The area of the square drawn on the hypotenuse of a right-angled triangle equals the sum of the areas of the squares drawn on the other two sides.

Quadrilateral: A polygon with 4 sides.

Radius: The length of the line segment that joins the centre and a point on the circumference of a circle.

Rate: A ratio of two measurements having different units.

Ratio: A comparison of two numbers.

Ray: A part of a line with one end point as shown.

Real Number: Any number belonging to the set of rational or irrational numbers.

Reciprocals: Two numbers that have a product of 1.

Rectangle: A parallelogram with four right angles.

Rectangular Prism: A prism whose bases are congruent rectangles.

Reflection: A transformation that maps an object onto its image by a reflection in a line.

Reflex Angle: An angle whose measure is greater than 180° but less than 360°.

Regular Polygon: A polygon in which all sides and angles are equal.

Relation: A set of ordered pairs.

Repeating Decimal: A decimal in which one or more digits repeat without end.

Rhombus: A parallelogram in which all sides are equal.

Right Angle: An angle whose measure is 90°.

Right Bisector: The line that cuts a line segment into 2 equal parts at right angles.

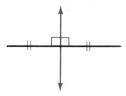

Right Triangle: A triangle with one right angle.

Root of an Equation: The value of the variable that makes the equation true.

Rotation: A transformation that maps an object onto its image by turning about a point.

Rotational Symmetry: A figure has rotational symmetry if it maps onto itself after a turn.

Rounding: A process of replacing a number by an approximate number.

RUN: The instruction to execute the computer program.

Sample: A representative part of the population.

Scale Drawing: A drawing in which distances are reductions or enlargements of actual distances.

Scalene Triangle: A triangle with no two sides equal.

Scientific Notation: Numbers written with one digit (not zero) to the left of the decimal point and with some power of 10 in exponential form.

Shell: A three-dimensional object whose interior is empty.

Similar Figures: Figures that have the same shape but not necessarily the same size.

Skeleton: A representation of the edges of a polyhedron.

Slope: The ratio: $\dfrac{\text{rise}}{\text{run}}$

Solid: A three-dimensional object whose interior is completely filled.

Solution Set: A replacement for a variable that results in a true sentence.

Square: A quadrilateral with 4 congruent sides and 4 right angles.

Square Root: The square root of a number is the number that multiplies itself to give the number.

Straight Angle: An angle whose measure is 180°.

Strip Pattern: A pattern formed by repeating a basic pattern using slides, half-turns and flips.

Supplementary Angles: Two angles whose sum is 180°.

Surface Area: The sum of the areas of all faces of a polyhedron.

Terminating Decimal: A decimal whose digits terminate.

Tessellation: A repeated pattern of geometric figures that will completely cover a surface.

Tetrahedron: A polyhedron with 4 triangular faces.

Translation: A transformation that maps an object onto its image so that each point in the object is moved the same distance and in the same direction.

Trapezoid: A quadrilateral with one pair of parallel sides.

Triangle: A polygon with 3 sides.

Variable: A letter or symbol used to represent a number.

Vertex (a) The common end point of two rays.

(b) The point where two adjacent sides meet in a polygon.

(c) The point where three or more edges of a polyhedron meet.

Volume: The number of cubic units required to fill a space.

Whole Numbers: Numbers in the set $\{0, 1, 2, 3, 4, 5, \ldots\}$

INDEX

PHOTOGRAPH CREDITS

p. 1: (upper left) CN; (upper centre) Nova Scotia Communication & Information Centre; (upper right) Courtesy of the Government of Quebec Tourist Branch; (middle centre) Travel Manitoba; (middle right) NFB Phototèque/Photo by Chris Lund — Sep 48; (lower left) New Brunswick Travel Bureau; (lower centre — two photos) Canadian Government Travel Bureau; (lower right) Ontario Ministry of Industry & Tourism. p. 12: Ontario Ministry of Industry & Tourism. p. 18: Courtesy of TRW Canada Limited, Dudley Lock Division. p. 20: Pete Romano/Sea Films, Inc. p. 31: CN. p. 34: Courtesy Litton Industries. p. 36: Courtesy Olivetti Canada Limited. p. 39: (lower) NASA. p. 41: (upper) CN. p. 41: (lower) Ontario Hydro. p. 43: Miller Services. p. 44: Canada Post Corporation. p. 45: (left, upper right, and lower right) Miller Services. p. 52: (upper and lower) Photo by Pauline Zvonarich. p. 55: (left) Photo by Scott Grant. p. 55: (right) Miller Services. p. 59: Photo by Pauline Zvonarich. p. 60: (lower right) The Globe and Mail, Toronto. p. 61: David Portigal. p. 63: (upper left) NASA. p. 63: (lower left) The Ministry of Transportation and Communications, Public and Safety Information Branch. p. 65: New Brunswick Travel Bureau. p. 80: Ford of Canada. p. 81: (upper and lower) Miller Services. p. 105: Photo by Pauline Zvonarich. p. 107: Canadian Government Travel Bureau. p. 109: Courtesy of IBM Canada Ltd. p. 112: The Bettmann Archive, Inc. p. 120: Ontario Ministry of Industry & Tourism. p. 123: The Bettmann Archive, Inc. p. 125: NFB Phototèque/Photo by Chris Lund — Sep 48. p. 135: Apple Computer Inc. p. 139: IBM. p. 141: Eastman Kodak Company. pp. 142, 143: Bar Code Artwork Courtesy of Photographic Sciences Corporation. p. 147: CN. p. 148: (lower) Miller Services. p. 149: Ford of Canada. p. 156: (upper) Miller Services. p. 156: (lower) The Ministry of Transportation and Communications, Public and Safety Information Branch.

p. 160: Miller Services. p. 163: Miller Services. p. 166: Miller Services. p. 167: Photo by Pauline Zvonarich. p. 170: Miller Services. p. 171: (left and right) Miller Services. p. 179: (upper) Miller Services. p. 179: (lower) Courtesy of IBM. p. 181: Travel Manitoba. p. 183: Miller Services. p. 191: Air Canada. p. 200: Miller Services. p. 201: Tourism B.C. p. 202: Photo by Pauline Zvonarich. p. 203: Miller Services. p. 261: Courtesy of the Government of Quebec Tourist Branch. p. 277: Noranda Mines. p. 299: Nova Scotia Communication & Information Centre. p. 301: Miller Services. p. 307: (upper left) RCAF. p. 307: (lower left and right) Air Canada. p. 310: (upper and lower) Miller Services. p. 311: Miller Services. p. 315: Miller Services. p. 319: (left) International Harvester. p. 320: (upper and lower) Miller Services. p. 321: (left) Florida State News Bureau. p. 321: (right) Miller Services. p. 325: Miller Services. p. 327: Canadian Government Travel Bureau. p. 330: Miller Services. p. 340: Gulf Oil Canada Limited. p. 342: Toronto Transit Commission. p. 344: (right) Miller Services. p. 355: Miller Services p. 357: Travel Manitoba. p. 362: Miller Services. p. 375: Hale Observatories. p. 380: Wayne van Exan, Host of the Owl's Nest; 12 midnight to 5 a.m., daily on CFRB 1010. p. 393: Miller Services. p. 400: The Bettmann Archive, Inc. p. 406: Canadian National. p. 411: J.A. Kraulis and Bo Curtis — From the book *Canada from the Air.* p. 414: Miller Services. p. 416: (upper) Alberta Government Photographic Services. p. 416: (lower) Miller Services. p. 426: The Ministry of Transportation and Communications, Public and Safety Information Branch. p. 428: Photo by Pauline Zvonarich. p. 457: Ontario Ministry of Industry & Tourism. p. 462: Miller Services. p. 466: (left and right) Photo by Pauline Zvonarich. p. 478: Consulate General of France. p. 479: Pan American World Airways.